PHYSICO-CHEMICAL CALCULATIONS IN SCIENCE AND INDUSTRY

ENGLAND:	BUTTERWORTH & CO. (PUBLISHERS) LTD. LONDON: 88 KINGSWAY, W.C.2
AUSTRALIA:	BUTTERWORTH & CO. (AUSTRALIA) LTD. SYDNEY: 6/8 O'CONNELL STREET MELBOURNE: 473 BOURKE STREET BRISBANE: 240 QUEEN STREET
CANADA:	BUTTERWORTH & CO. (CANADA) LTD. TORONTO: 1367 DANFORTH AVENUE, 6
NEW ZEALAND:	BUTTERWORTH & CO. (NEW ZEALAND) LTD. WELLINGTON: 49/51 BALLANCE STREET AUCKLAND: 35 HIGH STREET
SOUTH AFRICA:	BUTTERWORTH & CO. (SOUTH AFRICA) LTD. DURBAN: 33/35 BEACH GROVE
U. S. A.:	BUTTERWORTH INC. WASHINGTON, D.C.: 7235 WISCONSIN AVENUE, 14

PHYSICO-CHEMICAL CALCULATIONS

IN SCIENCE AND INDUSTRY

H. FROMHERZ, B. Sc., Ph. D.

Professor of Chemistry,
Maria Hilf College, Schwyz, Switzerland

Translated by

G. H. KINNER, B. Sc.

Principal Scientific Officer,
Royal Aircraft Establishment, Farnborough

LONDON
BUTTERWORTHS
1964

Suggested U.D.C. number: 541.1.083.3

Translated from
Physikalisch-chemisches Rechnen in Wissenschaft und Technik, 2nd ed.,

Printed in Leipzig by Oswald Schmidt KG

To My Teachers

PROFESSOR A.V. HILL, O.B.E., F.R.S.

SIR C.N. HINSHELWOOD, O.M., F.R.S.

CONTENTS

PREFACE TO THE ENGLISH EDITION

In this book, an attempt has been made to add a touch of realism to the theorems and formulae of physical chemistry by selecting, working out and explaining a variety of typical problems taken from the realms of science and industry.

It is hoped that the material will help students of chemistry, physics and related disciplines towards a better understanding of physical chemistry and its methods of calculation. As a practical reference book, the Exercises provide many examples of the almost limitless applications of physical chemistry to industrial problems. Ability to deal with these problems should prove useful in saving time and money and may even help in reducing loss of human life.

During his many years of experience as university teacher and industrial research chemist, and in his manifold dealings with students, discussion with professional colleagues and the tendering of advice, the author has had numerous opportunities to recognize just where the difficulties of appreciation and application of physical chemistry appear to lie.

Bearing in mind the purpose of the book, the order of the Exercises is such that, at any stage, it will generally be unnecessary to refer to later chapters. Moreover (with very few exceptions and at the risk of repetition), each problem is discussed so thoroughly that there is no need first to study other sections in order to understand it.

Corresponding to the diversity of practical problems, the Exercises will be found to vary between easy and more difficult, short and long. Rigid uniformity of expressions, terms and units of measurement, as used in textbooks, have been deliberately avoided. On the other hand, a uniform notation of formulae consistent with international usage has been adopted in order not to conflict with related sciences. This is especially so in the case of thermodynamic formulae.

For the sake of easy reference, the various Exercises are marked as follows:

Exercises particularly suitable for the practice of physical chemistry and its methods of calculation in connection with lecture demonstrations and problems are marked with an asterisk (*).

Difficult exercises which presuppose a certain command of the precepts of physical chemistry are unmarked.

Two bold asterisks are used to indicate those exercises which constantly recur in the typical calculations of physical chemistry and physico-chemical technology and which are presented in such a form as to be suitable for reference purposes.

This classification is to some extent arbitrary. Naturally, there are numerous examples which fall into more than one category.

The scientific requirements of the book have been related to those of the appropriate textbooks of physical chemistry from which derivations and explanations of fundamental formulae have been taken and introduced at the beginning of each Chapter. It was not possible to include a list of books consulted in assembling the Exercises, but it must be mentioned that the following works were particularly helpful to the author in providing numerous references:

D'ANS, J. and LAX, E., *Taschenbuch für Chemiker und Physiker*
BLADERGROEN, W., *Physikalische Chemie in Medizin und Biologie*
BONHOEFFER, K. F. and HARTECK, P., *Grundlagen der Photochemie*
EGGERT, J. (with HOCK, L. and SCHWAB, G.-M.), *Lehrbuch der physikalischen Chemie*
EMELÉUS, H. J. and ANDERSON, J. S., *Modern Aspects of Inorganic Chemistry*
EUCKEN, A. and JAKOB, M., *Der Chemieingenieur*
EUCKEN, A., *Lehrbuch der chemischen Physik*
EUCKEN, A. and WICKE, E., *Grundriß der physikalischen Chemie*
FAJANS, K. and WÜST, J., *Physikalisch-chemisches Praktikum*
FEITKNECHT, W., *Allgemeine und physikalische Chemie*
FIESER, L. F. and FIESER, M., *Organic Chemistry*
FINKELNBURG, W., *Einführung in die Atomphysik*
FROMHERZ, H. and KING, A., *German–English Chemical Terminology*
GATTERMANN, L. and WIELAND, H., *Die Praxis des organischen Chemikers*
GLASSTONE, S., *The Elements of Physical Chemistry*
GLASSTONE, S., *Thermodynamics for Chemists*
HERZFELD, K. F., *Kinetische Theorie der Wärme*
HILDEBRAND, J. H., *Solubility of Non-electrolytes*
HINSHELWOOD, C. N., *The Kinetics of Chemical Change in Gaseous Systems*
HOFMANN, K. A., *Lehrbuch der anorganischen Chemie*
HOLLEMAN, A. F. and WIBERG, E., *Lehrbuch der anorganischen Chemie*
HÜCKEL, W., *Theoretische Grundlagen der organischen Chemie*
JOST. W., *Explosions- und Verbrennungsvorgänge in Gasen*
JUSTI, E., *Spezifische Wärme, Enthalpie, Entropie, Dissoziation technischer Gase*
KARRER, P., *Lehrbuch der organischen Chemie*
KNOX, J., *Physico-chemical Calculations*
KOHLRAUSCH, F., *Praktische Physik*
KORTÜM, G., *Einführung in die chemische Thermodynamik*
KORTÜM, G. and BUCHHOLZ-MEISENHEIMER, H., *Theorie der Destillation und Extraktion von Flüssigkeiten*
KORTÜM, G., *Lehrbuch der Elektrochemie*
KUHN, W., *Physikalische Chemie*
LEWIS, G. and RANDALL, M., *Thermodynamics*
MICHAELIS, L., *Wasserstoffionenkonzentrationen*
MICHAELIS, L., *Oxydations- und Reduktionspotentiale*
MOELWYN-HUGHES, E. A., *The Kinetics of Reactions in Solution*
PAULING, L., *General Chemistry*
REMY, H., *Lehrbuch der anorganischen Chemie*
SCHUMACHER, H. J., *Chemische Gasreaktionen*
SCHWAB, G.-M., *Handbuch der Katalyse*
SCHWAB, G.-M., *Katalyse vom Standpunkt der chemischen Kinetik*

SCHWABE, K., *Fortschritte der pH-Meßtechnik*
SCHWABE, K., *Polarographie und chemische Konstitution organischer Verbindungen*
SKRABAL, A., *Homogenkinetik*
ULICH, H. and JOST, W., *Kurzes Lehrbuch der physikalischen Chemie*

The number and choice of the calculations dealt with in individual chapters have not been determined by the extent and completeness of relevant chapters in textbooks where didactic requirements must be borne in mind; rather have they been framed according to type and variety of applications in science and industry, with the intention of giving a picture of those points having importance and usefulness in practice.

Physical calculations are often required in the realms of atomic and molecular structures, spectroscopy and the statistical theory of matter, but experience shows that the difficulties lie more in understanding trains of thought and in deductions than in making purely practical application. The latter is mostly a simple matter of inserting numerical values in established formulae; if not, the problems range beyond the limits of normal routine calculations and belong to the field of physical research. Calculation of the efficiency and regulation of distillation columns on the basis of the mixture equilibrium curve has also not been included as an example of chemical engineering.

On the other hand, different questions relating to chemico-physical practice are discussed in the way in which they would be encountered by the industrial chemist. Thus it will be shown that by using semi-empirical laws and sufficient approximation, solutions may often be found the apparent basic value of which is comparatively limited. However, on the whole, these solutions satisfactorily fulfil their purpose, i.e. the speedy and adequate answering of a question.

My thanks are due to Mr. G. Kinner who undertook the task of translating the second German edition of this book, and to the staff of Butterworths for their friendly care in its production.

Finally, professional colleagues are requested to support the author in his endeavour to place in the hands of students and colleagues a book on the applicational possibilities and calculation procedures of physical chemistry, which is as versatile and generally useful as possible – by advising him of their experiences, giving examples from their own sphere of activities and by bringing tc his attention mistakes and suggesting improvements.

Schwyz, January 1964 H. F.

PREFACE TO THE SECOND EDITION

HEAVY demand has necessitated an early new edition of this book. Due account has been taken in the second edition of suggestions and critical remarks made by colleagues both in correspondence and in reviews. In particular, the dimensional notation has been made more precise and in the Chapter dealing with electromotive force a number of terms and formulae has been taken from the latest textbooks and publications in this field. I am indebted to Dr. E. Doehlemann, Trostberg (Obb.), for material regarding a new problem (No. 140.1) in electrometric titration. Four new Exercises on radioactivity have also been included; Nos. 207, 208, 209 on indicator analysis and No. 210 on protection against radiation. Thanks are due to Dr. E. Proksch, Vienna, for the material for Nos. 207, 208 and 209. The important eigenvalue method for the solution of differential equations, as well as the method for the variation of constants, given in problem No. 184 on the time dependence of a complex series of reactions, has been treated in a detailed and comparative manner.

Above all, I am grateful to Prof. Dr. G. Emschwiller, Paris, Prof. Dr. K. Huber, Berne, Prof. Dr. E. Lange, Erlangen, Prof. Dr. K. Peters, Vienna, and Prof. Dr. K. Schwabe, Dresden, for valuable suggestions and constructive criticism.

Schwyz, Autumn 1959

PROF. DR. HANS FROMHERZ

LIST OF SYMBOLS

A	work (fed into a system, or done on a system) activation energy surface area actual air consumption
A_0	theoretical air consumption
a	adsorbate, in millimoles per gramme adsorbent activity initial concentration constant in van der Waals equation of state quantity
α	degree of dissociation mole volume or surface fraction steric factor (probability factor) constant in Brønsted equation
α^{Bu}	Bunsen absorption coefficient
α^{Os}	Oswald absorption coefficient
B	constant in Freundlich adsorption isotherm second virial coefficient
b	constant in van der Waals equation of state constant in Langmuir adsorption isotherm
β	degree of dissociation constant for regular mixtures
C	Sutherland constant distribution coefficient conductivity
C, $C^\star$	number of components (in phase rule)
C_p	heat capacity of a system at constant pressure
C_v	heat capacity of a system at constant volume
c	concentration, litre molarity (molarity) speed of light constant in Brunauer–Emmett–Teller adsorption isotherm
c_2	Planck's second constant ($= hc/k$)
c_p	specific heat per molecule (molar heat) at constant pressure
c_v	specific heat per molecule (molar heat) at constant volume
D	torsional moment diffusion coefficient
d	layer thickness
δ	boundary layer thickness
E	electromotive force (e.m.f.) voltage, terminal voltage, cell voltage
E_h	reference e.m.f. against the standard hydrogen electrode
E_{oh}	standard reference e.m.f. against the hydrogen electrode under standard conditions
E_0	standard e.m.f.
E_b	ebullioscopic constant
E_f	cryoscopic constant
e	electronic charge ($= F/N_A$)
ε	dielectric constant
η	internal friction coefficient yield (chemical efficiency)

F	force melting point 1 faraday (Faraday constant) degrees of freedom (in phase rule)
f	activity coefficient
$f_{\pm}$	mean activity coefficient
f_{λ}	conductivity coefficient
f_{o}	osmotic coefficient
Φ	molar enzyme concentration in Michaelis–Menten equation light intensity, radiation intensity
φ	angle specific volume concentration of enzyme–substrate complex in Michaelis–Menten equation lattice energy quantum yield efficiency
G	mass, especially to indicate kilogramme molarity, m free enthalpy (thermodynamic potential); Gibbs free energy
g	acceleration due to gravity
g, g'	constants in the Brønsted equation
Γ	ionic concentration
γ	degree of hydrolysis constant for regular mixtures specific gravity
H	enthalpy (heat content)
H, H'	frequency factor (action constant)
ΔH^{E}	heat of formation
H_{G}, H_{N}	gross and net calorific value
h, H	height, fall
h	Planck's constant
I	electric current strength total radiation/sec unit matrix
J, J^{*}	ionic strength
i	van't Hoff coefficient
K	transformation matrix number of independent equilibrium constants (in phase rule)
K, K_{c}, K_{p}, K_{x}	law of mass action constants proportionality factor
Kp	boiling point
Kp_{100}	boiling point at 100 torr
K_{s}	solubility product
k	constant in Henry's law bulk modulus reaction rate constant Boltzmann constant ($= R/N_{A}$)
k_{A}	Smythe factor
k_{H_2O}	ionic product of water
$\varkappa$	ratio of the specific heats, c_{p}/c_{v} specific conductivity
L	tube or cell length
L_{f}	enthalpy of fusion
L_{s}	enthalpy of sublimation
L_{t}	enthalpy of transition
L_{v}	enthalpy of vaporization

l	mean free path
$^{d}l^{\star}$	final heat of solution
l_f	molar enthalpy of fusion
l_s	molar enthalpy of sublimation
l_t	molar enthalpy of transition
l_v	molar enthalpy of vaporization
$\Lambda_{c(mol)}$	molar conductivity
$\Lambda_{c(eq)}$	equivalent conductivity
$\Lambda_{K(eq)}, \Lambda_{A(eq)}$	ion equivalent conductivity
λ	wavelength excess air coefficient molar reaction variable radioactive decay constant eigenvalue
$'\lambda$	first heat of solution
λ_f	enthalpy of fusion per gramme
λ_v	enthalpy of vaporization per gramme
M	molecular weight, atomic weight in the meaning of (*i*) molar mass (g/mole), (*ii*) molecular weight (ratio)
$\overline{M}$	mean or apparent molecular weight of a mixture
M_r	reduced mass
m	mass concentration (mole/kg solvent), kilogramme molarity (molality)
m, μ	extinction modulus (absorption coefficient, attenuation coefficient)
Nm^3	cubic metres at s.t.p. (1 atm, 0 °C)
N	number of particles output, power
$\dot{N}$	particle velocity ($= dN/dt$)
^{1}N	number of particles per cm^3
$^{1}N_i$	number of particles of substance X_i per cm^3 of mixture
N_A	number of molecules in one mole (Avogadro constant)
n	quantity of moles, quantity of equivalents adsorption isotherm constant
n_e	electrochemical valency of an electrolyte; cell reaction charge number or number of faradays transported per mole–formula–weight change
n_A, n_K	transport numbers
$\{n_q\}$	number of mol. quanta
$\dot{n}_q$	number of mol. quanta per unit time and per unit volume
ν	number of fragments from a dissociating molecule
ν_i	stoichiometric mole number frequency ($= c/\lambda$)
ν	wave number ($= 1/\lambda$)
P	osmotic pressure pressure (only used in certain cases, especially for distinction from pH) number of phases (in phase rule)
$p, p^{\star}$	pressure fugacity statistical constant in Brønsted equation
pH	negative logarithm of hydrogen ion activity
p_i	partial pressure of substance X_i
p_{0i}	vapour pressure of pure substance X_i (saturation pressure)
p_k	critical pressure
π	Ludolph's number

Q	heat supplied to a system quantity of electricity, in coulombs
q	cross-sectional area statistical factor in Brønsted equation
$\mathfrak{Q}_p$	heat of reaction at constant pressure ($= -\Delta H$)
$\mathfrak{Q}_v$	heat of reaction at constant volume ($= -\Delta U$)
R	electrical resistance gas constant ($= N_A k$)
r	mixture ratio radius
rH	negative logarithm of hydrogen pressure
ϱ	density
S	entropy specific activity of a radioactive substance
[S]	substrate concentration
$S_{0\,298}$	standard entropy
Σ	summation symbol
σ	molecular diameter specific resistance
σ_{12}	mean molecular diameter ($= r_1 + r_2$)
T	absolute temperature, in degrees Kelvin half-life period
T_k	critical temperature
t	separation factor time
t_r	residence time
τ	mean life period
θ	temperature, in degrees Centigrade
U	(internal) energy
u_A, u_K	absolute migration velocity (per V/cm), ionic mobility
V	volume
$\dot{V}$	volumetric rate ($= dV/dt$)
v	molar volume reaction velocity ($= dx/dt$)
v_k	critical volume per mole
W	weight
w	speed; molecular speed
$\overline{w}$	mean molecular speed
X	frictional force; force
$\boldsymbol{x}$	eigenvector
x	coordinate value quantity (of adsorbate) mole fraction magnitude of an unknown
$100\,x$	mole per cent
ξ	weight or mass fraction
$100\,\xi$	per cent by weight
Y	Einstein constant for the mass–energy relation ($= c^2$)
y	magnitude of an unknown
Z	collision number constant in wave number–energy relation ($= N_A h c$) pore number
z, z_+, z_-	ionic charge; ion valency
z_s	number of adsorption centres

INTRODUCTORY REMARKS ON SYMBOLS AND EQUATIONS

In this book it has been assumed that the indication of dimensions should promote clarity in presentation, but should not become an end in itself.

In general, the following principles are adopted:

(1) As a rule the symbols signify physical quantities, i.e. the products of a numerical value and a dimension; not numerical values only.

Example—For the unit G one may put

$$G = 5{\cdot}3\ \text{g} = 5{\cdot}3 \times 10^{-3}\ \text{kg} \quad \text{but not} \quad 5{\cdot}3 \quad \text{or} \quad 5{\cdot}3 \times 10^{-3}$$

For the pressure, p, one may have

$$p = 10\ \text{atm} = 7600\ \text{torr} = 10{\cdot}33\ \text{kg cm}^{-2}, \text{ but not } 10 \text{ or } 7600.$$

As a rule, therefore, relations between symbols represent equations between quantities.

(2) If, in certain cases, for example for logarithms, only the coefficient $\{\}$ is used, without the selected unit of measurement (dimension), a special note is made, should clarity require it.

Example:

$$p = 10\ \text{atm} = 7600\ \text{torr}$$

$$\log p/\text{atm} = 1{\cdot}0 \quad \text{or} \quad \log p/\text{torr} = 3{\cdot}881$$

or just

$$T = 1000\ °\text{K} \quad \{T\} = 1000 \qquad \log\{T\} = 3$$

It is usually unnecessary to write $\log T/\text{deg.} = 3$, since, in scientific works, T is always measured in the same units.

(3) For the sake of clarity:

(*a*) in equations in which a combination of symbols and numerical quantities occurs, the units of measurement of the numerical quantities will, as a rule, be omitted, e.g. $T = T_0 + \theta = 273 + \theta$, and not $T = 273\ \text{deg.} + \theta$ or $T = (273 + \{\theta\})$ deg.

(*b*) as a rule, in making numerical calculations, only numerical values will be given in the intermediate steps, the unit of measurement being quoted only in the final result, provided that the dimensions are not changed during the calculation and a dimensional check is not required, e.g. $p = 677 + 8 = 685$ torr, and not $p = (677 + 8)$ torr $= 685$ torr

$$G = \frac{MpV}{RT} = \frac{32 \times 150 \times 40}{0{\cdot}082 \times 288} = 8130\ \text{g} = 8{\cdot}13\ \text{kg}$$

not, in general

$$G = \frac{32\ \text{g mole}^{-1} \times 150\ \text{atm} \times 40\ \text{l.}}{0{\cdot}082\,\dfrac{\text{l. atm}}{\text{deg. mole}} \times 288\ \text{deg.}} = \frac{32 \times 150 \times 40}{0{\cdot}082 \times 288}\,\frac{\text{g mole}^{-1}\,\text{atm l.}}{\text{l. atm deg.}^{-1}\,\text{mole}^{-1}\,\text{deg.}} = 8130\ \text{g}$$

(4) The symbol n represents the quantity of a substance in moles (gram mols), that is the molar quantity with the unit of measurement [mole], e.g. $n = 5{\cdot}2$ moles; the symbol $\{n\}$ represents the dimensionless number of moles, e.g. $\{n\} = 5{\cdot}2$, i.e. $n = \{n\}$ moles.

(5) In physico-chemical calculations it is preferable to use related quantities. Thus, in general, quantities will relate to 1 mole or 1 equivalent of substance.

Examples Gas constant $R = 1{\cdot}9865$ cal/(deg. mole)

and not molar gas constant $R = 1{\cdot}9865$ cal/deg.

Avogadro (Loschmidt) constant $N_A = 6{\cdot}0236 \times 10^{23}$ mole^{-1}

and not Avogadro (Loschmidt) number $N_A = 6{\cdot}0236 \times 10^{23}$

Faraday constant F (1 faraday) = 96,495 coulomb/equiv.

and not Faraday-equivalent F = 96,495 coulomb.

It is evident that what appears to be an unnecessary duplication of expressions is expedient in order to give a clear presentation; e.g. the *molar volume* of water is $v_{H_2O} = 18$ cm^3/mole, is used instead of the *volume* of water is $v_{H_2O} = 18$ cm^3/mole; or the *molar heat* of water is $\bar{c}_p = 18{\cdot}02$ cal/deg. mole instead of the *heat capacity* of water is $\bar{c}_p = 18{\cdot}02$ cal/deg. mole.

(6) A reaction equation will be written in the usual manner:

$$\nu_A A + \nu_B B + \Delta H \rightarrow \nu_E E + \nu_F F$$

or

$$\nu_A A + \nu_B B \rightarrow \nu_E E + \nu_F F - \Delta H$$

or

$$\nu_A A + \nu_B B \rightarrow \nu_E E + \nu_F F \Delta H$$

e.g.

$$N_2 + 3H_2 - 26 \text{ kcal/mole} \rightarrow 2NH_3$$

or

$$N_2 + 3H_2 \rightarrow 2NH_3 + 26 \text{ kcal/mole}$$

or

$$N_2 + 3H_2 \rightarrow 2NH_3 \; \Delta H = -26 \text{ kcal/mole}$$

It should indicate the conversion of molar quantities of the substances X_i. ΔH is the heat of reaction for a reaction in which the molar quantities n_i are converted, and therefore has the units [kcal/mole] or [joule/mole], as has also the external work, $p\Delta V$, appearing during the reaction. The molar quantity n_i (unit [mole]) is normally (see p. 101) broken down to $n_i = \nu_i \lambda$ or $dn_i = \nu_i d\lambda$, where ν_i is the stoichiometric mole number of the substance X_i (dimensionless) and λ is the molar 'reaction variable' (degree of advancement) (unit [mole]) of the relevant reaction. The name introduced above has been retained although, in accordance with the definitions in this book, λ represents a quantity of substance with the unit [mole]: when the reaction proceeds according to formula, λ is equal to 1 mole.

Example—5 moles N_2 and 15 moles H_2 are converted to 10 moles NH_3. As a result, 130 kcal are liberated at 500 °C. The stoichiometric mole numbers are $\nu_i = 1, 3$ and 2; the reaction variable is

$$\lambda = \frac{5 \text{ moles}}{1} = \frac{15 \text{ moles}}{3} = \frac{10 \text{ moles}}{2} = 5 \text{ moles}$$

The heat of reaction, per formula conversion, is

$$\Delta H = \frac{-130\,\text{kcal}}{5\,\text{moles}} = -26\,\text{kcal/mole}$$

(7) As is customary in textbooks of chemistry and physics, the symbol M has been taken to indicate molecular weight. However, in equations it may have a dual meaning – but the same numerical value – as follows:

(a) Molar weight in grammes (mass of a mole) with the dimensions (g/mole), e.g. $\mathrm{M}_{C_6H_6} = 78{\cdot}1$ g/mole means that the molar weight of benzene is 78·1 g.

(b) 'Molecular weight' which, as is well known, is neither a weight nor a mass but a non-dimensional ratio and should, therefore, correctly be designated by $\{M\}$ ($M = \{M\}$ grammes), e.g. $M_{C_6H_6} = 78{\cdot}1$, means that benzene has a molecular weight of 78·1.

Neither in designation nor in calculation is there any danger of confusion in establishing this point—even though international agreement of the concept may be desirable.

(8) In chemistry one is usually interested in the mass G of a substance, expressed in the units gramme (g) or kilogrammes (kg). The chemist's analytical balance serves to compare masses. In those cases where weight W is expressly used, gramme weight (g wt.) and kilogramme weight (kg wt.) are the terms used.

Example—The density of air is $\varrho = 1{\cdot}293 \times 10^{-3}$ g/cm^3 = 1·293 g/l., but the weight of air (specific gravity) is $\gamma = 1{\cdot}293 \times 10^{-3}$ g wt./cm^3 = 1·293 g wt./l.

1

IDEAL GASES

IF AN ideal gas has the pressure p_1 and volume V_1 at the absolute temperature T_1, and pressure p_2 and volume V_2 at absolute temperature T_2, then

$$\frac{p_1 V_1}{T_1} = \frac{p_2 V_2}{T_2} = \text{const} \qquad \ldots\ldots \quad (1)$$

T (degrees Kelvin, °K) $= T_0 + \theta = 273{\cdot}16 + \theta$ (θ in degrees Centigrade, °C)

In general:

$$pV = nRT = \frac{G}{M} RT \qquad \ldots\ldots \quad (2)$$

the equation of state for ideal gases.

$$n = \text{molar quantity (mole)} = \frac{\text{mass } G\,(\text{g})}{\text{mol. wt. } M\,(\text{g/mole})} \qquad \ldots\ldots \quad (3)$$

(See p. 2, paras. 4 and 6.) R is the gas constant.
If $p_0 = 1$ atm, $T_0 = 273{\cdot}16$ °K or 0 °C (standard conditions), the volume of 1 mole of a gas (molar volume) is $v_0 = V_0/n = 22{,}415\ \text{cm}^3/\text{mole}^{-1} = 22{\cdot}415\ \text{l. mole}^{-1}$*.

$$\left.\begin{aligned} \text{Thus:}\quad R &= \frac{p_0 V_0}{nT_0} = \frac{1 \times 22415}{1 \times 273{\cdot}16} = 82{\cdot}06\ \text{cm}^3\ \text{atm(deg. mole)} \\ &= 0{\cdot}80206\ \text{l. atm./(deg. mole)} = 1{\cdot}9865\ \text{cal/deg. mole} \end{aligned}\right\} \quad \ldots \quad (4)$$

$$\left.\begin{aligned} &\text{The density of an ideal gas} = \varrho_0 \\ &= \frac{\text{Mol. wt. } M}{\text{Molar volume } v_0} = \frac{\{M\}}{22{,}415}\,\frac{\text{g}}{\text{Ncm}^3} = \frac{\{M\}}{22{\cdot}415}\,\frac{\text{g}}{\text{l.}}\ \text{(see p. 3, para. 7)} \end{aligned}\right\} \quad \ldots \quad (5)$$

For an ideal gas mixture, the total pressure, p, is equal to the sum of the partial pressures p_i of the components X_i, thus

$$p = p_1 + p_2 + \cdots = \sum p_i \quad \text{Dalton's law} \qquad \ldots\ldots \quad (6)$$

If all mixture components X_i have the same pressure p and if p remains constant, then the volume of the mixture is equal to the sum of the individual volumes V_i, thus

$$V_m = V_1 + V_2 \cdots = \sum V_i \qquad \ldots\ldots \quad (7)$$

---

* Gas volume reduced to standard temperature and pressure (0 °C, 760 torr) is measured in normal cubic metres, Nm^3, or normal cubic centimetres, Ncm^3. Gas pressure is measured either in physical atmospheres [atm], or in mm Hg = torr (1 atm = 760 torr = 1033·23 g wt./cm²) or in kg wt./cm²; 1 kg wt./cm² = 1000 g wt./cm² = 735·559 torr.

In the c.g.s. system the unit of measurement for pressure is dyn/cm² = microbar. 1 atm = $1{\cdot}01325 \times 10^6$ dyn/cm² = 1013·25 millibars (mb); 1 torr = 1 mm Hg = $1{\cdot}33322 \times 10^3$ dyn/cm² = 1·33322 mb (see also p. 3, para. 7 and p. 8).

The equation of state for an ideal gas mixture is therefore

$$\left.\begin{aligned} pV_m &= (n_1 + n_2)\,RT = \sum n_i\,RT = \sum \frac{G_i}{M_i}\,RT = \frac{G}{\overline{M}}\,RT \\ p_i V_m &= n_i\,RT = \frac{G_i}{M_i}\,RT \quad \text{or} \quad p_i = \frac{n_i}{V_m}\,RT = c_i\,RT \end{aligned}\right\} \quad \ldots (8)$$

[c_i = concentration in moles per unit volume, see also eqn. (58)]

In this equation G_i is the mass (g) and M_i the molar weight (g/mole) of the component X_i. G, the total mass of the gas mixture, is given by $G = G_1 + G_2 + \cdots = \sum G_i$ and $\overline{M}$ is the mean or apparent molar weight.

According to eqn. (8) the mean molar weight, $\overline{M}$, will be

$$\overline{M} = \frac{G}{\sum n_i} = \frac{G_1 + G_2 + \cdots}{n_1 + n_2 + \cdots} = \frac{n_1 M_1 + n_2 M_2 + \cdots}{\sum n_i} = x_1 M_1 + x_2 M_2 + \cdots = \sum x_i M_i \quad \ldots (9)$$

x_i = the mole fraction of component X_i

$$x_i = \frac{n_i}{\sum n_i} = \frac{G_i/M_i}{\sum G_i/M_i} = \frac{p_i}{p} \text{ (according to Avogadro)} \quad \ldots\ldots (10)$$

$$\left.\begin{aligned} \text{The mole per cent (mole \%)} &= \text{mole fraction} \times 100 = x_i \times 100 \\ &= \frac{G_i/M_i}{\sum G_i/M_i} \times 100 \\ &= \text{volume per cent (vol.\%) for ideal gases} \end{aligned}\right\} \quad \ldots (11)$$

According to eqns. (10) and (11), the following may be used for conversion of weight per cent (wt. %) $100\xi_i$ (ξ_i = proportion by weight or mass) to mole per cent and vice versa:

$$\left.\begin{aligned} &\text{mole per cent:} && 100\,x_i = \frac{100\,\xi_i/M_i}{\sum \xi_i/M_i} \\ &\text{wt. per cent:} && 100\,\xi_i = \frac{x_i M_i}{\sum x_j M_i}\,100 = 100\,\frac{x_i M_i}{\overline{M}} \end{aligned}\right\} \quad \ldots (12)$$

For the mean molar weight, it follows from eqns. (9) and (12) that

$$\overline{M} = \frac{1}{\sum \xi_i/M_i} \quad \ldots\ldots (13)$$

and, from eqns. (12) and (13), for mole per cent:

$$100\,x_i = 100\xi_i \overline{M}/M_i \quad \ldots\ldots (14)$$

or mole % = wt. % × $\dfrac{\text{mean mol. wt.}}{\text{mol. wt.}}$

*Exercise 1

Calculate, from the molecular weight, the density ϱ_0 in g/l. for oxygen, nitrogen, carbon monoxide and nitric oxide [see eqn. (5)].

Solution 1. Density $\varrho_0 = \frac{\text{mol. wt. } M}{\text{molar volume } v_0}$

The molecular weights are: oxygen (O_2) = 32, nitrogen (N_2) = 28, carbon monoxide (CO) = 28 and nitric oxide (NO) = 30

Thus:
$$L_{O_2} = \frac{32}{22\cdot4} = 1\cdot43\ \text{g/l.} \qquad L_{N_2} = \frac{28}{22\cdot4} = 1\cdot25\ \text{g/l.}$$
$$L_{CO} = \frac{28}{22\cdot4} = 1\cdot25\ \text{g/l.} \qquad L_{NO} = \frac{30}{22\cdot4} = 1\cdot34\ \text{g/l.}$$

Note. The approximate density of non-ideal gases and vapours may also be calculated as above, with a maximum error of about 3—5 per cent.

*Exercise 2

When 150 tons of limestone (the daily output of a large lime kiln) are burnt, how much carbon dioxide is liberated at a temperature of $\theta = 15$ °C and a barometer reading of 710 mm Hg?

Solution 2. $CaCO_3 = CaO + CO_2$ Mol. wt. of $CaCO_3 = M = 100\cdot07$
100 g give 22·4 l. at s.t.p.
150 tons give x_0 l. at s.t.p.

Thus
$$x_0/22\cdot4 = 150 \times 10^6/100 \qquad \ldots\ \text{(i)}$$

x_0 l. at s.t.p. may be converted to x l. under the required conditions by means of eqn. (1): $p_1 = 760$ mm Hg, $V_1 = x_0$ l., $T_1 = 273$ °K, $p_2 = 710$ mm Hg, $V_2 = x$ l., $T_2 = 273 + 15 = 288$ °K

Thus:
$$\frac{x_0 \times 760}{273} = \frac{x \times 710}{288} \qquad \ldots\ \text{(ii)}$$

From (i) and (ii) the following is obtained:
$$x = \frac{760 \times 288 \times 22\cdot4 \times 150 \times 10^6}{710 \times 273 \times 100} = 37\cdot9 \times 10^6\ \text{l.} = 37{,}900\ \text{m}^3\ CO_2$$

*Exercise 3

How many kilogrammes of oxygen may be carried in a steel bottle of 40 l. capacity if the bottle is filled to a pressure of 150 atm at 15 °C?

Solution 3. Eqn. (2) is used:
$$pV = \frac{G}{M} RT \qquad \ldots\ \text{(i)}$$

$$p = 150\ \text{atm}, \quad V = 40\ \text{l.}, \quad M_{O_2} = 32$$
$$R = 0\cdot082 \frac{\text{l. atm}}{\text{deg. mole}}, \quad T = 273 + 15 = 288\ °\text{K}$$
(see eqn. (4))

$$G = \frac{MpV}{RT} = \frac{32 \times 150 \times 40}{0\cdot082 \times 288} = 8130\ \text{g} = 8\cdot13\ \text{kg}\ O_2$$

Note. The weight of steel bottles constitutes about 90 per cent of the carriage weight for condensed gases. The above-mentioned steel bottle has an empty weight of 75 kg.

*Exercise 4

A container filled with air and having a capacity of $V_1 = 162{\cdot}4\ \mathrm{cm}^3$ and a temperature of $\theta_1 = 15{\cdot}5\ °\mathrm{C}$ is heated. The air then escapes and is collected in a vessel, over water at a temperature of $\theta_2 = 14\ °\mathrm{C}$, when it occupies a volume $V_2 = 114{\cdot}3\ \mathrm{cm}^3$. During the experiment the barometer reading remains constant at $p_1 = 710$ torr. The final temperature of the heated container, θ_x, should be calculated, without taking into account its thermal expansion. (The partial pressure of water vapour $p_{\mathrm{H_2O}}$ at $14\ °\mathrm{C} = 12$ torr.)

Solution 4. Of the air originally in the container (molar quantity n_1), all that remains after the final temperature has been attained is the molar quantity n_3. The rest, molar quantity n_2, is in the collecting vessel, so that

$$n_1 = n_2 + n_3 \qquad \ldots\ldots \quad \text{(i)}$$

The various molar quantities are determined by means of eqn. (2).

$$n_1 = p_1 V_1 / R T_1 \qquad T_1 = 273{\cdot}2 + \theta_i \qquad n_2 = \frac{(p_1 - p_{\mathrm{H_2O}})V_2}{RT_2} \qquad \ldots\ldots \quad \text{(ii)}$$

The total pressure p_1 in the collecting vessel is the sum of the partial pressures of the water vapour, $p_{\mathrm{H_2O}}$, and of the collected air, p_2, therefore $p_2 = p_1 - p_{\mathrm{H_2O}}$ is the quantity required in (ii) for the calculation of n_2.

Finally:

$$n_3 = \frac{p_1 V_1}{RT_x} \qquad \ldots\ldots \quad \text{(iii)}$$

Combining (ii) and (iii) with (i), and simplifying, gives

$$\frac{1}{T_1} - \frac{(p_1 - p_{\mathrm{H_2O}})V_2}{p_1 V_1 T_2} = \frac{1}{T_x} \qquad \ldots\ldots \quad \text{(iv)}$$

By substitution of the numerical values, we get

$$\frac{1}{288{\cdot}7} - \frac{698 \times 114{\cdot}3}{710 \times 162{\cdot}4 \times 287{\cdot}2} = \frac{1}{T_x} \qquad \ldots\ldots \quad \text{(v)}$$

$$T_x = 948{\cdot}2\ °\mathrm{K} \qquad \theta_x = 675\ °\mathrm{C}.$$

Note. This exercise includes the principle of gas thermometer temperature measurement. To obtain useful results, measurements should be as accurate as possible (to 1 part in 1000). The numerical evaluation in eqn. (v) is best made by using logarithms or a 50 cm slide rule (with magnified readings) since, in this case, it is a matter of computing the difference between two relatively large numbers and unnecessary errors could occur through inaccurate calculation.

*Exercise 5

A glass flask, which is connected to a Hg-differential manometer, has an internal volume $V = 255{\cdot}0\ \mathrm{cm}^3$. It is heated in a water bath to $\theta = 98\ °\mathrm{C}$ while open to the atmosphere. A glass ball, filled with $G_1 = 0{\cdot}0912$ g of ether, is introduced into the flask after equilibrium has been established. The flask is then cut off from the outside atmosphere and the glass ball is broken inside the flask. Whilst the volume remains constant, a pressure difference of $\Delta p_1 = 111{\cdot}7$ mm Hg is noted with respect to the outside atmosphere. What is the molecular weight M_1 of the ether?

Solution 5. Using the second part of eqn. (8), the partial pressure of the ether ($=\Delta p_1$) is

$$\Delta p_1 V = \frac{G_1}{M_1} RT_1 \qquad (T_1 = 273 + \theta_1) \qquad \ldots\ldots \quad \text{(i)}$$

Substituting the given numerical values, with

$$R = 82 \text{ cm}^3 \text{ atm/(deg. mole)}$$

and

$$\Delta p_1 = 111{\cdot}7/760 \text{ atm}$$

one obtains

$$M_1 = \frac{760 \times 0{\cdot}0912 \times 371 \times 82}{111{\cdot}7 \times 255{\cdot}0} = 74{\cdot}1$$

Note. Since the gas constant is not dimensionless, care must be taken to ensure that the units of the numerical values used in the gas equation correspond to the units of the gas constant, i.e. if the above-mentioned value of R is used, the volume must be given in cubic centimetres and the pressure in atmospheres.

There are various methods, based on the gas law, for determining molecular weights. Sometimes three variables are fixed from the outset by the conditions of the experiment. The fourth appears during the experiment and is evaluated by it. In the above case V, T and G are fixed and Δp is measured.

*Exercise 6

In a laboratory with a room temperature of 20 °C and a barometer reading of $p = 750$ torr there is a glass bottle, filled with ethyl ether, whose mouth (diameter $= 2r = 2$ cm) is closed with a glass stopper. The bottle is partly emptied and re-stoppered quickly, so that, immediately after the operation and as a result of the entry of air, about 80 per cent of the gas-filled space over the ether in the bottle consists of air. How great is the force acting on the stopper of the bottle after equilibrium is established? The vapour pressure of ethyl ether at 20 °C is 460 torr.

Solution 6. Each time, immediately after the bottle has been closed, the total pressure in the vapour space ($p = 750$ torr) is due to the partial pressure of the air (80 per cent), $p_A = 750 \times 80/100 = 600$ torr, and that of the ether, $p_E = 750 - 600 = 150$ torr, which forms the remainder. As the equilibrium vapour pressure of ether at 20 °C is 460 torr, the partial pressure of the ether in the bottle will gradually rise from 150 torr to 460 torr, i.e. by 310 torr and this gives rise to an excess internal pressure. Since 760 torr = 1 atm = 1·033 kg wt./cm² (see p. 4), an internal excess pressure of $p_E = 1{\cdot}033 \times 310/760$ kg wt./cm² results and the force acting on the glass stopper from inside is

$$X_E = r^2 \times \pi \times 1{\cdot}033 \times 310/760 = 1{\cdot}32 \text{ kg wt.}$$

As only the weight (at most 50 g) of the stopper is opposed to this force, the stopper will be forced out.

Note. After ether has been poured from a bottle, it is regularly noticed that the stopper lifts after a short while — often, indeed, repeatedly — until equilibrium again becomes established in the vapour space over the liquid.

*Exercise 7

Ethyl ether, at a temperature of $\theta_1 = 15$ °C and with a barometer reading $p_1 = 750$ mm Hg, is introduced into an air-filled tube of volume $V = 100$ cm³, which is then sealed off and heated to $\theta_2 = 300$ °C. How many grammes of ether may be introduced if the pressure in the tube is not to exceed 50 atm?

Solution 7. At 300 °C all the ether is in the gas phase. The total pressure p is due to the partial pressure of the ether, p_E, and that of the air, p_A, in the tube and should not exceed 50 atm.

$$p = p_E + p_A = 50 \text{ atm.} \qquad \ldots \quad \text{(i)}$$

p_E and p_A are calculated from eqns. (2) and (1), respectively.

$$p_E = \frac{G R T_2}{74{\cdot}1 \times V} \quad \text{mol. wt. of ether} = 74{\cdot}1 \quad T_2 = 273 + \theta_2 \qquad \ldots \quad \text{(ii)}$$

$$p_A = \frac{p_1 T_2}{T_1} \qquad T_1 = 273 + \theta_1 \qquad \ldots \quad \text{(iii)}$$

Combining (i), (ii) and (iii) and introducing the numerical values, gives

$$50 = \frac{G \times 82 \times 573}{74{\cdot}1 \times 100} + \frac{750}{760} \times \frac{573}{288} \quad 50 = G \times 6{\cdot}35 + 1{\cdot}97 \quad \text{(atm)} \qquad \ldots \quad \text{(iv)}$$

The permissible mass of ether is therefore $G = 7{\cdot}6$ g.

Note. Since the value of the gas constant has the unit cm³ atm/(deg. mole), the pressure must be expressed in atmospheres and the volume in cubic centimetres. The mass is calculated in grammes (see Exercise 5).

Carius tubes will usually withstand an internal pressure of about 100 atm when properly sealed (length 35 cm, internal diameter up to 2·5 cm, wall thickness 1·2 mm, volume 100 to 150 cm³). For the sake of safety, the pressure is not raised above 50 atm. One can see from eqn. (iv) that the partial pressure of the air in the test tube (about 2 atm) has no practical significance. It must be borne in mind during the calculation that the effect of heat on a closed tube may promote decomposition or dissociation of the substance it contains, giving rise to an increase in the number of molecules (see Exercise 19).

*Exercise 8

The composition (in volume per cent) of dry air at the earth's surface is: 20·93 per cent O_2, 78·1 per cent N_2, 0·93 per cent Ar, 0·03 per cent CO_2 and 0·01 per cent H_2. What is the mean molecular weight ($\overline{M}$) of air and its density (ϱ_0) in grammes per litre? Give the composition of air in weight per cent and mole per cent.

Solution 8. According to Avogadro's hypothesis, volume per cent and mole per cent are identical for ideal gases [see also eqn. (11)]. The mean molecular weight $\overline{M}$ is computed from eqn. (9) in association with eqn. (11), from the known composition of air and the molecular weights of its constituents. There is obtained:

$$\overline{M} = \frac{1}{100}(20{\cdot}93 \times 32 + 78{\cdot}10 \times 28{\cdot}02 + 0{\cdot}93 \times 39{\cdot}99 + 0{\cdot}03 \times 44{\cdot}01 + 0{\cdot}01 \times 2{\cdot}02)$$

$$\overline{M} = 28{\cdot}96 \qquad \ldots \quad \text{(i)}$$

In accordance with eqn. (5), $\varrho_0 = 28{\cdot}96/22{\cdot}4 = 1{\cdot}293$ g/l. $\qquad \ldots \quad$ (ii)

Conversion to weight per cent by means of eqn. (14) gives

$$\text{wt. per cent} = \frac{\text{mole \%} \times \text{mol. wt.}}{\text{mean mol. wt.}} \qquad \ldots. \quad \text{(iii)}$$

e.g. for O_2

$$\frac{20{\cdot}93 \times 32}{28{\cdot}96} = 23{\cdot}12 \text{ wt. per cent } O_2$$

likewise

75·56 wt. per cent N_2 1·283 wt. per cent Ar 0·046 wt. per cent CO_2
0·001 wt. per cent H_2

*Exercise 9

What is the mean molecular weight of an ethyl alcohol/water mixture containing 30 per cent by weight of ethyl alcohol?

Solution 9. Molecular weight of ethyl alcohol = 46·07, of water = 18·02. From eqn. (13)

$$\bar{M} = \frac{100}{30/46{\cdot}07 + 70/18{\cdot}02} = 22{\cdot}1$$

*Exercise 10

Calculate the composition in mole per cent of a mixture containing 40 parts by weight of benzene and 60 parts by weight of ethyl alcohol.

Solution 10. Molecular weight of benzene = 78·11, of ethyl alcohol = 46·07. From eqn. (12)

Benzene: $$100\,x = \frac{10 \times 40/78{\cdot}11 \times 100}{40/78{\cdot}11 + 60/46{\cdot}07} = 28{\cdot}3 \text{ mole per cent}$$

Ethyl alcohol: 71·7 mole per cent.

**Exercise 11

A heating installation requires 300 kg of lignite per hour. The composition of the coal (in weight per cent) is: 5 per cent ash, 15 per cent H_2O, 53 per cent C, 6 per cent H_2, 18 per cent O_2, 1 per cent N_2 and 2 per cent S. Calculate (*a*) the oxygen requirement, (*b*) the theoretical air requirement A_0, (*c*) the theoretical exhaust gas volume V_0, (*d*) the actual air consumption A, and (*e*) the total exhaust gas volume V_f if excess air, given by

$$\lambda = \frac{\text{actual air consumption } A}{\text{theoretical air requirement } A_0}$$

is required for the complete combustion of lignite and $\lambda = 1{\cdot}6$. Finally, determine (*f*) the flue gas composition in vol. per cent and (*g*) the cross-section of the flue, if the exhaust gas escapes at a temperature of 150 °C, with a barometer reading of 720 torr and at a speed of 1·2 m/sec.

Solution 11. Let:

$$c + h + o + s + n + w + a = 1 \text{ kg} \qquad \ldots. \quad \text{(i)}$$

represent the composition of 1 kg of fuel containing carbon, hydrogen, oxygen, sulphur, nitrogen, water and ash. Bearing in mind the atomic weight or molecular weight and the molar volume of gases, it is then easily seen that, for complete combustion to CO_2, SO_2 and H_2O, the oxygen requirement per kilogramme of fuel may be expressed as follows:

$$O_2 \text{ req.} = c/12 + h/4 + s/32 - o/32 \text{ kmole/kg} \quad \ldots\ldots \quad \text{(ii)}$$

or

$$(c/12 + h/4 + s/32 - o/32)\ 22{\cdot}4 \text{ Nm}^3\text{/kg} \quad \ldots\ldots \quad \text{(iii)}$$

If the above-mentioned coal analysis figures are employed, the result is

$$\begin{aligned} O_2 \text{ req.} &= (53/12 + 6/4 + 2/32 - 18/32)\frac{22{\cdot}4}{100} \\ &= 0{\cdot}0542 \times 22{\cdot}4 \\ &= 1{\cdot}215 \text{ Nm}^3\text{/kg} \quad \ldots\ldots \quad \text{(iv)} \end{aligned}$$

$$\begin{aligned} \text{Therefore, for 300 kg, } O_2 \text{ req.} &= 300 \times 1{\cdot}215 \\ &= 364{\cdot}5 \text{ Nm}^3 \quad \ldots\ldots \quad \text{(v)} \end{aligned}$$

Since air consists of 20·9 per cent O_2 and 79·1 per cent N_2 by volume, the theoretical air requirement, A_0, will be

$$A_0 = \frac{1{\cdot}215 \times 100}{20{\cdot}9} = 5{\cdot}81 \text{ Nm}^3\text{/kg}$$

For 300 kg $= 1743 \text{ Nm}^3$ .... (vi)

In order to calculate the theoretical exhaust gas volume, the sum must be taken of the volumes of the individual combustion products. These are

$$\left.\begin{aligned} [CO_2] &= 22{\cdot}4\, c/12 = 1{\cdot}867\, c \text{ Nm}^3\text{/kg} \\ [H_2O] &= 22{\cdot}4\, (h/2 + w/18) = 11{\cdot}2\, h + 1{\cdot}245\, w \text{ Nm}^3\text{/kg} \\ [SO_2] &= 22{\cdot}4\, s/32 = 0{\cdot}70\, s \text{ Nm}^3\text{/kg} \\ [N_2] &= 22{\cdot}4 n/28 + A_0\, 79{\cdot}1/100 = 0{\cdot}80 n + 0{\cdot}791 A_0 \text{ Nm}^3\text{/kg} \end{aligned}\right\} \quad \ldots \quad \text{(vii)}$$

Using the analysis figures, the above example gives for V_0

$$\left.\begin{aligned} V_0 &= 0{\cdot}989[CO_2] + 0{\cdot}859[H_2O] + 0{\cdot}014[SO_2] + 4{\cdot}598[N_2] \\ &= 6{\cdot}46 \text{ Nm}^3\text{/kg} \\ \text{For 300 kg} \quad V_0 &= 300 \times 6{\cdot}46 = 1938 \text{ Nm}^3 \end{aligned}\right\} \quad \ldots \quad \text{(viii)}$$

The actual air consumption is

$$A = \lambda A_0 \quad \ldots\ldots \quad \text{(ix)}$$

thus, in accordance with (vi) and for $\lambda = 1{\cdot}6$

$$A = 1{\cdot}6 \times 5{\cdot}81 = 9{\cdot}30 \text{ Nm}^3\text{/kg} \text{ or, for the total, } 1{\cdot}6 \times 1743 = 2789 \text{ Nm}^3 \quad \ldots\ldots \quad \text{(x)}$$

The total exhaust gas volume (V_f) is made up from the theoretical volume (V_0) and the excess from actual air consumption (A) over the theoretical requirement (A_0).

Hence $$V_f = V_0 + A - A_0 = V_0 + (\lambda - 1)A_0 \quad \ldots . \text{(xi)}$$

Considering eqns. (viii), (x) and (vi), we obtain

$$V_f = 6{\cdot}46 + 9{\cdot}30 - 5{\cdot}81$$

$$= 9{\cdot}95\ \text{Nm}^3/\text{kg} \quad \text{or} \quad 2995\ \text{Nm}^3 \text{ total} \quad \ldots . \text{(xii)}$$

Thus: $$\frac{\text{exhaust gas volume, } V_f}{\text{vol. of air fed in, } A} = \frac{9{\cdot}95}{9{\cdot}30} = 1{\cdot}07 \quad \ldots . \text{(xiii)}$$

Thus 7 per cent more gas is evolved than is fed in. The flue gas composition is found from (vii) and increased by the amount of excess air $A - A_0$ which, according to (xii), amounts to $9{\cdot}30 - 5{\cdot}81 = 3{\cdot}49$ Nm³/kg and divides up into $0{\cdot}209 \times 3{\cdot}49 = 0{\cdot}73$ Nm³/kg oxygen and 2·76 Nm³/kg of atmospheric nitrogen. Accordingly, the flue gas volume $V_f = 9{\cdot}95$ Nm³/kg is made up from

$$\left.\begin{array}{rl} [CO_2]\ 0{\cdot}989\ \text{Nm}^3/\text{kg} = & 9{\cdot}94\% \\ [H_2O]\ 0{\cdot}859\ \text{Nm}^3/\text{kg} = & 8{\cdot}63\% \\ [SO_2]\ 0{\cdot}014\ \text{Nm}^3/\text{kg} = & 0{\cdot}14\% \\ [O_2]\ 0{\cdot}730\ \text{Nm}^3/\text{kg} = & 7{\cdot}34\% \\ [N_2]\ 7{\cdot}358\ \text{Nm}^3/\text{kg} = & 73{\cdot}95\% \\ \hline V_f = 9{\cdot}950\ \text{Nm}^3/\text{kg} = & 100{\cdot}00\% \end{array}\right\} \begin{array}{l}\text{gas composition} \\ \text{in vol. per cent}\end{array} \quad \ldots \text{(xiv)}$$

The flue gas volume in Nm³ is, according to the gas eqn. (1), converted for a temperature of 150 °C and a pressure of 720 torr as follows:

$$V = \frac{2995 \times (273 + 150) \times 760}{273 \times 720} = 4900\ \text{m}^3 \quad \ldots . \text{(xv)}$$

This is the quantity released in an hour. The figure for a second is therefore 4900/3600 m³. The volume $\dot{V}$ evolved each second is equal to the cross-section of the flue multiplied by the rate of flow (per second). Therefore, $\dot{V} = qw$.
Hence

$$q = \frac{4900}{3600 \times 1{\cdot}2} \left(\frac{\text{m}^3}{\text{sec m/sec}}\right) = 1{\cdot}13\ \text{m}^2$$

for the flue cross-section.

Note. Excess air corresponding to $\lambda = 2$ must usually be fed in to obtain complete combustion with steam coals.

**Exercise 12

What height, H, must a chimney be so that a pressure difference Δp (a negative pressure) of 1 torr is produced with respect to the outside air, i.e. in order to introduce the necessary feed air into the heating installation at the foot of the chimney?

The flue gases have the composition given in Exercise 11 and a temperature of $\theta_1 = 150$ °C; the mean barometer reading is $p_2 = 720$ torr and the outside temperature is $\theta_2 = 15$ °C. What are the theoretical and actual draughts in m/sec under these conditions?

The actual draught is, in practice, a factor $\varphi = 0{\cdot}3$ to $0{\cdot}7$ of the theoretical draught, due to friction in the flue and the nature of the firing. For rough calculation $\varphi = 1/3$ will be used. The rate of efflux (w) of gases from vents may be calculated from the formula for the speed of a falling body:

$$w = \sqrt{2gh}\ (\text{m/sec})$$

where $g = 9{\cdot}81$ m/sec², the acceleration due to gravity, and h (m) is the height of a column of gas in the flue maintaining a steady pressure difference Δp; h is, therefore, not equal to the height of the chimney (H).

Solution 12. The pressure of 1 torr corresponds to a weight of

$$\Delta p = 1033/760 = 1{\cdot}36 \text{ g wt./cm}^2 \quad \ldots\ldots \quad \text{(i)}$$

$\left(= \frac{1}{10}\right.$ of the specific gravity of Hg!$\left.\right)$; see p. 4. According to Archimedes' principle, the gas column (per cm²) in the flue must be lighter than the corresponding column of gas in the outside air by this amount. The specific gravity of air is $\gamma_{0A} = 1{\cdot}29 \times 10^{-3}$ g wt./Ncm³ [see Exercise 8, (ii)]; thus the specific gravity of air, γ_A, at 15 °C and 720 torr is, from gas eqn. (1):

$$\left.\begin{aligned} \gamma_A &= \gamma_{0A}\frac{p_2 T_0}{p_0 T_2} = 1{\cdot}29 \times 10^{-3} \times \frac{720 \times 273}{760 \times 288} \\ &= 1{\cdot}16 \times 10^{-3} \text{ g wt./cm}^3 \text{ for the outside air} \end{aligned}\right\} \quad \ldots \quad \text{(ii)}$$

The specific gravity of flue gas $\gamma_{0F} = \dfrac{\text{mean mol. wt. } \overline{M}}{22\,415}\ \dfrac{\text{g wt.}}{\text{Ncm}^3}$ from eqn. (5), where $\overline{M}$ is obtained from eqn. (9) as

$$\overline{M} = \frac{1}{100}(9{\cdot}94 \times 44 + 8{\cdot}63 \times 18 + 0{\cdot}14 \times 64 + 7{\cdot}34 \times 32 + 73{\cdot}95 \times 28) = 29{\cdot}1$$

i.e. based on the flue gas composition [see Exercise 11, (xiv)]. Thus the specific gravity of the flue gas

$$\gamma_{0F} = \frac{29{\cdot}1}{22\,415} = 1{\cdot}30 \times 10^{-3} \text{ g wt./Ncm}^3$$

Using gas eqn. (1), and converting to 150 °C and 720 torr

$$\gamma_F = \gamma_{0F} \times \frac{p_2 T_0}{p_0 T_1} = 1{\cdot}30 \times 10^{-3} \times \frac{720 \times 273}{760 \times 423} = 0{\cdot}794 \times 10^{-3} \text{ g wt./cm}^3 \quad \ldots\ldots \quad \text{(iii)}$$

for the gas in the chimney.

The height of the chimney (H) is calculated according to Archimedes' principle:

$$\left.\begin{aligned} &\text{Buoyancy/cm}^3 = \text{pressure difference } \Delta p = H(\gamma_A - \gamma_F) \\ &(\text{in g wt./cm}^2\text{: thus } H \text{ is in cm!}) \end{aligned}\right\} \quad \ldots \quad \text{(iv)}$$

Substituting the numerical values of (i), (ii) and (iii) into (iv) gives:

$$H = \frac{1{\cdot}36}{(1{\cdot}16 - 0{\cdot}794)10^{-3}} = 3{\cdot}72 \times 10^3 \text{ cm} = 37 \text{ m chimney height.} \quad \ldots\ldots \quad \text{(v)}$$

The draught is calculated from the previous formula for the speed of a falling body:

$$w = \sqrt{2gh} \quad \ldots\ldots \text{(vi)}$$

whereby

$$h\gamma_F = \Delta p \quad \ldots\ldots \text{(vii)}$$

and thus

$$\left.\begin{aligned} w &= \sqrt{\frac{2g\Delta p}{\gamma_F}}\ \text{(cm/sec)} \\ g = 981\ \text{cm/sec}^2 \quad &\Delta p\ (\text{g wt./cm}^2) \quad \gamma_F\ (\text{g wt./cm}^3) \end{aligned}\right\} \ldots \text{(viii)}$$

Usually the draught is calculated not from Δp but from the height of the chimney, H; thus, from (iv):

$$\Delta p = H(\gamma_A - \gamma_F)$$

Substituting this value in (viii) gives:

$$w = \sqrt{2gH\frac{(\gamma_A - \gamma_F)}{\gamma_F}}$$

and, with (ii) and (iii):

$$\left.\begin{aligned} w &= \sqrt{\frac{2gH(T_1\gamma_{0A}/\gamma_{0F} - T_2)}{T_2}}\ \text{(m/sec)} \\ g = 9{\cdot}81\ (\text{m/sec}^2) \quad &H(\text{m}) \quad \text{for the theoretical draught} \end{aligned}\right\} \ldots \text{(ix)}$$

Since the specific gravities of the flue gas and the air, when taken at s.t.p., are, in general, almost the same

$$\gamma_{0A}/\gamma_{0F} \approx 1$$

the actual draught may be simplified, in practice, to

$$w_{\text{eff}} = \varphi\sqrt{2 \times 9{\cdot}81\,H\frac{T_1 - T_2}{T_2}}\ \text{(m/sec)} \quad \ldots\ldots \text{(x)}$$

In the present case:

$$w_{\text{eff}} = \frac{1}{3}\sqrt{2 \times 9{\cdot}81 \times 37 \times \frac{135}{288}} = 6{\cdot}2\ \text{m/sec}$$

*Exercise 13

From an air stream saturated with carbon tetrachloride at a temperature of 20 °C and a barometer reading of $p = 710$ torr, the carbon tetrachloride is recovered by condensation, by means of compression and subsequent recooling to 20 °C. To what pressure p_x (atm) must the gas mixture be compressed in order to obtain a yield of $\eta = 90$ per cent? Vapour pressure of CCl_4 at 20 °C, $p_{CCl_4} = 91$ torr.

Solution 13. According to Dalton's law, eqns. (6) and (8), the molar quantities in a given gas mixture are proportional to the partial pressures of the components:

$$\frac{n_{CCl_4}}{n_{\text{air}}} = \frac{p_{CCl_4}}{p - p_{CCl_4}} \quad \ldots\ldots \text{(i)}$$

After compression to the pressure p_x and recooling to the original temperature of 20 °C, the molar ratio should still comprise the same molar quantity of air, but only the residue $1 - \eta$ of CCl_4. Therefore, the molar ratio after compression is

$$(1-\eta)\frac{n_{CCl_4}}{n_{air}} = \frac{p_{CCl_4}}{p_x - p_{CCl_4}} = (1-\eta)\frac{p_{CCl_4}}{p - p_{CCl_4}} \quad \ldots\ldots \text{(ii)}$$

[taking (i) into account], so that

$$p_x = \frac{p - \eta\, p_{CCl_4}}{1-\eta} \quad \ldots\ldots \text{(iii)}$$

Substituting the numerical values in (iii) gives, for p_x (atm),

$$p_x = \frac{710 - 0{\cdot}90 \times 91}{760\,(1 - 0{\cdot}90)} = 8{\cdot}26 \text{ atm compression pressure.}$$

*Exercise 14

An airstream saturated with carbon tetrachloride at a temperature of $\theta_1 = 20$ °C is cooled, at a constant barometer reading of $p = 710$ torr, to temperature $\theta_2 = -20$ °C; thus part of the carbon tetrachloride is condensed out. What is the yield of condensate and how many grammes of carbon tetrachloride are produced from a gas mixture of $V_1 = 15$ m³? Vapour pressure of CCl_4 at 20 °C is $p_1 = 91$ torr; at -20 °C, $p_2 = 10$ torr.

Solution 14. According to Dalton's law, eqns. (6), (8) and (10), the molar ratio in the original gas mixture is:

$$\frac{n_{CCl_4}}{n_{air}} = \frac{p_1}{p - p_1} \quad \ldots\ldots \text{(i)}$$

After condensation, the molar quantity of air remains at n_{air} but the molar quantity of CCl_4 has dropped from n_{CCl_4} to n'_{CCl_4}. Thus, after condensation (at constant barometer reading p)

$$\frac{n'_{CCl_4}}{n_{air}} = \frac{p_2}{p - p_2} \quad \ldots\ldots \text{(ii)}$$

Hence the condensed molar quantity of CCl_4, $n_{CCl_4} - n'_{CCl_4}$, is

$$\frac{n_{CCl_4} - n'_{CCl_4}}{n_{air}} = \frac{p_1}{p - p_1} - \frac{p_2}{p - p_2} \quad \ldots\ldots \text{(iii)}$$

Finally, dividing (iii) by (i), the yield is given by

$$\eta = \frac{n_{CCl_4} - n'_{CCl_4}}{n_{CCl_4}} = 1 - \frac{p_2\,(p - p_1)}{p_1\,(p - p_2)} \quad \ldots\ldots \text{(iv)}$$

The condensed mass of CCl_4 is $G_{CCl_4} \times \eta$, so that, from the gas law eqn. (8)

$$p_1 V_1 = \frac{G_{CCl_4}}{M_{CCl_4}} R T_1$$

Thus, for the condensate

$$\text{weight of condensate} = G_{CCl_4} \times \eta = \eta\,\frac{p_1 V_1 M_{CCl_4}}{R T_1} \quad \ldots\ldots \text{(v)}$$

Substituting the numerical values, and with due regard to dimensions, gives

$$\eta = 1 - \frac{10(710 - 91)}{91(710 - 10)} = 0{\cdot}903 = 90{\cdot}3 \text{ per cent yield}$$

$$\text{Mass of condensate} = G_{CCl_4} \times \eta = \frac{0{\cdot}903 \times 91 \times 15 \times 10^6 \times 154}{760 \times 82{\cdot}06 \times 293} = 10{\cdot}4\,\text{kg}$$

*Exercise 15

A sample of methane from natural gas is contaminated with helium. The density of the sample at s.t.p. is $\varrho_0 = 0{\cdot}70902$ g/l. What is the helium content in volume per cent? Atomic weights: $M_H = 1{\cdot}0080$, $M_{He} = 4{\cdot}003$, $M_C = 12{\cdot}010$ [for molar volume see eqn. (5)].

Solution 15. From eqn. (5) the apparent molecular weight of methane, $\overline{M}_{CH_4}$, is

$$\overline{M}_{CH_4} = \varrho_0 \times \text{molar vol.} = 0{\cdot}70902 \times 22{\cdot}415 = 15{\cdot}893 \quad \ldots\ldots \quad \text{(i)}$$

From eqn. (9) it follows that

$$\overline{M} = x_{He} M_{He} + (1 - x_{He}) M_{CH_4} \quad \text{or} \quad x_{He} = \frac{M_{CH_4} - \overline{M}}{M_{CH_4} - M_{He}} \quad \ldots\ldots \quad \text{(ii)}$$

Substituting the numerical values in (ii) gives

$$x_{He} = \frac{16{\cdot}042 - 15{\cdot}893}{16{\cdot}042 - 4{\cdot}003} = 0{\cdot}0124 \quad \ldots\ldots \quad \text{(iii)}$$

Since, from eqn. (11), molar and volume per cent are the same in the case of ideal gases, the methane sample contains 1·24 vol. per cent helium.

Note. The calculated helium content should be regarded only as an approximation. This is because of the nature of the difference calculation at (iii) and the slight uncertainty in the value for the molar volume (i.e. deviation from the ideal state).

*Exercise 16

On an average, 1000 vehicles per hour, at an average speed of 60 km/h and with a mean petrol consumption of 12 l./100 km, pass through a road tunnel 12 km long and having a cross-section of 38 m². The density of the petrol is 0·740 kg/l. and it is composed of 85·7 per cent C and 14·3 per cent H (wt. %). In the exhaust gas, there is, on average, 10 per cent CO_2 and 5 per cent CO (vol. per cent). How effective must the ventilation system be in order that the poisonous CO content of the tunnel should not exceed 0·5 parts per thousand? (The critical danger limit is 0·8 parts per thousand CO in air.) Making use of the result, what is the speed of ventilation through both tunnel exits? If the ventilation system fails, how long does it take for the CO content in the tunnel, previously free of CO, to reach the critical limit of 0·8 parts per thousand?

Solution 16. A vehicle uses 12 × 12/100 = 1·44 l. of petrol for the journey through the tunnel. Therefore, 1000 vehicles require 1440 l. or 1440 × 0·740 = 1065 kg of petrol per hour.

The carbon content of 1065 kg petrol $= 1065 \times 85{\cdot}7/100$ kg

$$= \frac{1065 \times 85{\cdot}7}{12 \times 100} \text{ kmol.}$$

This burns to give

$$\frac{1065 \times 85{\cdot}7}{12 \times 100} \times 22{\cdot}4 \text{ Nm}^3 \; CO_2 + CO$$

Hence, in accordance with the composition of the exhaust gas

$$\frac{5}{5 + 10} = \frac{1}{3} \text{ CO gas}$$

the CO production in the tunnel works out at

$$\frac{1065 \times 85{\cdot}7 \times 22{\cdot}4}{12 \times 100 \times 3} = 568{\cdot}5 \text{ Nm}^3 \text{ CO/h}$$

To maintain a constant level of CO, i.e. if the air in the tunnel contains 0·5 parts per thousand CO, the rate of air with this CO content discharged from the tunnel must balance the amount of CO produced.

If x is the amount of air passing through the tunnel (in Nm^3/h), then, to maintain a constant level of CO, one must have $x \times 5/10{,}000 = 568{\cdot}5$

$$x = 113{\cdot}7 \times 10^4 \text{ Nm}^3 \text{ air per hour}$$

This is the required degree of ventilation in the tunnel system. Since the cross-section of the tunnel is 38 m², the speed of the ventilating draught is given by

$$\frac{113{\cdot}7 \times 10^4}{38} \text{ m/h} \quad \text{or} \quad \frac{113{\cdot}7 \times 10^4}{38 \times 3600} \text{ m/sec} = 8{\cdot}31 \text{ m/sec}$$

This rate divided between the two tunnel exits gives a ventilation speed of 8·31/2 = 4·155 m/sec, which corresponds to an average wind speed in Europe.

The total internal volume of the tunnel is 12,000 × 38 m³. When the critical limit of 0·8 parts per thousand CO is reached, the tunnel therefore contains 12,000 × 38 × 8/10000 = 365 m³ CO. Since 568·5 Nm^3 of CO is produced in 60 min at s.t.p. (0 °C, 760 mm) the tunnel atmosphere will reach the critical limit in

$$\frac{365 \times 60}{568{\cdot}5} = 39 \text{ min}$$

For other conditions of temperature and pressure, the figure of 568·5 Nm^3 will have to be converted using the gas eqn. (1).

Note. These calculations clearly show the danger of CO in exhaust gases – because of its extremely poisonous nature. It is also very dangerous to leave a petrol engine running in a closed garage, since the CO content of the air will rapidly exceed the critical limit. Moreover, the ratio of the CO/CO_2 contents in the exhaust gases, being normally 1–5 per cent CO : 10–13 per cent CO_2, changes to 7–8 per cent CO : 9–10 per cent CO_2 during idling. On the other hand, with diesel engines, the CO content of the exhaust gases is low (0·1–0·2 per cent).

CO_2 is considerably less poisonous. The critical limit of CO_2 in air is about 3 per cent by volume so that, in the above calculation, CO_2 production need not be considered. On the other hand, there are similar calculations to the above, dealing with CO_2; e.g. the question of ventilation of air-raid shelters, bearing in mind the fact that a person exhales CO_2 at an average rate of 0·4 l./min. Special attention should be paid to the fact that, considering 3 per cent is the accepted critical limit of CO_2 in air, exhaled air is already completely 'used up' as a result of the increase in the CO_2 content – even though there is in fact still ample oxygen remaining in the air and available for breathing.

Experience shows that the critical limit for CO content must be taken, not as 0·8 part per thousand, but rather as 0·4 part per thousand because of the smoke elements in exhaust gas which impair the sight and cause the eyes to burn. These considerations would seem to indicate that, instead of longitudinal ventilation, it would be preferable to use the more expensive but safer transverse ventilation, operated by means of two ventilation channels running parallel along the tunnel and joined by cross channels.

2

GAS DISSOCIATION

THE degree of dissociation α is the fraction of the molecules which are dissociated under given conditions; $1 - \alpha$ is the fraction of undissociated molecules.

If n_0 is the total quantity of moles (before dissociation) and if one of these moles breaks up into ν fragments, then the molar quantity of dissociation products is

$$n_0 \nu \alpha \qquad \ldots . \quad (15)$$

and the total quantity of moles after dissociation is

$$n = n_0(1 - \alpha) + n_0 \nu \alpha = n_0[1 + \alpha(\nu - 1)] \qquad \ldots . \quad (16)$$

When dissociation takes place, the gas law becomes

$$pV = n_0[1 + \alpha(\nu - 1)]RT = nRT \qquad \ldots . \quad (17)$$

At constant pressure, comparison of eqn. (17) with eqns. (2) and (8) gives the following relationships

$$\left.\begin{aligned} \frac{\text{density after dissociation}}{\text{density before dissociation}} &= \varrho/\varrho_0 = V_0/V = n_0/n \\ &= \bar{M}/M_0 = 1[1 + \alpha(\nu - 1)] \end{aligned}\right\} \quad \ldots \quad (18)$$

Thus

$$\alpha = \frac{\varrho_0 - \varrho}{\varrho(\nu - 1)} = \frac{M_0 - \bar{M}}{\bar{M}(\nu - 1)} \qquad \ldots . \quad (19)$$

By using eqn. (18), the mean or apparent molecular weight $\bar{M}$ may be determined from the molecular weight M_0 of the undissociated substance and from the degree of dissociation.

*EXERCISE 17

Vapour density measurements showed that propane, owing to partial dehydrogenation to propylene, had an apparent molecular weight of 34·3 at a pressure of $p = 1$ atm and at an absolute temperature of $T = 800$ °K. Calculate the degree of dissociation, α, and the partial pressures of propane, propylene and hydrogen in the mixture.

Solution 17. Mol. wt. of propane (C_3H_8) $= M_0 = 44·1$. The dehydrogenation equation is $C_3H_8 = C_3H_6 + H_2$; the number of fragments on dissociation is, therefore, $\nu = 2$. Hence, from eqn. (19)

$$\alpha = \frac{44·1 - 34·3}{34·3} = 0·286, \text{ or } 28·6 \text{ per cent dissociation} \qquad \ldots . \quad \text{(i)}$$

From eqn. (10), we get

$$\frac{\text{partial pressure } p_i}{\text{total pressure } p} = \frac{n_i}{n} \qquad \ldots . \quad \text{(ii)}$$

The total pressure is $p = 1$ atm; the quantity of moles of undissociated propane is, from eqn. (16), $n_{\text{propane}} = n_0(1-\alpha) = n_0 \times 0{\cdot}714$; the quantity of moles of hydrogen is $n_{H_2} = n_0\alpha = n_0 \times 0{\cdot}286$ and, similarly, the quantity of moles of propylene is $n_0 \times 0{\cdot}286$. The total quantity of moles in the mixture is, from eqn. (16)

$$n = n_0[1+\alpha(\nu-1)] = n_0(1+\alpha) = n_0 \times 1{\cdot}286 \quad \ldots . \quad \text{(iii)}$$

Combining (iii) with (ii) gives the partial pressure of the undissociated propane as

$$p_{\text{propane}} \frac{p\,n_0(1-\alpha)}{n_0(1+\alpha)} = \frac{1 \times 0{\cdot}714}{1{\cdot}286} = 0{\cdot}555 \text{ atm} \quad \ldots . \quad \text{(iv)}$$

$$p_{H_2} = p_{\text{propylene}} = \frac{p\,n_0\,\alpha}{n_0(1+\alpha)} = \frac{1 \times 0{\cdot}286}{1{\cdot}286} = 0{\cdot}2225 \text{ atm} \quad \ldots . \quad \text{(v)}$$

Total pressure $p = p_{\text{propane}} + p_{\text{propylene}} + p_{H_2}$

$$= 0{\cdot}555 + 0{\cdot}2225 + 0{\cdot}2225 = 1{\cdot}000 \text{ atm.}$$

Note. It should be specially noted that, when calculating the partial pressures of dissociated gases, because of (ii), the term $n_0(1+\alpha)$ or, in general, $n_0[1+\alpha(\nu-1)]$, and not n_0, is used in the denominator in formulae (iv) and (v).

*Exercise 18

Equilibrium measurements showed that, at a temperature of 3000 °K and a pressure of $p = 10$ atm, 24·4 per cent of carbon dioxide dissociated into carbon monoxide and oxygen. Calculate the apparent molecular weight of carbon dioxide and the partial pressures of the mixture components under these conditions.

Solution 18. The dissociation equation for carbon dioxide ($M_0 = 44$) is: $CO_2 = CO + \frac{1}{2}O_2$. The degree of dissociation is $\alpha = 0{\cdot}244$. The dissociation equation shows that the number of fragments is $\nu = 3/2$.

Hence, by using eqn. (18), it follows that the apparent molecular weight is

$$\bar{M} = M_0/(1+\alpha/2) = 44/(1+0{\cdot}122) = 39{\cdot}2 \quad \ldots . \quad \text{(i)}$$

From eqn. (10), the relationship is

$$\frac{\text{partial pressure } p_i}{\text{total pressure } p} = \frac{n_i}{n} \quad \ldots . \quad \text{(ii)}$$

The total pressure is $p = 10$ atm; the quantity of moles of undissociated CO_2 is, from eqn. (16), $n_{CO_2} = n_0(1-\alpha) = n_0 \times 0{\cdot}756$; the quantity of moles of CO is $n_{CO} = n_0\alpha = n_0 \times 0{\cdot}244$; the quantity of O_2 moles is $n_{O_2} = n_0 \times \frac{1}{2}\alpha = n_0 \times 0{\cdot}122$ and the total quantity of moles is, therefore, $n = n_0[1+\alpha(1{\cdot}5-1)] = n_0 \times 1{\cdot}122$. Combining these values with (ii), the corresponding partial pressures become

$$p_{CO_2} = \frac{p\,n_0(1-\alpha)}{n_0(1+\alpha/2)} = \frac{10 \times 0{\cdot}756}{1{\cdot}122} = 6{\cdot}745 \text{ atm}$$

$$p_{CO} = \frac{p\,n_0\,\alpha}{n_0(1+\alpha/2)} = \frac{10 \times 0{\cdot}244}{1{\cdot}122} = 2{\cdot}17 \text{ atm}$$

$$p_{O_2} = \frac{p\,n_0 \times \alpha/2}{n_0(1+\alpha/2)} = \frac{10 \times 0{\cdot}122}{1{\cdot}122} = 1{\cdot}085 \text{ atm}$$

$$p = 6{\cdot}745 + 2{\cdot}17 + 1{\cdot}085 = 10{\cdot}00 \text{ atm.}$$

*Exercise 19

A Carius tube of capacity $V = 120\ cm^3$ is heated to 300 °C in order to oxidize an organic compound with pure nitric acid (density, $\varrho_4^{20} = 1{\cdot}5\ g/cm^3$). How many cubic centimetres of nitric acid may be introduced, (i) if the pressure in the tube is not to exceed $p = 50$ atm and (ii) if, in the interest of safety, allowance is made for the maximum possible dissociation of nitric acid into its elements at 300 °C? (See also Exercise 7.)

Solution 19. Allowance must be made for dissociation of the nitric acid according to the following equation: $2\ HNO_3 = H_2O + N_2 + 5\ O$ (not $\frac{5}{2}\ O_2$), bearing in mind the fact that, during the oxidation of an organic compound, oxygen converts hydrogen into steam and, at worst, carbon into carbon monoxide, one gas molecule of H_2O and CO, per O atom, resulting. Dissociation of nitric acid is complete at 300 °C. It must be assumed, therefore, that, under the given conditions, 2 moles of nitric acid will form seven fragments, or 1 mole half that number. Hence $\nu = 3{\cdot}5$ should be used in eqn. (17): $p = 50$ atm, $V = 120\ cm^3$, $T = 300 + 273 = 573$ °K, $R = 82\ cm^3$ atm/(mol. deg.) (see p. 4). The molecular weight of nitric acid is $M = 63$. Using the above data in eqn. (17) gives

$$n_0 = G/M = G/63 = \frac{50 \times 120}{3{\cdot}5 \times 82 \times 573} \text{ moles}$$

$$G = 2{\cdot}3\ g$$

$$\text{The volume} = \frac{G}{\varrho_4^{20}} = \frac{2{\cdot}3}{1{\cdot}5} = 1{\cdot}53\ cm^3$$

Thus a maximum of $1{\cdot}53\ cm^3$ of pure nitric acid may be introduced into the tube.

Note. Experiments such as those in this Exercise or in Exercise 17, where reactions are involved, must always be carried out in Carius tubes or in autoclaves. The above experiment plays its part in the Carius method for the determination of halogens and sulphur. In fact, Carius states that 1 to $1{\cdot}5\ cm^3$ of pure concentrated nitric acid is to be added.

In view of the explanation given in the note on Exercise 7, the partial pressure of the air in the tube (~ 2 atm) has been ignored as being insignificant.

3
REAL GASES AND LIQUIDS

THE van der Waals equation of state for real gases is

$$\left(p + \frac{a}{v^2}\right)(v - b) = RT \qquad v = \frac{V}{n} = \text{molar volume} \qquad \ldots . \quad (20)$$

At relatively low pressures, when $v \gg b$, eqn. (20) becomes

$$pv = RT\,(1 + B/v) = RT + Bp \quad \text{where } B = b - \frac{a}{RT} \qquad \ldots . \quad (21)$$

B is also called a second virial coefficient. When $B = 0$

$$T_B = \frac{a}{bR} \qquad \ldots . \quad (22)$$

This is the Boyle point, i.e. the limiting temperature to which the ideal gas equation may be applied up to high pressures.

Equations (20) and (21) become eqn. (2) for ideal gases in cases where the gas pressure is low and the molar volume large. Conversely, at higher pressures, the ideal gas equation must, in general, be replaced by an equation of state such as (21) or (20) – more so, the larger the molecules and the stronger the intermolecular attraction forces (i.e. especially when dipoles and quadripoles are present).

a and b are individual constants which must be empirically determined for each substance. They are, according to van der Waals equation, related to the critical constants, p_k, v_k and T_k, as follows:

$$a = 3\,p_k\,v_k^2 = \frac{27\,R^2\,T_k^2}{64\,p_k} \qquad b = v_k/3 = \frac{R\,T_k}{8\,p_k} \qquad \ldots . \quad (23)$$

$$v_k = 3\,b \qquad p_k = \frac{a}{27\,b^2} \qquad T_k = \frac{8\,a}{27\,b\,R} \qquad \ldots . \quad (24)$$

$$b = 4 \times \text{actual volume of molecules of one mole, } 4\pi \times N_A \times 4r_M^3/3 \qquad \ldots . \quad (25)$$

where r_M = molecular radius, N_A = Avogadro constant (see p. 28).

According to eqn. (25), b is a measure of the actual volume of molecules and increases with increase in molecular diameter; a is a measure of intermolecular attraction and also, in general, increases with increase in molecular diameter but has an abnormally high value in the case of dipolar and quadripolar substances, where the attraction forces are large.

It will be seen from eqns. (20)–(22) that a and b are not dimensionless numbers; their values - as in the case of the gas constant R – must therefore conform to the units of measurement used in the gas equation.

Taking van der Waals equation (20) for a gramme mole ($n = 1$ mole), with p in atm and v in cm³/mole, then

$$b \text{ has the unit (cm}^3\text{/mole) and } a \text{ the unit (cm}^6\text{ atm/mole}^2) \quad \ldots. \quad (26)$$

If eqn. (20) is applied for n gramme moles, then (after multiplication by n) we obtain

$$\left(p + \frac{a\,n^2}{(n\,v)^2}\right)(n\,v - n\,b) = n\,R\,T = \left(p + \frac{a'}{V^2}\right)(V - b') = R'\,T \quad \ldots. \quad (27)$$

where $V = n\,v\,(\text{cm}^3)$ $a' = n^2 a\,(\text{cm}^6\text{ atm})$ $b' = n\,b\,(\text{cm}^3)$ $R' = n\,R\,(\text{cm}^3\text{ atm/deg.})$.

If the van der Waals equation is applied for one normal cubic centimeter (1 Ncm³, see p. 4), then $n_0 = 1/22415$ mole, so that, according to eqn. (27), the constants $a^\star$, $b^\star$, $R^\star$ become

$$\left.\begin{aligned} a^\star &= n_0^2\,a = 1{\cdot}99 \times 10^{-9}\,a = \frac{a}{5{\cdot}03 \times 10^8} && (\text{cm}^6\text{ atm}) \\ b^\star &= n_0\,b = 4{\cdot}46 \times 10^{-5}\,b = \frac{b}{2{\cdot}24 \times 10^4} && (\text{cm}^3) \\ R^\star &= n_0\,R = 82{\cdot}06/22415 = 3{\cdot}661 \times 10^{-3} && (\text{cm}^3\text{ atm/deg.}) \end{aligned}\right\} \quad \ldots \quad (28)$$

If, in eqns. (20) and (27), the volumes v or V are expressed in litres, not in cubic centimetres, then the constants a and a' should be multiplied by 10^{-6}, the constants b and b' by 10^{-3} and R should be taken as 0·08206 l. atm/(deg. mole). Note the units in this case:

$$a\ (\text{l.}^2\text{ atm/mole}^2),\ a'\ (\text{l.}^2\text{ atm}),\ b\ (\text{l./mole}) \text{ and } b'\ (\text{l.}) \quad \ldots. \quad (29)$$

*Exercise 20

Verify the accuracy of the dimensions in the formula for the Boyle point [eqn. (22)].

Solution 20. The formula in eqn. (22) is $T_B = a/b\,R$. The units of a and b are given in eqn. (26) and those of R in eqn. (4). Therefore, applying eqn. (22), the dimensional equation will be

$$(\text{deg.}) = \frac{\left(\dfrac{\text{cm}^6\text{ atm}}{\text{mole}^2}\right)}{\left(\dfrac{\text{cm}^3}{\text{mole}}\right) \times \left(\dfrac{\text{cm}^3\text{ atm}}{\text{deg. mole}}\right)}$$

and the right-hand side reduces, in fact, to (deg.).

Note. A dimensional check is an important and necessary, even if inadequate, criterion for the accuracy of an equation. It is, therefore, always advisable. in propounding and deriving formulae, to check the accuracy of results and intermediate results by using a dimensional equation.

*Exercise 21

The critical temperature of propane is $\theta_k = 96{\cdot}8$ °C and the critical pressure $p_k = 42{\cdot}0$ atm. Calculate the van der Waals constants a and b and the Boyle point T_B.

Solution 21. Measuring the pressure in atmospheres and the volume in cubic centimetres for one gramme molecule according to eqn. (23) and with $R = 82{\cdot}06\,\dfrac{\text{cm}^3\text{ atm}}{\text{deg. mole}}$, the expressions for a and b are

$$a = \frac{27\,(82{\cdot}06)^2 \times T_k^2}{64 \times p_k} = 2841 \times T_k^2/p_k = \frac{2841\,(273{\cdot}2 + 96{\cdot}8)^2}{42}$$

$$= 9{\cdot}25 \times 10^6 \text{ cm}^6 \text{ atm/mole}^2$$

$$b = \frac{82{\cdot}06\,(273{\cdot}2 + 96{\cdot}8)}{8{\cdot}42} = 90{\cdot}4 \text{ cm}^3\text{/mole}$$

From eqn. (22), the Boyle temperature T_B is

$$T_B = \frac{9{\cdot}25 \times 10^6}{90{\cdot}4 \times 82{\cdot}06} = 1247\ °\text{K} \quad \text{or} \quad \theta_B = 974\ °\text{C}$$

Note. If the van der Waals equation is used for one gramme molecule, but in l.-atm, then the constants will, according to eqn. (29), become: $a = (9{\cdot}25 \times 10^6)\,10^{-6} = 9{\cdot}25$ l.^{2} atm/mole^2 and $b = 90{\cdot}4 \times 10^{-3} = 0{\cdot}0904$ l./mole, with $R = 0{\cdot}082$ l. atm/(deg. mole). If the van der Waals equation for 1 Ncm^3 is taken, then, in accordance with eqn. (28), the constants, $a^\star$ and $b^\star$, become: $a^\star = (9{\cdot}25 \times 10^6)\,1{\cdot}99 \times 10^{-9} = 0{\cdot}01841$ cm^6 atm, and $b^* = 90{\cdot}4 \times 4{\cdot}46 \times 10^{-5} = 0{\cdot}004033$ cm^3, with $R^\star = 3{\cdot}661 \times 10^{-3}$ cm^3 atm deg.$^{-1}$. In scientific literature $a^\star$ and $b^\star$ are often given. In this case the Boyle temperature may, of course, be similarly calculated, using eqn. (22), but it should be remembered that, instead of R, the value $n_0 R = R^\star$ of eqn. (28) must be used; thus

$$T_B = \frac{0{\cdot}01841}{0{\cdot}004033 \times 3{\cdot}661 \times 10^{-3}} = 1247\ °\text{K}$$

*Exercise 22

At what pressure, using the van der Waals equation, do the deviations from the ideal gas state reach 1 per cent and 5 per cent for propane at (a) the Boyle temperature, and (b) 100 °C? (For data on propane, see Exercise 21.)

Solution 22. Van der Waals equation (20) may easily be rewritten as

$$p = \frac{RT}{v - b} - \frac{a}{v^2} \quad \text{or} \quad pv = \frac{RTv}{v - b} - \frac{a}{v} \qquad \dots\dots \quad \text{(i)}$$

Since, according to the ideal gas equation (1), $(pv)_{\text{ideal}} = RT$, the relative deviation from the ideal gas state is

$$\frac{pv - (pv)_{\text{ideal}}}{(pv)_{\text{ideal}}} = \frac{b}{v - b} - \frac{a}{RTv} \qquad \dots\dots \quad \text{(ii)}$$

Using (ii), it is best first to determine by trial, i.e. by successive approximation, the value of v for which the deviations reach the required amount. It is also best to make the calculation in l. atm and per mole, because of the ease of handling the numbers*. The required relevant pressure is then obtained from (i). The values of a and b for propane are calculated in Exercise 21, also the Boyle temperature:

$$a = 9{\cdot}25 \text{ l.}^2 \text{ atm/mole}^2 \quad b = 0{\cdot}0904 \text{ l./mole} \quad \text{with} \quad R = 0{\cdot}082 \text{ l. atm/(deg. mole)}$$
$$T_B = 1247\ °\text{K} \qquad \dots\dots \quad \text{(iii)}$$

When $T_B = 1247$ °K, $RT_B = (pv)_{\text{ideal}} = 0{\cdot}082 \times 1247 = 102{\cdot}2$ l. atm/mole. A trial using $v = 1$ in (ii), gives

$$\frac{0{\cdot}0904}{1 - 0{\cdot}0904} - \frac{9{\cdot}25}{1 \times 102{\cdot}2} = 0{\cdot}90 \text{ per cent}$$

* Of course, one can, after rearrangement, also solve (ii) as a quadratic equation in v.

i.e. still somewhat below the imposed limit. On the other hand, $v = 0{\cdot}9$ gives a value of 1·12 per cent which is above the limit stipulated. The required value has therefore been deduced as lying in the region of $v = 0{\cdot}95$, and this value, in l./mole, substituted in (ii) does, in fact, give exactly +1·0 per cent. For the 5 per cent limit, a similar bracketing is made, using for v the two values 0·5 and 0·4, which give 4·0 per cent and 6·6 per cent, respectively. The correct value of v is therefore about $v = 0{\cdot}45$ and substitution of this figure in l./mole in (ii) actually gives

$$\frac{0{\cdot}0904}{0{\cdot}45 - 0{\cdot}0904} - \frac{9{\cdot}25}{0{\cdot}45 \times 102{\cdot}2} = +5{\cdot}0 \text{ per cent}$$

p is found by substituting in (i) the two values found for v:

$$p = \frac{102{\cdot}2}{0{\cdot}95 - 0{\cdot}0904} - \frac{9{\cdot}25}{0{\cdot}95^2} = 108{\cdot}7 \text{ atm}$$

for the 1 per cent limit for deviation from the ideal gas pressure, the latter being

$$RT_B/v = 102{\cdot}2/0{\cdot}95 = 107{\cdot}7 \text{ atm}$$

Similarly, substituting $v = 0{\cdot}45$ l./mole in (i) for the 5 per cent limit, gives

$$p = \frac{102{\cdot}2}{0{\cdot}45 - 0{\cdot}0904} - \frac{9{\cdot}25}{0{\cdot}45^2} = 238{\cdot}5 \text{ atm}$$

The ideal gas pressure would be $102{\cdot}2/0{\cdot}45 = 227{\cdot}3$ atm.

The problem is treated in a similar manner for the temperature of 100 °C; thus $T = 373$ °K, with $RT = 30{\cdot}6$ l. atm/mole.

It is found by trial that $v = 20$ l./mole gives a value close to the limit of 1 per cent deviation:

$$\frac{0{\cdot}0904}{20 - 0{\cdot}0904} - \frac{9{\cdot}25}{30{\cdot}6 \times 20} = -1{\cdot}06 \text{ per cent}$$

Trials with $v = 4$ and $v = 4{\cdot}5$, finally give a value of $v = 4{\cdot}2$ l./mole for the 5 per cent limit:

$$\frac{0{\cdot}0904}{4{\cdot}2 - 0{\cdot}0904} - \frac{9{\cdot}25}{30{\cdot}6 \times 4{\cdot}2} = -5{\cdot}0 \text{ per cent}$$

By a procedure similar to the above, the relevant pressures are found to be

$$p = \frac{30{\cdot}6}{20 - 0{\cdot}0904} = \frac{9{\cdot}25}{20^2} = 1{\cdot}51 \text{ atm for the 1 per cent limit}$$

the ideal gas pressure being $30{\cdot}6/20 = 1{\cdot}53$ atm, and

$$p = \frac{30{\cdot}6}{4{\cdot}2 - 0{\cdot}0904} - \frac{9{\cdot}25}{4{\cdot}2^2} = 6{\cdot}92 \text{ atm for the 5 per cent limit}$$

the ideal gas pressure in this case being $30{\cdot}6/4{\cdot}2 = 7{\cdot}28$ atm.

Note. These specimen calculations serve to illustrate clearly the special importance of the Boyle temperature. In the neighbourhood of this temperature, real gases behave, up to very high pressures, in almost the same way as ideal gases. This is because the repulsive forces embodied in term b

exactly balance the attractive forces expressed by a/v^2. It is seen, for example, on the one hand, that at the Boyle point, deviation from the ideal gas state reaches 5 per cent only at a pressure of 238·5 atm and is no more than 1 per cent at a pressure of 108·7 atm. On the other hand, at 100 °C (i.e. just above the critical temperature for propane, $\theta_k = 96{\cdot}8$ °C) the deviation is 1 per cent at a pressure of 1·51 atm and as much as 5 per cent at a pressure of only 7 atm.

*Exercise 23

In an isomerization experiment at 17 °C, 2·0 kg of liquid cyclohexane, C_6H_{12}, are introduced into a 20 l. autoclave and a pressure of 200 atm of hydrogen gas is applied. After closure, the autoclave is heated to 408 °C (for isomerization to methyl cyclopentane). What are the partial pressures of the components and the total pressure at this temperature?

Density of (liquid) C_6H_{12}, $\varrho_{C_6H_{12}} = 0{\cdot}7791$ kg/l.; van der Waals constants for C_6H_{12} (for 1 Ncm³; p in atm), $a^\star = 0{\cdot}04347$ cm⁶ atm, $b^\star = 0{\cdot}006359$ cm³. Hydrogen may be taken as an ideal gas. Gas constant, $R = 0{\cdot}08206$ l. atm/(deg. mole).

Solution 23. The hydrogen does not enter into the reaction. Its partial pressure, calculated from eqn. (1), is

$$p_{H_2} = \frac{p_{0\,H_2} V_0 T_1}{T_0 V_1} \quad \ldots\ldots \quad \text{(i)}$$

where $p_{0\,H_2} = 200$ atm $\quad V_1 = 20$ l. $\quad V_0 = 20 - 2{\cdot}0/0{\cdot}7791 = 17{\cdot}4$ l.

$$T_1 = 681\ ^\circ K \qquad T_0 = 290\ ^\circ K$$

Thus

$$p_{H_2} = \frac{200 \times 17{\cdot}4 \times 681}{20 \times 290} = 409 \text{ atm} \quad \ldots\ldots \quad \text{(ii)}$$

The partial pressure of cyclohexane, $p_{C_6H_{12}}$, is calculated from eqn. (27), taking eqns. (28) and (29) into account; since $a^\star$ and $b^\star$ are given and the volume is measured in litres, the quantity of moles is

$$n = G/M = \frac{2000}{84{\cdot}15} \text{ moles} \quad \ldots\ldots \quad \text{(iii)}$$

From eqns. (27)–(29):

$$\left.\begin{aligned} \frac{a'}{V_1^2} &= \frac{a^\star n^2 \times 5{\cdot}03 \times 10^8 \times 10^{-6}}{V_1^2} = \frac{0{\cdot}04347 \left(\frac{2000}{84{\cdot}15}\right)^2 5{\cdot}03 \times 10^8 \times 10^{-6}}{20^2} \\ &= 30{\cdot}89 \text{ atm} \end{aligned}\right\} \quad \ldots \quad \text{(iv)}$$

$$\left.\begin{aligned} b' &= b^\star n \times 2{\cdot}24 \times 10^4 \times 10^{-3} = 0{\cdot}006359 \frac{2000}{84{\cdot}15} \times 2{\cdot}24 \times 10^4 \times 10^{-3} \\ &= 3{\cdot}38 \text{ l.} \end{aligned}\right\} \quad \ldots \quad \text{(v)}$$

$$R' T_1 = n R T_1 = 0{\cdot}08206 \frac{2000}{84{\cdot}15} \times 681 = 1329 \text{ l. atm} \quad \ldots\ldots \quad \text{(vi)}$$

Thus, from eqn. (27)

$$(p_{C_6H_{12}} + 30{\cdot}89)(20 - 3{\cdot}38) = 1329 \text{ l. atm} \qquad p_{C_6H_{12}} = 49 \text{ atm}$$

$$\text{total pressure } p = p_{H_2} + p_{C_6H_{12}} = 409 + 49 = 458 \text{ atm.}$$

*Exercise 24

A partial pressure of benzene, $p_{C_6H_6} = 40$ atm is required in a hydrogenation experiment in a 5 l. autoclave at 327 °C. How many grammes of benzene should be introduced into the autoclave? The van der Waals constants for benzene (for 1 Ncm³, p in atm) are: $a^\star = 0{\cdot}03588$ atm cm⁶, $b^\star = 0{\cdot}005150$ cm³, $R = 0{\cdot}08206$ l. atm/(deg. mole).

Solution 24. Using eqns. (28) and (29) and measuring V in litres:

$$\left.\begin{aligned} a/V^2 &= 5{\cdot}03 \times 10^8 \times 10^{-6} \times 0{\cdot}03588/25 = 0{\cdot}722 \text{ atm/mole}^2 \\ b &= 2{\cdot}24 \times 10^4 \times 10^{-3} \times 0{\cdot}005150 = 0{\cdot}1153 \text{ l./mole} \end{aligned}\right\} \quad \ldots \quad \text{(i)}$$

With

$p = 40$ atm, $V = 5$ l. and $T = 327 + 273 = 600$ °K

$RT = 49{\cdot}236$ l. atm/mole, eqn. (27) becomes

$$(40 + 0{\cdot}722n^2)(5 - 0{\cdot}115n) - 49{\cdot}2n = 0 \quad \ldots\ldots \quad \text{(ii)}$$

This cubic equation is best solved graphically by putting y for the left-hand side of the equation; y may be taken as a function of n for a number of suitable numerical values of n on millimetre paper, and the intersection of the curve with the positive abscissa ($y = 0$) is the solution of n for equation (ii).

As a first approximation, a value of n is taken using the ideal gas equation (2); thus, with $pV = nRT$

$$n = \frac{40 \times 5}{49{\cdot}2} \approx 4$$

This value is certainly too low. Substitution in (ii) gives, for

$n = 4 \quad y = +37{\cdot}2$

$n = 5 \quad y = +11{\cdot}0 \qquad n = 5{\cdot}5 \quad y = -0{\cdot}6$

$n = 6 \quad y = -10{\cdot}7 \qquad n = 5{\cdot}4 \quad y = +1{\cdot}8$

Thus, by interpolation

$$n = 5{\cdot}475 \text{ moles} \quad \ldots\ldots \quad \text{(iii)}$$

Hence, the mass of benzene is

$$G = Mn = 78{\cdot}11 \times 5{\cdot}475 = 428 \text{ g}$$

4

KINETIC THEORY OF GASES. EFFUSION, FLOW, DIFFUSION

THE specific heat at constant volume (molecular heat) per degree of freedom is, for an ideal gas

$$c_V = \frac{R}{2} \qquad \ldots\ldots (30)$$

R, the gas constant [see eqn. (4)], will be

$$\left.\begin{aligned} R &= 82{\cdot}06\ \text{cm}^3\ \text{atm/(deg. mole)} = 8{\cdot}31439 \times 10^7\ \text{ergs/(deg. mole)} \\ &= 1{\cdot}9865\ \text{cal/(deg. mole)} \end{aligned}\right\} \quad \ldots (31)$$

The translational energy of an ideal gas (3 degrees of freedom of translational motion) is therefore

$$U_{\text{trans}} = \frac{3}{2} RT = \frac{1}{2} N_{\text{L}}\, m\, \overline{w^2} = \frac{1}{2} M\, \overline{w^2} \qquad \ldots\ldots (32)$$

N_{A} = number of molecules per mole = $6{\cdot}02368 \times 10^{23}$/mole (Avogadro or Loschmidt constant)

m = mass of one molecule

M = molecular weight

$\overline{w^2}$ = mean square velocity of the gas molecules

By rearrangement of eqn. (32)

$$\sqrt{\overline{w^2}} = \sqrt{\frac{3\,RT}{M}} = 1{\cdot}579 \times 10^4 \sqrt{T/M}\ \text{(cm/sec)} \qquad \ldots\ldots (33)$$

$$\bar{w} = \sqrt{\frac{8\,RT}{\pi M}} = 0{\cdot}921 \sqrt{\overline{w^2}} = 0{\cdot}921 \sqrt{\frac{3\,RT}{M}} = 1{\cdot}455 \times 10^4 \sqrt{T/M}\ \text{(cm/sec)} \qquad \ldots\ldots (34)$$

$\bar{w}$ = mean molecular velocity.

Hence, at a given temperature, the square of the molecular velocity is inversely proportional to the molecular weight, or to the gas density

$$\overline{w_1^2}/\overline{w_2^2} = M_2/M_1 = \varrho_2/\varrho_1 \qquad \ldots\ldots (35)$$

The number of collisions per second, Z_{11}, for a single particle in a homogeneous gas is given by

$$Z_{11} = \sqrt{2}\,{}^1N\,\pi\,\sigma^2\,\bar{w} = 4\,{}^1N\,\sigma^2 \sqrt{\frac{\pi\,RT}{M}} \qquad \ldots\ldots (36)$$

$\sigma = 2r$ = molecular diameter

The total number of collisions per second and per cubic centimetre in a homogeneous gas is

$$Z = {}^1N^2 \pi \sigma^2 \frac{\bar{w}}{\sqrt{2}} = Z_{11} \frac{{}^1N}{2} \quad \text{or, with eqn. (34)} \quad Z = 2\,{}^1N^2 \sigma^2 \left(\frac{\pi RT}{M}\right)^{1/2} \qquad \ldots . \; (37)$$

${}^1N = \frac{n N_A}{V} = c N_A = N_L \frac{p}{RT}$ = number of particles per cubic centimetre, at standard temperature and pressure (0 °C, 760 torr, see p. 4).

$${}^1N = \frac{6{\cdot}02368 \times 10^{23}}{22415} = 2{\cdot}686 \times 10^{19} \text{ molecules/Ncm}^3 \qquad \ldots . \; (38)$$

The mean free path, $\bar{l}$, of a molecule in an ideal gas is

$$\bar{l} = \frac{\text{mean velocity}}{\text{number of collisions/sec}} = \frac{\bar{w}}{Z_{11}} = \frac{1}{\sqrt{2}\,{}^1N \pi \sigma^2} \qquad \ldots . \; (39)$$

In a real gas there is a temperature dependence:

$$\bar{l}_T = \bar{l} \frac{T}{T + C} = \frac{1}{\sqrt{2}\,{}^1N \pi \sigma_T^2} \quad \text{where } \sigma_T^2 = \sigma^2 \left(1 + \frac{C}{T}\right) \qquad \ldots . \; (40)$$

C is an individual constant, known as the Sutherland constant (°K).

In a gas mixture containing the components X_1 and X_2, the number of collisions per second, Z_{12}, between a single particle of X_1 and the particles X_2 is

$$Z_{12} = {}^1N_2 \pi \sigma_{12}^2 \bar{w}_1 \sqrt{\frac{M_1 + M_2}{M_2}} = 2\,{}^1N_2 \sigma_{12}^2 \left(\frac{2 \pi RT}{M_r}\right)^{1/2} \qquad \ldots . \; (41)$$

where $\sigma_{12} = r_1 + r_2$ and $M_r = \frac{M_1 M_2}{M_1 + M_2}$ (the reduced mass).

The total number of collisions per second and per cubic centimetre between the particles X_1 and X_2 in the gas mixture is

$$Z = Z_{12}\,{}^1N_1 = 2\,{}^1N_1\,{}^1N_2 \sigma_{12}^2 \left(\frac{2 \pi RT}{M_r}\right)^{1/2} \qquad \ldots . \; (42)$$

It follows that the mean free path $\bar{l}_1$ of a particle of X_1 in an ideal gas mixture with the components X_1, X_2, X_3, ... will be

$$\bar{l}_1 = \frac{\text{mean velocity}}{\text{sum of number of collisions/sec}} = \frac{\bar{w}_1}{Z_{11} + Z_{12} + Z_{13} + \cdots} \qquad \ldots . \; (43)$$

The terms of the sum in eqn. (43) must, for a real gas mixture, be multiplied by the factors

$$\frac{T + C_{1i}}{T}, \quad \text{where } C_{11} = C_1 \quad \text{and } C_{1i} = \sqrt{C_1 C_i} \qquad \ldots . \; (44)$$

and the C_i represent the Sutherland constants of components X_i.

FLOW PHENOMENA

When considering internal friction of gases, the frictional force X is defined by

$$X = \eta q \frac{\partial w}{\partial d} \qquad \ldots . \; (45)$$

where X = frictional force, q = area (cross section) normal to the direction of the force and velocity, $\frac{\partial w}{\partial d}$ = velocity gradient along the flow layer of thickness d, normal to the direction of the velocity w.

The kinetic theory of gases (for elastic spheres) leads to the following expression or η, the coefficient of internal friction (viscosity)

$$\left.\begin{aligned} \eta &= \frac{5}{16}\,1{\cdot}016\sqrt{\frac{M\,RT}{\pi}} \times \frac{1}{N_A\,\sigma^2} = 0{\cdot}499\,c\,M\,\bar{w}\,\bar{l}_T = 0{\cdot}499\,\frac{{}^1N}{N_A}\,\bar{w}\,\bar{l}_T\,M \\ &= \frac{0{\cdot}499\,M\,\bar{w}}{\sqrt{2}\,N_A\,\sigma_T^2\,\pi} \quad \text{(poise) or } \left(\frac{\text{g}}{\text{cm sec}}\right) \end{aligned}\right\} \quad \ldots \quad (46)$$

where $c = {}^1N/N_2$ is the concentration in mole/cm^3, $\bar{w}$ is determined by eqn. (34) and $\bar{l}_T$ and σ_T by eqns. (40), (36) and (39).

The temperature dependence of η follows from eqn. (46)

$$\eta = K\,\frac{T^{3/2}}{T + C} \quad (K = \text{proportionality factor}) \quad \ldots\ldots \quad (47)$$

Since ${}^1N$ (number of molecules per cubic centimetre) does not feature or, rather, cancels out in eqn. (46), η is independent of pressure at a given temperature. Equation (46) permits determination of the gas-kinetic molecular diameter σ and the Sutherland constant C in conjunction with eqn. (40).

When gases flow through small apertures (at very low pressures), the number of gas particles which strike unit area (cm^2/sec), $\dot{N} = \mathrm{d}N/\mathrm{d}t$, is

$$\dot{N} = \frac{1}{4}\,{}^1N\,\bar{w} \text{ [for } {}^1N \text{ see eqn. (38), for } \bar{w} \text{ see eqn. (34)]} \quad \ldots\ldots \quad (48)$$

From eqn. (48) one may obtain the velocity of effusion through a small aperture of cross-section q (small in comparison with the mean free path $\bar{l}$, so that no collisions between gas molecules occur in the region of the aperture):

$$\text{Velocity of effusion} \qquad \dot{N}_q = q\,\dot{N} = \frac{1}{4}\,{}^1N\,\bar{w}\,q = \frac{n\,N_A\,\bar{w}\,q}{4V} \quad \ldots\ldots \quad (49)$$

The relation between the velocity of effusion through a small aperture and the pressure in a highly rarefied gas is obtained from the gas eqn. (2), $p = n\,RT/V$ and eqn. (49), also taking eqn. (34) into account:

$$\dot{N}_q = \frac{p\,N_A\,q}{\sqrt{2\pi\,M\,R\,T}} = \text{number of particles passing per second through the aperture } q \quad \ldots\ldots \quad (50)$$

(equation for the measurement of low vapour pressures)

$$\text{Units: } [p] = \left[\frac{\text{dyne}}{\text{cm}^2}\right] \qquad [R] = \left[\frac{\text{ergs}}{\text{deg. mole}}\right] \qquad [q] = [\text{cm}^2]$$

For flow through tubes (capillary diameter small in comparison with the mean free path):

$$\dot{N}_q = \frac{1}{2}\,K\,\frac{1}{\sqrt{2\,\pi\,MR}}\left(\frac{p_2}{\sqrt{T_2}} - \frac{p_1}{\sqrt{T_1}}\right) \times \frac{1}{L} \quad \ldots\ldots \quad (51)$$

(L = length of tube) where, for circular-section tubes, $K = \frac{2\,\pi\,(2\,r)^3}{3}$ ($2\,r$ = diam. of tube).

For isothermal flow through tubes (capillary diameter large in comparison with the mean free path, but still only for capillary tubes):

$$\dot{N}_q = \frac{\mathrm{d}N_q}{\mathrm{d}t} = \frac{(2r)^4 \pi N_A}{128 \eta L} \frac{1}{RT} \frac{p_2^2 - p_1^2}{2} \quad \text{(Poiseuille's equation)} \qquad \dots . \ (52)$$

($2r$ = diam. of tube, L = length of tube)

When considering the motion of spherical bodies in a gas (radius of sphere, r, large in comparison with the mean free path):

$$w = \frac{X}{6 \pi r \eta} \quad \text{Stokes' law} \quad (X = \text{force}) \qquad \dots . \ (53)$$

GAS DIFFUSION

$$\frac{\mathrm{d}N_q}{\mathrm{d}t} = \dot{N}_q = c N_L q w = -q D N_L \frac{\partial c}{\partial x} \approx -q N_A D \frac{c_1 - c_2}{x_1 - x_2} \qquad \dots . \ (54)$$

[diffusion equation: see also eqn. (266)]

$\dot{N}_q$ = number of particles passing through the cross-section q (cm²/sec)
c_i = molar concentration—note (mole/cm³)—in place of x_i (cm)
N_A = Avogadro constant (mol.$^{-1}$)
D = diffusion coefficient (cm²/sec) $= \frac{1}{3} \bar{w} \bar{l}$ to a first approximation .... (55)
w = velocity of flow (cm/sec)
$\bar{w}$ = mean velocity of the gas molecules (cm/sec)

*EXERCISE 25

A porous, volumetrically calibrated diffusion cell is filled with 80·2 cm³ of hydrogen and placed in an atmosphere of air. The internal and external pressures are balanced by means of a suitable liquid cut-off. During the experiment, the whole of the hydrogen diffuses outwards and air inwards. When the volume of gas in the diffusion cell becomes constant, indicating completion of the two-way diffusion, a gas volume reading of 21·2 cm³, i.e. of infused air, is taken in the diffusion cell. On repeating the experiment using a charge of 81·3 cm³ of propane, a volumetric reading of 100·4 cm³ is taken in the diffusion cell after adjusting for constancy of volume. The volumes are proportional to the diffusion velocities or, since the problem relates to effusion through apertures, to the molecular velocities, i.e. in accordance with eqn. (48). What is the molecular weight of propane if that of H_2 is taken as 2·016? See eqn. (35).

Solution 25. While 80·2 cm³ of H_2 diffuse outwards, 21·2 cm³ of air diffuse inwards. One has, therefore

$$\frac{w_{H_2}}{w_{air}} = \frac{80{\cdot}2}{21{\cdot}2} \quad \text{and} \quad \frac{w_{C_3H_8}}{w_{air}} = \frac{81{\cdot}3}{100{\cdot}4} \qquad \dots . \ \text{(i)}$$

thus

$$\frac{w_{H_2}}{w_{C_3H_8}} = \frac{80{\cdot}2}{21{\cdot}2} \Big/ \frac{81{\cdot}3}{100{\cdot}4} \qquad \dots . \ \text{(ii)}$$

From eqn. (35), this gives

$$M_{C_3H_8} = M_{H_2} \left(\frac{w_{H_2}}{w_{C_3H_8}}\right)^2 = 2{\cdot}016 \left(\frac{80{\cdot}2 \times 100{\cdot}4}{21{\cdot}2 \times 81{\cdot}3}\right)^2 = 44{\cdot}1$$

*Exercise 26

In diffusion experiments analogous to those in Exercise 25 and with mixtures of ozone–oxygen, oxygen–chlorine and oxygen–carbon dioxide, Soret found ratios as follows for the rates of diffusion $w_{Cl_2} : w_{O_2} : w_{CO_2} = 0{\cdot}227 : 0{\cdot}271 : 0{\cdot}290$. Calculate the molecular weight of ozone.

Solution 26. Mol. wt. of $Cl_2 = 70{\cdot}9$, of $CO_2 = 44{\cdot}0$. From eqn. (35), we get

$$\frac{M_{O_3}}{70{\cdot}9} = \left(\frac{0{\cdot}227}{0{\cdot}271}\right)^2 \qquad M_{O_3} = 49{\cdot}6 \qquad \frac{M_{O_3}}{44{\cdot}0} = \left(\frac{0{\cdot}290}{0{\cdot}271}\right)^2 \qquad M_{O_3} = 50{\cdot}2$$

Hence a mean value of $M_{O_3} = 49{\cdot}9$. It is thus shown that ozone is made up from three oxygen atoms, since $M_{O_3} = 48$, and the experimental results agree with this within the limits of accuracy of the method (approx. 5 per cent).

*Exercise 27

According to diffusion studies by Perkins, the rates of diffusion of mercury vapour and radium emanation are in the ratio 1·082 : 1. This leads to a first approximate value for the atomic weight of radium emanation (radon), since mercury vapour is known to be monatomic.

Solution 27. Atomic weight of mercury = 200·6, thus, from eqn. (35)

$$\frac{M_{Rn}}{200{\cdot}6} = \left(\frac{1{\cdot}082}{1}\right)^2 \qquad M_{Rn} = 235$$

instead of the correct value of 222. This represents an error of approximately 6 per cent.

*Exercise 28

The criterion for a separation process is the separation factor. If x_{A_1}/x_{A_2} and x_{E_1}/x_{E_2} represent the molar ratios of the mixture before and after separation, then the separation factor is

$$t = \frac{x_{E_1}/x_{E_2}}{x_{A_1}/x_{A_3}}$$

The ideal (initial) separation factor for a diffusion separation process is, therefore, given by the ratio of the initial rates of effusion. Calculate and compare the separation factors for the separation of a mixture of hydrogen and deuterium, of water vapour and heavy water vapour and a mixture of the isotopes of uranium hexafluoride, $^{238}UF_6$ and $^{235}UF_6$.

Solution 28. According to eqn. (35) the rates of diffusion are inversely proportional to the square roots of the molecular weights. The molecular weights are $H_2 = 2{\cdot}016$, $D_2 = 4{\cdot}028$, $H_2O = 18{\cdot}02$, $D_2O = 20{\cdot}03$ and the figures for the two UF_6 isotopes are 352 and 349.

$$t_{H_2-D_2} = \sqrt{4{\cdot}028/2{\cdot}016} = 1{\cdot}413$$

$$t_{H_2O-D_2O} = \sqrt{20{\cdot}03/18{\cdot}02} = 1{\cdot}055$$

$$t_{UF_6\text{-isot.}} = \sqrt{352/349} = 1{\cdot}0043$$

A marked decrease in the value of the diffusion separation process may be noted for the case of the isotopes with their high molecular weights.

*Exercise 29

A liquid hydrocarbon has the composition C – 91·25 per cent, H – 8·75 per cent by weight. 84·4 cm³ of the hydrocarbon vapour are introduced into a heated diffusion cell (see Exercise 25), which is then placed in an oxygen atmosphere. A volumetric reading of 143·2 cm³ (of oxygen) is recorded after adjustment for constancy of volume in the cell and after all the hydrocarbon has diffused out. What is the formula for the hydrocarbon?

Solution 29. From eqn. (35) the molecular weight of the hydrocarbon is

$$M_{\rm hc}/32 = \left(\frac{143 \cdot 2}{84 \cdot 4}\right)^2 \quad \text{thus } M_{\rm hc} = 92 \cdot 1 \qquad \ldots\ldots \quad \text{(i)}$$

The atomic weight of C is 12·01 and that of H = 1·008. From the weight ratio of H and C, one obtains the molecular ratio H/C by dividing the percentage weights by the actual atomic weights, thus

$$\text{Molecular ratio H/C} = \frac{8 \cdot 75}{1 \cdot 008} \Big/ \frac{91 \cdot 25}{12 \cdot 01} = 1 \cdot 142 : 1 \qquad \ldots\ldots \quad \text{(ii)}$$

(ii) gives the hypothetical formula $C_1H_{1\cdot142}$ with a hypothetical molecular weight of

$$M_{\rm hyp} = 1 \times 12 \cdot 01 + 1 \cdot 142 \times 1 \cdot 008 = 13 \cdot 15 \qquad \ldots\ldots \quad \text{(iii)}$$

The quotient of the true molecular weight and the hypothetical molecular weight, $M_{\rm hc}/M_{\rm hyp} = 92 \cdot 1/13 \cdot 15 = 7$. The hypothetical formula $C_1H_{1\cdot142}$ must be multiplied by this factor in order to obtain the actual formula of the hydrocarbon, i.e. $7 \times C_1H_{1\cdot142} = C_7H_8$ (toluene).

*Exercise 30

At what pressures will the mean free paths of nitrogen and hydrogen at 20 °C and 550 °C exceed 1 cm and 10^{-6} cm? The Sutherland constant for N_2, $C = 104$ °K, for H_2, $C = 71 \cdot 7$ °K. The molecular diameter for N_2, $\sigma = 3 \cdot 18$ Å, for H_2, $\sigma = 2 \cdot 47$ Å $= 2 \cdot 47 \times 10^{-8}$ cm.

Solution 30. From eqns. (38) and (1), the number of particles per cubic centimetre at 20 °C and 1 atm is:

$$^1N = 2 \cdot 686 \times 10^{19} \times \frac{273}{293} = 2 \cdot 51 \times 10^{19}/\text{cm}^3$$

and, correspondingly, at 550 °C

$$^1N = 0 \cdot 892 \times 10^{19}/\text{cm}^3 \qquad \ldots\ldots \quad \text{(i)}$$

Substitution in eqn. (39) gives $\bar{l}$ and, with eqn. (40), $\bar{l}_T$, e.g. for H_2 at 20 °C:

$$\bar{l} = 1/\sqrt{2}\,\pi \times 2 \cdot 51 \times 10^{19}\,(2 \cdot 47 \times 10^{-8})^2 = 14 \cdot 7 \times 10^{-6}\,\text{cm}$$

and

$$\bar{l}_{\mathrm{T}} = 14{\cdot}7 \times 10^{-6} \frac{293}{293 + 71{\cdot}7} = 11{\cdot}8 \times 10^{-6}\ \mathrm{cm}$$

$$\left.\begin{array}{lll} \text{Likewise for } H_2 \text{ at } 550\ {}^{\circ}\mathrm{C} & \bar{l} = 41{\cdot}7 \times 10^{-6}\ \mathrm{cm} & \bar{l}_{\mathrm{T}} = 38{\cdot}1 \times 10^{-6}\ \mathrm{cm} \\ N_2 \text{ at } 20\ {}^{\circ}\mathrm{C} & \bar{l} = 8{\cdot}87 \times 10^{-6}\ \mathrm{cm} & \bar{l}_{\mathrm{T}} = 6{\cdot}55 \times 10^{-6}\ \mathrm{cm} \\ N_2 \text{ at } 550\ {}^{\circ}\mathrm{C} & \bar{l} = 25{\cdot}0 \times 10^{-6}\ \mathrm{cm} & \bar{l}_{\mathrm{T}} = 22{\cdot}2 \times 10^{-6}\ \mathrm{cm} \end{array}\right\} \quad \ldots \quad \text{(ii)}$$

These values for the mean free path are valid for a pressure of 1 atm. According to eqn. (39), the mean free path is inversely proportional to ${}^1N$, the number of particles per cubic centimetre, and hence [see also eqns. (38) and (2)] also inversely proportional to the pressure. This gives

$$p\ \mathrm{atm} : 1\ \mathrm{atm} = \bar{l}_{\mathrm{T}}\ (\text{at } 1\ \mathrm{atm}) : \bar{l}_{\mathrm{T}}\ (\text{at } p\ \mathrm{atm}) \quad \ldots\ldots \quad \text{(iii)}$$

It follows that hydrogen at 20 °C has a mean free path of 1 cm at

$$11{\cdot}8 \times 10^{-6}\ \mathrm{atm} = 11{\cdot}8 \times 10^{-6} \times 760\ \mathrm{torr} = 8{\cdot}97 \times 10^{-3}\ \mathrm{torr}$$

Mean free paths of 1 cm are also obtained for

hydrogen at 550 °C at $29{\cdot}0 \times 10^{-3}$ torr
nitrogen at 20 °C at $4{\cdot}98 \times 10^{-3}$ torr
nitrogen at 550 °C at $16{\cdot}9 \times 10^{-3}$ torr

Similarly, the pressures at which the free path has a length of 10^{-6} cm will be

H_2 (20 °C) at 11·8 atm H_2 (550 °C) at 38·1 atm
N_2 (20 °C) at 6·55 atm N_2 (550 °C) at 22·2 atm.

Note. In practice, the mean free paths and the molecular diameters are calculated from the internal friction coefficient using eqn. (46); and the molecular radii may also be obtained from the van der Waals constant b by means of eqn. (25).

The path lengths of 1 and 10^{-6} cm given in the above Exercise are of particular practical interest. It should be especially noted that a mean free path of 1 cm corresponds to the range of pressures from 1/1000 to 1/100 mm Hg, attainable with a high-vacuum pump. In order to maintain satisfactory pumping efficiency at such pressures, one must ensure that the diameters of the pumping lines are least 1 cm, i.e. of the same order of magnitude as the mean free path, or at least one tenth of the latter. Moreover, the lines must be as straight as possible, since bends act as a resistance because of the small number of scattering and deflecting collisions. The range of 10^{-6} cm is of great significance because the pore width of many contact materials for technical catalytic processes is of this order of magnitude. It is now important to know above what pressure, in the pores of such contact materials, flow and diffusion is of the same kind and order of magnitude as in the channels between the contact mass. For, only in this case can the contact pore space be a determining factor in the catalytic contact effect. It will be seen from the results of the above Exercise that this is the case at temperatures of the order of 550 °C and at pressures above 50 atm. These are exactly the conditions found in technical catalytic high-pressure syntheses, such as the synthesis of ammonia by the Haber–Bosch process, methanol synthesis and the high-pressure hydrogenation of coal in fuel production.

*Exercise 31

Calculate the mean molecular velocities of hydrogen, oxygen, nitrogen and mercury vapour at 20 °C.

Solution 31. Eqn. (34) is used. R must be taken in c.g.s. units, in order to obtain the velocity in centimetres per second, i.e. in ergs/(deg. mole) [see eqn. (31)]. We then obtain for

$$H_2: \quad \bar{w} = 1{\cdot}455 \times 10^4 \sqrt{\frac{273 + 20}{2{\cdot}016}} = 1754 \text{ m/sec}$$

The velocities for the other molecules are inversely proportional to the roots of the molecular weights, hence for

$$O_2: \quad \bar{w} = 1754 \sqrt{\frac{2{\cdot}016}{32}} = 440 \text{ m/sec}$$

$$N_2: \quad \bar{w} = 1754 \sqrt{\frac{2{\cdot}016}{28{\cdot}016}} = 470{\cdot}5 \text{ m/sec}$$

$$Hg: \quad \bar{w} = 1754 \sqrt{\frac{2{\cdot}016}{200{\cdot}6}} = 175{\cdot}9 \text{ m/sec}$$

Exercise 32

Estimate the retarding effect, as a percentage of the velocity, experienced by a neutron if it collides elastically in direct central impact with, on the one hand, deuterium (e.g. in heavy water) or, on the other hand, with graphite as moderator. Deviations from elastic impact and the influence of chemical bonding of collision partners should be neglected. The velocity of the neutrons should, in any given case, be 200 times the speed of the moderators.

Solution 32. According to the laws of mechanics for elastic collision, if a particle of mass m_1 with a velocity w_{a1} meets a particle of mass m_2 with a velocity w_{a2} (same direction), then the velocities after impact, w_{e1} and w_{e2}, are

$$w_{e1} = w_{a1} - \frac{2\, m_2 (w_{a1} - w_{a2})}{m_1 + m_2} \qquad w_{e2} = w_{a2} + \frac{2\, m_1 (w_{a1} - w_{a2})}{m_1 + m_2} \quad \ldots \quad \text{(i)}$$

Since the atomic weights of a neutron, deuteron and carbon are 1, 2 and 12, respectively, the neutron velocities after impact are:

$$\text{with D:} \quad w_{e1} = w_{a1} - \frac{2{\cdot}2(1 - 1/200)\, w_{a1}}{1 + 2} = 0{\cdot}327\, w_{a1}$$

$$\text{with C:} \quad w_{e1} = w_{a1} - \frac{2{\cdot}12(1 - 1/200)\, w_{a1}}{1 + 12} = 0{\cdot}837\, w_{a1}$$

With a D-compound as moderator (e.g. D_2O) the neutron loses $100 - 32{\cdot}7 = 67{\cdot}3$ per cent of its absolute velocity in such an impact. With graphite the values are $100 - 83{\cdot}7 = 16{\cdot}3$ per cent. An appreciably greater number of collisions are required with graphite as moderator than with D_2O in order to moderate the neutrons to the thermal velocity conditioned by the temperature.

*Exercise 33

Calculate the mean molecular velocity (Brownian movement) of colloidal gold particles at the limit of microscopic visibility ($\theta = 17$ °C). The density of gold is approximately 20 g/cm³. The limit of microscopic visibility is approximately half the wavelength of visible (violet) light, i.e. approx. 200 mμ, which is taken as the length of the edges of the gold particles.

Solution 33. Use eqn. (34). The mass of a gold particle is: volume × density, i.e. 20 g/cm³ $(2 \times 10^{-5}\ \text{cm})^3 = 1{\cdot}6 \times 10^{-13}$ g. From this, the molecular weight M is obtained by multiplying by the Avogadro number $N_A = 6{\cdot}023 \times 10^{23}\ \text{mol}^{-1}$ [see eqn. (32)], i.e. $M = 1{\cdot}6 \times 10^{-13} \times 6{\cdot}023 \times 10^{23} = 9{\cdot}6 \times 10^{10}\ \text{mole}^{-1}$. Substituting in eqn. (34) gives:

$$\bar{\omega} = 1{\cdot}455 \times 10^4 \sqrt{\frac{(273 + 17)}{9{\cdot}6 \times 10^{10}}} = 0{\cdot}80\ \text{cm/sec}$$

Note. The observation of Brownian movement under the microscope shows that the distance travelled by a particle is only a few thousandths of a millimetre per second. This is due to the fact that the eye can only register a mean path and not the rapid changes of direction in the fine zig-zag movements which the particles execute as a result of the many collisions.

Exercise 34

Estimate the limit, determined by Brownian movement, of the accuracy of measurement of a needle or moving-coil galvanometer at room temperature (18 °C).

Solution 34. From eqns. (30) and (32), the kinetic energy per mole (Brownian movement energy) for one degree of freedom is $u_{\text{kin}} = \frac{1}{2} RT$ or, for one degree of freedom per molecule, or per unit of movement, $U_{\text{kin}} = RT/2N_A$. This is the amount of energy transmitted in irregular fluctuations, as a result of collisions of air molecules and other thermal vibrations, to the suspended needle or coil of the galvanometer, thus imparting to it a corresponding torsional energy. In general, at low torsional energies $U_{\text{tor}} = \frac{1}{2} D\varphi^2$, where φ is the angular deflection in radians and D the torsional moment [torsional moment for angular deflection $\varphi = 1$, in (dyne cm)]. As a mean therefore

$$U_{\text{kin}} = U_{\text{tor}} \quad \text{i.e.} \quad \frac{1}{2} \times \frac{RT}{N_A} = \frac{1}{2} D\bar{\varphi}^2 \quad \text{or} \quad \sqrt{\bar{\varphi}^2} = \sqrt{\frac{RT}{DN_A}}$$

this being the mean angle of fluctuation of the galvanometer arising from the thermal motion (Brownian movement). Electric currents causing deflections smaller than this cannot be measured, since such deflections could not be distinguished from those associated with the thermal effects.

Taking the numerical values $R = 8{\cdot}31439 \times 10^7$ ergs/(deg. mole) [see eqn. (31)], $T = 291$ °K, $N_A = 6{\cdot}0236 \times 10^{23}$ mol.⁻¹, one obtains for the angle, $\sqrt{\bar{\varphi}^2} \approx 2 \times 10^{-7}/\sqrt{D}$ in radians, or $2 \times 10^{-4}/\sqrt{D}$ mm deflection at a scale distance of 1 m.

**Exercise 35

Determine the vapour pressure of solid coronene, $C_{24}H_{12}$ by the effusion method. For this purpose, equilibrium was established between solid coronene and its vapour contained in a flask at a temperature of 198·5 °C. The coronene vapour was then allowed to effuse through an opening of 1·69 mm², the mass transfer in a period of 9 hours being $G = 13{\cdot}72$ mg. What is the vapour pressure of coronene in mm Hg (torr)? (Method for the determination of small vapour pressures.)

Solution 35. Use eqn. (50). It is important that all quantities should be given in c.g.s. units. Equation (50) is rewritten as

$$p = \frac{\dot{N}_q}{N_A} \times \frac{\sqrt{2\pi MRT}}{q} \quad (\text{dyne/cm}^2) \quad \ldots\ldots \quad \text{(i)}$$

The molecular weight, $M = 300$. The effusion time $t = 9 \times 3600$ sec. The mass of coronene effused is $G = 13{\cdot}72 \times 10^{-3}$ g. It follows that the number of molecules per second is $\dfrac{\dot{N}_0}{N_A} = \dfrac{G}{Mt}$

Thus

$$\frac{\dot{N}_q}{N_A} = \frac{13{\cdot}72 \times 10^{-3}}{300 \times 9 \times 3600} \text{ mole/sec}$$

$$q = 1{\cdot}69 \times 10^{-2} \text{ cm}^2 \text{ (cross-sectional area of opening, cm}^2\text{)}$$

$$T = 198{\cdot}5 + 273{\cdot}2 = 471{\cdot}7\ ^\circ\text{K}$$

$$R = 8{\cdot}31439 \times 10^7 \text{ ergs/(deg. mole) [see eqn. (31)]}$$

$$1 \text{ torr} = 1{\cdot}3332 \times 10^3 \text{ dyne/cm}^2 \text{ (see note on p. 4).}$$

Hence

$$p = \frac{13{\cdot}72 \times 10^{-3}\sqrt{2 \times 3{\cdot}14 \times 300 \times 8{\cdot}314 \times 10^7 \times 471{\cdot}7}}{1{\cdot}3332 \times 10^3 \times 300 \times 9 \times 3600 \times 1{\cdot}69 \times 10^{-2}} = 5{\cdot}38 \times 10^{-4} \text{ mm Hg}$$

Exercise 36

In the lenticels (bark pores) of the aerial roots of mangroves one finds a large number of fine, irregular and scattered air passages. One can take, as the 'effective pore number', the number of straight capillaries which possess the same flow resistance as the irregular air passages of the lenticels. Estimate the effective pore number.

In order to do this, a rubber tube connected to a pressure chamber of volume V was drawn over a cut aerial root and the time taken for the pressure to fall to that of the outside atmosphere. The effective pore number, Z, may be determined by using the Poiseuille equation [eqn. (52)].

Experimental data:

capillary length $L = 60 \times 10^{-4}$ cm
capillary diameter $2r = 1{\cdot}86 \times 10^{-4}$ cm
viscosity of air at 25 °C $\eta = 1{\cdot}84 \times 10^{-4}$ poise
total volume of pressure chamber $V = 20$ cm³
external pressure $p_0 = 760$ torr $= 1{\cdot}013 \times 10^6$ dyne/cm²
excess internal pressure
at beginning of experiment $p_A - p_0 = 66$ torr
at end of experiment $p_E - p_0 = 5$ torr
duration of experiment $t = 300$ sec

Solution 36. According to the Poiseuille eqn. (52), the total flow in moles (n) through the Z capillaries of the aerial roots, per unit of time, is

$$-\frac{dn}{dt} = -\frac{\dot{N}_q}{N_A} = \frac{(2r)^4 \pi (p^2 - p_0^2)}{128 L \eta RT \times 2} Z \quad \ldots\ldots \quad \text{(i)}$$

For small pressure differences, this becomes

$$-\frac{dn}{dt} = \frac{(2r)^4 \pi (p - p_0) p_0 Z}{128 L \eta RT} \quad \ldots . \quad \text{(ii)}$$

With the gas equation (2), $pV = nRT$, we get

$$\frac{dn}{dt} = \frac{V}{RT} \frac{dp}{dt} \quad \ldots . \quad \text{(iii)}$$

and (ii) becomes

$$-\frac{dp}{dt} = \frac{(2r)^4 \pi p_0 Z}{128 L \eta V} (p - p_0) \quad \ldots . \quad \text{(iv)}$$

Integrating with respect to t, the duration of the experiment, over the limits p_A to p_E, gives

$$\int_{p_A}^{p_E} \frac{dp}{p - p_0} = \int_0^t \frac{(2r)^4 \pi p_r Z}{128 L \eta V} dt \quad \ldots . \quad \text{(v)}$$

This gives

$$\ln \left(\frac{p_A - p_0}{p_E - p_0}\right) = \frac{(2r)^4 \pi p_0 Z}{128 L \eta V} t \quad \text{or} \quad \log \left(\frac{p_A - p_0}{p_E - p_0}\right) = \frac{0{\cdot}4343\, d^4 \pi p_0 Z t}{128 L \eta V} \quad \ldots . \quad \text{(vi)}$$

and substituting the experimental data in (vi), one has:

$$\log \frac{66}{5} = 1{\cdot}121 = \frac{0{\cdot}4343 \times (1{\cdot}86 \times 10^{-4})^4 \times 3{\cdot}14 \times 1{\cdot}013 \times 10^6 \times 300 Z}{128 \times 60 \times 10^{-4} \times 1{\cdot}84 \times 10^{-4} \times 20} = 1{\cdot}759 \times 10^{-4} Z$$

Thus, the effective pore number is

$$Z = \frac{1{\cdot}121}{1{\cdot}759 \times 10^{-4}} = 6380$$

Exercise 37

How many normal cubic centimetres of CO_2 can diffuse out from the interior of a mangrove aerial root through the lenticels in the course of 6 h (ebb time), if the aerial root is of the type described in Exercise 36?

Experimental data:

CO_2 content in the intercellular space = 0·93 per cent by volume
CO_2 content in the outside air = 0·03 per cent by volume
capillary length $L = 60 \times 10^{-4}$ cm
capillary diameter $2r = 1{\cdot}86 \times 10^{-4}$ cm
temperature $\theta = 34{\cdot}5$ °C
pore number $Z = 6380$
diffusion coefficient (CO_2 – air) $D = 0{\cdot}15$ cm²/sec
barometer reading $p = 760$ torr
duration of experiment $t = 6 \times 3600 = 21{,}600$ sec

Solution 37. From the diffusion eqn. (54), the number of moles diffusing in unit time through surface area $q = Z(2r)^2\pi/4$ is given by:

$$\frac{dn}{dt} = \frac{d(N_q/N_A)}{dt} = \frac{-DZ(2r)^2 \pi}{4} \frac{c_{CO_2\,\text{int}} - c_{CO_2\,\text{ext}}}{L} \quad \ldots . \quad \text{(i)}$$

With the gas equation (2), $n = pV/RT$ in which $p = p_0 = 760$ torr and $T = T_0 = 273$ °K (normal volume V_0 of CO_2 involved) there is obtained:

$$\frac{dn}{dt} = \frac{dV_0}{dt} \times \frac{p_0}{RT_0} \quad \ldots\ldots \text{(iii)}$$

and

$$c_{CO_2\,int} = \frac{p_{CO_2\,int}}{RT} \qquad T = 273 + \theta = 307{\cdot}5\ °K \quad \ldots\ldots \text{(iv)}$$

Substituting (iii) and (iv) in (i) gives

$$\frac{dV_0}{dt} = \frac{-DZ(2r)^2 T_0 \pi (p_{CO_2\,int} - p_{CO_2\,ext})}{4LTp_0} \quad \ldots\ldots \text{(v)}$$

Since, from eqns. (11) and (10), vol. % $= \dfrac{p_{CO_2}}{p_{total}} \times 100$, therefore

$$p_{CO_2\,int} - p_{CO_2\,ext} = (\text{vol. \%}_{int} - \text{vol. \%}_{ext})\, p_{total}/100 \quad \ldots\ldots \text{(vi)}$$

Hence, from (v), the volume (Ncm³ CO_2) of CO_2 effusing outwards in a given time is

$$-V_0 = \frac{\pi DZ(2r)^2 T_0 p_{total}}{4 \times 100 \times Tp_0L} (\text{vol. \%}_{int} - \text{vol. \%}_{ext})\, t \quad \ldots\ldots \text{(vii)}$$

Substituting the numerical values given in the experimental data, there is obtained

$$-V_0 = \frac{0{\cdot}15 \times 3{\cdot}14(1{\cdot}86 \times 10^{-4})^2 \times 6380 \times 273 \times 760(0{\cdot}93 - 0{\cdot}03) \times 21\,600}{4 \times 100 \times 307{\cdot}5 \times 60 \times 10^{-4} \times 760} = 0{\cdot}75\ \text{Ncm}^3$$

5

CONCENTRATION OF MIXTURES AND SOLUTIONS

CONCENTRATION can be measured in the following ways:

(a) The proportion by weight or mass, ξ_i, of a substance X_i is

$$\xi_i = \frac{G_i}{\Sigma G_i} \quad [G_i = \text{total mass of the components } X_i \text{ (g)}] \qquad \ldots . \; (56)$$

The percentage by weight $= \xi_i \times 100$.

(b) The mole fraction x_i [see eqn. (10), p. 5] of a substance X_i is

$$x_i = \frac{n_i}{\Sigma n_i} = \frac{G_i N_i}{\Sigma G_i/M_i} \quad (n_i = \text{quantity of moles, } M = \text{mol. wt.}) \qquad \ldots . \; (57)$$

The mole per cent $= x_i \times 100 =$ per cent by volume in the case of ideal gases. [For the conversion of mole fractions to parts by weight, and vice versa, see eqn. (12), p. 5.]

(c) The molarity, c_i (molar concentration, moles per litre), i. e. quantity of moles of substance X_i per litre of solution [see also eqn. (8)], is

$$c_i = \frac{n_i}{V_{\text{soln}}} = \frac{G_i/M_i}{\Sigma G_i/1000\,\varrho} = \frac{1000\,\varrho\, G_i}{M_i \Sigma G_i} = 1000\,\varrho\,\xi/M_i \text{ (mole/l.)} \qquad \ldots . \; (58)$$

where ϱ = density of the mixture (solution) in g/cm³
$\sum G_i$ = total weight of mixture (solution) in g
V_{soln} = volume of solution in litres.

(d) The molality, m_i (kilogramme-molarity), i. e. the quantity of moles of dissolved substance X_i per kilogramme of solvent, is

$$m_i = \frac{G_i/M_i}{G_{\text{solv.}}/1000} = \frac{G_i \times 1000}{M_i G_{\text{solv.}}} \quad \text{(mol./kg)} \qquad \ldots . \; (59)$$

where $G_{\text{solv.}}$ = mass of solvent in g.

For very dilute solutions of a substance X_1 in a solvent $X_{\text{solv.}}$, the concentration measurements listed in *(a)* to *(d)* are proportional to one another. Thus, when $G_1 \ll G_{\text{solv.}}$

$$\left.\begin{aligned} \xi_1 &= G_1/G_{\text{solv.}} \\ x_1 &= n_1/n_{\text{solv.}} = \frac{G_1 M_{\text{solv.}}}{G_{\text{solv.}} M_1} = \frac{c_1 M_{\text{solv.}}}{1000\,\varrho} \\ c_1 &= \frac{G_1}{G_{\text{solv.}}} \times \frac{1000\,\varrho}{M_1} = \frac{x_1 \times 1000\,\varrho}{M_{\text{solv.}}} \\ m_1 &= \frac{G_1}{G_{\text{solv.}}} \times \frac{1000}{M_1} \end{aligned}\right\} \qquad \ldots \; (60)$$

For the general conversion of c_1 to x_1

$$x_1 = \frac{M_{\text{solv.}}}{\dfrac{1000}{c_1} + M_{\text{solv.}} - M_1} \qquad \ldots\ldots (61)$$

Volumes are additive in perfectly ideal mixtures. If φ_i is the specific volume (volume of 1 g) of a substance X_i, and φ_m is that of the mixture, we have

$$\sum \xi_i \varphi_i = \varphi_m = \frac{V_m}{\Sigma G_i} = \frac{1}{\varrho} = \sum \xi_i/\varrho_i \qquad \ldots\ldots (62)$$

where V_m = volume of the mixture
ϱ = density of the mixture
ϱ_i = density of the mixture component X_i

If $v_i = M_i/\varrho_i$ is the molar volume of the component X_i,

and $v_m = V_m/\sum n_i = \overline{M}_m/\varrho$ is that of the mixture, then

$$\sum x_i v_i = v_m = \sum x_i M_i/\varrho_i = \overline{M}_m/\varrho \qquad \ldots\ldots (63)$$

where $\overline{M}_m$ = mean molecular weight of the mixture [see eqn. (9)].

The following is true for the dilution of a dilute ideal solution of volume V_1:

$$\Delta V = V_1\left(\frac{c_1}{c_2} - 1\right) \qquad \ldots\ldots (64)$$

where ΔV = volume of solvent required for dilution from concentration c_1 to c_2.

Equations for mixing, dilution or similar studies can also be derived by postulating that the amount of each substance present in the solution, or mixture, before mixing, must be equal to the amount of such substance after solution, or mixing, has been effected. Thus, in the case of dilution [eqn. (64)], the quantity of dissolved substance X, before dilution, is

$$V_1 c_1 + \Delta V \times 0$$

since ΔV litres of solvent, containing none of X, are added to V_1 litres of solution of concentration c_1. After dilution, the amount of X is given by

$$(V_1 + \Delta V) c_2$$

since, assuming volume additivity, $V_1 + \Delta V$ litres are then present with a final concentration of c_2. Equating the above expressions gives

$$V_1 c_1 = (V_1 + \Delta V) c_2 \quad \text{or} \quad \Delta V = V_1 c_1/c_2 - V_1 = V_1\left(\frac{c_1}{c_2} - 1\right)$$

which is the same as eqn. (64).

The formula for the following problem is arrived at in a similar way.

It is required to obtain a parts (kg* or l.) of a solution (concentration c_m) of a substance X from concentrated (c_1) and dilute (c_2) solutions of the same substance. What are the required proportions?

* The assumption of volume additivity is, of course, not valid when calculations are made in kilogrammes or with molalities.

If x is the fraction of stronger solution, that for the more dilute solution is $a - x$. Thus, the equation of quantities is

$$c_m a = c_1 x + c_2 (a - x) \quad \text{or} \quad x = \frac{a(c_m - c_2)}{c_1 - c_2} \qquad \ldots\ldots (65)$$

*Exercise 38

A cane sugar solution, where $c = 0{\cdot}399$ m, has a density of $\varrho_s = 1{\cdot}05066$ g/cm³ at 20 °C. How many grammes of water does the solution contain per gramme of cane sugar? What is the specific volume of sugar $\varphi_{\text{sug.}}$ in solution, assuming that the specific volume of water is unaffected by the process of solution? Compare the specific volume of sugar in solution with that of solid sugar, which has a density of $\varrho_{\text{sol. sug.}} = 1{\cdot}5860$ g/cm³.

Solution 38. The formula for cane sugar is $C_{12}H_{22}O_{11}$. The molecular weight therefore is $M = 342{\cdot}29$. A litre of the solution weighs $1000\,\varrho_s$ grammes and contains cM grammes of sugar. The water in the solution weighs $1000\,\varrho_s - cM$ grammes and has a volume of the same number of cubic centimetres. The number of grammes of water in the solution, per gramme of sugar, is therefore

$$\frac{1000\,\varrho_s - cM}{cM} = \frac{1000 \times 1{\cdot}05066 - 0{\cdot}399 \times 342{\cdot}29}{0{\cdot}399 \times 342{\cdot}29} = 6{\cdot}693\,\frac{\text{g H}_2\text{O}}{\text{g}_{\text{sug.}}} \qquad \ldots\ldots \text{(i)}$$

After deducting the volume of water, the residual volume—that of the sugar in one litre of solution—is $1000 - (1000\,\varrho_s - cM)$ cm³. The specific volume of sugar in solution is, therefore

$$\left.\begin{aligned}\varphi_{\text{sugar dissolved}} &= \frac{1000 - (1000\,\varrho_s - cM)}{cM}\,\frac{\text{cm}^3}{\text{g}} = \frac{1000 + cM - 1000\,\varrho_s}{cM} \\ &= \frac{1000 + 0{\cdot}399 \times 342{\cdot}29 - 1000 \times 1{\cdot}05066}{0{\cdot}399 \times 342{\cdot}29} = 0{\cdot}6290\ \text{cm}^3/\text{g}\end{aligned}\right\} \quad \ldots \text{(ii)}$$

The specific volume of solid sugar is

$$\varphi_{\text{sol. sug.}} = 1/\varrho_{\text{sol. sug.}} = 1/1{\cdot}5860\ \text{cm}^3/\text{g} = 0{\cdot}6305\ \text{cm}^3/\text{g} \qquad \ldots\ldots \text{(iii)}$$

Comparison of (ii) and (iii) shows that the specific volume of sugar is little affected by the process of solution and that additivity of volumes virtually holds good.

*Exercise 39

What is the molar concentration c of a cane sugar solution, $100\xi = 7$ per cent by weight, if no volumetric change takes place during the solution process, and the density of solid cane sugar is $\varrho_{\text{sol. sug.}} = 1{\cdot}5860$ g/cm³?

Solution 39. 1000 g of the solution contain 1000ξ g of sugar and $1000 - 1000\xi$ g of water. The respective volumes are $1000\xi/\varrho_{\text{sol. sug.}}$ cm³ and $1000\,(1 - \xi)$ cm³, making a total of $1000\,(1 - \xi + \xi/\varrho_{\text{sol. sug.}})$ cm³ of solution. Thus the molar concentration c of the cane sugar solution ($M = 342{\cdot}29$, see Exercise 38) is

$$c = \frac{\xi}{M(1 - \xi + \xi/\varrho_{\text{sol. sug.}})}\ \text{mole/cm}^3 \quad \text{or} \quad c = \frac{1000\,\xi\,\varrho_{\text{sol. sug.}}}{M(\varrho_{\text{sol. sug.}} - \varrho_{\text{sol. sug.}} \times \xi + \xi)}\ \text{mole/l.} \qquad \text{(i)}$$

Substituting the numerical values: $\xi = 0{\cdot}07$, $\varrho_{\text{sol. sug.}} = 1{\cdot}5860$, $M = 342{\cdot}3$, gives

$$c = \frac{1000 \times 0{\cdot}07 \times 1{\cdot}5860}{342{\cdot}3\,(1{\cdot}5860 - 1{\cdot}5860 \times 0{\cdot}07 + 0{\cdot}07)} = 0{\cdot}210 \text{ mole/l.} \quad \ldots\ldots \text{(ii)}$$

*Exercise 40

The density of carbon tetrachloride is $\varrho_{CCl_4} = 1{\cdot}6239$ g/cm³ at 15 °C, and that of toluene is $\varrho_{\text{tol.}} = 0{\cdot}8716$ g/cm³ at the same temperature. What is the composition (as a weight percentage) of a mixture of these substances such that the density is the same as that for water ($\varrho = 1$ g/cm³)?

Solution 40. Eqn. (62) shows that the density of the mixture is

$$1/\varrho = \xi_1/\varrho_1 + (1 - \xi_1)/\varrho_2 \quad \ldots\ldots \text{(i)}$$

where ξ_1 is the proportion by weight of component X_1 (CCl_4). Substituting the numerical values gives

$$1/\varrho = \xi_1/1{\cdot}6239 + (1 - \xi)/0{\cdot}8716 \quad \ldots\ldots \text{(ii)}$$

In general, ξ_1 will therefore be

$$\xi_1 = \frac{\varrho_1(\varrho - \varrho_2)}{\varrho(\varrho_1 - \varrho_2)} \quad \ldots\ldots \text{(iii)}$$

and, in the present case

$$\xi_1 = \frac{1{\cdot}6239\,(1 - 0{\cdot}8716)}{1{\cdot}6239 - 0{\cdot}8716} = 0{\cdot}2772 \text{ parts by weight } CCl_4 \quad \ldots\ldots \text{(iv)}$$

The mixture contains 27·72 per cent carbon tetrachloride and 72·28 per cent toluene.

*Exercise 41

In order to prepare 450 kg of sulphuric acid containing 75 per cent H_2SO_4, using existing solutions of 34 and 83 per cent concentrations, how much of each solution must be taken?

Solution 41. The required fraction x, for the more concentrated acid, is from eqn. (65)

$$x = \frac{450\,(75 - 34)}{83 - 34} = 376 \text{ kg}$$

and 450 — 376 = 74 kg of the more dilute acid.

*Exercise 42

A 24 per cent by weight solution of potassium carbonate, K_2CO_3, has a density of 1·232 g/cm³, or kg/l., at 20 °C. What is the molarity, the molality and the mole fraction?

Solution 42. The volume of 1 kg of the solution is 1/1·232 l. The molecular weight of K_2CO_3 is 138·2. The molarity [see eqn. (58)] therefore is

$$c = \frac{240 \times 1{\cdot}232}{138{\cdot}2} = 2{\cdot}140 \text{ mole/l.} \quad \ldots\ldots \text{(i)}$$

1 kg of solution contains 240 g of K_2CO_3 and 1000 − 240 = 760 g of water. The molality [see eqn. (59)] is therefore

$$m = \frac{240 \times 1000}{138{\cdot}2 \times 760} = 2{\cdot}284 \text{ mole/kg of solvent} \quad \ldots\ldots \quad \text{(ii)}$$

The solution contains 240/138·2 moles of K_2CO_3 and 760/18·02 moles of water. The mole fraction of K_2CO_3 [see eqn. (57)] therefore is

$$x_{K_2CO_3} = \frac{240/138{\cdot}2}{240/138{\cdot}2 + 760/180{\cdot}2} = 0{\cdot}0396 \quad \text{or} \quad 3{\cdot}96 \text{ mole per cent} \quad \ldots\ldots \quad \text{(ii)}$$

*Exercise 43

How many litres of oxygen are obtained from the catalytic decomposition of hydrogen peroxide into water and oxygen at 18 °C and 720 mm Hg, (*a*) from 1 l. of pure hydrogen peroxide, (*b*) from 1 l. of a 30 per cent aqueous solution, (*c*) from 1 l. of a 3 per cent aqueous solution (percentage by weight), taking the density of pure hydrogen peroxide at 18 °C as $\varrho = 1{\cdot}4465$ and that of the two solutions as 1·1122 and 1·0094 g/cm³?

Solution 43. The reaction equation is

$$H_2O_2 = H_2O + \frac{1}{2} O_2$$

1 mole (= 34·02 g) of H_2O_2 therefore yields 1/2 mole of O_2 [= 1/2 × mole volume = 1/2 v (in litres)].

The volume of oxygen, V, may be determined in two ways (in principle the same):

(*a*) from gas equation (2)

$$V = \frac{RTn}{p} \qquad R = 0{\cdot}08206 \frac{\text{l. atm}}{\text{deg. mol.}} \qquad T = 273 + 18 = 291 \text{ °K}$$

$$p = 720 \text{ torr} = 720/760 \text{ atm} \qquad n_{O_2} = \frac{1}{2} n_{H_2O_2} = \frac{1}{2} \frac{\text{mass of } H_2O_2}{\text{mol. wt. of } H_2O_2}$$

$$= \frac{1}{2} \frac{1000\,\varrho \times \text{wt. \%}}{34{\cdot}02 \times 100}$$

Substitution in the gas equation gives

$$V_{O_2} = \frac{0{\cdot}08206 \times 291 \times 1000\,\varrho \,\text{wt. \%} \times 760}{2 \times 34{\cdot}02 \times 100 \times 720} = \frac{370{\cdot}2\,\varrho \,\text{wt. \%}}{100} \text{ l.} \quad \ldots\ldots \quad \text{(i)}$$

(*b*) the stoichiometric ratio is stated in the usual way:

$$V_{O_2} : \frac{\text{mol. vol. of } O_2\ (v_{O_2})}{2} = \text{mass of } H_2O_2 : 34{\cdot}02 \quad \ldots\ldots \quad \text{(ii)}$$

where, from eqn. (1), v_{O_2} is calculated from the molar volume (22·42 l./mole) at s.t.p. (0 °C, 760 mm Hg) [see eqn. (4)] as

$$\frac{v_{O_2} \times 720}{291} = \frac{22{\cdot}42 \times 760}{273} \quad \ldots\ldots \quad \text{(iii)}$$

and

$$\text{mass of } H_2O_2 = \frac{1000\,\varrho \text{ wt. per cent}}{100} \quad \text{as before} \quad \ldots\ldots \quad \text{(iv)}$$

Substitution of (iii) and (iv) in (ii) gives

$$V_{O_2} = \frac{1000\,\varrho\,\text{wt. per cent} \times 22{\cdot}42 \times 760 \times 291}{2 \times 720 \times 273 \times 100 \times 34{\cdot}02} = \frac{370{\cdot}2\,\varrho\,\text{wt.}\,\%}{100}\ \text{l. as at (i)}$$

Note that $22{\cdot}42/273 = \{R\} = 0{\cdot}08206$ [see eqn. (4)].

Substituting the numerical values for the density and weight per cent gives the following results.

100 per cent H_2O_2 yields 535 l. of oxygen
30 per cent H_2O_2 yields 123·5 l. of oxygen
3 per cent H_2O_2 yields 11·21 l. of oxygen

per litre of H_2O_2 solution at 18 °C and 720 mm Hg.

Note. It will be seen that oxygen, in the form of pure liquid H_2O_2 at atmospheric pressure and normal temperatures, is 'condensed down' to about 1/500 of its normal volume and is available in this form in ordinary liquid containers. With oxygen gas, such a concentration is only obtainable either by compressing it to over 500 atm pressure and storing in heavy steel bottles, or by liquefaction after cooling to very low temperatures (approx. − 220 °C).

Despite a heat of decomposition of 23 kcal/mole, pure syrupy hydrogen peroxide is relatively stable in the absence of catalytic impurities. It may be stored in aluminium vessels, where a skin of Al_2O_3 forms on the metal. It is a useful oxygen carrier, e.g. for rocket fuels.

*Exercise 44

A precipitate in a filter funnel retains 4 cm³ of $n/10$ NaCl solution. How many times must the precipitate be washed, by filtering successive 60 cm³ quantities of distilled water through the funnel, in order to reduce the total weight of NaCl retained in the precipitate to less than 1/100 mg?

It is assumed that the water flows uniformly through the filter (no flaws) and that there is no appreciable adsorption of NaCl.

Solution 44. The initial quantity of NaCl (mass G) retained on the filter, in 4 cm³ of liquid, is diluted by the addition of 60 cm³ of distilled water to $4 + 60 = 64$ cm³. After filtration, 4 cm³ of these washings will still be retained within the filter. Thus the mass G_1 of NaCl then remaining in the precipitate will be

$$G_1 = G \times \frac{4}{64}$$

After washing x times, the equation will be

$$G_x = G\left(\frac{4}{64}\right)^x$$

or, in general,

$$G_x = G\left(\frac{V_F}{V_F + V_W}\right)^x \quad \ldots\ldots \quad \text{(i)}$$

where V_F is the volume of liquid retained in the filter and V_W the volume of washing water added each time. In the present example

$$G = 58{\cdot}45 \times \frac{1}{10} \times \frac{4}{1000}\,\text{g} \quad \text{(mole weight of NaCl} = 58{\cdot}45)$$

Hence

$$\frac{58{\cdot}45 \times 4}{10\,000}\left(\frac{4}{64}\right)^x = 10^{-5}\,(\mathrm{g}) \quad \text{or} \quad 16^x = 2338$$

$$x = \frac{\log 2338}{\log 16} = 2{\cdot}8$$

The deposit must therefore be washed three times to reduce the NaCl content to less than 1/100 mg.

Note. This example deals with conditions similar to those occurring in quantitative analysis. Thus, as a rule, it is necessary to wash a crystalline deposit three times in order to remove all soluble material. Gelatinous deposits usually require more washing, because their nature prevents a uniform flow of water through the filter. Apart from this, impurities tend to remain obstinately adsorbed on the gel.

Formula (i) shows that washing a deposit with a given volume of water a is more effective the smaller the individual volumes of washing water ($V_W = a/x$) and the greater the value of x. We have the following relationships

$$G_x = G\left(\frac{V_F}{V_F + a/x}\right)^x = G\left(\frac{x\,V_F}{a + x\,V_F}\right)^x = G\left(1 + \frac{a/V_F}{x}\right)^{-x} \quad \ldots\ldots \quad \text{(ii)}$$

i.e. a function which decreases uniformly with increase of x and which has a limiting value, when $x \to \infty$, of

$$G_\infty = G\mathrm{e}^{-a/V_F} \quad \ldots\ldots \quad \text{(iii)}$$

G_∞ represents the maximum washing effect that can be obtained with a given volume a of washing water, when the filter has a retention volume of V_F.

6

VAPOUR PRESSURE OF LIQUID MIXTURES AND SOLUTIONS AZEOTROPY; MISCIBILITY GAPS

IDEAL MIXTURES

IN PERFECTLY ideal mixtures, i.e. in mixtures formed without evolution of heat, or contraction or dilation of volume, the vapour pressure of the mixture component X_i (partial pressure p_i) is proportional to the mole fraction x_{Li} [see eqn. (10)] at all mixture strengths (Raoult's law):

$$p_i = x_{Li}\, p_{0i} \qquad \ldots . \quad (66)$$

where p_{0i} = vapour pressure of the pure component X_i as a temperature function (saturation pressure)

p_i = partial pressure of the component X_i

x_{Li} = mole fraction of the component X_i in the mixture

$p = p_1 + p_2 + p_3 + \cdots = \sum p_i$ = total vapour pressure of the mixture [Dalton's law, see eqn. (6)] .... (67)

$x_{Vi} = p_i/p$ = mole fraction of the component X_i in the vapour phase over the mixture (in accordance with Avogadro's principle) .... (68)

These equations, together with the identities

$$x_{L1} + x_{L2} + x_{L3} + \cdots = 1 = \sum x_{Li} \qquad \ldots . \quad (69)$$

$$x_{V1} + x_{V2} + x_{V3} + \cdots = 1 = \sum x_{Vi} \qquad \ldots . \quad (70)$$

describe the relationship between the composition of the liquid phase and that of the vapour phase existing in equilibrium, dependent upon pressure and temperature.

These relationships may be clearly represented in the following way (by simple generalization for n components):

Binary system	*Ternary system*
$x_{L1} + x_{L2} = 1$	$x_{L1} + x_{L2} + x_{L3} = 1$
$x_{V1} + x_{V2} = 1$	$x_{V1} + x_{V2} + x_{V3} = 1$
$x_{L1} p_{01} = p_1 = x_{V1} p$	$x_{L1} p_{01} = p_1 = x_{V1} p$
$x_{L2} p_{02} = p_2 = x_{V2} p$	$x_{L2} p_{02} = p_2 = x_{V2} p$
	$x_{L3} p_{03} = p_3 = x_{V3} p$

.. (71)

From these, one may develop dual systems for calculating liquid–vapour boiling point curves or surfaces. Eliminating x_{Vi} from eqn. (71) gives

$x_{L1} + x_{L2} = 1$ $x_{L1}\dfrac{p_{01}}{p} + x_{L2}\dfrac{p_{02}}{p} = 1$	$x_{L1} + x_{L2} + x_{L3} = 1$ $x_{L1}\dfrac{p_{01}}{p} + x_{L2}\dfrac{p_{02}}{p} + x_{L3}\dfrac{p_{03}}{p} = 1$

.. (72)

When p and T are constant, the system shows

a point of intersection of two straight lines on the liquid composition curve.	a line of intersection of two planes on the liquid composition surface.

Eliminating x_{Li} from eqn. (71) gives

$x_{V1} + x_{V2} = 1$ $x_{V1}\dfrac{p}{p_{01}} + x_{V2}\dfrac{p}{p_{02}} = 1$	$x_{V1} + x_{V2} + x_{V3} = 1$ $x_{V1}\dfrac{p}{p_{01}} + x_{V2}\dfrac{p}{p_{02}} + x_{V3}\dfrac{p}{p_{03}} = 1$

.. (73)

When p and T are constant, the system shows

a point of intersection of two straight lines on the vapour composition curve.	a line of intersection of two planes on the vapour composition surface coordination; of corresponding (conjugated) points x_{Li} and x_{Vi} on the two lines of intersection, by $x_{Vi} = x_{Li}\dfrac{p_{0i}}{p}$.

Several relationships taken from eqns. (71), (72) and (73) are of practical importance.

(1) $p = x_{L1}p_{01} + x_{L2}p_{02}$ | $p = x_{L1}p_{01} + x_{L2}p_{02} + x_{L3}p_{03}$ .... (74)

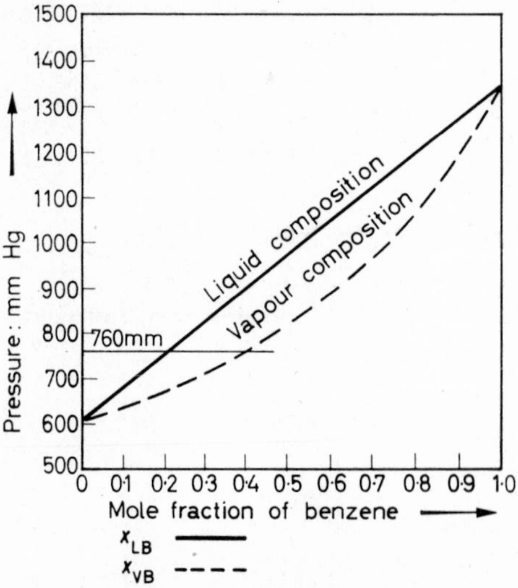

Figure 1. Boiling diagram for benzene–toluene at 100 °C

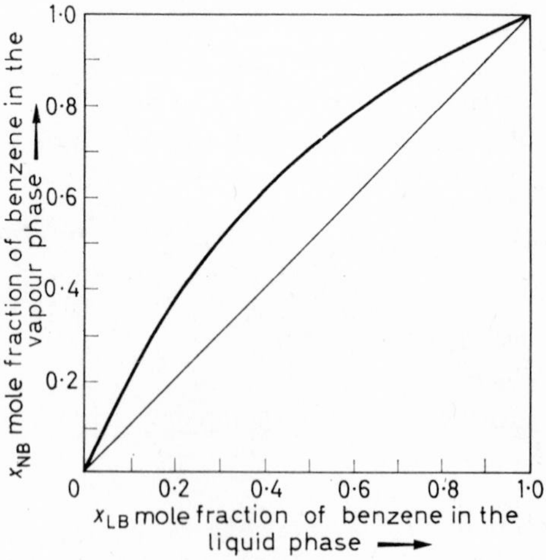

Figure 2. Equilibrium curve for benzene–toluene at 100 °C

for calculating the total pressure and hence the liquid composition curve (or surface) at constant temperature, as a function of x_{Fi} (see *Figure 1*).

(2) $1/p = x_{V1}/p_{01} + x_{V2}/p_{02}$ | $1/p = x_{V1}/p_{01} + x_{V2}/p_{02} + x_{V3}/p_{03}$ .... (75)

for calculating the total pressure and hence the vapour composition curve (or surface) at constant temperature, as a function of x_{Vi} (see *Figure 1*).

(3) $x_{Vi} = x_{Li}\, p_{0i}/p$ $x_{Li} = x_{Vi}\, p/p_0$ .... (76)

for calculating the concentration of vapour x_{Vi} in equilibrium with a concentration of x_{Li} in the liquid phase, in association with (1) and, in reverse, in association with (2).

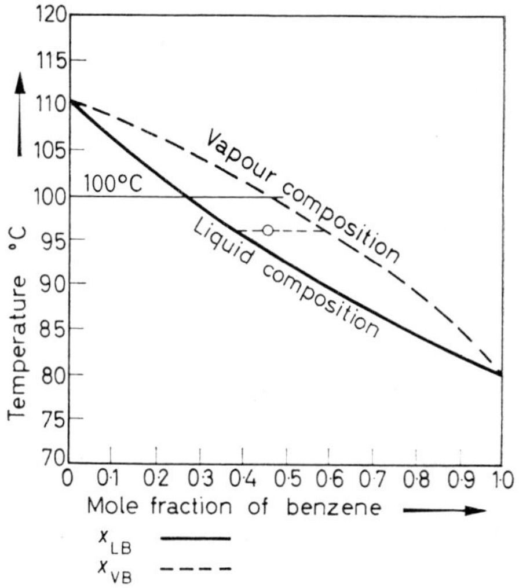

Figure 3. Boiling-point composition diagram for benzene–toluene at 760 mm Hg *pressure*

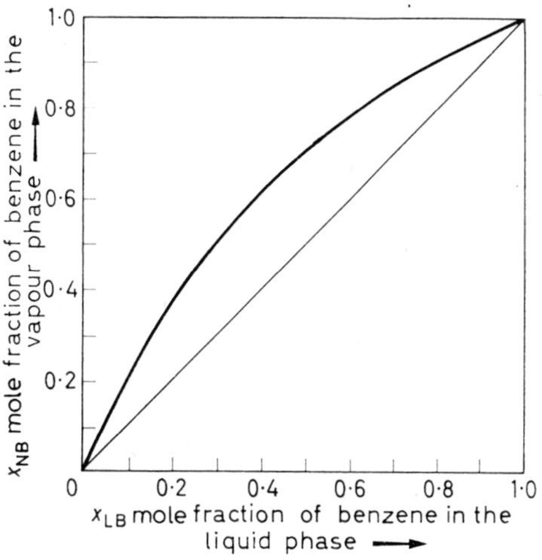

Figure 4. Equilibrium curve for benzene–toluene at 760 mm Hg

In considering the equilibrium curve, the question also arises as to the behaviour of x_{Vi} as a function of x_{Li}, either at constant temperature (*Figure 2*) or at constant pressure (*Figure 4*).

(4) $x_{L1} = \dfrac{p - p_{02}}{p_{01} - p_{02}}$ | $x_{L1} = \dfrac{p - p_{02} - x_{L3}(p_{03} - p_{02})}{p_{01} - p_{02}}$ .... (77)

for calculating the liquid composition curve, or surface, at constant total pressure, as a function of temperature (as a parameter of p_{0i}) and as a function of x_{L3}, see *Figure 3*. The corresponding vapour composition curve (or surface), at constant total pressure, may be calculated as a function of temperature from eqn. (76), see *Figure 3*.

IDEAL DILUTE SOLUTIONS

Raoult's law is valid, at least for the solvent component X_0, for ideal dilute solutions (which represent the limiting state of real mixtures) in which a component X_0 is present in great excess ($x_{L0} \approx 1$), i.e. as solvent [see eqn. (66)]:

$$p_0 = x_{L0}\, p_{00} \quad \ldots. \quad (78)$$

Henry's law holds for the solute X_i ($x_{Li} \approx 0$):

$$p_i = x_{Li}\, k_i \quad \ldots . \quad (79)$$

where k_i is an individual, temperature-dependent constant for the component X_i; it differs, in general, from p_{0i} in Raoult's law [eqn. (66)].

REGULAR MIXTURES

The laws for regular mixtures describe the equilibria for a large number of binary mixtures, especially for those having small heats of mixing, of less than 600–800 cal/mole, and where the effects of dipole moments and chemical association are absent. Equation (66) then takes the place of Raoult's law.

In the symmetrical case: initial heat of solution ${}^1\lambda_{12} \approx {}^1\lambda_{21} = {}^1\lambda$ (${}^1\lambda_{12}$ = heat of solution of 1 mole of X_1 in an unlimited quantity of X_2, ${}^1\lambda_{21}$ = heat of solution of 1 mole of X_2 in an unlimited quantity of X_1, hence, to a first approximation, ${}^1\lambda$ is independent of temperature):

$$\left.\begin{aligned} p_1 &= p_{01}\, x_{L1} \exp\frac{\beta}{2} x_{L2}^2 = p_{01} \exp\frac{\beta}{2}(1 - x_{L1})^2 \\ p_2 &= p_{02}\, x_{L2} \exp\frac{\beta}{2} x_{L1}^2 = p_{02}(1 - x_{L1}) \exp\frac{\beta}{2} x_{L1}^2 \end{aligned}\right\}^{*} \quad \ldots \quad (80)$$

and

$$\frac{\beta}{2} = \frac{{}^1\lambda}{RT} \quad \ldots . \quad (81)$$

is seen to be an individual, temperature-dependent constant describing the special system. Its variation with temperature is, from eqn. (81), given by

$$\frac{\beta_1}{\beta_2} = \frac{T_2}{T_1} \quad \ldots . \quad (82)$$

Analytical evaluation of eqn. (80) shows that, for the existence and position of an azeotropic point [vapour pressure maximum ($\beta > 0$) or minimum ($\beta < 0$), boiling point maximum ($\beta < 0$) or minimum ($\beta > 0$)] x_{az}, p_{az}, T_{az}

$$x_{az1} = \frac{\ln(p_{01}/p_{02})}{\beta} + \frac{1}{2} = \frac{\log(p_{01}/p_{02})}{0{\cdot}4343\,\beta} + \frac{1}{2} \quad \text{where} \quad 0 < x_1 < 1 \quad \ldots . \quad (83)$$

thus

$$\left| \frac{\log(p_{01}/p_{02})}{0{\cdot}4343\,\beta} \right| < \frac{1}{2}$$

and

$$p_{az} = p_{01} \exp\frac{\beta}{2}(1 - x_{az1})^2 \quad \text{or} \quad p_{az} = p_{02} \exp\frac{\beta}{2}(x_{az1})^2 \quad \ldots . \quad (84)$$

From eqn. (83) we get

$$\beta_{az} = \frac{2 \log(p_{01}/p_{02})}{0{\cdot}4343\,(2\,x_{az1} - 1)} \quad \ldots . \quad (85)$$

and from eqn. (84)

$$\beta_{az} = \frac{2\,(\log p_{az} - x_{az1} \log p_{01} - x_{az2} \log p_{02})}{0{\cdot}4343\, x_{az1}\, x_{az2}} \quad \ldots . \quad (86)$$

As is shown by eqns. (83) and (84), the existence and position of an azeotropic point are dependent not only on the individual constants β for the special mixing system

* $\exp x = e^x$

and on its heat of solution, but also on p_{01}/p_{02}, i.e. on a physical and, more or less, random number.

The following holds for the two phase boundaries I and II, $x_{L\,I\,1}$ and $x_{L\,II\,1}$, of a (symmetrical) miscibility gap:

$$x_{L\,I\,1} = 1 - x_{L\,II\,1} = x_{L\,II\,2} \qquad x_{L\,I\,2} = 1 - x_{L\,II\,2} = x_{L\,II\,1}$$

$$\ln \frac{1 - x_{L\,I\,1}}{x_{L\,I\,1}} = \frac{\beta}{2}(1 - 2\,x_{L\,I\,1}) \quad \text{or} \quad \log \frac{1 - x_{L\,I\,1}}{x_{L\,I\,1}} = \frac{\beta}{2}(1 - 2\,x_{L\,I\,1}) \times 0{\cdot}4343 \qquad (87)$$

This equation is best solved graphically $\left(\text{points of intersection of the straight lines } y = \frac{\beta}{2}(1 - 2\,x_{L\,I\,1})\ 0{\cdot}4343 \text{ with the curve } y = \log \frac{1 - x_{L\,I\,1}}{x_{L\,I\,1}}\right)$.

The critical separation point lies at $\beta_K = 4$ (separation when $\beta > 4$). .... (88)

The critical separation temperature would be

$$T_K = \frac{{}^1\lambda}{2\,R} \qquad (89)$$

This expression is, however, of hardly any practical value because of lack of exactitude in the preceding assumptions.

In the unsymmetrical case: ${}^1\lambda_{12} \neq {}^1\lambda_{21}$ (unsymmetrical mixture gaps); the mixture equilibrium may be expressed by means of an (unsymmetrical) cubic version of eqn. (80)

$$\left.\begin{aligned} p_1 &= p_{01}\,x_{L1} \exp\left(\frac{\beta}{2}\,x_{L2}^2 + \frac{\gamma}{3}\,x_{L2}^3\right) \\ p_2 &= p_{03}\,x_{L2} \exp\left(\frac{\beta + \gamma}{2}\,x_{L1}^2 - \frac{\gamma}{3}\,x_{L1}^3\right) \end{aligned}\right\} \qquad (90)$$

where $x_{L2} = 1 - x_{L1}$.

The following equations are valid for a ternary regular system (symmetrical case) where ${}^1\lambda_{12} = {}^1\lambda_{21}$, ${}^1\lambda_{13} = {}^1\lambda_{31}$ and ${}^1\lambda_{23} = {}^1\lambda_{32}$

$$\left.\begin{aligned} p_1 &= p_{01}\,x_{L1} \exp \frac{1}{RT}\left[{}^1\lambda_{12}\,x_{L2}^2 + {}^1\lambda_{13}\,x_{L3}^2 + ({}^1\lambda_{12} + {}^1\lambda_{13} - {}^1\lambda_{23})\,x_{L2}\,x_{L3}\right] \\ p_2 &= p_{02}\,x_{L2} \exp \frac{1}{RT}\left[{}^1\lambda_{12}\,x_{L1}^2 + {}^1\lambda_{23}\,x_{L3}^2 + ({}^1\lambda_{12} + {}^1\lambda_{23} - {}^1\lambda_{13})\,x_{L1}\,x_{L3}\right] \\ p_3 &= p_{03}\,x_{L3} \exp \frac{1}{RT}\left[{}^1\lambda_{13}\,x_{L1}^2 + {}^1\lambda_{23}\,x_{L2}^2 + ({}^1\lambda_{13} + {}^1\lambda_{23} - {}^1\lambda_{12})\,x_{L1}\,x_{L2}\right] \end{aligned}\right\} \qquad (91)$$

where $x_{L1} + x_{L2} + x_{L3} = 1$.

The shape of the liquid and vapour composition surfaces, and the existence of binary and ternary azeotropic points and miscibility gaps, are dependent on the signs and the relative magnitudes of the initial heats of solution, ${}^1\lambda_{12}$, ${}^1\lambda_{13}$, ${}^1\lambda_{23}$.

The law of moments, based directly on the law of conservation of mass, may be used for arithmetical or graphical determination of the quantitative distribution of mixture components on either side of a miscibility gap (or, in the general case, for determining a phase boundary) where the so-called conjugated points are linked by a tie line in the phase diagram. According to this law, the quantitative ratios for conjugated phase points are inversely proportional to the lengths of the segments into which the state point, for the given mixture, divides the tie line.

Example. In *Figure 3*, a mixture X (composition x_1) is split into a liquid phase X_L (composition x_{L1}) and a vapour phase X_V (composition x_{V1}), i.e. into the quantitative ratios (here in moles)

$$n_L : n_V = (x_{V1} - x_1) : (x_1 - x_{L1})$$

or

$$\frac{n_V}{n_L + n_V} = \frac{x_1 - x_{L1}}{x_{V1} - x_{L1}} \qquad \frac{n_L}{n_L + n_V} = \frac{x_{V1} - x_1}{x_{V1} - x_{L1}} \quad \ldots\ldots (92)$$

*Exercise 45

Ascertain the vapour pressure and vapour composition (per cent by volume) of a mixture of 67 mole per cent benzene and 33 mole per cent toluene at 20 °C. The benzene–toluene system may be regarded as an ideal mixture. It is found from tables that the vapour pressure of benzene at 20 °C is $p_{0\,B} = 74{\cdot}4$ mm Hg and that of toluene, $p_{0\,T} = 22{\cdot}3$ mm Hg.

Solution 45. Equation (74) shows the total pressure p to be

$$p = 0{\cdot}67 \times 74{\cdot}7 + 0{\cdot}33 \times 22{\cdot}3 = 50{\cdot}05 + 7{\cdot}36 = 57{\cdot}41 \text{ mm} \quad \ldots\ldots (i)$$

From eqn. (68) or (76), we find that

$$x_{V\,T} = 7{\cdot}36/57{\cdot}41 = 0{\cdot}128 \qquad x_{V\,B} = 1 - 0{\cdot}128 = 0{\cdot}872 \quad \ldots\ldots (ii)$$

Since, according to Avogadro's principle, volumetric and molar concentrations are identical in the ideal gas state [see also eqn. (11)], (ii) shows that the vapour over a liquid mixture of 67 mole per cent benzene/33 mole per cent toluene contains

87·2 vol. per cent benzene and 12·8 vol. per cent toluene . . . . (iii)

*Exercise 46

Ascertain the vapour pressure and vapour composition (per cent by weight) of a mixture of 39·4 per cent by weight benzene and 60·6 per cent by weight toluene at 20 °C, by way of comparison with Exercise 45.

Solution 46. The molecular weight of benzene, C_6H_6, is $M_B = 78{\cdot}1$, that of toluene, $C_6H_5CH_3$, is $M_T = 92{\cdot}1$. The conversion of weight per cent into mole fractions is made by using eqn. (12).

$$x_{L\,B} = \frac{39{\cdot}4}{78{\cdot}1}\bigg/\left(\frac{39{\cdot}4}{78{\cdot}1} + \frac{60{\cdot}6}{92{\cdot}1}\right) = \frac{0{\cdot}504}{0{\cdot}504 + 0{\cdot}658} = 0{\cdot}434 \qquad x_{L\,T} = 1 - 0{\cdot}434 = 0{\cdot}566$$

Taking the vapour pressures for benzene and toluene at 20 °C (as given in Exercise 45), the total pressure, p, will be

$$p = 0{\cdot}434 \times 74{\cdot}7 + 0{\cdot}566 \times 22{\cdot}3 = 32{\cdot}44 + 12{\cdot}61 + 45{\cdot}05 \text{ mm} \quad \ldots\ldots (i)$$

From eqn. (68) or (76), $x_{V\,T}$ and $x_{V\,B}$ will be

$$x_{V\,T} = 12{\cdot}61/45{\cdot}05 = 0{\cdot}280 \qquad x_{V\,B} = 1 - 0{\cdot}280 = 0{\cdot}720 \quad \ldots\ldots (ii)$$

Hence the vapour composition, in per cent by weight, may be calculated from eqn. (12)

$$\xi_{VT} = \frac{0{\cdot}28 \times 92{\cdot}1}{0{\cdot}28 \times 92{\cdot}1 + 0{\cdot}72 \times 78{\cdot}1} = \frac{25{\cdot}79}{25{\cdot}79 + 56{\cdot}25} = 0{\cdot}315 \qquad \xi_{VB} = 1 - 0{\cdot}315 = 0{\cdot}685 \quad \ldots\ldots \text{(iii)}$$

Eqn. (iii) shows that the vapour composition over a liquid mixture of 39·4 per cent by weight benzene/60·6 per cent by weight toluene is

68·5 per cent by weight benzene and 31·5 per cent by weight toluene.

Note. When one has to determine a quantity based on a difference, as in (ii) of Exercises 45 and 46, it is best to make the calculation in such a way that the error in subtraction is as small as possible. This is achieved by first calculating the smaller fraction (x_{VT} or ξ_{VT} in the above examples), thus avoiding having to compute the difference between two large numbers with a large relative error.

If one is obliged to make a considerable number of conversions from mole per cent to weight per cent, it is convenient and time-saving to prepare a reference curve.

Mixtures of benzene and toluene (and of almost all hydrocarbons) can be regarded, to a close approximation, as ideal non-polar and chemically similar substances.

The vapour pressures of pure substances at the various temperatures encountered in different problems can be ascertained from tables, usually by interpolation, e. g. *International Critical Tables;* Landolt-Börnstein, *Physikalisch-chemische Tabellen;* J. d'Ans–E. Lax, *Taschenbuch für Chemiker und Physiker.* A suitable portion of the almost linear plot of log p_0 against $1/T$ is best taken for the purpose of interpolation; the required values may then be read off directly [see also Chapter 8, eqn. (107) and Exercise 66].

*Exercise 47

Ascertain the composition (in mole per cent) of a mixture of benzene and toluene having a boiling point of 100 °C at atmospheric pressure. Tables show the vapour pressure of benzene at 100 °C as $p_{0B} = 1344$ mm, and that of toluene as $p_{0T} = 559$ mm Hg.

Solution 47. From eqn. (77) and $p = 760$ for benzene

$$x_{LB} = \frac{760 - 559}{1344 - 559} = 0{\cdot}256 \qquad x_{LT} = 1 - 0{\cdot}256 = 0{\cdot}744 \quad \ldots\ldots \text{(i)}$$

Hence, by using eqn. (76)

$$x_{VB} = \frac{0{\cdot}256 \times 1344}{760} = 0{\cdot}453 \qquad x_{VT} = 1 - 0{\cdot}453 = 0{\cdot}547 \quad \ldots\ldots \text{(ii)}$$

It follows that a mixture of 25·6 mole per cent benzene and 74·4 mole per cent toluene boils at a temperature of 100 °C at atmospheric pressure, and that the composition of the vapour which distils off is 45·3 mole or vol. per cent benzene and 54·7 mole or vol. per cent toluene. As a result of the distillation, the concentration of benzene is increased in the vapour phase and that of toluene in the liquid. See also *Figures 1* and *4*.

Note. In order to obtain a boiling point composition diagram for a binary mixture of the type existing for benzene–toluene at constant pressure, values of x_L and x_V are calculated (as above) for a series of temperatures lying between the boiling points of the pure components. The vapour composition curve, for constant pressure (see *Figure 4*), is also determined, whilst obtaining the boiling diagram at constant temperature (see *Figure 1*), in accordance with the examples in Exercises 45 and 46.

*Exercise 48

$G = 300$ g of a benzene–toluene mixture, containing $x_B = 45$ mole per cent benzene, is heated to 96 °C under a pressure of 1 atm. What are the compositions, masses and volumes of the two phases?

Density of benzene (liq.), $\varrho_B = 0{\cdot}8786$ g/cm³, mol. wt. $M_B = 78{\cdot}1$

Density of toluene (liq.), $\varrho_T = 0{\cdot}8716$ g/cm³, mol. wt. $M_T = 92{\cdot}1$

See boiling diagram (*Figure 4*) and eqn. (92).

Solution 48. Locate the given point ($x_B = 0{\cdot}45, \theta = 96$ °C) in the boiling diagram for benzene–toluene (*Figure 4*). The point is found to lie between the liquid composition and vapour composition curves, i.e. in a 'miscibility gap'. The composition is therefore split between two conjugated phases (liquid and vapour), having the compositions

$$x_{LB} = 0{\cdot}38 \quad \text{and} \quad x_{VB} = 0{\cdot}60 \qquad \ldots\ldots \quad \text{(i)}$$

and linked by a tie line in the diagram.

The phase composition, x_{LB} and x_{VB}, can, of course, also be calculated from Exercise 47 without using the boiling diagram, i.e. after referring to tables and finding that the vapour pressures of benzene and toluene at 96 °C are $p_{0B} = 1{\cdot}570$ and $p_{0T} = 0{\cdot}646$ atm, respectively. One then has, from eqns. (77) and (76), and when $p = 1$ atm:

$$x_{LB} = \frac{1 - 0{\cdot}646}{1{\cdot}570 - 0{\cdot}646} = 0{\cdot}383 \qquad x_{VB} = 1{\cdot}570 \times 0{\cdot}383 = 0{\cdot}601$$

Since the state point x_B divides the tie line in the ratio 7:15 [as is read from the diagram or obtained by calculation from (i)], we find that

$$(x_B - x_{LB})/(x_{VB} - x_B) = (0{\cdot}45 - 0{\cdot}38)/(0{\cdot}60 - 0{\cdot}45) = 0{\cdot}07/0{\cdot}15$$

Thus the ratio of the total number of moles in the liquid and vapour phases is

$$\left.\begin{aligned} n_L/n_V &= (x_{VB} - x_B)/(x_B - x_{LB}) = 15/7 \\ \text{or} \qquad n_L/(n_L + n_V) &= (x_{VB} - x_B)/(x_{VB} - x_{LB}) = \frac{15}{15 + 7} \end{aligned}\right\} \quad \ldots \quad \text{(ii)}$$

[see eqn. (92)].

The total molar quantity, $n = n_L + n_V$, is obtained [from eqn. (9)] by taking $G = 300$ g and dividing by the mean molecular weight ($\overline{M}$) of the mixture:

$$n = n_L + n_V = \frac{G}{\overline{M}} = \frac{G}{x_B M_B + x_T M_T} = \frac{300}{0{\cdot}45 \times 78{\cdot}1 + 0{\cdot}55 \times 92{\cdot}1}\ \text{mole} \qquad \ldots\ldots \quad \text{(iii)}$$

Thus, from (i), (ii) and (iii), the required distribution into liquid and vapour phases is, in moles

$$\left.\begin{aligned} n_L &= \frac{G}{x_B M_B + x_T M_T} \times \frac{x_{VB} - x_B}{x_{VB} - x_{LB}} = \frac{300}{85{\cdot}8} \times \frac{15}{22} = 2{\cdot}383 \text{ moles} \\ n_V &= \frac{G}{x_B M_B + x_T M_T} \times \frac{x_B - x_{LB}}{x_{VB} - x_{LB}} = \frac{300}{85{\cdot}8} \times \frac{7}{22} = 1{\cdot}112 \text{ mole} \end{aligned}\right\} \quad \ldots \quad \text{(iv)}$$

The mass distribution is obtained by multiplying the molar quantities by the mean molecular weights, $\bar{M}_L$ and $\bar{M}_V$, for the liquid and vapour phases, respectively:

$$\left.\begin{aligned}\bar{M}_L &= x_{LB} M_B + x_{LT} M_T = 0{\cdot}38 \times 78{\cdot}1 + 0{\cdot}62 \times 92{\cdot}1 = 86{\cdot}8 \\ \bar{M}_V &= x_{VB} M_B + x_{LT} M_T = 0{\cdot}60 \times 78{\cdot}1 + 0{\cdot}40 \times 92{\cdot}1 = 83{\cdot}7\end{aligned}\right\} \quad .. \quad \text{(v)}$$

hence

$$\left.\begin{aligned}G_L &= n_L \bar{M}_L = 2{\cdot}383 \times 86{\cdot}8 = 206{\cdot}9 \text{ g} \\ G_V &= n_V \bar{M}_V = 1{\cdot}112 \times 83{\cdot}7 = \underline{93{\cdot}1 \text{ g}} \\ &\qquad\qquad\qquad\quad \text{Total } 300{\cdot}0 \text{ g}\end{aligned}\right\} \quad .. \quad \text{(vi)}$$

Finally, the phase volumes are determined as follows. For the vapour phase, the mole quantity (n_V) is multiplied by the molar volume at 96 °C, in accordance with eqns. (1) and (4):

$$V_V = n_V \times 22{\cdot}4 \text{ l./mole} \times T/T_0 = 1{\cdot}112 \times 22{\cdot}4(273 + 96)/273 = 33{\cdot}7 \text{ l.} \quad .... \quad \text{(vii)}$$

For the liquid phase, the molar quantity (n_L) is multiplied by the molar volume (v_L) of the liquid phase (ignoring a very slight temperature dependence), using eqn. (63):

$$\left.\begin{aligned}V_L = n_L v_L &= n_L(x_{LB} v_B + x_{LT} v_T) = n_L(x_{LB} M_B/\varrho_B + x_{LT} M_T/\varrho_T) \\ &= 2{\cdot}383 \left(\frac{0{\cdot}38 \times 78{\cdot}1}{0{\cdot}8786} + \frac{0{\cdot}62 \times 92{\cdot}1}{0{\cdot}8716}\right) = 237 \text{ cm}^3\end{aligned}\right\} \quad .. \quad \text{(viii)}$$

Note. There are many ways of solving this problem by calculation. It should be specially noted that it is very often convenient to use a boiling-point composition diagram where the abscissa gives the composition of the mixture in parts by weight. This is especially so when the problem involves the mass distribution of the various phases. After determining the proportion by weight of benzene in both phases (ξ_{LB} and ξ_{VB}), one then immediately [analogously to (iv)] finds the total mass distribution in both phases (G_L and G_V) by using the law of moments:

$$G_L = G \frac{\xi_{VB} - \xi_B}{\xi_{VB} - \xi_{LB}}$$

(ξ_B = mass fraction of benzene in the given mixture, of mass $G = G_L + G_V$)

$$G_V = G \frac{\xi_B - \xi_{LB}}{\xi_{VB} - \xi_{LB}} \quad .... \quad \text{(ix)}$$

*Exercise 49

A lubricating oil was refined by treatment with propane to remove asphaltic material. Analysis showed that the lubricating oil still contained 0·075 per cent by weight of propane. Is it possible to ignore this low propane content, or might its vapour pressure lead to the formation of explosive propane/air mixtures in the storage tanks? If so, to what extent must the oil be freed from residual propane (by stripping with steam)? Adopt a safety factor of 5.

The explosion limits for propane are 2·4 to 9·5 per cent by volume of propane in air. Molecular weight of propane, C_3H_8, $M_P = 44$; vapour pressure at 24 °C, $p_{0P} = 10$ atm; molecular weight of lubricating oil, M = approx. 300; the vapour pressure of the oil may be ignored.

Solution 49. The mole fraction of propane is calculated from the propane content. The partial pressure of propane, p_P, is then obtained by using Raoult's law [eqn. (66)]. This gives, for a total pressure of $p = 1$ atm, the volumetric fraction of propane in the air over the oil, using eqn. (68).

The mole fraction of propane in the oil is, from eqn. (12) (and ignoring quantities of small magnitude in the denominator sum):

$$x_{LP} = \frac{0{\cdot}075/44}{100/300} = 0{\cdot}0051 \quad \ldots\ldots \quad \text{(i)}$$

The partial pressure (p_P) of propane over the oil is, from (i) and eqn. (66)

$$p_P = x_{LP} p_{0P} = 0{\cdot}0051 \times 10 = 0{\cdot}051 \text{ atm} \quad \ldots\ldots \quad \text{(ii)}$$

For an external pressure of 1 atm, (ii) shows that

$$\frac{100\, p_P}{p} = \frac{0{\cdot}051}{1} 100 = 5{\cdot}1 \text{ per cent by volume propane} \quad \ldots\ldots \quad \text{(iii)}$$

will be present over the lubricating oil in a closed tank. The vapour therefore has a composition lying midway between the explosion limits (2·4 to 9·5 per cent by volume propane), and the propane content, even though not high, cannot be tolerated.

If a safety factor of 5 is adopted, the propane content must be reduced to a figure of not more than 0·5 per cent by volume. Hence

$$p_P = \frac{0{\cdot}5}{100} \times 1 = 0{\cdot}005 \text{ atm} \qquad x_{LP} = p_P/p_{0P} = 0{\cdot}005/10 = 0{\cdot}0005$$

and, from eqn. (12)

$$\xi_{LP} = \frac{0{\cdot}0005 \times 44}{1 \times 300} = 0{\cdot}0073 \times 10^{-2} = 0{\cdot}0073 \text{ per cent by weight of propane}$$

as an upper limit in the oil .... (iv)

Note. A qualitative assessment of lubricating oil is obtained by measuring the flash point. Lubricating oils have flash points lying between 160° and 320 °C, depending on the viscosity and proposed application. The flash point is lowered by contamination, e.g. by dilution with petrol or diesel fuel. When making a flash point test on lubricating oil containing propane, special care must be taken to make observations even at ordinary temperatures (flash point of propane) and not merely when the oil has been heated to, say, 50° or 100 °C. The latter is the usual procedure when measuring the normal flash points of oils, i.e. in order to save time. If this is done when propane is present, there is a risk that the first flash point, due to the propane, will be overlooked, since a large proportion of it will have been driven off by heating to 50° or 100 °C. As a result, only the flash point of the propane-free oil will be obtained and the test will be valueless.

**Exercise 50

In order to stabilize the composition of fuels containing dissolved gases, such as butane (C_4), propane (C_3), ethane (C_2), methane (C_1) and the inert gases, H_2, N_2, CO_2, etc., these gases must be removed. Butane and propane are liquefied by compression, stored in bottles and used as 'liquid gas'. A proportion of cheap ethane may by added, so long as the permissible charging pressure of the bottles is not exceeded. The following problem now arises.

How much ethane may be added to the liquid gas if the composition of the gas removed from the fuel is known, in order to be able to market the product at the high price commanded by liquid gas? Also, how much ethane has to be added to the fuel gas (the price of which is much lower, depending on its calorific value)?

The maximum charging pressure for the bottles is. according to regulations, 17 atm at 40 °C.

Two samples of gas obtained from fuel stabilization were found, by analysis, to have the following compositions (volume per cent):

	C_4	C_3	C_2	C_1	H_2	N_2	CO_2	*Total*
Case I	47·0	48·0	3·6	0·1	0·1	0·8	0·4	100·0
Case II	35·0	38·0	21·0	2·4	0·8	2·8	—	100·0

Butane consists of 60 per cent n-butane and 40 per cent iso-butane.

Vapour pressure, at 40 °C, of: C_2 (ethane) $p_{02} = 58$ atm*
C_3 (propane) $p_{03} = 15$ atm
n-butane n-$p_{04} = 4{\cdot}3$ atm
iso-butane i-$p_{04} = 5{\cdot}7$ atm } $p_{04} = 4{\cdot}86$ atm†

Solution 50. The composition of the samples is adjusted by subtracting the figures (1·4 and 6·0 per cent by volume) for C_1 and the inert gases. The adjustment to $C_2 + C_3 + C_4 = 100$ is made by multiplying the gas analysis figures by 100/(100 − 1·4) or 100/(100 − 6·0), respectively. In accordance with Avogadro's law for ideal gases, the resulting volume per cent figures are also equivalent to mole per cent; see also eqn. (11). This gives the following figures for the mole fractions in the two samples.

	x_4 (C_4)	x_3 (C_3)	x_2 (C_2)	*Total*
Case I	0·476	0·487	0·037	1·00
Case II	0·372	0·404	0·224	1·00

.... (i)

Using the quoted values for vapour pressure, the total pressure, p, at 40 °C for liquid gas of composition as at (i), will be, from eqn. (74)

$$p = 58x_2 + 15x_3 + 4{\cdot}86x_4 \qquad \text{.... (ii)}$$

* Strictly speaking, one should not talk of the vapour pressure of ethane at 40 °C, since the critical temperature is about 35 °C, at a critical pressure of 49 atm. Experience shows, however, that the correct result is obtained in this and similar cases if, in accordance with eqn. (108), the vapour pressure curve of the substance is extrapolated beyond the critical point. See also Exercise 68. The above value for the vapour pressure of ethane was obtained in this way.

† Methane and the inert gases have such high vapour pressures that their solubility in the liquid phase can virtually be ignored. The two butanes have very similar vapour pressures. An average value, in accordance with the composition, may therefore be taken without detracting from the accuracy of the calculation. In this way, the above system is reduced to a ternary system and the calculation thereby considerably simplified, especially so in the case of graphical presentation. Thus

$$p_{04} = \frac{60 \times 4{\cdot}3 + 40 \times 5{\cdot}7}{100} = 4{\cdot}86 \text{ atm}$$

will be the vapour pressure of the butane mixture at 40 °C.

(*a*) *Algebraic calculation*

By substituting in (ii) the values for the mole fractions given at (i), one obtains the total pressures:

$$\left.\begin{array}{ll}\text{Case I} & p = 58 \times 0{\cdot}037 + 15 \times 0{\cdot}487 + 4{\cdot}86 \times 0{\cdot}476 = 11{\cdot}76 \text{ atm} \\ \text{Case II} & p = 58 \times 0{\cdot}224 + 15 \times 0{\cdot}404 + 4{\cdot}86 \times 0{\cdot}372 = 20{\cdot}86 \text{ atm}\end{array}\right\} \quad \ldots \text{(iii)}$$

In Case I, the total pressure of the condensed liquid gas is less than 17 atm and all the ethane may therefore be left in the gas obtained during fuel stabilization.

In Case II, however, the total pressure exceeds 17 atm, the maximum permissible bottle pressure. A proportion of the ethane must therefore be removed. If pure ethane is removed, the ratio C_3/C_4 remains constant. Thus, in Case II

$$x'_3/x'_4 = x_3/x_4 = 0{\cdot}404/0{\cdot}372 \quad \ldots\ldots \text{(iv)}$$

and, in addition,

$$x'_3 + x'_4 = 1 - x'_2 \quad \ldots\ldots \text{(v)}$$

Finally, for a maximum pressure of $p = 17$ atm, (ii) gives

$$17 = 58\,x'_2 + 15\,x'_3 + 4{\cdot}86\,x'_4 \quad \ldots\ldots \text{(vi)}$$

The composition of the liquid gas which, in Case II, has the maximum permissible vapour pressure of 17 atm after removal of ethane, may be calculated from the three eqns. (iv), (v) and (vi). Eliminating x'_3 and x'_4 gives an expression for x'_2

$$17 = 58\,x'_2 + (15 \times 0{\cdot}404 + 4{\cdot}86 \times 0{\cdot}372)\,(1 - x'_2)/(0{\cdot}404 + 0{\cdot}372) \quad \ldots\ldots \text{(vii)}$$

whence x'_2 is

$$x'_2 = 0{\cdot}143 \quad \text{and } x'_3 = 0{\cdot}446 \qquad x'_4 = 0{\cdot}411 \quad \ldots\ldots \text{(viii)}$$

In Case II, the gas mixture (i) must therefore be divided into ethane and acceptable liquid gas. The proportions, in mole fractions or by volume, may be calculated using the law of moments [eqn. (92)].

$$\frac{n_{\text{ethane (separated)}}}{n_{\text{total gas mixture}}} = \frac{x_2 - x'_2}{x_{V2} - x'_2} = \frac{0{\cdot}224 - 0{\cdot}143}{1{\cdot}000 - 0{\cdot}143} = 0{\cdot}0945 = 9{\cdot}45 \text{ vol. per cent} \quad \ldots\ldots \text{(ix)}$$

(The vapour phase is pure ethane, hence $x_{V2} = 1{\cdot}000$)

9·45 per cent by volume of ethane must therefore be removed from the gas mixture (i), Case II. On the basis of the original gas analysis, this gives

$$9{\cdot}45\,(100 - 6{\cdot}0)/100 = 8{\cdot}9 \text{ vol. per cent}$$

Thus, apart from C_1 and the inert gases (total = 6·0 per cent), 8·9 per cent of the 21·0 per cent ethane content must be removed from the gas, in order to obtain an acceptable product with a maximum vapour pressure of 17 atm at 40 °C.

(*b*) *Graphical Calculation*

The result may be obtained much more simply, clearly and quickly, especially when a series of values is required, by graphical treatment of the ternary system, using triangular co-ordinates.

Triangular Co-ordinates—An equilateral triangle is used for graphical representation of ternary mixtures. The sum of the co-ordinates x_1, x_2, x_3 of a point P (*Figure 5*) is, by geometry, obviously equal to the length of one side, i.e. $x_1 + x_2 + x_3 = 1$ or 100, according to whether mole fractions or percentages are considered.

In the reference triangle, two characteristic lines should be noted.

(1) The concentration of one component remains constant for a line parallel to a side of the triangle.

(2) The ratio of two concentrations remains constant for a straight line through any corner of the triangle, e.g. in the case of dilution or concentration by the addition or removal of a third constituent.

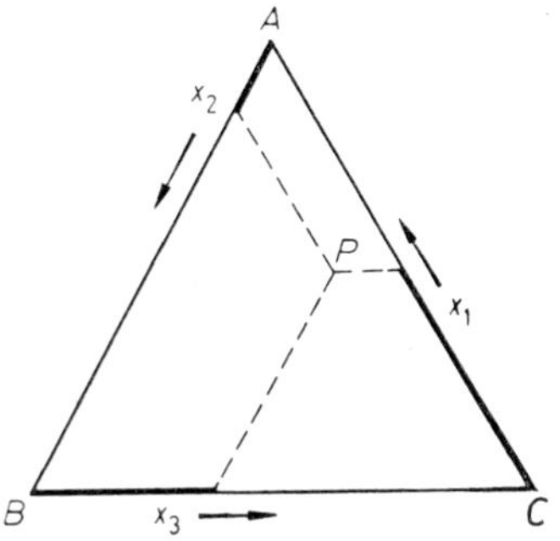

Figure 5. Representation of a ternary mixture in triangular co-ordinates

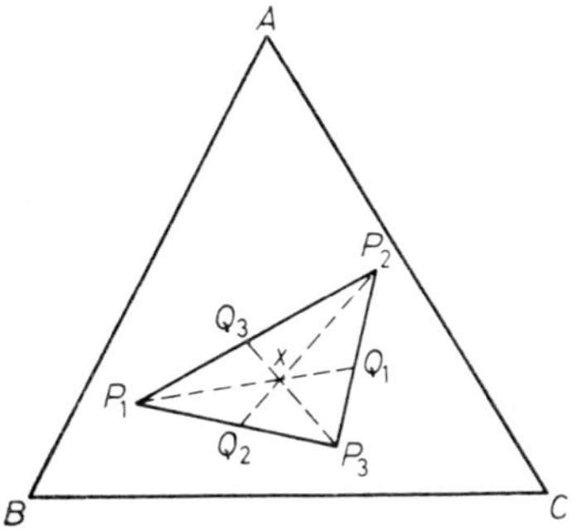

Figure 6. Representation of the mixing of ternary mixtures in triangular co-ordinates

The law of moments [eqn. (92)] is valid for the mixing or separation of two systems or phases. In mixing or separating three systems or phases, P_1, P_2, P_3 (*Figure 6*), the point x is at the centre of gravity of the triangle determined by the points P_1, P_2 and P_3 and at the corners of which the respective quantities hang as weights. If lines are drawn from P_1, P_2 and P_3 through x, three points of intersection, Q_1, Q_2 and Q_3, are obtained on the opposite sides of the triangle. The quantitative proportions of the three mixtures are then given by the ratios of the lengths of the lower segments to those of the whole transversals drawn through the corners, e.g. for P_1, by $xQ_1 : P_1Q_1$.

In the reference triangle (*Figure 7*), the mole fractions of $C_2(x_2)$, $C_3(x_3)$ and $C_4(x_4)$ are plotted in the usual manner. The equation for the total pressure p of the liquid gas at 40 °C, for a maximum permissible value $p = 17$ atm, and as defined at (ii) is first introduced into the diagram. Eliminating x_2 $(= 1 - x_3 - x_4)$ gives

$$\left.\begin{aligned} 17 &= 58\,(1 - x_3 - x_4) + 15x_3 + 4{\cdot}86\,x_4 \\ \text{or} \quad 41 &= 43\,x_3 + 53{\cdot}14\,x_4 \quad \text{as a straight-line equation} \end{aligned}\right\} \quad .. \quad \text{(x)}$$

When $x_4 = 0$, $x_3 = 0{\cdot}954$; when $x_3 = 0$, $x_4 = 0{\cdot}771$.

These two points (shown in *Figure 7*) determine the straight-line boundary limit (isotherm at 40 °C) for $p = 17$ atm. Mixtures at 17 atm and 40 °C, which are represented by points lying above this limit, i.e. on the side nearer the corner C_2, contain too much ethane and have vapour pressures greater than 17 atm. Points lying below the limit represent mixtures with vapour pressures less than 17 atm. If, for Cases I and II [see (i)], the compositions are represented by the points X_1 and X_2 given in *Figure 7*, it will be seen that X_1 lies below and X_2 above the limiting isotherm. This means that, in Case I, the gas removed from the fuel can, without further treatment,

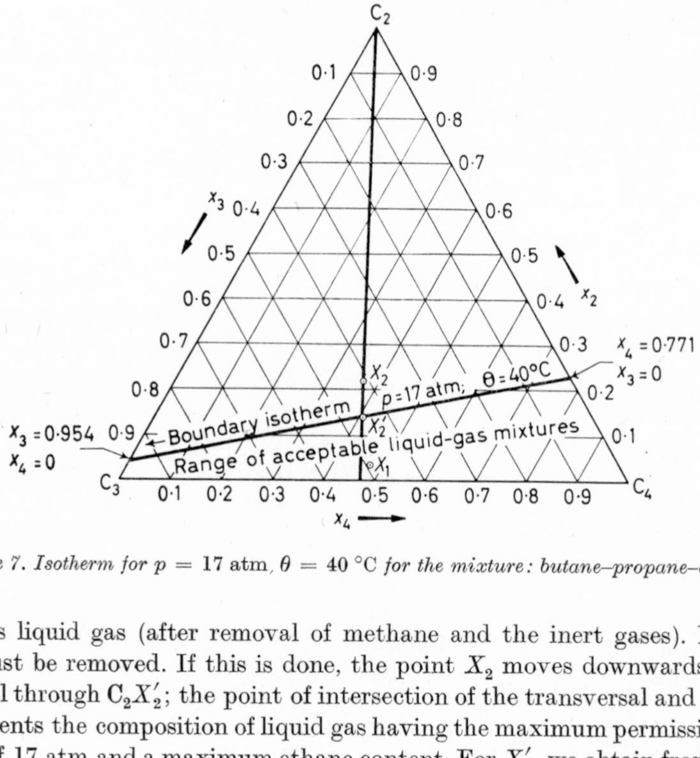

Figure 7. Isotherm for $p = 17$ atm, $\theta = 40$ °C *for the mixture: butane–propane–ethane*

be used as liquid gas (after removal of methane and the inert gases). In Case II, ethane must be removed. If this is done, the point X_2 moves downwards along the transversal through C_2X_2'; the point of intersection of the transversal and the 17 atm line represents the composition of liquid gas having the maximum permissible vapour pressure of 17 atm and a maximum ethane content. For X_2', we obtain from *Figure 7*: $x_2' = 0{\cdot}143$, $x_3' = 0{\cdot}446$, $x_4' = 0{\cdot}411$. The mole or volume fraction of ethane to be removed is found either as in (ix) or by direct measurement of the lengths $X_2'X_2$ and $X_2'C_2$ in the diagram, which gives $X_2'X_2/X_2'C_2 = 0{\cdot}0945$ or 9·45 per cent by volume.

**Exercise 51

A gas, free from methane and inert gases, and obtained during the stabilization of fuel, has the composition X [see Exercise 50 (i), Case II].

$$\left.\begin{array}{ll}\text{Butane:} & 37{\cdot}2 \text{ per cent by vol. } (x_4 = 0{\cdot}372)\\ \text{Propane:} & 40{\cdot}4 \text{ per cent by vol. } (x_3 = 0{\cdot}404)\\ \text{Ethane:} & 22{\cdot}4 \text{ per cent by vol. } (x_2 = 0{\cdot}224)\end{array}\right\} \text{X}$$

A maximum amount of the gas is condensed by compression in a compressor with a cooling water temperature of 17 °C, so that the vapour pressure at 40 °C will not exceed the permissible limit of 17 atm*. To what pressure must be gas be subjected and what is the composition (X_L) of the condensed liquid gas and that (X_V) of the non-condensed residual gas?

Use the results from Exercise 50:

(*a*) The composition X′ of the given liquid gas after removal of the appropriate amount of pure ethane from X [Exercise 50 (viii) and *Figure 7*] is:

$$x_2' = 0{\cdot}143 \qquad x_3' = 0{\cdot}446 \qquad x_4' = 0{\cdot}411$$

(*b*) The limiting isotherm defining the area for permissible liquid gas mixtures is as shown in Exercise 50 (x) and *Figure 7*. One finds from tables that the vapour pressures at 17 °C are as follows:

Ethane: $p_{02} = 37$ atm

Propane: $p_{03} = 8{\cdot}5$ atm

Butane: $p_{04} = 2{\cdot}5$ atm (The last figure is the mixture value obtained from n-C_4, ${}^{n}p_{04} = 2{\cdot}2$ atm and i-C_4, ${}^{i}p_{04} = 2{\cdot}7$ atm)

Solution 51. A boundary isotherm is shown in *Figure 7*, defining the upper limit for the permissible compositions of liquid gases. The question now arises as to what pressure, p, should be applied to the mixture so that, at 17 °C, liquid gas, having the most economic composition X_L and represented by a point lying on the boundary isotherm and in the neighbourhood of X′ (see above), immediately condenses from the gas mixture X. In addition, what is the equilibrium composition (X_V) of the associated vapour phase?

Using the values of the co-ordinates of X′ given above, the vapour pressure of the required liquid gas mixture, with a composition corresponding to the limiting isotherm for 17 °C, is obtained from eqn. (74). The compression pressure is:

$$p = 37 \times 0{\cdot}143 + 8{\cdot}5 \times 0{\cdot}446 + 2{\cdot}5 \times 0{\cdot}411 = 10{\cdot}1 \text{ atm} \quad \ldots\ldots \quad \text{(i)}$$

Similarly to Exercise 50 (x), the equation for this liquid isotherm is found to be

$$10{\cdot}1 = 37\,(1 - x_{L3} - x_{L4}) + 8{\cdot}5\,x_{L3} + 2{\cdot}5\,x_{L4} \quad \text{or} \quad 26{\cdot}9 = 28{\cdot}5\,x_{L3} + 34{\cdot}5\,x_{L4} \quad \ldots\ldots \quad \text{(ii)}$$

The extreme points of this straight line are $x_{L4} = 0$, $x_{L3} = 0{\cdot}944$ and $x_{L3} = 0$, $x_{L4} = 0{\cdot}780$. Comparison between the limiting isotherm (x) in Exercise 50 and that calculated (ii) above for 17 °C and 10·1 atm shows that they virtually coincide and pass exactly through the point X′ in *Figure 7*.

The isotherm (ii) is now drawn and the associated vapour isotherm, which is best calculated from (ii) by means of eqn. (76), on paper suitable for triangular co-ordinates (*Figure 8*) and includes some tie lines [see notes to eqn. (92)] in the region of the

* A Linde fractionating plant can be used for the industrial production of liquid gas to specification, i.e. for removal of the prescribed amount of ethane (including methane and the inert gases) from gas obtained during fuel stabilization, as mentioned in Exercise 50.

point X. It is easy, by interpolation, to draw the tie line which actually passes through X. The conjugated points, X_L and X_V, which lie on the liquid and vapour isotherms, respectively, and on a tie line through X, may be determined graphically, as below.

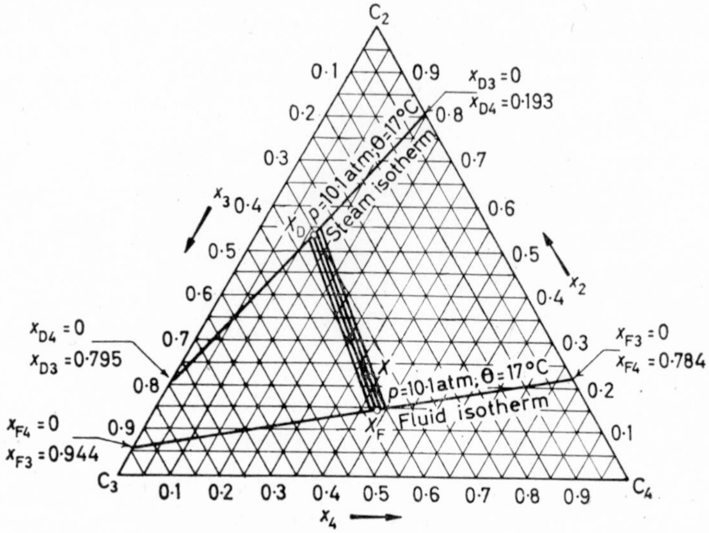

Figure 8. Vapour isotherm with tie lines for the mixture butane–propane–ethane (p = 10·1 atm, θ = 17° C)

The extreme points of the vapour isotherm, conjugated with those for the liquid isotherm (ii) (*Figure 8*) are, from eqn. (76)

$$\left.\begin{aligned} x_{V3} &= x_{L3}p_{03}/p = 0{\cdot}944 \times 8{\cdot}5/10{\cdot}1 = 0{\cdot}795 \quad x_{V4} = 0 \\ x_{V3} &= 0 \quad x_{V4} = x_{L4}p_{04}/p = 0{\cdot}780 \times 2{\cdot}5/10{\cdot}1 = 0{\cdot}193 \end{aligned}\right\} \quad \text{(iii)}$$

These values fix the position of the vapour isotherm (*Figure 8*). A number of tie lines are now drawn in the vicinity of X for Case II ($x_2 = 0{\cdot}224$, $x_3 = 0{\cdot}404$, $x_4 = 0{\cdot}372$), e. g. for points on the liquid isotherm with the co-ordinates $x_{L3} = 0{\cdot}40$, $0{\cdot}41$, $0{\cdot}42$, $0{\cdot}43$; the conjugated values x_{V3} on the vapour isotherm are, from eqn. (76) and (iii), $x_{V3} = 0{\cdot}337$, $0{\cdot}345$, $0{\cdot}354$, $0{\cdot}362$.

Using these values and drawing the appropriate tie lines in *Figure 8*, it is seen that the point X is bracketed by the tie lines between $x_{L3} = 0{\cdot}41$, $x_{V3} = 0{\cdot}345$ and $x_{L3} = 0{\cdot}42$, $x_{V3} = 0{\cdot}354$, respectively. By means of interpolation, values may be read off straight away for conjugated points, X_L and X_V, whose tie line passes exactly through X. One finds that

$$\left.\begin{aligned} &\text{for } X_L\text{:} \quad x_{L2} = 0{\cdot}147 \quad x_{L3} = 0{\cdot}418 \quad x_{L4} = 0{\cdot}435 \\ &\text{for } X_V\text{:} \quad x_{V2} = 0{\cdot}540 \quad x_{V3} = 0{\cdot}352 \quad x_{V4} = 0{\cdot}108 \end{aligned}\right\} \quad \text{(iv)}$$

Eqn. (iv) gives the composition (X_L) of the liquid phase (liquid gas of required composition) and (X_V) that of the vapour phase (residual gas) existing in equilibrium with it. This is the manner in which the gas obtained during fuel stabilization, and free from C_1 and inert gases, condenses under the effect of compression to 10·1 atm and cooling to 17 °C.

Note. Graphical resolution of the type dealt with in the above problem, i.e. by dividing an ideal ternary mixture X (x_2, x_3, x_4), at a given temperature and pressure, into a liquid phase $X_L(x_{L2}, x_{L3}, x_{L4})$ and a corresponding vapour phase X_V (x_{V2}, x_{V3}, x_{V4}) existing in equilibrium with it, is of general importance. This type of problem may also be solved algebraically.

For this, one has the following six equations from which to determine the six unknowns, $x_{L2}, x_{L3}, x_{L4}, x_{V2}, x_{V3}, x_{V4}$

(1) $x_{L2} + x_{L3} + x_{L4} = 1$ }
(2) $x_{V2} + x_{V3} + x_{V4} = 1$ } definition eqns. (69) and (70)

(3) $p = p_{02}x_{L2} + p_{03}x_{L3} + p_{04}x_{L4}$ liquid isotherm (74)

(4) $x_{V3} = x_{L3}p_{03}/p$ }
(5) $x_{V4} = x_{L4}p_{04}/p$ } conjugated points on the vapour isotherm (76)

(6) The algebraic expression for the condition that the three points X_V, X, X_L in the diagram lie on a straight line (their tie line):

$$\begin{vmatrix} x_{V2} & x_{V3} & x_{V4} \\ x_2 & x_3 & x_4 \\ x_{L2} & x_{L3} & x_{L4} \end{vmatrix} = 0 \text{ or, when written out } \frac{x_{V4} - x_{L4}}{x_4 - x_{L4}} = \frac{x_{V2} - x_{L2}}{x_2 - x_{L2}}$$

**Exercise 52

In Exercise 51, a gas was obtained during fuel stabilization, having the following composition by volume (see Exercise 50, Case II): C_4 35·0 per cent, C_3 38·0 per cent, C_2 21·0 per cent, C_1 2·4 per cent, H_2 0·8 per cent, N_2 2·8 per cent.

The residual gas (6·0 per cent) = C_1 + the inert gases H_2 and N_2, or, after separation of the C_1 fraction and inert gases, of composition X (see Exercise 51), where $x_4 = 0·372$, $x_3 = 0·404$ and $x_2 = 0·224$. This gas was condensed by compression to $p = 10·1$ atm and cooling to 17 °C. After this treatment, the liquid phase had the composition X_L ($x_{L4} = 0·435$, $x_{L3} = 0·418$, $x_{L2} = 0·147$), in equilibrium with a vapour phase of composition X_V ($x_{V4} = 0·108$, $x_{V3} = 0·352$, $x_{V2} = 0·540$) [see Exercise 51 (iv)].

(*a*) What is the quantitative distribution of X (in mole or volume per cent) between the liquid and vapour phases?

(*b*) What must the compression pressure, *P*, be if the original gas (see above) is directly compressed and condensed without separation of the C_1 fraction and inert gases?

(*c*) What, in the latter case, is the volumetric fraction (per cent by volume) and composition of the residual gas passing into the fuel gas?

Solution 52. (*a*) The quantitative distribution between the two phases is found by applying the law of moments [eqn. (92)]. As a result, the mole or volume fraction (α) of vapour phase (X_V) is

$$\alpha = \frac{n_V}{n_L + n_V} = \frac{x_1 - x_{L2}}{x_{V2} - x_{L2}} = \frac{0·224 - 0·147}{0·540 - 0·147} = 0·196 = 19·6 \text{ vol. per cent} \quad \ldots . \quad \text{(i)}$$

This value can also, of course, be obtained by direct measurement of the lengths of the segments on the tie line in *Figure 8*.

(*b*) The methane and inert gases (present in the original gas to the extent of $2{\cdot}4 + 0{\cdot}8 + 2{\cdot}8 = 6{\cdot}0$ per cent by volume) are virtually insoluble in the liquid phase (see Exercise 50, Note 2) and do not therefore influence either the yield or composition (X_L) of the liquid gas. The methane passes into the fuel gas as a vapour-phase component where it exerts a partial pressure, according to the amount present, and which must be added to the compression pressure ($p = 10{\cdot}1$ atm) calculated for gas of composition X and containing no C_1 fraction or inert gases.

The resulting vapour phase therefore comprises 6·0 vol. per cent of residual gas (R) from the original gas and α (100 – R) per cent by volume of product free from inert gas [$\alpha = 0{\cdot}196$, see eqn. (i); $(100 - R) = 94{\cdot}0$]. The latter fraction must (from above) exert a partial pressure of 10·1 atm. On the basis of proportionality between mole fraction and partial pressure [Avogadro's law and Dalton's law, eqns. (6) and (8)], the required compression pressure (P) is obtained as

$$\frac{P}{p} = \frac{\alpha(100 - R) + R}{\alpha(100 - R)}$$

hence

$$P = 10{\cdot}1 \times \frac{0{\cdot}196\,(100 - 6{\cdot}0) + 6{\cdot}0}{0{\cdot}196\,(100 - 6{\cdot}0)} = 13{\cdot}4 \text{ atm} \quad \ldots\ldots \quad \text{(ii)}$$

(*c*) The fraction of original gas, obtained during fuel stabilization, which passes into the fuel gas is, accordingly

$$\text{Fuel gas fraction} = \frac{\alpha(100 - R) + R}{100} = \frac{0{\cdot}196\,(100 - 6) + 6}{100}$$

$$= 0{\cdot}244 = 24{\cdot}4 \text{ vol. per cent} \quad \ldots\ldots \quad \text{(iii)}$$

The composition of this fraction is, from (ii) and (iii), for (C_2):

$$x_{V2} \times \frac{\alpha(100 - R) \times 100}{\alpha(100 - R) + R} = \frac{0{\cdot}540 \times 0{\cdot}196\,(100 - 6) \times 100}{0{\cdot}196\,(100 - 6) + 6}$$

$$= 40{\cdot}7 \text{ vol. per cent}$$

and, similarly, for (C_3), where $x_{V3} = 0{\cdot}352$, $(C_3) = 26{\cdot}6$ vol. per cent

and for (C_4), where $x_{V4} = 0{\cdot}108$, $(C_4) = 8{\cdot}1$ vol. per cent

For (C_1) and the inert gases, one has, from (iii) and the initial data

$$C_1 = \frac{C_1 \times 100}{\alpha(100 - R) + R} = \frac{2{\cdot}4 \times 100}{0{\cdot}196\,(100 - 6) + 6} = 9{\cdot}8 \text{ vol. per cent} \quad \ldots\ldots \quad \text{(iv)}$$

for (H_2), where $H_2 = 0{\cdot}8$ $(H_2) = 3{\cdot}3$ vol. per cent

and for (N_2), where $N_2 = 2{\cdot}8$ $(N_2) = 11{\cdot}5$ vol. per cent

Total = 100·0.

Note on Exercise 50, 51 and 52. Exercise 50 deals with the yield of liquid gas, from gas obtained during the stabilization of fuel, and with the removal of pure ethane [see Exercise 50 (i)]. In this case, it is seen that when a costly separation of pure ethane is effected in a Linde fractionating plant, about 90 per cent by volume of the original gas may be converted to liquid gas. On the other hand (Exercises 51 and 52), a yield of only about 80 per cent by volume of liquid gas is obtained when a relatively cheap and simple procedure is adopted, i.e. treatment in compressor plant. The residue of about 20 per cent contains a quantity of ethane similar to that calculated in Exercise 50, i.e. $0{\cdot}540 \times 19{\cdot}6 = 10{\cdot}6$ per cent [calculated from X_V and (i)], together with 9 per cent of propane and butane. Choice between the two methods of treatment is largely a matter of economics, depending on local conditions.

**EXERCISE 53

Liquid sulphur dioxide, SO_2, is used as a refrigerant and extraction solvent and, in the pure state, either as a gas or liquid, does not corrode iron containers or piping. However, 1 per cent of water in SO_2 renders it a highly corrosive liquid. Care must therefore be taken that, in industrial use, the water content is always considerably less than 0·1 per cent by weight. The water content may be reduced to 0·2 per cent by weight in a distillation column. Is it possible to lower it still further by treatment with anhydrous $CaCl_2$ and, if so, to what extent? Alternatively, is the cheap, readily available $CaCl_2$ useless for removing such small traces of water?

Vapour pressure of SO_2 at 20 °C, $p_{0\,SO_2} = 3{\cdot}37$ kg wt./cm² (see p. 4).

Vapour pressure of water at 20 °C, $p_{0\,H_2O} = 17{\cdot}5$ mm Hg. The SO_2–water system has a wide miscibility gap; at 20 °C the compositions of the two liquid phases are

5 mole per cent SO_2: 95 mole per cent H_2O

and

93 mole per cent SO_2: 7 mole per cent H_2O

i.e. one with a high water content and one of low water content, both being in equilibrium with the accompanying vapour phase.

At 20 °C, calcium chloride can absorb water vapour down to a partial pressure of 0·2 mm Hg.

Solution 53. In order to answer the question, it is necessary to establish at what composition of the liquid SO_2–H_2O mixture the partial pressure of water will be about 0·2 mm Hg.

In order to do this, and quite generally for the construction of the boiling diagram for SO_2–H_2O, the existence of a very large miscibility gap is essential. In this sort of case, where a homogeneous mixture only occurs near the extremes of the state diagram (within 0–10 mole per cent and 90–100 mole per cent), one practically enters the area of ideal dilute solutions, where Raoult's law is valid for the excess component (solvent) and Henry's law for the solute [see eqns. (78) and (79)]. It is then possible, to a close approximation, to establish a linear relation between partial pressure and concentration. Equilibrium between both phases signifies that their temperature, pressure and partial pressures are equal. The vapour phase is common.

The above considerations provide an adequate basis for the construction of the boiling diagram for SO_2–H_2O at 20 °C [*Figure 9 (a)*]. At very high concentrations of SO_2, i.e. in the region where $x_{L\,(SO_2)} \approx 1$, the partial pressure curve for this component starts at $p_{0\,SO_2} = 3{\cdot}37$ kg wt./cm² $= 3{\cdot}37 \times 736 = 2480$ mm Hg and follows the Raoult straight line [$p_{SO_2} = x_{L\,(SO_2)}\, p_{0\,SO_2}$] as far as the miscibility gap [$x_{L\,(SO_2)} = 0{\cdot}93$]. Over the miscibility gap, the partial pressure is constant and can either be read from the figure or calculated as $2480 - 0{\cdot}07 \times 2480 = 2306$ mm Hg. The line from the other side of the miscibility gap $[x_{L(SO_2)} = 0{\cdot}05]$ to the edge of the diagram, i.e. in the region $x_{L(SO_2)} \approx 0$, represents the partial pressure of SO_2 as calculated from Henry's law. A corresponding opposed path exists as the partial pressure curve for H_2O. Starting at $p_{0\,H_2O} = 17{\cdot}5$ mm Hg [i.e. in the region where $x_{L(H_2O)} \approx 1$ and $x_{L(SO_2)} \approx 0$], the curve follows the Raoult straight line $[p_{H_2O} = x_{L(H_2O)} p_{0\,H_2O}]$ as far as the miscibility gap $[x_{L(H_2O)} = 0{\cdot}95,\ x_{L(SO_2)} = 0{\cdot}05]$. As for SO_2, the partial pressure of H_2O is constant over the miscibility gap. The value may again be read from the diagram, or calculated as $17{\cdot}5 - 0{\cdot}05 \times 17{\cdot}5 = 16{\cdot}6$ mm Hg. The line from the opposite side of

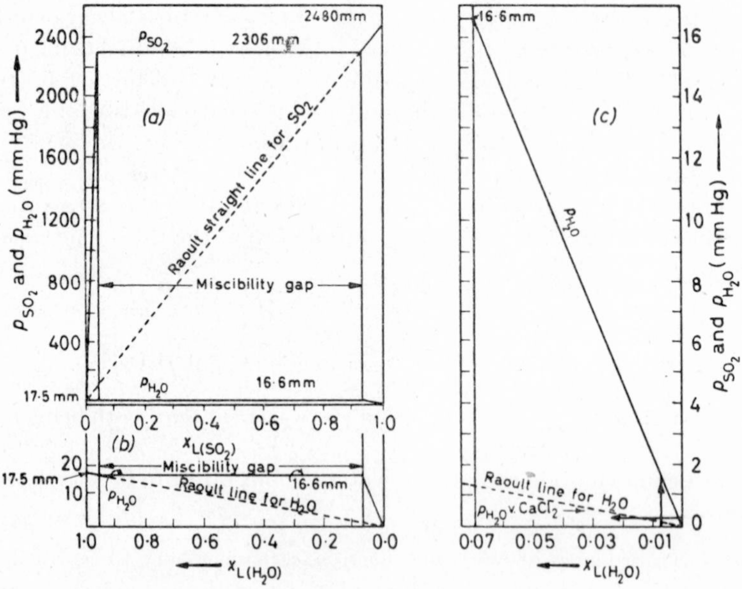

Figure 9. Boiling diagram, with miscibility gap, for the SO_2-H_2O *system at* 20 °C

the miscibility gap $[x_{L(H_2O)} = 0{\cdot}07]$ to the edge of the diagram [i.e. in the region where $x_{L(H_2O)} \approx 0$ and $x_{L(SO_2)} \approx 1$], represents the linear relationship calculated from Henry's law for $H_2O: p_{H_2O} = k_{H_2O} \times x_{L(H_2O)}$.

The complete partial pressure curve for H_2O can be seen more clearly in *Figure 9(b)*, where the ordinate scale has been increased by a factor of 20. *Figure 9(c)* shows the range of concentrations and partial pressures of interest in the present problem. In this figure, the scales on both axes have been multiplied by a factor of 10 in comparison with *Figure 9(b)*. The main curve shows the linear relationship calculated from Henry's law. The Raoult relationship is also shown as a broken line.

The concentration of water in question (viz. 0·2 per cent by weight) is converted to mole per cent by using eqn. (12), where $M_{H_2O} = 18$ and $M_{SO_2} = 64$:

$$[H_2O] = \frac{100 \times 0{\cdot}2/18}{99{\cdot}8/64 + 0{\cdot}2/18} = 0{\cdot}71 \text{ mole per cent } H_2O \quad \ldots\ldots \quad \text{(i)}$$

Figure 9(c) shows that a concentration of 0·71 mole per cent H_2O in SO_2 [$x_{L(H_2O)} = 0{\cdot}0071$] corresponds to a partial pressure of water of 1·7 mm Hg. (ii)

It is therefore seen that the drying of SO_2 can be considerably improved by the use of $CaCl_2$, which absorbs water down to a partial pressure of 0·2 mm. *Figure 9(c)* shows that a concentration of 0·1 mole per cent H_2O ($x_{L(H_2O)} = 0{\cdot}001$) corresponds to a partial pressure of water of 0·2 mm, i.e. from eqn. (12):

$$\frac{0{\cdot}1 \times 18 \times 100}{0{\cdot}1 \times 18 + 99{\cdot}9 \times 64} = 0{\cdot}028 \text{ wt. per cent } H_2O \text{ in } SO_2 \quad \ldots . \text{ (iii)}$$

as against the initial concentration of 0·2 per cent by wt. H_2O.

Note. It should be noted that grossly inaccurate results would be obtained if the existence of the large miscibility gap in the SO_2-H_2O system were ignored, i.e. if the calculations were made on the assumption that Raoult's law for ideal mixtures was applicable. If this were done, a reading of only 0·12 mm Hg would be taken for the partial pressure of water at a concentration of 0·71 mole per cent H_2O in SO_2 [$x_{L(H_2O)} = 0{\cdot}0071$] and the incorrect conclusion would be reached that $CaCl_2$, capable of absorbing down to a partial pressure of 0·2 mm Hg, was not suitable for drying SO_2 to the required degree.

The considerations outlined are useful for constructing acceptably accurate boiling diagrams for systems where a wide miscibility gap occurs. (The applications include determination of the general shape of boiling point curves, the approximate calculation of the equilibrium curve [see eqn. (76)], general appraisal of the possibilities for separation and calculation of the required efficiency in distillation columns*, i.e. with a view to effecting separation of such systems.)

Equation (87), together with eqns. (80) or (90), provides a satisfactory basis for the analytical mathematical treatment of systems where a wide miscibility gap exists (at least over the mole fraction range between 0·1 and 0·9), i.e. by applying the laws for ideal dilute solutions (Raoult's law for excess components, Henry's law for the solute) and permitting rectilinear partial pressure curves to be set up over a mixture range. Evaluation of eqn. (87) leads to a constant $\beta > 5{\cdot}5$ as describing a system having a miscibility gap covering the range given above. (In the case of H_2O-SO_2, $\beta \approx 6{\cdot}2$.) Inspection of eqn. (80), however, shows that, due to the size of the constant β, and in the narrow mixture range ($x_{L1} \approx 1$), the partial pressure curve p_2 for the solute virtually becomes a steep straight line (Henry's line) of slope $k = p_{02} \exp(\beta/2)$. On the other hand, the partial pressure curve p_1 for the excess component ($x_{L2} \approx 0$) is still virtually defined by $p_{01} x_{L1}$, i.e. by Raoult's law.

**Exercise 54

At atmospheric pressure, the binary mixture methyl alcohol–cyclohexane shows a boiling point minimum of 54·2 °C at a concentration of 38 per cent by weight methyl alcohol. By using eqns. (85), (82) and (88), calculate whether and when the mixture will separate, if the temperature is lowered. The following data are obtained from tables by means of interpolation:

vapour pressure of methyl alcohol at 54·2 °C, $p_{0(\text{met})} = 491$ torr

vapour pressure of cyclohexane at 54·2 °C, $p_{0(\text{cy})} = 310$ torr.

Solution 54. To a first approximation, hydrocarbon/alcohol mixtures may be taken as obeying the laws for regular mixtures. Alcohols have a dipole moment (OH group)

---

* Calculation of the arrangement and efficiency of distillation columns, on the basis of the equilibrium curve, will not be dealt with in this book as an example of chemical engineering [see *Technique of Organic Chemistry IV. Distillation.* New York (Interscience) 1951].

but, from the point of view of solvation, behave similarly to hydrocarbons, on account of the presence of the hydrocarbon chain in the molecule. The formulae for the symmetrical case can be used, providing quantitative data regarding the miscibility gap are not required. From eqn. (85) β_{az} for 54·2 °C is calculated first and, on the assumption that β is inversely proportional to T [see eqn. (82)]

$$\beta_1/\beta_2 = T_2/T_1 \qquad \text{(i)}$$

one then determines the temperature which, with $\beta = 4$ [according to eqn. (88)], represents the critical point for separation. Thus, from (i),

$$T_k = \frac{\beta_{az}\, T_{az}}{4} \qquad \text{(ii)}$$

The molecular weight of methyl alcohol, CH_3OH, $M_{met} = 32$, for cyclohexane, C_6H_{12}, $M_{cy} = 84$. From eqn. (12), and for 38 per cent by weight methyl alcohol

$$x_{az\,(met)} = \frac{38/32}{38/32 + 62/84} = 0{\cdot}6167 \qquad \text{(iii)}$$

Eqn. (85) gives, for β_{az}:

$$\beta_{az} = \frac{2 \log (p_{0\,(met)}/p_{0\,(cy)})}{0{\cdot}4343\,(2\,x_{az\,(met)} - 1)} = \frac{2 \log (491/310)}{0{\cdot}4343\,(2 \times 0{\cdot}6167 - 1)} = 3{\cdot}94 \qquad \text{(iv)}$$

The above result shows that, at the azeotropic point in the methyl alcohol–cyclohexane system, the constant β is only slightly less than the critical value of 4 for separation. The critical separation temperature can be estimated from (ii):

$$T_k = \frac{3{\cdot}92\,(54{\cdot}2 + 273{\cdot}2)}{4} = 322{\cdot}5\,°K = 49{\cdot}5\,°C$$

This indicates that the methyl alcohol–cyclohexane mixture will separate at a temperature a few degrees below that for the azeotropic point.

Note. Accurate measurements have shown that the critical separation temperature in fact lies only a few degress below that of the azeotropic point, viz. at 45·6 °C. The agreement between the calculated value and the experimental figure must be regarded as more or less accidental and largely due to the very limited extrapolation of formula (ii), which is certainly only applicable over a narrow temperature range. In general, discrepancies of 10°, or more, may be expected in this type of calculation. The value of β_{az} empirically calculated from eqn. (85) gives a good approximation to the experimental curve, bearing in mind the location (x_{az}) of the azeotropic point. On the other hand, agreement for the pressures is poor.

**Exercise 55

The liquid mixture ethyl alcohol–benzene has a boiling point minimum of 67·9 °C at a concentration of 32·5 per cent by weight ethyl alcohol. As a basis for designing a fractionating column (calculation of number and arrangement of plates), deduce, to a first approximation, the boiling diagram and equilibrium curve of the system at atmospheric pressure. For the sake of simplicity, assume that the mixture behaves as a regular symmetrical system (see Exercise 54). Equations (86) and (82) will be used.

The following data are obtained from tables:

Substance	*Molecular weight* M	*Boiling point* °C	*Vapour pressure at* 67·9 °C mm Hg
Ethyl alcohol, C_2H_5OH	46·05	78·3	$p_{0\,E}$: 495·5
Benzene, C_6H_6	78·11	80·3	$p_{0\,B}$: 510·5

Solution 55. Equation (12) is used for the conversion of 32·5 per cent by weight ethyl alcohol to the mole fraction ($x_{az\,E}$):

$$x_{az\,E} = \frac{32{\cdot}5/46}{32{\cdot}5/46 + 67{\cdot}5/78} = 0{\cdot}449 \qquad \ldots. \quad \text{(i)}$$

From (i) and eqn. (86), and with the values $\log p_{0\,E} = \log 495{\cdot}5 = 2{\cdot}695$, $\log p_{0\,B} = \log 510{\cdot}5 = 2{\cdot}708$, $\log p_{az} = \log 760 = 2{\cdot}881$, we find that

$$\beta_{az} = \frac{2\,(2{\cdot}881 - 0{\cdot}449 \times 2{\cdot}695 - 0{\cdot}551 \times 2{\cdot}708)}{0{\cdot}4343 \times 0{\cdot}449 \times 0{\cdot}551} = 3{\cdot}33 \qquad \ldots. \quad \text{(ii)}$$

Estimation of the constant β, which describes the system, from eqn. (85), i.e. as in Exercise 54, would involve the difference of two almost equal and large numbers, both in the case of the numerator and in the denominator, and would give a very unreliable result. In such cases (and always when the azeotropic point lies close to $x_{az} = 0{\cdot}5$, eqn. (86) is used for calculating β. Agreement with experimental values, both as regards pressures and temperatures, is generally satisfactory when β_{az} is calculated from eqn. (86); location of the azeotropic point (x_{az}) is less accurate.

Since, as will be seen from eqn. (82), β is dependent on temperature, it follows that

$$\beta_i = \beta_{az} T_{az}/T_i \qquad \ldots. \quad \text{(iii)}$$

Equation (80) gives the partial pressures p_E and p_B; it is assumed that the total pressure, $p = p_A + p_B$, remains constant at 760 mm Hg.

In order to calculate the boiling diagram, one therefore has the following transcendental equation for $x_{L\,E}$ (and where $p_{0\,E}$, $p_{0\,B}$ and β are functions of temperature):

$$760 = x_{L\,E}\, p_{0\,E} \exp \frac{\beta}{2} (1 - x_{L\,E})^2 + (1 - x_{L\,E})\, p_{0\,B} \exp \frac{\beta}{2} (x_{L\,E})^2 \quad \ldots. \quad \text{(iv)}$$

$$x_{L\,B} = 1 - x_{L\,E} \qquad 1 - x_{L\,B} = x_{L\,E}$$

In making the calculation, the correct values of β are first determined from (iii) for a number of temperatures between 80 °C and 67·9 °C and the associated values of $p_{0\,E}$ and $p_{0\,B}$ are then ascertained from tables by interpolation. We find that

θ (°C)	T (°K)	β	$p_{0\,E}$ (mm)	$p_{0\,B}$ (mm)
76·5	349·7	3·25	708	676
74·0	347·2	3·27	640	624
71·6	344·8	3·30	578	576
69·3	342·5	3·32	522	532
68·7	341·9	3·32	509	522
68·1	341·3	3·33	497	512
67·9	341·1	3·33	495·5	510·5

.. (v)

The technique for the numerical evaluation of (iv), for the various temperatures and corresponding values in (v), consists in bracketing as closely as possible the correct values of x_{LE} by two trial values and then determining the correct value by interpolation (*regula falsi* method).

The determination of x_{LE} for $\theta = 69{\cdot}3$ °C is given as an example of the method of calculation, taking $\beta = 3{\cdot}32$, $\beta/2 = 1{\cdot}66$, $p_{0E} = 522$ mm, $p_{0B} = 532$ mm. After preparing a rough sketch of the probable shape of the boiling curve, a trial calculation is made for $x_{LE} = 0{\cdot}20$ and $0{\cdot}21$.

	x_L	p_0	$(1 - x_L)$	$(1 - x_L)^2$	$\frac{\beta}{2}(1 - x_L)^2$	$\exp \frac{\beta}{2}(1 - x_L)^2$	p (mm)
For E	0·20	522	0·80	0·64	1·061	2·890	301·9
	0·21	522	0·79	0·624	1·036	2·817	308·7
For B	0·80	532	0·20	0·04	0·066	1·069	455
	0·79	532	0·21	0·044	0·073	1·076	454

. . (vi)

$$\text{Thus, for} \quad x_{LE} = 0{\cdot}20: \quad p_E + p_B = 301{\cdot}9 + 455 = 756{\cdot}9 \text{ mm}$$

$$\text{for} \quad x_{LE} = 0{\cdot}21: \quad p_E + p_B = 308{\cdot}7 + 454 = 762{\cdot}7 \text{ mm.}$$

It will be seen that the correct value for x_{LE} (for $p_E + p_B = 760$ mm) must, in fact, lie between 0·20 and 0·21. Linear interpolation (*regula falsi* method) on a graph leads to a sufficiently accurate value of $x_{LE} = 0{\cdot}205$ as the root of eqn. (iv) . . . . (vii)

As a second root, a symmetrically opposed value will be surmised, i.e. in the region of $1 - 0{\cdot}205 = 0{\cdot}795$. A similar calculation to (vi) is then made taking the values of 0·80 and 0·79 for x_{LE}. This gives the following result:

$$x_{LE} = 0{\cdot}80, \quad p_E = 446{\cdot}5 \text{ mm} \qquad p_B = 307{\cdot}5 \text{ mm} \qquad p_E + p_B = 754 \text{ mm}$$

$$x_{LE} = 0{\cdot}79, \quad p_E = 444 \text{ mm} \qquad p_B = 314{\cdot}5 \text{ mm} \qquad p_E + p_B = 758{\cdot}5 \text{ mm}$$

This shows that bracketing has not been effected and a further calculation must be made for $x_{LE} = 0{\cdot}78$, giving

$$x_{LE} = 0{\cdot}78, \quad p_E = 441{\cdot}5 \text{ mm} \qquad p_B = 321{\cdot}5 \text{ mm} \qquad p_E + p_B = 763 \text{ mm}$$

It will be seen that the correct value of x_{LE} (for 760 mm) must lie between 0·79 and 0·78, and interpolation gives $x_{LE} = 0{\cdot}787$ . . . . (viii)

The corresponding values of x_{VE} [$= p_E/760$ from eqn. (68)] are found by interpolation of the above-determined values for p_E, as follows:

$$p_E = 301{\cdot}9 + 0{\cdot}5\,(308{\cdot}7 - 301{\cdot}9) = 305{\cdot}3 \text{ mm}$$

$$x_{VE} = p_E/760 = 305{\cdot}3/760 = 0{\cdot}402 \quad \text{for} \quad x_{LE} = 0{\cdot}205 \qquad \text{(ix)}$$

and

$$p_E = 441{\cdot}5 + 0{\cdot}7\,(444 - 441{\cdot}5) = 443{\cdot}2$$

$$x_{VE} = p_E/760 = 443{\cdot}2/760 = 0{\cdot}583 \quad \text{for} \quad x_{LE} = 0{\cdot}787 \qquad \text{(x)}$$

The other roots (x_{LE}) of eqn. (iv) are determined in a similar manner for the remaining temperatures.

The values of the roots (x_{VE}) of eqn. (iv) and the associated values of x_{LE} are collected in the following table.

θ (°C)	$x_{L'E}$	$x_{V'E}$	$x_{L''E}$	$x_{V''E}$
80·3	0·000	0·000	—	—
78·3			1·000	1·000
76·5	0·032	0·137	0·980	0·916
74·5	0·0644	0·227	0·9425	0·798
71·6	0·112	0·313	0·888	0·688
69·3	0·205	0·402	0·787	0·583
68·7	0·260	0·431	0·732	0·552
68·1	0·350	0·463	0·635	0·519
67·9	0·491	0·491	—	—

. . (xi)

These values lead to a boiling diagram as in *Figure 10* and an equilibrium curve as shown in *Figure 11*.

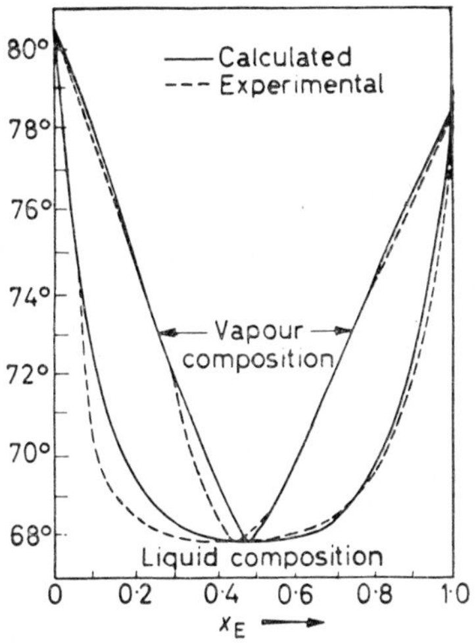

Figure 10. Boiling diagram ethyl alcohol–benzene at 760 mm Hg *pressure*

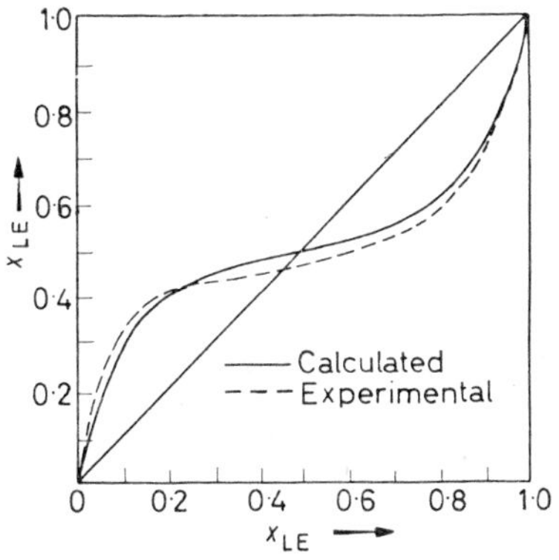

Figure 11. Equilibrium curve ethyl alcohol–benzene at 760 mm Hg *pressure*

Note. The experimentally determined curves are shown in *Figures 10* and *11* for the purpose of comparison. It will be seen that there is good agreement, bearing in mind the assumption on which the calculation is based, i.e. that the system can be regarded as a normal symmetrical one, and that only one experimental value (the temperature of the boiling point minimum) has been used in the calculation (excluding, of course, the vapour pressure curves for the pure components). β_{az} is calculated from eqn. (ii) as 3·33 for the minimum boiling point temperature. Multiplying by $RT_{az}/2$ [see eqn. (81)] gives the value of the temperature-independent constant:

$$^{1}\lambda = \beta RT_{az}/2 = 3{\cdot}33 \times 1{\cdot}987 \times 341/2 = 1129 \text{ cal}$$

which is of the nature of an initial heat of solution, and is the characteristic constant describing the system. When the concentration, x_{azE} [in eqn. (86)], has a value of about 0·5, it has practically no effect on the calculation of β. It appears only as a mean of the two values of β, separately obtained from the two eqns. (84), the difference between which [for ${}^1\lambda_{12} \neq {}^1\lambda_{21}$ see eqn. (90)] indicates the extent of departure from regular symmetry. *Figures 10* and *11* show that the differences between the calculated and experimental results are largely due to a pronounced assymetry (displacement of the azeotropic point towards the left at the same temperature); the effect could be eliminated by introducing a correction factor into eqn. (90). For the majority of practical purposes, however, the methods of calculation described in this exercise should suffice for the preparation of an orientating boiling diagram, unless both components have a dipole character and association tendencies.

**Exercise 56

It is required to distil (*a*) benzene and (*b*) toluene by means of steam distillation. Determine the distillation temperature at atmospheric pressure and the weight of steam necessary to distil 100 grammes of either substance. Benzene and toluene are practically insoluble in water.

Solution 56. Since benzene and toluene are not miscible with water, the vapour pressure over the heterogeneous mixture, i.e. the sum of the partial pressures, is determined by the vapour pressures of the pure components at the distillation temperature. Thus

$$p = 760\,\text{mm Hg} = p_{0(\text{H}_2\text{O})} + p_{0(\text{B})} \quad \text{or} \quad p = 760\,\text{mm Hg} = p_{0(\text{H}_2\text{O})} + p_{0(\text{T})} \quad \ldots . \quad \text{(i)}$$

The distillation temperature may be determined from eqn. (i) when the dependence on temperature is known for the vapour pressure curves of the components. In practice, the distillation temperature is then ascertained graphically, by drawing the curves for total vapour pressure and noting the point of intersection with the 760 mm line. Alternatively, a curve for $760 - p_{0(\text{H}_2\text{O})}$ can be added to a diagram showing the vapour pressure curves of benzene and toluene. The points of intersection of the $760 - p_{0(\text{H}_2\text{O})}$ curve with the benzene and toluene vapour pressure curves give the respective boiling temperatures and the corresponding partial pressures of water and benzene or toluene at the boiling point, since it follows from (i) that

$$760 - p_{0(\text{H}_2\text{O})} = p_{0(\text{B})} \quad \text{or} \quad p_{0(\text{T})} \quad \ldots . \quad \text{(ii)}$$

determines the boiling points.

Reference to tables gives the following data (if necessary, by interpolation):

θ (°C)	$p_{0\,(\text{Benzene})}$ (mmHg)	$p_{0\,(\text{H}_2\text{O})}$ (mmHg)	$p_{0\,(\text{Benzene})} + p_{0\,(\text{H}_2\text{O})}$ (mmHg)
65	456·0	187·5	643·5
66	472·1	196·1	668·2
67	489·2	205·0	694·2
68	506·4	214·2	720·6
69	524·8	223·7	748·5
70	543·2	233·7	776·9
69·4	532	228	760 (by interpolation)

. . (iii)

θ (°C)	$p_{0\,(\text{Toluene})}$ (mmHg)	$p_{0\,(H_2O)}$ (mmHg)	$p_{0\,(\text{Toluene})} + p_{0\,(H_2O)}$ mmHg
82	309·0	384·9	693·9
83	319·9	400·6	720·5
84	331·1	416·8	747·9
85	342·0	433·6	775·6
86	354·0	450·9	804·9
87	365·0	468·7	833·7
84·4	336	424	760 (by interpolation)

. . (iv)

According to Avogadro's law [eqn. (10)], the partial pressures of the vapour phase are proportional to the mole numbers, thus

$$p_{0(H_2O)} : p_{0(B)} = x_{V\,(H_2O)} : x_{V\,(B)} = \frac{G_{H_2O}}{M_{H_2O}} : \frac{G_B}{M_B} \quad \ldots\ldots \text{(v)}$$

and similarly for toluene.

Taking the molecular weights as $M_B = 78$, $M_T = 92$ and $M_{H_2O} = 18$, and since the given mass (G) of the hydrocarbons is 100 grammes, from (v) we get:

for benzene: $G_{H_2O} = \dfrac{228 \times 18 \times 100}{532 \times 78} = 9{\cdot}9$ g H_2O/100 g benzene at 69·4 °C

for toluene: $G_{H_2O} = \dfrac{424 \times 18 \times 100}{336 \times 92} = 24{\cdot}7$ g H_2O/100 g toluene at 84·4 °C

while the boiling points of pure benzene and pure toluene are 80·3 °C and 110·6 °C, respectively.

Note. Steam distillation is a special case of azeotropic distillation where the boiling temperature is changed by the addition of another component and a constant-boiling mixture of constant composition (azeotrope) distils off. Examples: separation of alcohol and water by the addition of benzene; removal of water from fatty acids by addition of suitable esters; separation of aromatic and aliphatic hydrocarbons of similar boiling point, by the addition of alcohol (especially methyl alcohol). Since, in the above examples, the constant boiling mixture lies within the range of the miscibility gap, there is no actual azeotropic point but rather a so-called pseudoazeotropic point.

The above technique can also be applied in reverse. For example, benzene, toluene or xylene can be used to remove the last traces of water from substances not soluble in these hydrocarbons. The benzene or toluene are usually circulated by means of refluxing and a water separator is included in the circuit.

Steam distillation is usually cheaper than vacuum distillation.

It follows from eqn. (v) that steam distillation can be used in order to determine molecular weights, i.e. by measuring the distillation temperature and the quantities of the components in the distillate. $p_{0\,(H_2O)}$ is obtained from tables for a given boiling temperature; $p - p_{0\,(H_2O)}$ is therefore known, for a barometer reading of p, and gives the partial pressure of the component being steam distilled. The molecular weight of the component can then be determined from eqn. (v).

7

DETERMINATION OF MOLECULAR WEIGHT IN SOLUTIONS

OSMOTIC PRESSURE, LOWERING OF VAPOUR PRESSURE, ELEVATION OF BOILING POINT, DEPRESSION OF FREEZING POINT. CORRELATION WITH HEATS OF VAPORIZATION AND FUSION

AN EQUATION corresponding exactly to the ideal gas equation (2) is valid for the osmotic pressure, P, of a dilute solution of volume V:

$$P = RTn/V = RTc \quad \left\{ \begin{array}{l} P = \text{osmotic pressure, in atm} \\ c = \text{concentration, in moles/l., see eqn. (58)} \\ R = \text{gas constant} = 0{\cdot}08206\ \text{l. atm/(deg. mole)} \end{array} \right\} \quad \ldots (93)$$

When an increase in the number of particles occurs as a result of (usually electrolytic) dissociation of a molecule into ν fragments (usually ions), and where the degree of dissociation is $\alpha\,[= f_\lambda =$ conductivity coefficient; see Chapter 12, eqn. (216)], the following relationships, analogous to eqn. (16), hold good:

$$\left. \begin{array}{l} n = n_0[1 + \alpha(\nu - 1)] = n_0 i = n_0 f_0 \nu \\ i = 1 + \alpha(\nu - 1) \ = \text{van't Hoff's coefficient} \\ f_0 = i/\nu = [1 + \alpha(\nu - 1)]/\nu = \text{osmotic coefficient} \end{array} \right\} \quad \ldots (94)$$

One also has, analogous to eqn. (17)

$$\left. \begin{array}{r} P = RTn/V = RTn_0[1 + \alpha(\nu - 1)]/V = RTn_0 i/V = RTn_0 \nu f_0/V = P_0 \nu f_0 \\ f_0 = P/P_0\nu \end{array} \right\} \quad \ldots (95)$$

If no dissociation occurs, the osmotic pressure $P = P_0 = RTn_0/V$, whereas, in the case of complete dissociation ($\alpha = 1$)

$$P = P_0\nu \quad \text{and} \quad f_0 = 1 \qquad \ldots\ldots (96)$$

The following is the expression derived from eqn. (78) for the lowering of the vapour pressure of a solvent ($\Delta p = p_{0\,\text{St}} - p_{\text{St}}$) when a quantity ($n_{\text{Se}}$) of solute is dissolved in a quantity (n_{St}) of solvent:

$$\frac{\Delta p}{p_{0\,\text{St}}} = \frac{p_{0\,\text{St}} - p_{\text{St}}}{p_{0\,\text{St}}} = \frac{n_{\text{Se}}}{n_{\text{Se}} + n_{\text{St}}} \approx \frac{n_{\text{Se}}}{n_{\text{St}}} = \frac{G_{\text{Se}} M_{\text{St}}}{G_{\text{St}} M_{\text{Se}}} \qquad \ldots\ldots (97)$$

The above holds for dilute solutions where $n_{\text{Se}} \ll n_{\text{St}}$, n = mole quantity, G = mass, M = mol. wt.

The expression for the elevation of the boiling point (ΔT_b) of a solvent when a quantity of solute (m) is dissolved in 1000 grammes of solvent [molality = m, see eqn. (59)] is

$$\Delta T_b = m E_b = \frac{G_{Se} E_b \times 1000}{M_{Se} G_{St}} \quad \text{where } E_b = \frac{R T_b^2}{1000\,\lambda_v} \qquad \dots\dots (98)$$

ΔT_b = elevation of boiling point, °C or °K
T_b = boiling point of the pure solvent, °K
E_b = elevation of boiling point for 1 mole of solute per 1000 g of solvent, in °C or °K (ebullioscopic constant), (deg. mole^{-1} kg)
λ_v = heat of vaporization, i.e. latent heat of vaporization for 1 g of pure solvent, at constant pressure, in cal/g, and taken as positive when the system absorbs heat
$l_v = M_{St}\lambda_v$ = molar heat of vaporization, cal/mole
M_{Se} = mol. wt. of solute
G_{Se} = mass of solute, in grammes
G_{St} = mass of solvent, in grammes
R = gas constant = 1·9865 cal/(deg. mole), see eqn. (4)

The following expression [corresponding to eqn. (98) for the elevation of boiling point] holds for the depression of the freezing point (ΔT_f) when a molar quantity of solute (m) is dissolved in 1000 g of solvent [m = molality, see eqn. (59)]:

$$\Delta T_f = m E_f = \frac{G_{Se} \times E_f \times 1000}{M_{Se} G_{St}} \quad \text{where } E_f = \frac{R T_f^2}{1000\,\lambda_f} \qquad \dots\dots (99)$$

T_f = freezing point of the pure solvent, °K
E_f = depression of freezing point for 1 mole of solute per 1000 g of solvent, in °C or °K (cryoscopic constant), deg. mole^{-1} kg
λ_f = heat of fusion, i.e. latent heat of fusion for 1 g of pure solvent, at constant pressure, in cal/g
$l_f = M_{St}\,\lambda_f$ = molar heat of fusion, cal/mol.

The remaining terms are as defined under eqn. (98).

From eqns. (99) and (94) one derives the following expressions for depression of freezing point ($\Delta T_f'$ and E_f') in the case of dissociated substances:

$$\left.\begin{aligned} &\frac{\Delta T_f'}{\Delta T_f} = \frac{E_f'}{E_f} = \frac{n}{n_0} = 1 + \alpha(\nu - 1) = \text{van't Hoff coefficient, } i \\ &i = \nu f_0 = \frac{M_0}{\bar{M}} \quad \text{see eqn. (18)} \\ &\text{Osmotic coefficient } f_0 = \frac{E_f'}{\nu E_f} = \frac{M_0}{\nu \bar{M}} = \frac{i}{\nu} = \frac{1 + \alpha(\nu - 1)}{\nu} \quad \text{[see also eqn. (227)]} \\ &\bar{M} = \text{mean or apparent molecular weight} \end{aligned}\right\} \quad \dots (100)$$

In solutions of practically completely dissociated strong electrolytes, α should be regarded purely as a mathematical quantity (i.e. the apparent degree of dissociation). According to context, such systems will be described by the osmotic coefficients, f_0, the conductivity coefficients, f_λ, or activity coefficients, f, whichever is the more suitable. See Chapter 12, eqns. (227), (216), (228) and (230)–(235).

*Exercise 57

Calculate the osmotic pressure of a 5 per cent (50 g/l.) solution of dextrose at 20 °C.

Solution 57. Dextrose, $C_6H_{12}O_6$, has a molecular weight, $M = 180{\cdot}15$. The molar concentration is, therefore, $c = 50/180$ mole/l. and, from eqn. (93)

$$P = 0{\cdot}0821\,(273 + 20)\,50/180 = 6{\cdot}68 \text{ atm.}$$

*Exercise 58

What is the vapour pressure (p_{St}) of a solution of 5·130 grammes of urea in 104·9 grammes of water at 18·0 °C? The vapour pressure of water at 18·0 °C is $p_{0\,St} = 15{\cdot}477$ torr. Urea, $CO(NH_2)_2$, has a molecular weight of 60·1; the mol. wt. of water is 18·016.

Solution 58. Equation (97) is used in order to calculate the lowering of the vapour pressure:

$$\frac{15{\cdot}477 - p_{St}}{15{\cdot}477} = \frac{5{\cdot}130 \times 18{\cdot}02}{104{\cdot}9 \times 60{\cdot}1} \qquad 15{\cdot}477 - p_{St} = 0{\cdot}227 \qquad p_{St} = 15{\cdot}250 \text{ torr}$$

Exercise 59

An elevation of boiling point of 0·364 °C is observed when 0·645 grammes of naphthalene, $C_{10}H_8$, are dissolved in 43·25 grammes of dioxan, $C_4H_8O_2$ (boiling point, $Kp = 100{\cdot}8$ °C). When 0·784 grammes of benzil, of unknown molecular weight, are dissolved in 45·75 grammes of the same solvent, the elevation of the boiling point is 0·255 °C. Calculate the elevation of boiling point per mole (E_b), the molar heat of vaporization (l_v) for dioxan and the molecular weight of benzil.

Solution 59. Naphthalene has a molecular weight of 128·2. Equation (98) gives

$$0{\cdot}364 = \frac{0{\cdot}645 \times E_b \times 1000}{128{\cdot}2 \times 43{\cdot}25} \qquad E_b = 3{\cdot}13 \text{ deg. kg/mole} \qquad \ldots. \quad \text{(i)}$$

From this result, and eqn. (98), one obtains the latent heat of vaporization per gramme of dioxan (λ_v):

$$3{\cdot}13 = \frac{1{\cdot}987\,(273{\cdot}2 + 100{\cdot}8)^2}{1000\,\lambda_v} \qquad \lambda_v = 88{\cdot}75 \text{ cal/g} \qquad \ldots. \quad \text{(ii)}$$

The molecular weight of dioxan is 88·1, hence the molar heat of vaporization is

$$l_v = 88{\cdot}1 \times 88{\cdot}75 = 7820 \text{ cal/mole} \qquad \ldots. \quad \text{(iii)}$$

Thus, the molecular weight of benzil is, from eqn. (98),

$$0{\cdot}255 = \frac{0{\cdot}784 \times 3{\cdot}13 \times 1000}{45{\cdot}75\,M} \qquad M = 210{\cdot}1 \qquad \ldots. \quad \text{(iv)}$$

*Exercise 60

A boiling point elevation of 0·0291 °C is observed when 0·241 grammes of lactic acid, $CH_3CH(OH)COOH$, are dissolved in 53·50 grammes of water. The boiling point elevation of water per mole (E_b) is 0·515 deg. kg/mole. Calculate the apparent molecular weight ($\bar{M}$) and the degree of dissociation of lactic acid under these conditions.

Solution 60. Equation (98) gives the apparent molecular weight of lactic acid as

$$0{\cdot}0291 = \frac{0{\cdot}241 \times 0{\cdot}515 \times 1000}{\bar{M} \times 53{\cdot}50} \qquad \bar{M} = 79{\cdot}7 \qquad \ldots. \quad \text{(i)}$$

The true molecular weight of lactic acid is $M_0 = 90{\cdot}1$. The acid is therefore partially dissociated. The degree of dissociation (α) is obtained from the apparent molecular weight by means of eqn. (19), taking into account the fact that lactic acid, with only one COOH group, can only dissociate to give one hydrogen ion; i.e. it can only split into two fractions, so that $\gamma = 2$:

$$\alpha = \frac{90{\cdot}1 - 79{\cdot}7}{79{\cdot}7} = 0{\cdot}13 \qquad \ldots. \quad \text{(ii)}$$

In this case, i.e. at 100 °C and a concentration of $m = \frac{0{\cdot}241 \times 1000}{53{\cdot}50 \times 90{\cdot}1} = 0{\cdot}05$ mole/1000 g H_2O [see eqn. (59)] the acid is therefore dissociated to the extent of 13 per cent.

*Exercise 61

The depression of the freezing point for human blood is about 0·56 °C (0·54–0·58 °C). What is the osmotic pressure of blood, and what concentration of common salt solution has the same osmotic pressure as blood (a physiological common salt solution), if one takes the degree of dissociation of a dilute common salt solution as being 0·85? The depression of the freezing point of water per mole (E_f) is 1·86 deg. kg/mole.

Solution 61. The number of moles, m, per 1000 g of water may be determined from eqn. (99) and equated to the concentration, c (mole/l.), (for a very dilute aqueous solution). The osmotic pressure of blood, at a body temperature of 37 °C, can then be calculated from eqn. (93):

$$m \approx c = \frac{0{\cdot}56}{1{\cdot}86} = 0{\cdot}301 \text{ mole/l.}; \quad P = 0{\cdot}0821\,(273 + 37)\,\frac{0{\cdot}56}{1{\cdot}86} = 7{\cdot}66 \text{ atm.} \quad \ldots. \quad \text{(i)}$$

As a result of strong dissociation (into Na^+ and Cl^- ions), a common salt solution of concentration c_{NaCl} (mole/l.) has a molar concentration of dissociation products of $c_{dis} = c_{NaCl}\,(1 + \alpha)$ [from eqn. (16)] and this determines the osmotic pressure. One must therefore equate $c_{dis} = c_{NaCl}\,(1 + 0{\cdot}85)$ with $m \approx c\ (blood) = 0{\cdot}301$ mole/l. Hence

$$c_{NaCl}\,(1 + 0{\cdot}85) = 0{\cdot}301 = \frac{G_{NaCl}}{58{\cdot}5}\,(1 + 0{\cdot}85) \quad \text{(mol. wt. NaCl} = 58{\cdot}5)$$

$G_{NaCl} = 9{\cdot}5$ g NaCl/l. H_2O, i.e about 1 per cent common salt solution . . . . (ii)

*Exercise 62

In order to determine the degree of polymerization of sulphur and iodine in those organic solvents where iodine dissolves to give a violet colour, 3·826 g of sulphur are dissolved in 43·54 g of carbon disulphide (boiling point, $Kp = 46{\cdot}2$ °C) and a boiling point elevation of $\Delta T_b = 0{\cdot}785$ °C is observed. An elevation of 0·912 °C is also noted when 4·575 g of iodine are dissolved in 45·28 g of the same solvent. The boiling point elevation per mole for carbon disulphide is $E_b = 2{\cdot}29$ deg. kg/mole.

Solution 62. Substitution in eqn. (98), gives, for sulphur

$$0{\cdot}785 = \frac{3{\cdot}826 \times 2{\cdot}29 \times 1000}{43{\cdot}54\,M} \qquad M_{\text{sulph}} = 256{\cdot}2 \quad \ldots\ldots \quad \text{(i)}$$

Since the atomic weight of sulphur is 32·06, and 256·2/32·06 = 8, sulphur must exist in solution in carbon disulphide as S_8 molecules.

Similarly, for iodine

$$0{\cdot}912 = \frac{4{\cdot}575 \times 2{\cdot}29 \times 1000}{45{\cdot}25\,M} \qquad M_{\text{iodine}} = 253{\cdot}9 \quad \ldots\ldots \quad \text{(ii)}$$

and, since the atomic weight of iodine is 126·9, and 253·9/126·9 = 2, iodine with a violet colour must exist in solution in carbon disulphide as I_2 molecules.

*Exercise 63

For the purpose of comparison, 1000 grammes of diphenylamine, [$(C_6H_5)_2NH$, mol. wt. = 169·2] are added to 50·00 grammes of naphthalene, $C_{10}H_8$, mol. wt. = 128·2, m. pt. = 80·4 °C, b. pt. = 217·9 °C, and also to 50·00 grammes of camphor, $C_{10}H_{16}O$, mol. wt. = 152·2, m. pt. = 178·8 °C, b. pt. = 204 °C. Freezing point depressions of 0·815 °C and 4·73 °C are observed for naphthalene and camphor, respectively. Calculate the cryoscopic constant, E_f (depression of freezing point per mole), and the latent heat of fusion per mole, λ_f, for naphthalene and camphor, and note the reason for the marked difference in depression of freezing point as between the two solvents.

Solution 63. Substitution of the numerical values in eqn. (99) gives, for naphthalene:

$$0{\cdot}815 = \frac{1{\cdot}000\,E_f \times 1000}{50{\cdot}00 \times 169{\cdot}2} \qquad E_f = 6{\cdot}9 \text{ deg. mole}^{-1}\text{kg} = \frac{1{\cdot}987\,(273{\cdot}2 + 80{\cdot}4)^2}{1000\,\lambda_f} \quad \ldots\ldots \quad \text{(i)}$$

It follows that $\lambda_f = 36{\cdot}0$ cal/g .... (ii)

and $l_f = \lambda_f M_{\text{napht}} = 36{\cdot}0 \times 128{\cdot}2 = 4{\cdot}6$ kcal/mole as the latent heat of fusion per mole for naphthalene at 80·4 °C .. (iii)

Similarly, for camphor:

$$4{\cdot}73 = \frac{1{\cdot}000\,E_f \times 1000}{50{\cdot}00 \times 169{\cdot}2} \qquad E_f = 40{\cdot}0 \text{ deg. mole}^{-1}\text{ kg} = \frac{1{\cdot}987\,(273{\cdot}2 + 178{\cdot}8)^2}{1000\,\lambda_f} \quad \ldots\ldots \quad \text{(iv)}$$

Hence $\lambda_f = 10{\cdot}15$ cal/g .... (v)

and $l_f = \lambda_f M_{\text{camph}} = 10{\cdot}15 \times 152{\cdot}2 = 1{\cdot}55$ kcal/mole as the latent heat of fusion per mole for camphor at 178·8 °C .. (vi)

Note. It will be seen from (i) and (iv) that the high value of the cryoscopic constant for camphor is due, first, to the relatively low latent heat of fusion and, second, to the relatively high melting point. On the other hand, camphor and naphthalene have similar molecular weights, boiling points and latent heats of vaporization and therefore similar ebullioscopic constants (5·80 deg. mole⁻¹ kg and 6·09 deg. mole^{-1} kg, respectively). A more basic reason for the marked difference between their cryoscopic constants is to be found from consideration of their molecular structure. Whilst naphthalene has a flat-shaped molecule, a model of the camphor molecule shows it to be highly symmetrical and almost spherical, and this leads to an abnormally high melting point (see also Chapter 8, especially Exercises 68—71, and the note to Exercise 71).

On account of the high value of the cryoscopic constant, camphor is used to determine the molecular weights of organic substances. Ordinary thermometers are quite satisfactory for this purpose; there is no need to use a highly sensitive Beckmann thermometer (Rast's method).

*Exercise 64

A stream of air, at room temperature, is passed first through a set of small wash bottles containing a solution of 11·67 g phenanthrene in 102·4 g of benzene, and then through a set containing pure benzene. After cutting off the air flow, a check shows that the solution has decreased in weight by 2·9492 g. The pure benzene, on the other hand, has decreased by only 0·1548 g. What is the molecular weight of phenanthrene?

Solution 64. In the first set of wash bottles, the stream of air becomes saturated with benzene to an extent governed by the partial pressure of benzene over the solution. This charge of benzene is then fed to the second set of bottles. It should be borne in mind that the partial pressure of benzene differs in the two sets of bottles on account of the lowering of the vapour pressure in the case of the solution. If care is taken to ensure that the air stream is fully saturated, the partial pressures must, according to Avogadro's law [eqn. (10)], be proportional to the amounts of benzene taken up. The lowering of the vapour pressure of the solution is proportional to the extra weight of benzene absorbed in the second set of bottles and the vapour pressure over the pure benzene is proportional to the total weight of benzene absorbed in both sets of bottles. Taking the molecular weight of benzene as 78·1, therefore from eqn.(97)

$$\frac{0{\cdot}1548}{2{\cdot}9492 + 0{\cdot}1548} = \frac{11{\cdot}67 \times 78{\cdot}1}{102{\cdot}4\, M} \qquad M_{\text{phenanthrene}} = 178{\cdot}5$$

*Exercise 65

When mercuric cyanide, $Hg(CN)_2$, is added to an excess of potassium cyanide solution, a complex anion is formed according to the equation

$$Hg(CN)_2 + xCN^- = [Hg(CN)_{x+2}]^{x(-)} \qquad \ldots. \quad \text{(i)}$$

The freezing point of a potassium cyanide solution containing 0·5 mole KCN per 1000 g H_2O is $-1{\cdot}635$ °C. If 1·348 g of mercuric cyanide are added to 46·84 g of such a solution, the freezing point rises to $-1{\cdot}453$ °C. What formula should be ascribed to the complex anion? The cryoscopic constant for water is $E_f = 1{\cdot}86$ deg. mole^{-1} kg.

Solution 65. Equation (i) shows that if 1 mole of $Hg(CN)_2$ is added to KCN solution, $1 + x$ moles become associated to give 1 mole of complex. Over all, therefore, and after adding 1 mole of Hg $(CN)_2$, there is an increase of 2 moles and a decrease of $1 + x$ moles, i.e. a total decrease of $(1 + x) - 2 = x - 1$ moles, in comparison with the initial KCN solution. In the present case, 1·348/252·6 moles $Hg(CN)_2$, with a mol. wt. for Hg $(CN)_2$ of 252·6, are added to the KCN solution, which is therefore reduced in strength by $(x - 1)$ 1·348/252·6 moles, and this causes a change of freezing point of 1·635 – 1·453 = 0·182 °C. Since the molecular weight of KCN is 65·1, one has in 46·84 g of the above KCN solution

$$\frac{46{\cdot}84 \times 1000}{(1000 + 0{\cdot}5 \times 65{\cdot}1)} = 45{\cdot}36 \text{ g } H_2O$$

Hence, from eqn. (99)

$$0{\cdot}182 = \frac{(x - 1)\, 1{\cdot}348 \times 1{\cdot}86 \times 1000}{252{\cdot}6 \times 45{\cdot}36}\ ; \quad \text{thus } x - 1 = 0{\cdot}832$$

$$x = 1{\cdot}832 \qquad \ldots . \qquad \text{(ii)}$$

and $x + 2$ is equal to 3·832 and lies between values of 3 and 4. The complex in eqn. (i) is therefore a mixture of $[Hg(CN)_4]^{2-}$ and $[Hg(CN)_3]^-$ ions.

8

TEMPERATURE DEPENDENCE OF VAPOUR PRESSURE. DETERMINATION OF HEATS OF VAPORIZATION, SUBLIMATION AND FUSION

(1) For the equilibrium between two states of aggregation, I and II, with one degree of freedom, the following equation holds for transition from I → II:

$$\frac{\mathrm{d}p}{\mathrm{d}T} = \frac{\Delta H}{T(V_{\mathrm{II}} - V_{\mathrm{I}})} \quad \text{(Clausius–Clapeyron equation)} \qquad \ldots . (101)$$

where ΔH = change in heat content during the transition I → II. Thus, during the transition from liquid to vapour: $\Delta H = L_v$ = (external) heat of vaporization; during the transition from solid to vapour: $\Delta H = L_s$ = (external) heat of sublimation, and during the transition from solid to liquid: $\Delta H = L_f$ = heat of fusion.

V_{I} and V_{II} are the volumes before and after transition at temperature T; p is the equilibrium pressure and $\mathrm{d}p/\mathrm{d}T$ is the rise of the equilibrium pressure–temperature curve.

(2) V_{I} can be ignored in comparison with V_{II} for the transitions liquid → vapour (vaporization) and solid → vapour (sublimation) when the temperature is sufficiently removed from the critical temperature. The ideal gas equation [eqn. (2)] can then be applied to V_{II}. Under these conditions, one has (for 1 mole):

$$\frac{\mathrm{d}\ln p}{\mathrm{d}T} = \frac{l_t}{RT^2} \qquad \ldots . (102)$$

where l_t, according to the transition in question, is the molar heat of vaporization l_v, or molar heat of sublimation l_s, in cal/mole, and R, the gas constant, is 1·9865 cal/(deg. mole).

(3) Over small temperature intervals, where l_v can be taken either as constant, or a mean value $\bar{l}_v$ ascribed to it, the following approximate equation [obtained by integration of eqn. (102)] is valid:

$$\log p_1 - \log p_2 = \frac{\bar{l}_v}{4{\cdot}574}(1/T_2 - 1/T_1) \qquad \ldots . (103)$$

so that

$$\bar{l}_v = 4{\cdot}574 \frac{T_1 T_2}{T_1 - T_2} \log(p_1/p_2) \text{ (cal)} \qquad \ldots . (104)$$

A corresponding expression holds for $\bar{l}_s$, with values of p_1' and p_2' for the solid-state vapour pressure curve.

For the heat of fusion, at the melting point, one has

$$l_f = l_s - l_v \qquad \ldots. (105)$$

and, for the molar heat of transition l_t in the solid state

$$l_t = l_{s(b)} - l_{s(a)} \qquad \ldots. (106)$$

where $l_{s(b)}$ and $l_{s(a)}$ represent the molar heats of sublimation immediately below and above the transition point, respectively.

(4) Equation (103) can also be written as

$$\left.\begin{array}{l} \log p = -A/T + B \\ \text{where} \\ A = \bar{l}_v/4{\cdot}574 \quad \text{and} \quad B = \log p_0 + \bar{l}_v/4{\cdot}574\,T_0 \end{array}\right\} \quad \ldots (107)$$

and p_0, T_0, represent any point of measurement on the vapour pressure curve.

Equation (107) is a useful approximation, giving a straight-line relationship when $\log p$ is plotted against $1/T$. Given two points (p, T) on the vapour pressure curve, the above plot may be used, with good approximation, to obtain intermediate values by means of linear interpolation, provided that the interval between the points is not too great and they are sufficiently removed from the critical point.

(5) More accurate interpolation over a larger interval between two given points p_1, T_1 and p_2, T_2 is possible by using the equation

$$\log p = -A'/T + B' \log T + C' \qquad \ldots. (108)$$

where $B' = \dfrac{c_{pV} - c_{pL}}{1{\cdot}9865}$ c_{pV} and c_{pL} being the mean molar specific heats (molar heats), at constant pressure, in the vapour and condensed states, respectively.

$$A' = \log (p_1/p_2) - B' \log (T_1/T_2) \times T_1T_2/(T_1 - T_2)$$

$$C' = \log p_1 + A'/T_1 - B' \log T_1$$

If B' is ignored, eqn. (108) and its constants then become eqn. (107). If the molar heats are unknown, but given three pairs of p, T values, eqn. (108) may be used for interpolation [three eqns. (108), with three unknowns A', B' and C'].

(6) If only one pair of values (p, T) is known, i.e. the boiling point T_{760} at 760 mm Hg, and making use of Trouton's rule,

$$l_v/T_{760} \approx 21{\cdot}5 \text{ cal/(deg. mole)} \qquad \ldots. (109)$$

The following formula for approximate interpolation of vapour pressure, may be obtained by substituting eqn. (109) in (107):

$$\log p/\text{mm Hg} = -\frac{21{\cdot}5}{4{\cdot}574} \times \frac{T_{760}}{T} + \left(\log 760 + \frac{21{\cdot}5}{4{\cdot}574}\right) = -4{\cdot}7\,T_{760}/T + 7{\cdot}6 \qquad \ldots. (110)$$

According to this formula, $\log p/\text{mm Hg}$ *vs* $1/T$ plots of the vapour pressure curves of all substances should meet at the vanishing point, $1/T_0 = 0$; $\log p_0/\text{mm Hg} = 7{\cdot}6$.

Experience shows that the following rules apply:

(*a*) Equation (110) and the vanishing point $1/T_0 = 0$, $\log p_0/\text{mm Hg} = 7{\cdot}6$, may well be used for locating boiling points at different pressures in the case of low-molecular weight inorganic and organic substances, without large dipole moments (in particular, without OH groups).

(*b*) For a whole range of organic substances, of a generally higher molecular weight, a vanishing point, $1/T_0 = 0$, $\log p_0/\text{mm Hg} = 8{\cdot}3$ is obtained. This is based on a survey of boiling points at various barometer readings or during distillation at reduced pressure. (For aliphatic hydrocarbons at 760 mm Hg, the boiling points are actually slightly too high; for alcohols and phenols, too low.) Here, one therefore has

$$\log p/\text{mm Hg} = -5{\cdot}4 \times T_{160}/T + 8{\cdot}3 \qquad \ldots . \ (112)$$

Considering the frequent application of the useful vapour pressure relation of eqn. (112) in organic chemistry practice, it is advisable to draw a diagram on graph paper (see *Figure 12*).

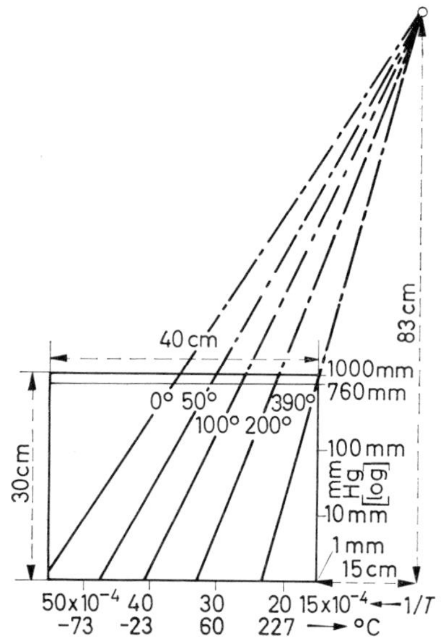

Figure 12
Preparation of a vapour pressure table

Using millimetre paper (30 × 40 cm) one plots reciprocal absolute temperature ($1/T$) ($1 \times 10^{-4} \triangleq$* 1 cm) on the x-axis, from right to left, starting with 15×10^{-4} (which corresponds to 667 °K or 394 °C). The logarithm of the pressure in mm ($\log 10 = 1 \triangleq 10$ cm) is plotted on the y-axis, from bottom to top, starting with $\log 1 = 0$, to $\log 1000 = 3 \triangleq 30$ cm. The appropriate temperatures and pressures in °C and mm Hg are then written in.

* Signifies 'corresponding to'.

The 760 mm line is then drawn at log 760 = 2·881 ≙ 28·81 cm and reciprocal absolute temperatures ($1/T$) marked on it using the point of a pin, i.e. starting from the right with 390 °C [$= 1/(390 + 273) = 15{\cdot}08 \times 10^{-4} \triangleq 15{\cdot}08 - 15 = 0{\cdot}08$ cm] and proceeding by 10°C intervals to 0°C ($= 1/273 = 36{\cdot}63 \times 10^{-4} \triangleq 36{\cdot}63 - 15 = 21{\cdot}63$ cm). The temperature values may then be written in on the 760 mm line.

Next, the graph paper is squarely fixed to a drawing board and the vanishing point located by first drawing a horizontal line 15 cm in length to the right, from the lower right-hand corner of the graph paper, followed by a vertical line of length 83 cm upwards.

Straight lines, representing the vapour pressure curves, are then drawn radiating from the vanishing point and passing through the points marked on the 760 mm line, i.e. corresponding to intervals of 10 °C. It is convenient to fix a pin firmly at the vanishing point, since this facilitates handling the ruler.

By means of interpolation, such a diagram permits rapid and easy location of change of boiling points with change in barometer reading or in distillation at reduced pressure.

(*c*) In the case of hydrocarbons, which have a special importance in the fuel and allied industries, eqns. (103), (107) and (110) may be expressed more specifically:

(*i*) For pure aromatic and polyaromatic hydrocarbons and their methyl derivatives, vapour pressure curves for the liquid phase can be prepared from a plot of log p/mm Hg against $1/T$, and having a common point of intersection (the vanishing point), by taking

$$\log p_0/\text{mm Hg} = 7{\cdot}18 \quad T_0 = 3000\ {}^\circ\text{K}\ (1/T_0 = 3{\cdot}33 \times 10^{-4}\ \text{deg.}^{-1}) \qquad \ldots. (113)$$

If the boiling point, $Kp_{760} = T_{760}$ °K, is known, the mean molar heat of vaporization, $\bar{l}_v$, can be determined to a first approximation by using eqn. (104):

$$\bar{l}_v = 4{\cdot}574 \times 3000\,(7{\cdot}18 - \log 760)\frac{T_{760}}{3000 - T_{760}} = 59\,\frac{T_{760}}{3000 - T_{760}}\ \text{kcal/mole} \qquad \ldots. (114)$$

The empirical formula

$$\bar{l}_v = 2{\cdot}5 + 0{\cdot}070\,M\ \text{kcal/mole} \quad (M = \text{mol. wt.}) \qquad \ldots. (115)$$

may also be used (especially when the boiling point is not known), but with less accuracy.

(*ii*) For polyaromatic hydrocarbons and their methyl derivatives, the following values provide an approximately common point of intersection (vanishing point) for the vapour pressure curves of the solid phase (sublimation pressure curves):

$$\log p_0'/\text{mm Hg} = 9{\cdot}7 \quad T_0' = 3000\ {}^\circ\text{K}\ (1/T_0' = 3{\cdot}33 \times 10^{-4}\ \text{deg.}^{-1}) \qquad \ldots. (116)$$

provided there is no transition point in the solid state.

If the melting point, $F = T_F$ (°K), is known together with the corresponding vapour pressure, p_F (pressure at the triple point, as the point of intersection of the vapour pressure curves of the liquid and solid phases with the solid–liquid phase boundary), the mean molar heat of sublimation, $\bar{l}_s$, can be approximately determined from eqn. (104):

$$\left.\begin{aligned}\bar{l}_s &= 4{\cdot}574 \times 3000\,(9{\cdot}7 - \log p_F/\text{mm Hg})\,\frac{T_F}{3000 - T_F} \\ &= 13{\cdot}72\,(9{\cdot}7 - \log p_F/\text{mm Hg})\,\frac{T_F}{3000 - T_F}\ \text{kcal/mole}\end{aligned}\right\} \quad \ldots (117)$$

and the mean molar heat of fusion $\bar{l}_f = \bar{l}_s - \bar{l}_v$ [see eqn. (105)] is found from eqns. (117) and (114) (by substituting for log 760 and T_{760} with $\log p_F$/mm Hg and T_F) to be approximately

$$\left.\begin{aligned}\bar{l}_f &\approx 4{\cdot}574\,[(9{\cdot}7 - \log p_F/\text{mm Hg}) - (7{\cdot}18 - \log p_F/\text{mm Hg})]\,\frac{3000\,T_F}{3000 - T_F} \\ &= 34{\cdot}6\,\frac{T_F}{3000 - T_F}\ \text{kcal/mole}\end{aligned}\right\} \quad \ldots (118)$$

(*d*) The vapour pressure curves of the aliphatic hydrocarbons (plots of $\log p$/mm Hg against $1/T$) show a more pronounced deflection to the right (concave curvature) than those of the aromatics. For the range between 1 mm and 760 mm Hg, one can take the following values as giving a common point of intersection (vanishing point):

$$\log p_0/\text{mm Hg} = 6{\cdot}68 \quad T_0 = 1750\ ^\circ\text{K}\ (1/T_0 = 5{\cdot}71 \times 10^{-4}\ \text{deg.}^{-1}) \quad \ldots . (119)$$

For the range close to 760 mm the values are:

$$\log p_0/\text{mm Hg} = 6{\cdot}83 \quad T_0 = 3510\ ^\circ\text{K}\ (1/T_0 = 2{\cdot}85 \times 10^{-4}\ \text{deg.}^{-1}) \quad \ldots . (120)$$

In the case of cyclic paraffins and alkyl-substituted aromatic hydrocarbons, the vanishing point lies between that for the polyaromatics and that for the aliphatic hydrocarbons.

It is not possible to give data for calculating the sublimation pressure curves of aliphatic hydrocarbons, because of the frequent existence of transition points in the solid state.

In the general absence of boiling point data for normal paraffins, the mean molar heat of vaporization $\bar{l}_v$, between 760 and 1 mm Hg, may be estimated from the formula

$$\bar{l}_v = 1{\cdot}42\,\sqrt{M + 40} - 8{\cdot}6\ \text{kcal/mole} \quad \ldots . (121)$$

At 760 mm itself, the values of $\bar{l}_v$ are from 5 per cent (for C_5) to 15 per cent lower (C_{10} and above). .... (122)

Given the boiling point as $Kp_{760} = T_{760}$ °K, $\bar{l}_v$ can be calculated [analogously to eqn. (114)] for aliphatic hydrocarbons, between 1 and 760 mm, by using the formula:

$$\bar{l}_v = 30{\cdot}4\ T_{760}/(1750 - T_{760})\ \text{kcal/mole} \quad \ldots . (123)$$

and, in the region of 760 mm, one has

$$\bar{l}_v = 63{\cdot}4\ T_{760}/(3510 - T_{760})\ \text{kcal/mole} \quad \ldots . (124)$$

(7) For more accurate calculation of vapour pressure curves, when the standard entropy is known, see Chapter 11.

*Exercise 66

Eight litres of air are bubbled through n-pentane, n-C_5H_{12}, boiling point, $Kp = 36{\cdot}2\,°C$, at a temperature of 18 °C and barometer reading of 710 mm Hg. What is the volume of the pentane-saturated air after passing through the liquid and how many grammes of pentane has it absorbed?

Make the calculation, (*a*) without any additional data regarding the vapour pressure of pentane and (*b*) using the fact that the boiling point of pentane at 100 mm Hg is − 12·4 °C.

Solution 66. One must first determine the vapour pressure of pentane at 18 °C. For case (*a*), using eqn. (121), together with (103), gives

$$\bar{l}_v = 1{\cdot}42\sqrt{72 + 40} - 8{\cdot}6 = 6{\cdot}43 \text{ kcal/mole* } (M_{\text{pent}} = 72) \quad \ldots\ldots \quad \text{(i)}$$

and by substituting (i) in eqn. (103), we get

$$\left.\begin{aligned}\log p/\text{mm Hg} &= \log 760 - \frac{6430}{4{\cdot}574}(1/291 - 1/309{\cdot}2) = 2{\cdot}5963\\ p_{\text{pent}} &= 395 \text{ mm Hg at } 18\,°\text{C}\dagger\end{aligned}\right\} \quad \ldots \quad \text{(ii)}$$

Since the total pressure is equal to the barometer reading (710 mm Hg), the partial pressure of the air in the air–pentane mixture must be 710 − 395 = 315 mm Hg. .... (iii)

The volume of air used, at an initial pressure of 710 mm Hg, must be adjusted, for a final pressure of 315 mm Hg, by using the ideal gas equation (1). Eight litres of air will therefore become

$$V_A \times 315 = 8 \times 710$$

$$V_A = 18 \text{ l. of pentane-saturated air} \quad \ldots\ldots \quad \text{(iv)}$$

When $V = 18$ l., $p = 395$ mm Hg and $\theta = 18\,°C$, gas equation (2) shows that the weight of pentane absorbed is

$$\frac{395}{760} \times 18 = \frac{G(273 + 18) \times 0{\cdot}082}{72} \qquad G_{\text{pent}} = 28{\cdot}2 \text{ grammes} \quad \ldots\ldots \quad \text{(v)}$$

In case (ii), one may (*a*) either calculate $\bar{l}_v$ and p_{pent} and find from eqn. (104) that

$$\bar{l}_v = \frac{4{\cdot}574(273 + 36{\cdot}2)(273 - 12{\cdot}4)\log(760/100)}{36{\cdot}2 - (-12{\cdot}4)} = 6680 \text{ cal/mole} \quad \ldots\ldots \quad \text{(vi)}$$

---

* At 760 mm Hg and 36 °C, $\bar{l}_v$ will be about 5 per cent too low [see eqn. (122)], i.e. 6·11 kcal/mol. The experimental values determined for 30 °C and 40 °C are 6·19 and 6·08 kcal/mol, respectively. Equation (123) may be used in place of (121). This gives the following result, as opposed to (i):

$$\bar{l}_v = 30{\cdot}4\,\frac{273 + 36{\cdot}2}{1750 - (273 + 36{\cdot}2)} = 6{\cdot}51 \text{ kcal/mole}$$

† Equation (110) would give

$$\log p/\text{mm Hg} = -4{\cdot}7\,\frac{273 + 36{\cdot}2}{273 + 18} + 7{\cdot}6 = 2{\cdot}605$$

$$p_{\text{pent}} = 403 \text{ mm Hg at } 18\,°\text{C}$$

Substituting (vi) in eqn. (103) then gives

$$\log p/\text{mm Hg} = \log 760 - \frac{6680}{4{\cdot}574}(1/291 - 1/309{\cdot}2) = 2{\cdot}5855$$

$$p_{\text{pent}} = 385 \text{ mm Hg at } 18\ ^\circ\text{C} \qquad \ldots. \quad \text{(vii)}$$

(*b*) or determine log p/mm Hg more easily by means of graphical interpolation [eqn. (107), see also note to Exercise 46]. In this case, the logarithms (2·881 and 2·0) of the two given pressures (760 and 100 mm Hg) are plotted on the y-axis, with $1/T$ as abscissa, i.e. $1/(273 + 36{\cdot}2) = 32{\cdot}34 \times 10^{-4}$ deg.$^{-1}$ and $1/(273 - 12{\cdot}4) = 38{\cdot}37 \times 10^{-4}$ deg.$^{-1}$ on the x-axis. These two points are joined by a straight line and a reading for 18 °C, i.e. at $1/(273 + 18) = 34{\cdot}36 \times 10^{-4}$ deg.$^{-1}$, gives log p/mm Hg = 2·586, p = 385 mm Hg.

Having determined the above value for the vapour pressure of pentane at 18 °C, the volume of pentane-saturated air is calculated, in the manner previously shown, as

$$V_{\text{A}} = \frac{8 \times 710}{710 - 385} = 17{\cdot}4 \text{ l. of pentane-saturated air} \qquad \ldots. \quad \text{(viii)}$$

The weight of pentane absorbed then is

$$G = 27{\cdot}4 \text{ grammes}$$

Note. Vapour pressure values given in earlier Exercises (45-47, 49-51, 54-56) were obtained by graphical interpolation, using the above method.

Exercise 67

The following three values are given for the vapour pressure of methylene chloride, which is used as a refrigerant:

$$p_1 = 0{\cdot}0355 \text{ kg wt./cm}^2 \text{ at } -30\ ^\circ\text{C}$$
$$p_2 = 0{\cdot}190 \text{ kg wt./cm}^2 \text{ at } 0\ ^\circ\text{C}$$
$$p_3 = 1{\cdot}020 \text{ kg wt./cm}^2 \text{ at } 40\ ^\circ\text{C}$$

Prepare the interpolation curve which gives the most accurate intermediate values and, by way of example, give the vapour pressures for −15 °C and +20 °C.

Solution 67. Formula (108) is used for interpolation:

$$-1/T \times A' + \log T \times B' + C' = \log p \qquad \ldots. \quad \text{(i)}$$

Substituting the three given (p, T) values gives three equations with the three unknowns, A', B' and C'. These are solved by the usual method of elimination or using the determinant formula*. One then has:

$$-1/T_1 \times A' + \log T_1 \times B' + C' = \log p_1$$
$$-1/T_2 \times A' + \log T_2 \times B' + C' = \log p_2$$
$$-1/T_3 \times A' + \log T_3 \times B' + C' = \log p_3$$

* It is not necessary to be familiar with the theory of determinants to solve this problem. The units of p (kg wt./cm²) and T (°K) are omitted.

where

$$\left.\begin{aligned}
-1/T_1 &= -41{\cdot}152\times 10^{-4}\\
\log T_1 &= 2{\cdot}38561\\
\log p_1 &= 0{\cdot}55023-2 = -1{\cdot}44977\\
-1/T_2 &= -36{\cdot}630\times 10^{-4}\\
\log T_2 &= 2{\cdot}43616\\
\log p_2 &= 0{\cdot}27875-1 = -0{\cdot}72125\\
-1/T_3 &= -31{\cdot}949\times 10^{-4}\\
\log T_3 &= 2{\cdot}49554\\
\log p_3 &= 0{\cdot}00860
\end{aligned}\right\} \quad \ldots \quad \text{(ii)}$$

It follows from this that

$$A' = \frac{\begin{vmatrix} \log p_1 & \log T_1 & 1\\ \log p_2 & \log T_2 & 1\\ \log p_3 & \log T_3 & 1\end{vmatrix}}{\begin{vmatrix} -1/T_1 & \log T_1 & 1\\ -1/T_2 & \log T_2 & 1\\ -1/T_3 & \log T_3 & 1\end{vmatrix}} \quad \ldots\ldots \quad \text{(iii)}$$

$$B' = \frac{\begin{vmatrix} -1/T_1 & \log p_1 & 1\\ -1/T_2 & \log p_2 & 1\\ -1/T_3 & \log p_3 & 1\end{vmatrix}}{\begin{vmatrix} -1/T_1 & \log T_1 & 1\\ -1/T_2 & \log T_2 & 1\\ -1/T_3 & \log T_3 & 1\end{vmatrix}} \quad \ldots\ldots \quad \text{(iv)}$$

which, on solving, gives (as is also obtained from (ii) by direct use of the method of elimination):

$$A' = \frac{(\log p_2 - \log p_1)(\log T_3 - \log T_1) - (\log p_3 - \log p_1)(\log T_2 - \log T_1)}{(1/T_1 - 1/T_2)(\log T_3 - \log T_1) - (1/T_1 - 1/T_3)(\log T_2 - \log T_1)} \quad \ldots\ldots \quad \text{(v)}$$

$$B' = \frac{(1/T_1 - 1/T_2)(\log p_3 - \log p_1) - (1/T_1 - 1/T_3)(\log p_2 - \log p_1)}{(1/T_1 - 1/T_2)(\log T_3 - \log T_1) - (1/T_1 - 1/T_3)(\log T_2 - \log T_1)} \quad \ldots\ldots \quad \text{(vi)}$$

C' is obtained by substituting the values of A' and B' in one of the original equations.

Using the values at (ii), numerical substitution in (v) and (vi) gives

$$A' = \frac{0{\cdot}72852\times 0{\cdot}10993 - 1{\cdot}45837\times 0{\cdot}05055}{4{\cdot}522\times 10^{-4}\times 0{\cdot}10993 - 9{\cdot}203\times 10^{-4}\times 0{\cdot}05055} = \frac{0{\cdot}6366\times 10^{-2}}{3{\cdot}19\times 10^{-6}} = 1995{\cdot}6 \text{ deg.} \quad \ldots\ldots \quad \text{(vii)}$$

$$B' = \frac{4{\cdot}522\times 10^{-4}\times 1{\cdot}45837 - 9{\cdot}203\times 10^{-4}\times 0{\cdot}72852}{4{\cdot}522\times 10^{-4}\times 0{\cdot}10993 - 9{\cdot}203\times 10^{-4}\times 0{\cdot}05055} = \frac{-0{\cdot}10982\times 10^{-4}}{3{\cdot}19\times 10^{-6}} = -3{\cdot}4426 \quad \ldots\ldots \quad \text{(viii)}$$

$$\left.\begin{aligned}
C' &= +\log p_2 + A'/T_2 - B'\log T_2 = -0{\cdot}72125 + \frac{1995{\cdot}6}{273} + 3{\cdot}4426\times 2{\cdot}43616\\
&= -0{\cdot}72125 + 7{\cdot}3099 + 8{\cdot}3867 = 14{\cdot}9754
\end{aligned}\right\} \quad \ldots \quad \text{(ix)}$$

Note. The accuracy of the formula for interpolation may be judged from the fact that the values for + 20 °C and − 15 °C, i.e. for temperatures furthest away from the given temperatures of + 40, 0 and − 30 °C, are exactly the same as the experimentally determined figures.

By substituting in eqn. (108) the numerical values found for the three constants, the following expression is obtained for the variation of the vapour pressure of methylene chloride in the range -30 °C to $+40$ °C:

$$\log p/\text{kg wt./cm}^2 = -\frac{1995{\cdot}6}{T} - 3{\cdot}4426 \log T/\text{deg.} + 14{\cdot}9754 \quad \ldots . \quad (\text{x})$$

This formula then gives

for $+20$ °C ($=293$ °K): $\log p/\text{kg wt./cm}^2 = 0{\cdot}6720 - 1$ $\quad p = 0{\cdot}470$ kg wt./cm²

for -15 °C ($=258$ °K): $\log p/\text{kg wt./cm}^2 = 0{\cdot}9383 - 2$ $\quad p = 0{\cdot}0867$ kg wt./cm²

Problems requiring the solution of sets of equations with two or more unknowns cannot usually be worked out by means of a slide rule; they require a rather greater accuracy, which can only be obtained by using logarithms (and a corresponding accuracy in any experimental data required). The reason is that the calculations usually involve the determination of small differences between large numbers where errors easily creep in (see also note to Exercise 4).

Exercise 68

Determine, for the purpose of comparison, the trend of the vapour pressure curve (liquid–solid), the triple point p_F (vapour pressure at the melting point) and the molar heat of fusion l_f for the following pairs of isomers, which differ as regards molecular symmetry: (1) anthracene and phenanthrene, $C_{14}H_{10}$, and (2) *p*- and *m*-xylene, $C_6H_4(CH_3)_2$. The following data are given:

Anthracene: 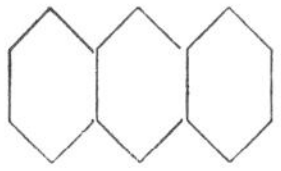 $Kp_{760} = 342$ °C $\quad Kp_{100} = 249$ °C
m. pt. = 219 °C

Phenanthrene: 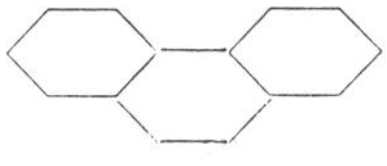 $Kp_{760} = 339$ °C $\quad Kp_{100} = 245$ °C
m. pt. = 101 °C

p-Xylene: 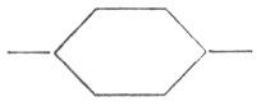 $Kp_{760} = 138$ °C $\quad$ m. pt. = 13·2 °C

m-Xylene: 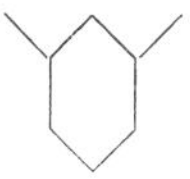 $Kp_{760} = 139$ °C $\quad$ m. pt. = $-53{\cdot}5$ °C
(Kp = boiling point)

The substances in question show no transitions in the solid state.

Solution 68. The vapour pressure at the melting point (pressure at the triple point) is first obtained by calculation or by graphical interpolation of the given values. Eqn. (103) is used for case (1) and eqn. (113) for case (2). The trend of the vapour pressure curve for the solid state (this also passes through the triple point) can then be determined from eqns. (116) and (117).

(1) In this case, two vapour pressure values are given for the liquid state. The pressure at the triple point may either be determined graphically from eqn. (117) (see *Figure 13*) or calculated from eqn. (103), after obtaining $\bar{l}_v$ from eqn. (104). Thus, for anthracene:

from eqn. (104)

$$\bar{l}_v = \frac{4{\cdot}574\,(342 + 273)\,(249 + 273) \times \log (760/100)}{342 - 249} = 13{\cdot}92 \text{ kcal/mole} \quad \ldots\ldots \quad \text{(i)}$$

and from eqn. (103)

$$\log p_F/\text{mm Hg} = \log 760 - \frac{13{,}920}{4{\cdot}574}[1/(219 + 273) - 1/(342 + 273)] = 1{\cdot}644 \quad \ldots\ldots \quad \text{(ii)}$$

$$p_F = 44 \text{ mm Hg}$$

The vapour pressure curve for solid anthracene passes through the triple point ($p_F = 44$ mm, m. pt. = 219 °C). According to eqn. (116) it also approximately passes through the vanishing point ($\log p_0'/\text{mm Hg} = 9{\cdot}7$, $T_0' = 300$ °K). Hence, from eqn. (117)

$$\bar{l}_s = 13{\cdot}72\,(9{\cdot}7 - 1{\cdot}644)\frac{492}{3000 - 492} = 21{\cdot}7 \text{ kcal/mole} \quad \ldots\ldots \quad \text{(iii)}$$

The sublimation temperature of solid anthracene, e.g. at a vapour pressure of $p = 1/100$ mm, $\log p/\text{mm Hg} = -2$, is, from eqn. (103), therefore, approximately

$$(-2 - 9{\cdot}7) = \frac{21{,}700}{4{\cdot}574}(1/T - 1/3000) \quad 1/T = 28{\cdot}00 \times 10^{-4} \text{ deg.}^{-1} \quad \ldots\ldots \quad \text{(iv)}$$

The approximate course of the vapour pressure curve for solid anthracene below its melting point may either be calculated from these values or by extrapolation through the vanishing and triple points. This gives a rough idea of the whole of the vapour pressure curve (see *Figure 13*). An estimation of the molar heat of fusion l_f is obtained from eqn. (105) from the difference between l_s and l_v. This is based on the assumptions, valid in the case of polyaromatic substances, that l_s and l_v are only slightly temperature-dependent and that no transitions take place in the solid state. Thus

$$\bar{l}_f \approx 21{\cdot}7 - 13{\cdot}92 \approx 7{\cdot}8 \text{ kcal/mole} \quad \ldots\ldots \quad \text{(v)}$$

Experimental measurements shows that $l_f = 6{\cdot}89$ kcal/mole. Similar calculations or extrapolation can be made in the case of phenanthrene, so that

$$\bar{l}_v = \frac{4{\cdot}574\,(339 + 273)\,(245 + 273) \times \log (760/100)}{339 - 245} = 13{\cdot}60 \text{ kcal/mole} \quad \ldots\ldots \quad \text{(vi)}$$

$$\left.\begin{aligned} \log p_F/\text{mm Hg} &= \log 760 - \frac{13{,}600}{4{\cdot}574}[1/(101 + 273) - 1/(339 + 273)] = 0{\cdot}789 - 1 \\ p_F &= 0{\cdot}6 \text{ mm Hg} \end{aligned}\right\} \quad \ldots \quad \text{(vii)}$$

$$\bar{l}_s = 13{\cdot}72\,[9{\cdot}7 - (0{\cdot}789 - 1)]\frac{374}{3000 - 374} = 19{\cdot}4 \text{ kcal/mole} \quad \ldots\ldots \quad \text{(viii)}$$

For a vapour pressure of solid phenanthrene of $p = 1/100$ mm Hg, $\log p/\text{mm Hg} = -2$, one has the approximation that

$$(-2 - 9{\cdot}7) = -\frac{19{,}400}{4{\cdot}574}(1/T - 1/3000) \quad 1/T = 30{\cdot}93 \times 10^{-4} \text{ deg.}^{-1} \quad \ldots\ldots \quad \text{(ix)}$$

The course of the vapour pressure curve is shown in *Figure 13*.

$\bar{l}_f \approx 19{\cdot}4 - 13{\cdot}6 \approx 5{\cdot}8$ kcal/mole (the experimental value being $l_f = 4{\cdot}45$ kcal/mole) $\ldots\ldots$ (x)

(2) In the case of xylene, only the boiling point $Kp\,(=T_v)$ is given. The vanishing point defined by eqn. (113) must therefore be taken as a second fixed point for the purpose of extrapolation of the vapour pressure curve. For *p*-xylene, $Kp = 138$ °C, $T_v = 138 + 273 = 411$ °K.

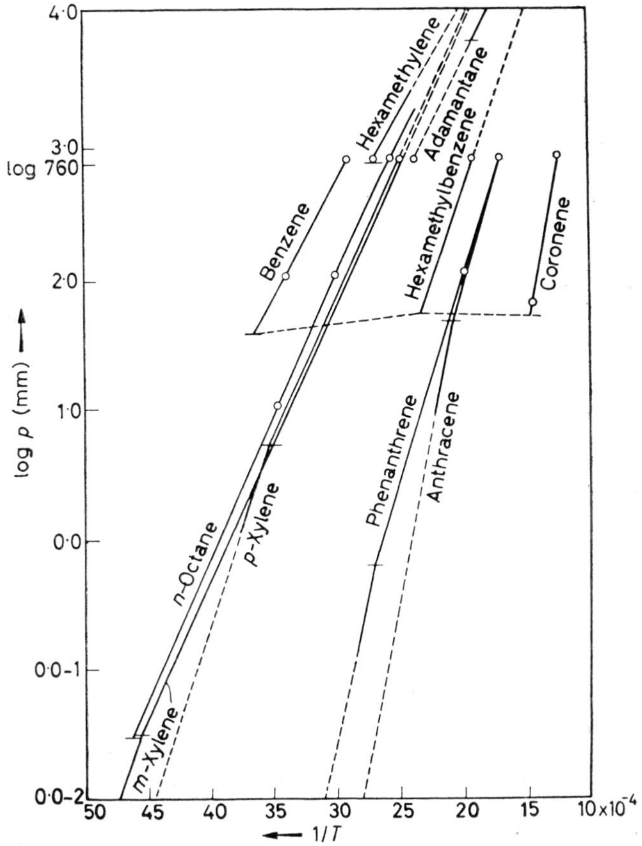

Figure 13. Vapour pressure curves and triple points of hydrocarbons

Referring back to eqn. (114), we find that

$$\bar{l}_v = 59 \frac{411}{3000 - 411} = 9{\cdot}36 \text{ kcal/mole} \qquad \ldots. \quad \text{(xi)}$$

[the experimentally determined value of l_v at the boiling point (760 mm Hg) is 8·60 kcal/mole].

The pressure p_F at the triple point, for a melting point of 13·2 °C, is found by means of eqns. (103), (113) and (114):

$$\log p_F/\text{mm Hg} = 7{\cdot}18 - \frac{9360}{4{\cdot}574}\,[1/(13{\cdot}2 + 273) - 1/3000] = 0{\cdot}71$$

or

$$\left.\begin{aligned}\log p_F/\text{mm Hg} &= \log 760 - \frac{9360}{4{\cdot}574}[1/(13{\cdot}2 + 273) - 1/(138 + 273)] = 0{\cdot}71\\ p_F &= 5{\cdot}1 \text{ mm Hg}\end{aligned}\right\} \quad \ldots \text{(xii)}$$

Also, from eqn. (117), and similarly to the case of anthracene and phenanthrene:

$$\bar{l}_s = 13{\cdot}72\,(9{\cdot}7 - 0{\cdot}71)\,\frac{286{\cdot}2}{3000 - 286{\cdot}2} = 13{\cdot}01 \text{ kcal/mole} \qquad \ldots \text{(xiii)}$$

The approximate value of $1/T$, when $p = 1/100$ mm, $\log p/\text{mm Hg} = -2$, is given by

$$-2 - 9{\cdot}7 = -\frac{13010}{4{\cdot}574}(1/T - 1/3000) \quad 1/T = 44{\cdot}48 \times 10^{-4} \text{ deg.}^{-1} \qquad \ldots \text{(xiv)}$$

The course of the vapour pressure curve is shown in *Figure 13.*

In the absence of any transition points, eqn. (105) gives the molar heat of fusion as

$$\bar{l}_f \approx \bar{l}_s - \bar{l}_v \approx 13{\cdot}01 - 9{\cdot}36 \approx 3{\cdot}65 \text{ kcal/mole}$$

(the experimental value being 4·04 kcal/mole) .... (xv)

Again, in the absence of any transition point, the molar heat of fusion can be directly calculated from the melting point by means of eqn. (118). It is found that

$$\bar{l}_f \approx 34{\cdot}6\,\frac{286{\cdot}2}{3000 - 286{\cdot}2} = 3{\cdot}65 \text{ kcal/mole [the same as (xv)]} \qquad \ldots \text{(xvi)}$$

The following values are obtained in a similar way for *m*-xylene where $Kp_{760} = 139$ °C and $T_v = 139 + 273 = 412$ °K:

$$\bar{l}_v = 59\,\frac{412}{3000 - 412} = 9{\cdot}4 \text{ kcal/mole}$$

[the experimental value of l_v at the boiling point (760 mm Hg) is 8·93 kcal/mole] .... (xvii)

The pressure p_F at the triple point is

$$\left.\begin{aligned}\log p_F/\text{mm Hg} &= 7{\cdot}18 - \frac{9400}{4{\cdot}574}[1/(-53{\cdot}5 + 273) - 1/3000] = 0{\cdot}50 - 2\\ p_F &= 0{\cdot}032 \text{ mm Hg}\end{aligned}\right\} \quad \ldots \text{(xviii)}$$

$$\bar{l}_s = 13{\cdot}72\,[9{\cdot}7 - (0{\cdot}50 - 2)]\,\frac{219{\cdot}5}{3000 - 219{\cdot}5} = 12{\cdot}13 \text{ kcal/mole} \qquad \ldots \text{(xix)}$$

The approximate value of $1/T$, e.g. at a pressure of $1/100$ mm Hg, $\log p/\text{mm Hg} = -2$, is

$$-2 - 9{\cdot}7 = -\frac{12130}{4{\cdot}574}(1/T - 1/3000) \quad 1/T = 47{\cdot}48 \times 10^{-4} \text{ deg.}^{-1} \qquad \ldots \text{(xx)}$$

The course of the vapour pressure curve is shown in *Figure 13.*

From eqn. (118) $\bar{l}_f \approx 34{\cdot}6\,\dfrac{219{\cdot}5}{3000 - 219{\cdot}5} \approx 2{\cdot}73$ kcal/mole

[= (12·13 − 9·4) from eqn. (105) and using (xvii) and (xix)]
(experimental value = 2·74 kcal/mole) .. (xxi)

It will be seen from *Figure 13* for both pairs of isomers that, over the liquid phase, the vapour pressure curves are almost coincident. On the other hand, the position of the triple point is affected, in the case of the isomer with the greater degree of symmetry, by a break in the vapour pressure curve. The pressure at the triple point is therefore considerably higher for the symmetrical molecule (44 mm for anthracene as opposed to 0·6 mm for phenanthrene, 5·1 mm for *p*-xylene, 0·032 mm for *m*-xylene), so that the melting points and heats of fusion are also higher, assuming no transition points exist. See also the note at the end of Exercise 71.

Exercise 69

Estimate the pressure p_F at the triple point (vapour pressure at the melting point) for two of the C_8H_{18} isomers, viz. for the linear molecule n-octane, $CH_3(CH_2)_6CH_3$, and for hexamethylethane, $(CH_3)_3C—C(CH_3)_3$, which has an essentially spherically-shaped molecule. For the purpose of comparison, derive the results both by calculation and by graphical extrapolation. The following data are given:

n-octane: $Kp_{760} = 125{\cdot}8$ °C, $Kp_{100} = 66{\cdot}0$ °C, $Kp_{10} = 19{\cdot}0$ °C, m. pt. $-56{\cdot}5$ °C

hexamethylethane: $Kp_{765} = 107$ °C, m.pt. $= 104$ °C (Kp = boiling point).

Solution 69. The quickest way to determine the pressure at the triple point for n-octane is to plot the given values as a curve of log p against $1/T$ and to extrapolate linearly to the melting point, in accordance with eqn. (107). In this way, the pressure p_F at the triple point (see *Figure 13*) is

$$\log p_F/\text{mm Hg} = 0{\cdot}482 - 2 \qquad p_F = 0{\cdot}03 \text{ mm Hg} \quad \ldots. \quad \text{(i)}$$

In general, it is only necessary to make an arithmetical calculation when information regarding the mean heat of vaporization is required. From eqn. (104), we find

$$\bar{l}_v = 4{\cdot}574 \frac{339 \times 292}{339 - 292} \log(100/10) = 9{\cdot}64 \text{ kcal/mole} \quad \ldots. \quad \text{(ii)}$$

and, from eqn. (103), [the same as at (i)],

$$\log p_F/\text{mm Hg} = \log 10 - \frac{9640}{4{\cdot}574}(1/216{\cdot}5 - 1/292) = 0{\cdot}482 - 2 \quad \ldots. \quad \text{(iii)}$$

Because of the marked temperature dependence of the heat of vaporization in the case of paraffins, an extrapolation of this length gives only the order of magnitude of the pressure at the triple point, i.e. an upper limit, in view of the increase of heat of vaporization with fall in temperature. This assessment is, however, sufficient for the purpose of comparison.

In order to estimate the pressure at the triple point for hexamethylethane by means of graphical extrapolation, the vanishing point [preferably that given by eqn. (120)] must be introduced. This is because only the boiling and melting points are given and, on account of their closeness in value, the pressure at the triple point will not be much less than 760 mm Hg. It is found (see *Figure 13*) that

$$\log p_F/\text{mm Hg} = 2{\cdot}85 \qquad p_F = 708 \text{ mm Hg} \quad \ldots. \quad \text{(iv)}$$

Arithmetic calculation from eqn. (120), using eqns. (104) and (103), gives

$$\bar{l}_v = 4{\cdot}574 \frac{3510 \times 380}{3510 - 380}(6{\cdot}83 - \log 765) = 7{\cdot}69 \text{ kcal/mole} \quad \ldots . \quad \text{(v)}$$

(in the neighbourhood of the boiling point, $Kp = 107$ °C)

$$\left.\begin{aligned} \log p_F/\text{mm Hg} &= \log 765 - \frac{76{,}900}{4{\cdot}574}(1/377 - 1/380) = 2{\cdot}8837 - 0{\cdot}0352 = 2{\cdot}8485 \\ p_F &= 706 \text{ mm Hg} \end{aligned}\right\} \quad .. \quad \text{(vi)}$$

As in the case of Exercise 68, a large difference is revealed between the pressures of the two isomers at the respective triple points, and therefore a large difference between the melting points. This is again due to differences in molecular symmetry. One isomer has an almost spherical molecule, the other a flexible cluster forming long-chain structure. It should be noted that the difference in pressure at the triple point is, in the present case, very large indeed (706 mm, in contrast to 0·03 mm Hg).

Note. The polyaromatics and other large molecules (see Exercise 68) exhibit no transition points in the solid state. This behaviour is in contrast to that of the paraffins and similar compounds where, because of their structure, free rotation about molecular bonds takes place. This leads to the existence of transition points, and heats of transition must be taken into account. For this reason, in the absence of actual vapour pressure data for the solid state, it is inadmissible to assess the trend of vapour pressure for the solid state or the heat of sublimation at temperatures below the melting point, let alone the heat of fusion; see also Exercise 70 and the note to Exercise 71.

Exercise 70

Calculate the pressure p_F at the triple point (vapour pressure at the melting point) for benzene, C_6H_6, hexamethylbenzene, $C_6(CH_3)_6$, and coronene, $C_{24}H_{12}$, i.e. for substances with very different molecular weights, boiling points and melting points but having a similar symmetry. The following data are given:

Benzene 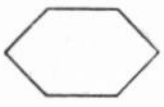 $Kp_{760} = 80{\cdot}2$ °C, $Kp_{100} = 26{\cdot}4$ °C, m. pt. = 5·5° C

Hexamethylbenzene 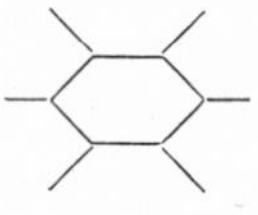 $Kp_{760} = 265$ °C, m. pt. = 166 °C

Coronene 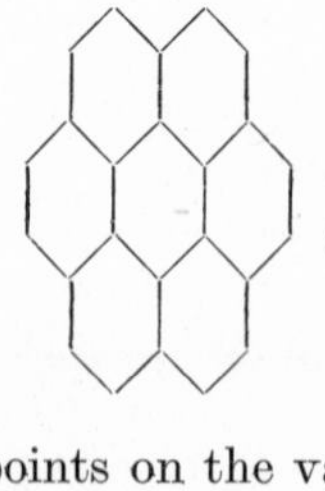 $Kp_{760} = 575$ °C, $Kp_{56{\cdot}5} = 443$ °C, m. pt. = 435 °C
(Kp = boiling point)

Solution 70. Two points on the vapour pressure curve are given for benzene and coronene. It is therefore possible, with reasonable accuracy, to make a linear extrapolation to the freezing point by using eqn. (107) and a plot of log p against $1/T$. In the case of hexamethylbenzene, the vanishing point must be introduced as a second point of reference before extrapolating (see *Figure 13*).

Arithmetic calculation of the pressure at the triple point for benzene and coronene follows from eqns. (104) and (103):

for benzene:

$$\bar{l}_v = \frac{4{\cdot}574 \times 353{\cdot}1 \times 299{\cdot}4}{353{\cdot}1 - 299{\cdot}4} \times \log(760/100) = 7{\cdot}93 \text{ kcal/mole} \quad \ldots\ldots \quad \text{(i)}$$

$$\left.\begin{aligned} \log p_F/\text{mm Hg} &= \log 760 - \frac{7{\cdot}93 \times 10^3}{4{\cdot}574}(1/278{\cdot}5 - 1/353{\cdot}1) = 2{\cdot}881 - 1{\cdot}315 \\ &= 1{\cdot}566 \\ p_F &= 36{\cdot}8 \text{ mm Hg} \end{aligned}\right\} \quad \ldots \quad \text{(ii)}$$

for coronene:

$$\bar{l}_v = \frac{4{\cdot}574 \times 848 \times 716}{848 \times 716} \times \log(760/56{\cdot}5) = 23{\cdot}75 \text{ kcal/mole} \quad \ldots\ldots \quad \text{(iii)}$$

$$\left.\begin{aligned} \log p_F/\text{mm Hg} &= \log 56{\cdot}5 - \frac{23{\cdot}75 \times 10^3}{4{\cdot}574}(1/708 - 1/716) = 1{\cdot}752 - 0{\cdot}082 \\ &= 1{\cdot}670 \\ p_F &= 46{\cdot}8 \text{ mm Hg} \end{aligned}\right\} \quad \ldots \quad \text{(iv)}$$

In the case of hexamethylbenzene, only the boiling point, Kp_{760}, is given. Calculation of the pressure at the triple point may therefore be made by using eqns. (104) and (103) and introducing the vanishing point as in eqn. (113); alternatively, the formula in eqn. (114) for $\bar{l}_v$ may be taken:

$$\bar{l}_v = \frac{59\,(265 + 273)}{3000 - (265 + 273)} = 12{\cdot}9 \text{ kcal/mole} \quad \ldots\ldots \quad \text{(v)}$$

(the experimental value is 12·87 kcal/mole at 263·5 °C)

$$\left.\begin{aligned} \log p_F/\text{mm Hg} &= \log 760 - \frac{12{\cdot}9 \times 10^3}{4{\cdot}574}(1/439 - 1/538) = 1{\cdot}697 \\ p_F &= 49{\cdot}8 \text{ mm Hg} \end{aligned}\right\} \quad \ldots \quad \text{(vi)}$$

The above calculations show that benzene, hexamethylbenzene and coronene display approximately the same pressures at the triple points. The three substances have very different molecular weights, boiling and melting points, but have a very similar symmetry, the molecules being in the form of hexagonal discs. This result is in contrast to those noted in Exercises 68 and 69, where differences in triple-point pressures were found between isomers having dissimilar molecular structures (see also note to Exercise 71).

Exercise 71

In view of the results in Exercises 68, 69 and 70, indicating the connection between molecular structure and pressure at the triple point, calculate the latter in the case of adamantane (diamantine), $C_{10}H_{16}$, a molecule which shows the highest degree of symmetry in its molecular structure and where the carbon skeleton is practically a spherical replica of the diamond lattice.

Textbook data give the melting point (in a sealed capillary) as 268 °C (268 °C from petroleum, 267·5 to 269 °C for the synthetic product). Bicyclononane, C_9H_{16}, with similar but dual (boat and chair) structures has a boiling point of 169 °C. Camphane, $C_{10}H_{18}$, and camphene, $C_{10}H_{16}$, have more rigid structures and boiling points of 161 and 160 °C. Finally, *d*-limonene, $C_{10}H_{16}$, with its open structure of a doubly-substituted, six-membered ring, has a boiling point of 177·6 °C. It therefore seems reasonable to take a boiling point of 160 °C at 760 mm Hg (i.e. the same as that of camphene) as a close approximation in regard to the vapour pressure of liquid (metastable) adamantane.

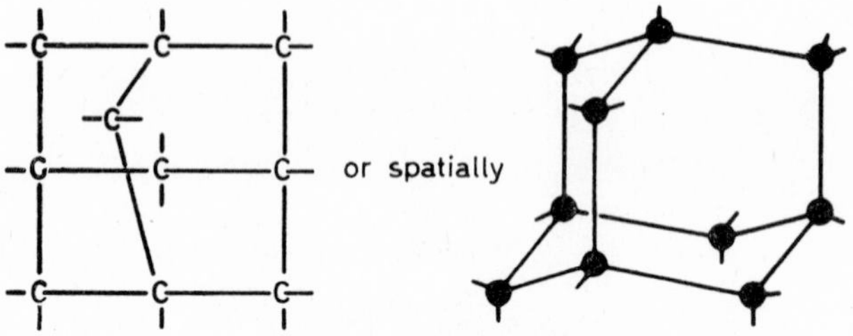

Structure of adamantane

Solution 71. Adopting the value of the vanishing point given for paraffins in eqn. (120), the vapour pressure curve is obtained by plotting $\log p$ against $1/T$ between the assumed (metastable) value and the vanishing point. The vapour pressure at the melting point is then determined by interpolation by means of eqn. (107) (see *Figure 13*).

Calculation from eqns. (120), (124) and (103) then gives

$$\bar{l}_v = \frac{63{\cdot}4 \times (160 + 273)}{3510 - (160 + 273)} = 8{\cdot}93 \text{ kcal/mole} \qquad \ldots\ldots \quad \text{(i)}$$

$$\left.\begin{aligned} \log p_{\mathrm{F}}/\text{mm Hg} &= \log 760 - \frac{8{\cdot}93 \times 10^3}{4{\cdot}574}(1/541 - 1/433) = 2{\cdot}881 + 0{\cdot}900 = 3{\cdot}781 \\ p_{\mathrm{F}} &= 6040 \text{ mm Hg, or about 8 atm.} \end{aligned}\right\} \quad \ldots \quad \text{(ii)}$$

This estimated value of 8 atm for the vapour pressure of adamantane at its melting point is a reflection of its spherically symmetrical structure and may be taken as the highest value of its type for any organic compound. It follows that only sublimation of adamantane can occur at atmospheric pressure.

Note. The solution of Exercises 68—71 effectively draws attention to the influence of molecular symmetry on the pressure at the triple point, and on melting point and heat of fusion. Highly symmetrical compounds are associated with close-knit solid structures which can withstand high internal pressures up to the point where the structure collapses due to liquefaction. On the other hand, non-symmetrical molecular structures have a low pressure at the melting point and the substances are difficult to solidify.

*Exercise 72

Calculate the lower explosion limit (in mm Hg and volume per cent) in air at atmospheric pressure, and also the explosion temperature (flash point), (*a*) for xylene, $C_6H_4(CH_3)_2$, (boiling point approx. 140 °C) and (*b*) for transformer oil (mol. wt.

approx. 300; composition 13·3 per cent by weight H, the remainder C; boiling point approx. 350 °C). It should be borne in mind that, for hydrocarbons rich in carbon, the partial pressure in air, for ignition by an external source, is shown by experience to be about half the partial pressure stoichiometrically required for combustion to CO_2 and H_2O. Use eqn. (112) for the relation between partial pressure and temperature. Air contains 20·9 per cent by vol. of O_2.

Solution 72. (*a*) The combustion equation for xylene is

$$C_6H_4(CH_3)_2 + 10{\cdot}5\ O_2 = 8CO_2 + 5H_2O$$

i.e. 10·5 vols. of oxygen react with 1 vol. of xylene or $\frac{10{\cdot}5 \times 100}{20{\cdot}9} = 50{\cdot}2$ vols. of air.

The stoichiometric partial pressure of xylene is, therefore

$$\left.\begin{aligned} 760\,\frac{1}{1+50{\cdot}2} &= 14{\cdot}8 \text{ mm Hg, which corresponds to } \frac{1}{1+50{\cdot}2}\times 100 \\ &= 1{\cdot}95 \text{ per cent by vol. of xylene} \end{aligned}\right\} \quad \text{(i)}$$

The lower explosion limit may, therefore, be estimated as approximately 1·95/2 = 0·98 per cent by vol. xylene or 7·4 mm Hg.

From eqn. (112)

$$\log p/\text{mm Hg} = -5{\cdot}4 \times T_{760}/T + 8{\cdot}3 \quad \text{(ii)}$$

The explosion temperature T is then found by substituting the value of the boiling point of xylene, 140 °C or $T_{760} = 413$ °K and $p = 7{\cdot}4$ mm Hg or $\log p/\text{mm Hg} = 0{\cdot}87$:

$$0{\cdot}87 = -5{\cdot}4 \times 413/T + 8{\cdot}3 \quad \text{or} \quad T = 300 \text{ °K (27 °C)}$$

Thus the lower explosion limit for xylene is about 0·98 per cent by vol. and the flash point 27 °C. In practice the figures are 1 per cent by volume and 24 °C.

(*b*) The composition of the transformer oil is 13·3 per cent by wt. H and 86·7 per cent by wt. C. It follows that the molecular ratio C:H is given by

$$86{\cdot}7/12{\cdot}01 : 13{\cdot}3/1{\cdot}008 = 7{\cdot}22 : 13{\cdot}2$$

These figures would correspond to a molecular weight of 100. Since the molecular weight is actually 300, they must be multiplied by three, giving an empirical formula for the oil of $C_{21\cdot66}H_{39\cdot6}$.

This leads to a combustion equation

$$1 \text{ molecule of oil} + 31{\cdot}56\ O_2 = 21{\cdot}66\ CO_2 + 19{\cdot}8\ H_2O$$

so that 31·5 molecules of O_2 react with 1 molecule of oil or 1 vol. of oil vapour requires $31{\cdot}56 \times 100/20{\cdot}9 = 151$ vols. of air.

Stoichiometrically, therefore, the air must contain $\frac{1}{1+151} \times 100 = 0{\cdot}66$ per cent by vol. of oil vapour, equivalent to a partial pressure of $0{\cdot}66 \times 760/100 = 5{\cdot}0$ mm Hg.

Half this value is taken for the lower explosion limit, i.e. 0·33 per cent by volume or 2·5 mm Hg.

Using (ii), a boiling point value of 350 °C or 623 °K and $p = 2{\cdot}5$ mm or $\log p/\text{mm Hg} = 0{\cdot}398$, gives the flash point as

$$0{\cdot}398 = -5{\cdot}4 \times 623/T = 8{\cdot}3 \qquad T = 426 \text{ °K (153 °C)}$$

Note. The explosion hazards associated with petrol fraction hydrocarbons when mixed with air – i.e. initiated by flames, sparks (from static electricity) or local heating (electric hotplates, filings and drillings) – are usually underestimated, and not only by laymen. As a result, serious industrial accidents often occur. Containers which have held petrol, diesel fuel or petroleum should not, therefore, be worked on with a blow-lamp, drill or file, even after they have apparently been completely emptied. Workers who have to repair or reconstruct fuel containers (tanks or tank wagons) should, therefore, seek the advice of an expert. Providing regulations are not infringed, such containers should be filled with CO_2 or, in certain circumstances, rendered non-explosive by the addition of carbon tetrachloride. Obviously, such containers must also not be entered without wearing an oxygen mask. Serious domestic accidents with petrol occur because it is not sufficiently widely known that (a) carbon tetrachloride may almost always serve in place of petrol and (b) one should always work in the open air when using petrol. It is not safe to work at open windows; the heavy vapours sink towards the floor and then spread, so that no odour is detected. Should the door now be opened, the vapours will spiral upwards, reaching such sources of ignition as electric or gas fires. An explosion will then occur.

9

THERMOCHEMISTRY

HEATS OF REACTION; SPECIFIC HEATS; TEMPERATURE DEPENDENCE OF HEATS OF REACTION

U = intrinsic energy of a system
ΔU = change in intrinsic energy = $U_2 - U_1$ (positive for an increase)
$+Q$ = heat absorbed by a system, heat requirement
$+A$ = work fed into a system, or work done on the system

$\Delta U = A + Q$ first law of thermodynamics (energy principle) .... (125)

The increase in the intrinsic energy of a system is the sum of the heat absorbed and the work done on the system. It is independent of the sequence and stages of the process (independent of the path) and only depends on the initial and final states. U is a variable of state. Thus

$$\left.\begin{array}{l}\Delta U = \Delta U_1 + \Delta U_2 + \cdots + \Delta U_n \\ \text{(Hess' law of constant heat summation)}\end{array}\right\} \quad \text{.. (126)}$$

If the initial and final states of a system are the same (cyclic process), then

$$\Delta U = 0 \quad \text{.... (127)}$$

$$H = \text{enthalpy or heat content} \equiv U + pV \quad \text{.... (128)}$$

$$\Delta H = \text{change of enthalpy} = H_2 - H_1$$

Like U, H is also a variable of state.

Where necessary for the purpose of differentiation, variables referring to one mole will be written in small letters.

C_v = heat capacity of a system at constant volume, i.e. the quantity of heat necessary, at constant volume, to raise the temperature of the system by one degree.
c_v = specific heat per mole (molar heat) at constant volume.

Absorption of heat at constant volume ($A = 0$):

$$Q_v = \Delta U = C_v \Delta T = n c_v \Delta T \quad \text{.... (129)}$$

(n = quantity of moles in the system);
or in differential form

$$Q_v = \Delta U = U_{T_2} - U_{T_1} = n \int_{T_1}^{T_2} c_v \, \mathrm{d}\, T \qquad C_v = n\, c_v = \left(\frac{\partial U}{\partial T}\right)_v \quad \text{.... (130)}$$

C_p = heat capacity of a system at constant pressure
c_p = specific heat per mole (molar heat) at constant pressure.

Absorption of heat at constant pressure ($A = -p\Delta V$):

$$Q_p = \Delta U - A = \Delta U + p\Delta V = \Delta H = C_p\Delta T = nc_p\Delta T \qquad \ldots (131)$$

or in differential form

$$Q_p = \Delta H = H_{T_2} - H_{T_1} = n\int_{T_1}^{T_2} c_p \,\mathrm{d}T \qquad C_p = n c_p = \left(\frac{\partial H}{\partial T}\right)_p \qquad \ldots (132)$$

Work done $A = -p\Delta V$ (external work), at constant pressure

$$A = -p(V_2 - V_1) \qquad \ldots (133)$$

or in differential form

$$\mathrm{d}A = -p\,\mathrm{d}V \qquad A = -\int_{V_1}^{V_2} p\,\mathrm{d}V \qquad \ldots (134)$$

The work done during the reversible isothermal expansion of an ideal gas [$pV = nRT$, see eqn. (2)] is

$$\left.\begin{aligned} A &= -\int_{V_1}^{V_2} p\,\mathrm{d}V = -\int_{V_1}^{V_2} \frac{nRT}{V}\mathrm{d}V = -nRT\ln(V_1/V_2) \\ &= nRT\ln(p_1/p_2) = -4{\cdot}574\,nT\log(p_1/p_2)\ (\mathrm{cal}) \\ &\qquad [R = 1{\cdot}9865\ \mathrm{cal/(deg.\ mole)},\ \text{see eqn. (4)}] \end{aligned}\right\} \quad \ldots (135)$$

For an ideal gas

$$c_p = c_v + R \qquad \ldots (136)$$

If a process takes place such that $\Delta U = 0$, i.e. $A = -Q$, this is said to be isothermal, since the temperature remains constant, as ΔU is independent of the volume.

If $Q = 0$, i.e. $A = \Delta U$, the process is adiabatic and no heat enters or leaves the system. In the case of the adiabatic expansion or contraction of an ideal gas, the adiabatic gas equation is used: $pV^{\varkappa} =$ const. or $TV^{\varkappa-1} =$ const., where

$$\left.\begin{aligned} \varkappa = c_p/c_v.\ \text{The theoretical value is for monatomic gases } \varkappa &= 1{\cdot}667 \\ \text{for diatomic gases } \varkappa &= 1{\cdot}4 \end{aligned}\right\} \quad \ldots (137)$$

The heat evolved during a chemical reaction or transition is called the heat of reaction (or transition). In accordance with the definitions at the beginning of the chapter, the heat of reaction is taken as positive when the system absorbs heat (endothermic reaction) and negative when heat is evolved (exothermic reaction). Distinction is made between

the heat of reaction at constant volume or energy of reaction per mole, formula $Q_v = \Delta U$, and

the heat of reaction at constant pressure or reaction enthalpy per mole, formula $Q_p = \Delta H = \Delta U + p\Delta V$, this being the more commonly used;

thus $A + B + \Delta H = AB$ or $A + B = AB - \Delta H$*. ... (138)

* The units of ΔH and ΔU [per mole of reactant(s)] are usually (cal/mole) or (Joule/mole); the units of ΔV are usually (l./mole) or (cm^3/mole); see p. 2.

It is still customary, however, to take the heat evolved (exothermic reaction) as positive and heat absorbed (endothermic reaction) as negative in the case of chemical reactions. (This is not the case for transitions such as fusion, sublimation and vaporization.) The quantity of heat absorbed or evolved per mole of reactant(s) is then known as the heat effect ('heat tonality')

$$\left.\begin{aligned} &\text{heat effect at constant volume} && \mathfrak{Q}_v = -Q_v = -\Delta U \\ &\text{heat effect at constant pressure} && \mathfrak{Q}_p = -Q_p = -\Delta H \\ &\text{(most commonly given)} && \quad = -\Delta U - p\Delta V = \mathfrak{Q}_v - p\Delta V \end{aligned}\right\} \quad ..(139)^*$$

Under ordinary conditions of pressure, the supplementary term $p\Delta V$ is only taken into account when the enthalpy changes of gaseous products of reaction are involved. Thus

$$Q_p = \Delta H = \Delta U + p\Delta V = \Delta U + \Delta\sum \nu_{i(\text{gas})} RT \quad .... (140)$$

$$\text{or} \quad \mathfrak{Q}_p = -\Delta H = -\Delta U - p\Delta V = \mathfrak{Q}_v - \Delta\sum \nu_{i(\text{gas})} RT \quad .... (141)$$

where $n_i = \nu_i \lambda$ or $dn_i = \nu_i d\lambda$ (see pp. 2 and 121), the gas constant, $R = 1{\cdot}9865$ cal/(deg. mole) and $\Delta\sum \nu_{i(\text{gas})}$ is the difference between the stoichiometric number of moles of gaseous products before and after reaction; λ is the molar reaction variable (mole) or molar degree of advancement of the reaction (see p. 2).

Heat of formation or enthalpy of formation, ΔH^F, is defined as the heat of reaction, at 1 atm and given temperature (usually 18° or 25 °C), for the formation of 1 mole of a substance from the free molecules of the constituent elements in the standard state at room temperature. .... (142)†

The atomic heat of formation or enthalpy of formation refers to the heat of formation of 1 mole of a substance from the free atoms. .... (143)

The lattice energy, φ, is defined as the energy required to build a crystal lattice (in the static state) from the free units making up the crystal, i.e. in the case of ionic crystals, from the free ions (at 0 °K). .... (144)

It follows from Hess' law, eqn. (126), that

(*a*) the enthalpy of formation of a compound is equal to the difference between the enthalpies of combustion ΔH^C of its constituents (enthalpy of formation of the combustion products) and the enthalpy of combustion of the compound itself. .... (145)

(*b*) the enthalpy of reaction is equal to the difference between the enthalpy of formation of the products (right-hand side of the reaction equation) and that of the initial reactants (left-hand side of the equation), due note being taken of the number of molecules involved in the reaction. .... (146)

---

* The definitions in eqn. (139) are really superfluous and inconsistent, bearing in mind it has been established that the energy introduced into a system is to be taken as positive. They represent a concession to practical usage.

† For reactions between elements, one should always check the tables as to which substances or allotropic modifications are used as initial or reference reactants (with an enthalpy of formation, $\Delta H^F = 0$). In the case of organic substances, it should be specially noted whether diamond or graphite (so-called β-graphite) is used as reference.

Calorific value: gross calorific value, H_G, refers to the enthalpy of combustion of fuel burnt to form CO_2 and liquid water. The units of measurement for solids and liquids are usually kcal/kg; for gases, the units kcal/Nm³ (i.e. m³ at s.t.p.) are taken. .... (147)

Net calorific value refers to the enthalpy of combustion of fuels burnt to form CO_2 and water vapour. .... (148)

The calorific value is usually taken as positive when heat is evolved from the system; eqns. (139), for heat of reaction, are therefore used.

Temperature dependence of heat of reaction or heat of transition:
at constant volume

$$\frac{\partial Q_v}{\partial T} = \left(\frac{\partial \Delta U}{\partial T}\right)_v = C_{v\,(\text{final})} - C_{v\,(\text{initial})} \left(= -\frac{\partial \mathfrak{Q}_v}{\partial T}\right) \qquad \ldots . (149)$$

at constant pressure

$$\frac{\partial Q_p}{\partial T} = \left(\frac{\partial \Delta U}{\partial T}\right)_p = C_{p\,(\text{final})} = C_{p\,(\text{initial})} \left(= -\frac{\partial \mathfrak{Q}_p}{\partial T}\right) \qquad \ldots . (150)$$

where $C_{(\text{initial})}$ and $C_{(\text{final})}$ are the respective heat capacities of the left-hand side and right-hand side of the reaction equation [Kirchhoff's law, see also eqn. (195)].

*Exercise 73

The enthalpy of formation of acetylene, C_2H_2 (from graphite and H_2), is $\Delta H_1^F = +53{\cdot}9$ kcal/mole; that of benzene vapour, C_6H_6, is $\Delta H_2^F = +19{\cdot}1$ kcal/mole. What is the enthalpy of reaction, ΔH, when acetylene is catalytically polymerized to benzene vapour?

Solution 73. The reaction equation is [see eqn. (138)]

$$3\,C_2H_2 = C_6H_6 - \Delta H_x \qquad \ldots . \quad (i)$$

The equation for the formation of $3\,C_2H_2$ is

$$6\,C + 3\,H_2 = 3\,C_2H_2 - 3\Delta H_1^F \qquad \ldots . \quad (ii)$$

and for C_6H_6

$$6\,C + 3\,H_2 = C_6H_6 - \Delta H_2^F \qquad \ldots . \quad (iii)$$

In accordance with Hess' law [eqn. (126)], the reaction equations (and the heats of reaction) can be treated as algebraic equations. As an example, addition of (ii) (after transposing the left- and right-hand sides) to (iii) gives

$$3\,C_2H_2 - 3\Delta H_1^F + 6\,C + 3\,H_2 = 6\,C + 3\,H_2 + C_6H_6 - \Delta H_2^F \qquad [(ii) + (iii)]$$

or, after cancelling

$$3\,C_2H_2 = C_6H_6 - \Delta H_2^F + 3\Delta H_1^F \qquad \ldots . \quad (iv)$$

Comparing (iv) with (i), it is seen that $\Delta H_2^F - 3\Delta H_1^F = \Delta H_x$ [see also (146)], thus

$$\Delta H_x = \Delta H_2^F - 3\Delta H_1^F = +19{\cdot}1 - 3{\cdot}53 \times 9 = -142{\cdot}6 \text{ kcal/mole} \qquad \ldots . \quad (v)$$

The reaction enthalpy is negative, i.e. heat is evolved during the reaction which is, in fact, strongly exothermic (heat of reaction $\mathfrak{Q}_p = -\Delta H_x = +142{\cdot}6$ kcal/mole).

Note. The expression at (v) can, of course, be taken directly from (146). However, it is often useful in this type of thermochemical calculation to proceed stepwise, by addition or subtraction of algebraic equations, especially when one has no experience with this type of calculation. For example, (iii) may also be subtracted from (ii), giving

$$0 = 3C_2H_2 - C_6H_6 - 3\Delta H_1^F + \Delta H_2^F \quad \text{or} \quad 3C_2H_2 - C_6H_6 = -(\Delta H_2^F - 3\Delta H_1^F) \qquad \ldots . \quad \text{(vi)}$$

Comparison with (i)

$$3C_2H_2 - C_6H_6 = -\Delta H_x$$

gives

$$\Delta H_x = \Delta H_2^F - 3\,\Delta H_1^F \qquad \ldots . \quad \text{(vii)}$$

which is the same as (v).

*Exercise 74

Calculate the enthalpy of reaction in the solid state, ΔH_x, when sodium nitrate reacts with potassium chloride to give potassium nitrate and sodium chloride.

Reference to tables* gives the following values for the enthalpy of formation at 18 °C:

$$\Delta H^F_{NaNO_3} = -111{\cdot}72 \text{ kcal/mole} \qquad \Delta H^F_{KNO_3} = -118{\cdot}09 \text{ kcal/mole}$$

$$\Delta H^F_{KCl} = -104{\cdot}36 \text{ kcal/mole} \qquad \Delta H^F_{NaCl} = -98{\cdot}33 \text{ kcal/mole}$$

Solution 74. The reaction equation is $NaNO_3 + KCl = KNO_3 + NaCl - \Delta H_x$.

According to (146), the enthalpy of reaction is equal to the difference between the enthalpies of formation of the final products and those of the initial reactants. Thus

$$\Delta H_x = (-118{\cdot}09 - 98{\cdot}33) - (-111{\cdot}72 - 104{\cdot}36) = -0{\cdot}34 \text{ kcal/mole}$$

*Exercise 75

Determine the enthalpy of reaction, ΔH, when tricalcium orthophosphate is reduced to red phosphorus by reaction with graphite and sand to give calcium silicate and gaseous carbon monoxide at 18 °C.

The enthalpies of formation at 18 °C are obtained from tables:

$\Delta H^F_{Ca_3(PO_4)_2} = -983$ kcal/mole

$\Delta H^F_{SiO_2} = -203$ kcal/mole (for quartz)

$\Delta H^F_{C(graphite)} = -0{\cdot}45$ kcal/mole (transition enthalpy, graphite from diamond)

$\Delta H^F_{CaSiO_3} = -376{\cdot}6$ kcal/mole

$\Delta H^F_{CO} = -26{\cdot}84$ kcal/mole [from C (diamond)]

$\Delta H^F_{P(red)} = -4{\cdot}22$ kcal/mole (heat of transition, white to red phosphorus, in the solid state)

* International Critical Tables; Rossini, F. D., Selected Values of Chemical Thermodynamic Properties; Kelley, K. K., High Temperature Heat Content, Heat Capacity and Entropy Data; Chemical Engineers Handbook; Landolt-Börnstein, Physikalisch-chemische Tabellen; D'Ans, J., Lax, E., Taschenbuch für Chemiker und Physiker; Justi, E., Spezifische Wärme, Enthalpie, Entropie und Dissoziation technischer Gase.

Solution 75. The reaction equation is

$$Ca_3(PO_4)_2 + 3\,SiO_2 + 5\,C_{(graphite)} = 3\,CaSiO_3 + 5\,CO + 2\,P_{(red)} - \Delta H_x$$

The enthalpy of reaction, as the difference between the enthalpy of formation on the right- and left-hand sides of the equation [see (146)], will be

$$\Delta H_x = (-3 \times 376{\cdot}6 - 5 \times 26{\cdot}84 - 2 \times 4{\cdot}22) - (-983 - 3 \times 203{\cdot}3 - 5 \times 0{\cdot}45)$$
$$= +322{\cdot}7 \text{ kcal/mole}$$

The reaction is, therefore, strongly endothermic.

*Exercise 76

Determine the enthalpy of reaction, ΔH_x, for the catalytic oxidation of ammonia to NO and water vapour at room temperature. Tables give the values of enthalpy of formation (at 18 °C) as

$$\Delta H^F_{NH_3} = -11{\cdot}00 \text{ kcal/mole}$$
$$\Delta H^F_{O_2} = 0{\cdot}0 \text{ kcal/mole (reference substance)}$$
$$\Delta H^F_{NO} = +21{\cdot}6 \text{ kcal/mole}$$
$$\Delta H^F_{H_2O(g)} = -57{\cdot}84 \text{ kcal/mole [(g) denotes gas] at 18 °C (sic)}$$

Solution 76. The reaction equation is

$$4\,NH_3 + 5\,O_2 = 4\,NO + 6\,H_2O - \Delta H_x$$

The enthalpy of reaction, as the difference between the heats of formation on the right- and left-hand sides of the equation [see (146)], will be

$$\Delta H_x = (+4 \times 21{\cdot}6 - 6 \times 57{\cdot}84) - (-4 \times 11{\cdot}00) = -216{\cdot}6 \text{ kcal/mole}$$

*Exercise 77

Calculate the enthalpy of formation of ethyl alcohol (C_2H_5OH), ΔH^F_{alc}, from its enthalpy of combustion, ΔH^C_{alc} (at 25 °C), to $H_2O_{(liq)}$ and $CO_{2\,(g)}$ and from the enthalpies of formation of H_2O, $\Delta H^F_{H_2O}$, and of CO_2, $\Delta H^F_{CO_2}$. Tables (see p. 103) give the following values.

$$\Delta H^C_{alc} = -326{\cdot}48 \text{ kcal/mole}$$
$$\Delta H^F_{H_2O\,(liq)} = -68{\cdot}313 \text{ kcal/mole (= heat of combustion of } H_2 \text{ to } H_2O_{(liq)} \text{ at 25 °C)}$$
$$\Delta H^F_{CO_2} = -94{\cdot}052 \text{ kcal/mole (= heat of combustion of graphite to } CO_{2\,(g)} \text{ at 25 °C).}$$

Solution 77. The combustion equation is

$$CH_3CH_2OH + 3\,O_2 = 2\,CO_2 + 3\,H_2O - \Delta H^C_{alc} \quad \ldots\ldots \text{(i)}$$

The required equation for ΔH^F_{alc} is, from (145)

$$\Delta H^F_{alc} = \left(2\,\Delta H^F_{CO_2} + 3\,\Delta H^F_{H_2O}\right) - \Delta H^C_{alc} \quad \ldots\ldots \text{(ii)}$$

Substituting the numerical values gives the enthalpy of formation of ethyl alcohol from graphite, H_2 and O_2 as:

$$\Delta H^F_{\text{alc}} = -2 \times 94{\cdot}052 - 3 \times 68{\cdot}313 - (-326{\cdot}48) = -66{\cdot}56 \text{ kcal/mole} \quad \ldots. \quad \text{(iii)}$$

*Exercise 78

What is the enthalpy of solution at 18 °C of 1 mole $CaCl_2 \cdot 6H_2O$ in 200 mol. H_2O if the enthalpy of solution of 1 mole anhydrous $CaCl_2$ in 200 mol. of H_2O at 18 °C is $\Delta H^{\text{sol}}_{CaCl_2} = -18{\cdot}0$ kcal/mole and the enthalpy of hydration of anhydrous $CaCl_2$ to $CaCl_2 \cdot 6H_2O$ at 18 °C is $\Delta H^{\text{hyd}}_{CaCl_2} = -22{\cdot}63$ kcal/mole?

Solution 78. The hydration reaction

$$CaCl_2 + \nu H_2O = CaCl_2 \text{ (dissolved in } \nu \text{ mol. } H_2O) - \Delta H^{\text{sol}}_{CaCl_2} \quad \ldots. \quad \text{(i)}$$

can be considered in stages

$$\left.\begin{array}{ll} \text{I} & CaCl_2 + 6H_2O = CaCl_2 \cdot 6H_2O - \Delta H^{\text{hyd}}_{CaCl_2} \\ \text{II} & CaCl_2 \cdot 6H_2O + (\nu - 6)\, H_2O \\ & \qquad = CaCl_2 \text{ (dissolved in } \nu \text{ mol. } H_2O) - \Delta H^{\text{sol}}_{CaCl_2 \cdot 6H_2O} \end{array}\right\} \quad \ldots \quad \text{(ii)}$$

Addition of I and II gives

$$CaCl_2 + \nu H_2O = CaCl_2 \text{ (dissolved in } \nu \text{ mol. } H_2O) - \Delta H^{\text{hyd}}_{CaCl_2} - \Delta H^{\text{sol}}_{CaCl_2 \cdot 6H_2O} \quad \ldots. \quad \text{(iii)}$$

Comparison of (i) and (iii) gives the enthalpy as

$$\Delta H^{\text{sol}}_{CaCl_2} = \Delta H^{\text{hyd}}_{CaCl_2} + \Delta H^{\text{sol}}_{CaCl_2 \cdot 6H_2O} \quad \ldots. \quad \text{(iv)}$$

Inserting the numerical values gives

$$-18{\cdot}0 = -22{\cdot}36 + \Delta H^{\text{sol}}_{CaCl_2 \cdot 6H_2O} \quad \text{or} \quad \Delta H^{\text{sol}}_{CaCl_2 \cdot 6HO_2} = +4{\cdot}63 \text{ kcal/mole}$$

The hydration of anhydrous $CaCl_2$ to $CaCl_2 . 6H_2O$ and solution of anhydrous $CaCl_2$ in a large volume of water are exothermic reactions, but solution of $CaCl_2 \cdot 6H_2O$ in excess water is endothermic, i.e. it is accompanied by cooling and suitable, therefore, for the preparation of freezing mixtures.

*Exercise 79

Prepare a table comparing the hydrogenation of cyclic and aliphatic hydrocarbons, i.e. by determining the heat of hydrogenation (*a*) during the progressive hydrogenation of benzene vapour to cyclohexa-1,3-diene, cyclohexene, cyclohexane, n-hexane and propane, (*b*) of butadiene to *cis*-but-2-ene, n-butane and ethane and (*c*) of acetylene to ethylene and ethane. What is the heat of hydrogenation, $\mathfrak{Q}_p$, [see eqn. (139)] per Nm^3 of hydrogen used, during hydrogenation (*d*) of benzene to cyclohexane, (*e*) of *cis*-but-2-ene to butane and (*f*) for the formation of ethane from butane?

The following data are given for 25 °C.

Compound	*State*	*Enthalpy of formation*, ΔH^F (kcal/mole)	*Enthalpy of vaporization*, l_v (kcal/mole)
Benzene, C_6H_6	Liq.	+ 11·1	+ 8·0
Cyclohexa-1,3-diene, C_6H_8	Liq.	+ 16·7	+ 8·0
Cyclohexene, C_6H_{10}	Liq.	− 9·7	+ 8·0
Cyclohexane, C_6H_{12}	Liq.	− 37·75	+ 7·85
n-Hexane, C_6H_{14}	Liq.	− 50·5	+ 7·4
Propane, C_3H_8	Gas	− 24·75	—
Butadiene, C_4H_6	Gas	+ 27·3	—
cis-But-2-ene, C_4H_8	Gas	− 1·44	—
n-Butane, C_4H_{10}	Gas	− 29·76	—
Ethane, C_2H_6	Gas	− 20·19	—
Acetylene, C_2H_2	Gas	+ 53·9	—
Ethylene, C_2H_4	Gas	+ 12·56	—

Solution 79. Tables usually give the enthalpy of formation for the liquid state for the first five compounds listed above. The enthalpy of formation for the vapour state is therefore obtained by adding the enthalpy of vaporization. The required enthalpy of hydrogenation is then obtained from the difference between the enthalpies of formation, in accordance with (146).

Thus

(*a*) enthalpy of hydrogenation for ΔH

benzene → cyclohexa-1,3-diene = (16·7 + 8·0) − (11·1 + 8·0) = + 5·6 kcal/mole

cyclohexadiene → cyclohexene = (−9·7 + 8·0) − (16·7 + 8·0) = −26·4 kcal/mole

cyclohexene → cyclohexane = (−37·75 + 7·85) − (−9·7 + 8·0) = −28·2 kcal/mole

enthalpy of hydrogenation and scission for

cyclohexane → n-hexane = (−50·5 + 7·4) − (−37·75 + 7·85) = −13·2 kcal/mole

n-hexane → 2 propane = (−2 × 24·75) − (−50·5 + 7·4) = − 6·4 kcal/mole

(*b*) (aliphatic) enthalpy of hydrogenation for

butadiene → *cis*-butane = (−1·44) − (+27·3) = −28·74 kcal/mole

cis-butene → n-butane = (−29·76) − (−1·44) = −28·32 kcal/mole

enthalpy of hydrogenation and scission for

n-butane → 2 ethane = (−2 × 20·19) − (−29·76) = −10·62 kcal/mole

(*c*) enthalpy of hydrogenation for

acetylene → ethylene = (+12·56) − (+53·9) = −41·34 kcal/mole

ethylene → ethane = (−20·19) − (+12·56) = −32·75 kcal/mole

(*d*) enthalpy of hydrogenation for

benzene (+ $3H_2$) → cyclohexane
= (−37·75 + 7·85) − (+11·1 + 8·0) = −49·0 kcal/mole.

It follows that 49/3 = 16·33 kcal of heat are liberated per mole of hydrogen taken up. Since the volume of 1 mole of H_2 at s.t.p. is 22·4 l. [eqn. (4)], the heat of hydrogenation of benzene $\mathfrak{Q}^{\text{hyd}}_{p\,(\text{benzene})}$, per $\text{Nm}^3\ H_2$ is

$$\mathfrak{Q}^{\text{hyd}}_{p\,(\text{benzene})} = \frac{16{\cdot}33 \times 1000}{22{\cdot}4} = 729\ \text{kcal/Nm}^3\ H_2$$

(*e*) Similarly, the heat of hydrogenation per $\text{Nm}^3\ H_2$, when the hydrogenation of aliphatic double bonds is involved (*cis*-butene → butane), is

$$\mathfrak{Q}^{\text{hyd}}_{(\text{butene})} = \frac{28{\cdot}32 \times 1000}{22{\cdot}4} = 1265\ \text{kcal/Nm}^3\ H_2$$

(*f*) and for the hydrogenation and scission of butane to ethane

$$\mathfrak{Q}^{\text{hyd + sci}}_{p\,(\text{butane})} = \frac{10{\cdot}62 \times 1000}{22{\cdot}4} = 474\ \text{kcal/Nm}^3\ H_2$$

The above calculations show that about 28 kcal/mole are liberated during hydrogenation of a double bond but, in the case of the conversion of energy-rich acetylene to ethylene, the figure exceeds 40 kcal/mole. If, however, hydrogenation is accompanied by the rupture of a C—C bond, by scission of a molecule or opening of a ring, then only about 10 kcal/mole are evolved, because of the additional energy required. The first stage in the hydrogenation of an aromatic ring is of a special nature. The ring is so stable that the input of energy required in this stage results in an endothermic reaction. Subsequent stages are so strongly exothermic that the overall reaction for hydrogenation of benzene to cyclohexane is also exothermic. Similar relations hold in the case of the hydrogenation of naphthalene. It follows that cyclohexadiene cannot be obtained by the direct hydrogenation of benzene. If this reaction is attempted, only more fully hydrogenated derivatives will be obtained. The change in enthalpy for three separate double bonds, as opposed to that for the three conjugated double bonds in the benzene ring, is deduced from the reaction $C_6H_6 + 2C_6H_{12} + \Delta H = 3C_6H_{10}$, i.e. by combining the reaction at (*d*) with the third reaction at (*a*) (multiplied by 3):

$$C_6H_6 + 3H_2 - 49{\cdot}0\ \text{kcal/mole} = C_6H_{12}$$

$$3C_6H_{12} + 3 \times 28{\cdot}2\ \text{kcal/mole} = 3C_6H_{10} + 3H_2$$

addition gives $$C_6H_6 + 2C_6H_{12} + 35{\cdot}6\ \text{kcal/mole} = 3C_6H_{10}$$

$\Delta H = +35{\cdot}6$ kcal/mole is a measure of the stability of the benzene ring and also characterizes its so-called resonance energy.

*Exercise 80

Given the enthalpies of formation [for creation from molecules of the constituent elements see (142)], calculate the atomic enthalpy of formation [see (143)] for production from the atoms of methane, ethane, ethylene and acetylene.

The following data are obtained by reference to tables (*cf* p. 103).

Enthalpy of formation, ΔH^F, for

Methane	$-17{\cdot}87$ kcal/mole	H (atomic) from $\frac{1}{2}$ H_2 + 51 kcal/mole
Ethane	$-20{\cdot}19$ kcal/mole	C (atomic) from $C_{solid} \approx +170{\cdot}89$ kcal/mole
Ethylene	$+12{\cdot}56$ kcal/mole	
Acetylene	$+53{\cdot}9$ kcal/mole	(= enthalpy of sublimation of carbon*)

The given enthalpies of formation refer, in order, to C—H, C—C, C=C and C≡C bonds. Assuming constancy between the various molecules, the mean bond energies may then be determined. Because of the uncertainty of the value for the heat of sublimation of carbon, the difference between the heat of formation at constant pressure and that at constant volume may be neglected.

Solution 80. For methane:

$$C_{solid} + 2H_2 = CH_4 + 17{\cdot}87 \text{ kcal/mole} \quad \ldots\ldots \quad \text{(i)}$$

$$C_{solid} = C_{gas} - 170{\cdot}89 \text{ kcal/mole} \quad \ldots\ldots \quad \text{(ii)}$$

$$2H_2 = 4H - 4{\cdot}51 \text{ kcal/mole} \quad \ldots\ldots \quad \text{(iii)}$$

Subtracting (ii) and (iii) from (i), it follows that

$$0 = CH_4 - C_{gas} - 4H + 17{\cdot}87 + 170{\cdot}89 + 4 \times 51 \quad \ldots\ldots \quad \text{(iv)}$$

or

$$C_{gas} + 4H = CH_4 + 17{\cdot}87 + 170{\cdot}89 + 4 \times 51 \quad \ldots\ldots \quad \text{(v)}$$

It is now necessary to add the enthalpies of formation of the atoms (from their molecules) to the normal enthalpy of formation; thus (v) gives the atomic enthalpy of formation of methane as

$$C_{gas} + 4H = CH_4 + 393 \quad \Delta H = -393 \text{ kcal/mole} \quad \ldots\ldots \quad \text{(vi)}$$

For ethane:

$$2C_{gas} + 6H = C_2H_6 + 20{\cdot}19 + 2 \times 170{\cdot}89 + 6 \times 51 \quad \Delta H = -668 \text{ kcal/mole} \quad \ldots\ldots \quad \text{(vii)}$$

For ethylene:

$$2C_{gas} + 4H = C_2H_4 - 12{\cdot}56 + 2 \times 170{\cdot}89 + 4 \times 51 \quad \Delta H = -533 \text{ kcal/mole} \quad \ldots\ldots \quad \text{(viii)}$$

For acetylene:

$$2C_{gas} + 2H = C_2H_2 - 53{\cdot}9 + 2 \times 170{\cdot}89 + 2 \times 51 \quad \Delta H = -390 \text{ kcal/mole} \quad \ldots\ldots \quad \text{(ix)}$$

From the atomic energy of formation of methane (vi), it follows that the energy of the C—H bond is

$$-393/4 = -98{\cdot}25 \text{ kcal/mole} \quad \ldots\ldots \quad \text{(x)}$$

By subtracting six times the C—H bond energy (x) from the atomic energy of formation of ethane (vii), the energy for the C—C bond is given as

$$-668 - (-6 \times 98{\cdot}25) = -78{\cdot}5 \text{ kcal/mole} \quad \ldots\ldots \quad \text{(xi)}$$

* Regarding the new value of 170·89 ± 0·5 for the enthalpy of sublimation of carbon, based on eqn. (101), p. 81 and eqn. (50), p. 30, see PORTER, G., *Endeavour* 16 (1957) 224.

The energy of the C=C bond is similarly obtained from (viii) and (x):

$$-533 - (-4 \times 98{\cdot}25) = -140 \text{ kcal/mole} \quad \ldots. \quad \text{(xii)}$$

and that for the C≡C bond from (ix) and (x):

$$-390 - (-2 \times 98{\cdot}25 = -193{\cdot}5 \text{ kcal/mole} \quad \ldots. \quad \text{(xiii)}$$

*Exercise 81

The enthalpies of neutralization ΔH^n of NaOH with (*a*) HCl, (*b*) HF and (*c*) HCN were determined under the same conditions (18 °C with 0·5 molar solutions), and found to be −13·75, −16·27 and −2·85 kcal/mole, respectively. NaOH and HCl are practically completely dissociated into Na^+ and OH^-, and H^+ and Cl^- ions, whilst HF and HCN are practically undissociated under these conditions. It is assumed that all the salts formed may be regarded as completely dissociated. Calculate the enthalpies of dissociation of HF and HCN in solution.

Solution 81. The heat of reaction during neutralization is made up from that for the reaction $H^+ + OH^- = H_2O$, together with the heat of dissociation of the undissociated compounds. When NaOH is neutralized with HCl, both of which are virtually completely dissociated, only the reaction $H^+ + OH^- = H_2O - \Delta H^n$ takes place and this has an enthalpy of neutralization of $\Delta H^n = -13{\cdot}75$ kcal/mole. The difference between this value and those for HF and HCN represents the enthalpy of dissociation. One therefore has

$$HF + Na^+ + OH^- = Na^+ + F^- + H_2O + 16{\cdot}27 \text{ kcal/mole} \quad \ldots. \quad \text{(i)}$$

$$H^+ + OH^- = H_2O \qquad + 13{\cdot}75 \text{ kcal/mole} \quad \ldots. \quad \text{(ii)}$$

$$HF - H^+ = F^- + 16{\cdot}27 - (+13{\cdot}75) \text{ [by subtracting (ii) from (i)]} \quad \ldots. \quad \text{(iii)}$$

or

$$HF = H^+ + F^- + 2{\cdot}52 \quad \Delta H^d = -2{\cdot}52 \text{ kcal/mole (in aqueous solution)} \quad \ldots. \quad \text{(iv)}$$

Correspondingly

$$HCN = H^+ + CN^- + 2{\cdot}85 - (+13{\cdot}75) \quad \Delta H^d = +10{\cdot}9 \text{ kcal/mole} \quad \ldots. \quad \text{(v)}$$

The enthalpy of dissociation of HF in aqueous solution is $\Delta H^d = -2{\cdot}52$ kcal/mole; this is therefore an exothermic reaction. The figure of $\Delta H^d = +10{\cdot}9$ kcal/mole for HCN results in absorption of heat, so that, in this case, the reaction is endothermic.

Note. For completely dissociated acids and bases in dilute aqueous solution, the enthalpy of neutralization may be expressed by means of the empirical formula $\Delta H^n = -14{\cdot}70 + 0{\cdot}05\theta$ kcal/mole, where θ is the temperature in °C. A more accurate calculation in the above exercise would need to take hydrolysis into account.

**Exercise 82

Calculate the heats of hydration of Na^+, Cl^- and F^- ions, given the heats (enthalpies) of solution of $NaCl_{solid}$ and NaF_{solid}, their lattice energies and the enthalpy of solution of HCl gas. The energy of formation of HCl gas from H^+_{gas} and Cl^-_{gas}, required for the calculation, should be derived from the known enthalpies of formation of H, Cl and HCl and from the ionization energy of H [$H = H^+ + e^-$ (electron)] and the electron affinity of Cl [$Cl + e^-$ (electron) $= Cl^-$]. The heat of hydration of H^+ will be taken as given. The slight difference between enthalpy, ΔH, and energy, ΔU, can be neglected, being less than the probable error associated with individual values, particularly that for the heat of hydration of H^+. See also note to Exercise 82. The following numerical values are given:

$$\text{Enthalpy of solution of } HCl_{gas},\ \Delta H^{sol}_{HCl} = -17{\cdot}56 \text{ kcal/mole}$$
$$\text{Enthalpy of solution of } NaCl_{solid},\ \Delta H^{sol}_{NaCl} = +0{\cdot}96 \text{ kcal/mole}$$
$$\text{Enthalpy of solution of } NaF_{solid},\ \Delta H^{sol}_{NaF} = +0{\cdot}46 \text{ kcal/mole}$$
$$\text{Lattice energy of } NaCl_{solid},\ \varphi = -180 \text{ kcal/mole}$$
$$\text{Lattice energy of } NaF_{solid},\ \varphi = -213 \text{ kcal/mole}$$

Lattice energy is defined as the energy required for the formation of 1 mole of salt crystal from the free ions [see (144)].

Enthalpy of formation of HCl_{gas} (from $\frac{1}{2}H_2 + \frac{1}{2}Cl_2$)	ΔH^F_{HCl}	$= -21{\cdot}9$ kcal/mole
Enthalpy of formation of H_{gas} (from $\frac{1}{2}H_2$)	ΔH^F_H	$= +51{\cdot}9$ kcal/mole
Enthalpy of formation of Cl_{gas} (from $\frac{1}{2}Cl_2$)	ΔH^F_{Cl}	$= +28{\cdot}9$ kcal/mole
Ionization energy of H (to H^+)	ΔU^I_H	$= +312$ kcal/mole
Electron affinity of Cl (to Cl^-)	ΔU^{Af}_{Cl}	$= -86{\cdot}5$ kcal/mole
Heat of hydration of H^+	$\Delta H^{hyd}_{H^+}$	≈ -270 kcal/mole

Solution 82. We have

$$Na^+_{gas} + C^-_{gas} = NaCl_{solid} - \text{lattice energy } \varphi$$
$$NaCl_{solid} = Na^+_{aq} + Cl^-_{aq} - \text{heat of solution } \Delta H^{sol}_{NaCl}$$
$$Na^+_{aq} + C^-_{aq} = Na^+_{gas} + C^-_{gas} + \text{heat of hydration } \Delta H^{hyd}_{NaCl}$$

i.e. a cyclic process, back to the starting point. Thus, from eqn. (127):

$$0 = -\text{lattice energy } \varphi - \text{heat of solution } \Delta H^{sol}_{NaCl} + \text{heat of hydration } \Delta H^{hyd}_{NaCl} \quad \ldots\ldots \text{(i)}$$

or

$$\text{heat of hydration } \Delta H^{hyd}_{NaCl} = \text{lattice energy } \varphi + \text{heat of solution } \Delta H^{sol}_{NaCl} \quad \ldots\ldots \text{(ii)}$$

The heat of hydration of a salt (note: for gaseous ions) obtained in this way is the sum of the relevant heats of hydration of the ions.

From (ii), the heat of hydration of NaCl (gaseous ions) is

$$\Delta H^{hyd}_{NaCl} = -180 + 0{\cdot}96 = -179 \text{ kcal/mole} \quad \ldots \text{(iii)}$$

and for NaF (gaseous ions)

$$\Delta H^{hyd}_{NaF} = -213 + 0{\cdot}46 = -212{\cdot}5 \text{ kcal/mole} \quad \ldots\ldots \text{(iv)}$$

In the case of HCl_{gas}, and for a cyclic process similar to that shown above, the energy of formation of HCl gas from H^+ and Cl^- replaces the lattice energy. In place of (ii), one therefore has

heat of hydration ΔH^{hyd}_{HCl} = energy of formation of HCl_{gas} from the free ions + heat of solution of HCl_{gas}, ΔH^{sol}_{HCl}.

The energy of formation of HCl_{gas} from the free ions is obtained from the given data by combination of the following equations:

$$H^+_{gas} + Cl^-_{gas} = HCl_{gas} - \text{energie of formation from the free ions } \Delta H^{F(ion)}_{HCl} \quad \ldots\ldots \text{(vi)}$$

$$\tfrac{1}{2} H_2 + \tfrac{1}{2} Cl_2 = HCl_{gas} - \Delta H^F_{HCl} \quad \ldots\ldots \text{(vii)}$$

$$\tfrac{1}{2} H_2 = H_{gas} - \Delta H^F_H \quad \ldots\ldots \text{(viii)}$$

$$\tfrac{1}{2} Cl_2 = Cl_{gas} - \Delta H^F_{Cl} \quad \ldots\ldots \text{(ix)}$$

$$H_{gas} = H^+_{gas} + e^- - \Delta U^I_H \quad \ldots\ldots \text{(x)}$$

$$Cl_{gas} + e^- = Cl^-_{gas} - \Delta U^{Af}_{Cl} \quad \ldots\ldots \text{(xi)}$$

Taking the sum of (vii)-(xi) and cancelling gives

$$0 = HCl_{gas} - H^+_{gas} - Cl^-_{gas} - \Delta H^F_{HCl} + \Delta H^F_H + \Delta H^F_{Cl} + \Delta U^I_H + \Delta U^{Af}_{Cl} \quad \ldots\ldots \text{(xii)}$$

Comparison with (vi) shows that the sum of the energies on the right-hand side of (xii) is equal to the energy of formation of HCl_{gas} from the free ions. Substituting the numerical values therefore gives

Energy of formation (from the free ions)

$$\Delta H^{F(ion)}_{HCl} = -21{\cdot}9 - 51{\cdot}9 - 28{\cdot}9 - 312 - (-86{\cdot}5) = -328{\cdot}2 \text{ kcal/mole} \quad \ldots\ldots \text{(xiii)}$$

Substituting in (v) gives the heat of hydration of HCl (gaseous ions) as

$$\Delta H^{hyd}_{HCl} = -328{\cdot}2 - 17{\cdot}56 = -346 \text{ kcal/mole} \quad \ldots\ldots \text{(xiv)}$$

Subtracting the given heat of hydration of H^+, one obtains the heat of hydration of Cl^- as

$$\Delta H^{hyd}_{Cl^-} = -346 - (-270) = -76 \text{ kcal/mole} \quad \ldots\ldots \text{(xv)}$$

and when this value is in turn subtracted from (iii), the heat of hydration of Na^+ is

$$\Delta H^{hyd}_{Na^+} = -179 - (-76) = -103 \text{ kcal/mole} \quad \ldots\ldots \text{(xvi)}$$

Finally, subtracting the above value from (iv) gives the heat of hydration of F^- as

$$\Delta H^{hyd}_{F^-} = -212{\cdot}5 - (-103) = -109{\cdot}5 \text{ kcal/mole} \quad \ldots\ldots \text{(xvii)}$$

Note. There is considerable uncertainty regarding the value for the hydration of gaseous H^+ to H^+_{aq} ($= H_3O^+$), formerly taken as about 250 kcal/mole. When more accurate assessment of the heats of hydration of ions is required, it is, of course, better to take several salt combinations and average the results. This is because individual errors mount up when making, for example, a series of subtractions such as those at (xiv), (xv), (xvi) and (xvii) above, for calculating the heat of hydration of F^-.

More precise calculations should be based on a temperature of 0 °K, i.e. the heats of formation at 18 °C must be converted to 0 °K by using Kirchhoff's equation (150). This is because the values for lattice energy, ionization energy and electron affinity are only valid for 0 °K and contain no temperature parameter.

**EXERCISE 83

Calculate the lattice energy [see (144)] of AgI. The following data are given:

Enthalpy of formation of AgI [from Ag_{solid} and $\frac{1}{2}I_{2(solid)}$], $\Delta H^F_{AgI} = -15$ kcal/mole

Heat of sublimation of Ag, $l_{s(Ag)} = +63$ kcal/mole

Enthalpy of formation of I_{gas} [from $\frac{1}{2}I_{2(solid)}$], $\Delta H^F_I = +25$ kcal/mole

Ionization energy of Ag, $\Delta U^I_{Ag} = +174$ kcal/mole

Electron affinity of I (to I^-), $\Delta U^{Af}_I = -74$ kcal/mole.

Solution 83. Consider the following cyclic process

$$Ag^+_{gas} + I^-_{gas} = AgI_{solid} - \text{lattice energy } \varphi$$
$$AgI_{solid} = Ag_{solid} + \tfrac{1}{2}I_{2(solid)} + \text{enthalpy of formation } \Delta H^F_{AgI}$$
$$Ag_{solid} = Ag_{gas} - \text{heat of sublimation } l_{s(Ag)}$$
$$\tfrac{1}{2}I_{2(solid)} = I_{gas} - \text{enthalpy of formation } \Delta H^F_I$$
$$I_{gas} + e^- = I^-_{gas} - \text{electron affinity } \Delta U^{Af}_I$$
$$Ag_{gas} = Ag^+_{gas} + e^- - \text{ionization energie } \Delta U^I_{Ag}$$

From eqn. (127), the energy equation is

$0 = -$lattice energy $\varphi_{AgI} +$ enthalpy of formation $\Delta H^F_{AgI} -$ heat of sublimation $l_{s(Ag)} -$ enthalpy of formation $\Delta H^F_I -$ electron affinity $\Delta U^{Af}_I -$ ionization energy ΔU^I_{Ag}.

After substituting the numerical values:

$$\text{lattice energy } \varphi_{AgI} = (-15) - 63 - 25 - (-74) - 174 = -203 \text{ kcal/mole}$$

Note. For more precise calculation, see note to Exercise 82. The best value for the lattice energy of AgI is probably -199 kcal/mole. The same cyclic process may by used to determine the electron affinity of halogen atoms in those cases where the lattice energy can be accurately calculated (e.g. that of the alkali halides).

*EXERCISE 84

The following heats of combustion at constant volume, ($Q_v = \Delta U^C$), to $CO_{2(gas)}$, $H_2O_{(liq)}$ and $N_{2(gas)}$ at 25 °C, were determined in a bomb calorimeter:

(1) Propane (gas), C_3H_8	$\Delta U^C = -528{,}810$ cal/mole
(2) Ethyl alcohol (liq.), C_2H_5OH	$\Delta U^C = -325{,}890$ cal/mole
(3) Acetic acid (liq.), CH_3COOH	$\Delta U^C = -208{,}600$ cal/mole
(4) Oxalic acid (solid), $(COOH)_2$	$\Delta U^C = -60{,}990$ cal/mole
(5) Urea (solid), $CO(NH_2)_2$	$\Delta U^C = -151{,}900$ cal/mole
(6) Uric acid (solid), $C_5H_4O_3N_4$	$\Delta U^C = -460{,}880$ cal/mole

Calculate the heats of combustion at constant pressure, Q_p, i.e. the enthalpies of combustion ΔH^C at 25 °C.

Solution 84. The conversion is obtained from eqn. (140) where $T = 273 + 25 = 298$ °K. The difference between the stoichiometric number of moles of gaseous final products and initial reactants, $\Delta\nu_{\text{gas}}$, must be determined, in each case, from the reaction equation. We find that*

(1) $(C_3H_8) + 5(O_2) = 3(CO_2) + 4H_2O \quad \Delta\sum\nu_{i(\text{gas})} = 3 - 6 = -3$
i.e. from eqn. (140): $\Delta H^C = -528{,}810 - 3 \times 1{\cdot}987 \times 298 = -530{,}590$ cal/mole

(2) $C_2H_5OH + 3(O_2) = 2(CO_2) + 3H_2O \quad \Delta\sum\nu_{i(\text{gas})} = 2 - 3 = -1$
i.e. $\Delta H^C = -325{,}890 - 1 \times 1{\cdot}987 \times 298 = -326{,}480$ cal/mole

(3) $CH_3COOH + 2(O_2) = 2(CO_2) + 2H_2O \quad \Delta\sum\nu_{i(\text{gas})} = 2 - 2 = 0$
i.e. $\Delta H^C = \Delta U^C = -208{,}600$ cal/mole

(4) $[(COOH)_2] + \frac{1}{2}(O_2) = 2(CO_2) + H_2O \quad \Delta\sum\nu_{i(\text{gas})} = 2 - \frac{1}{2} = +1\frac{1}{2}$
i.e. $\Delta H^C = -60{,}990 + 1{\cdot}5 \times 1{\cdot}987 \times 298 = -60{,}100$ cal/mole

(5) $[CO(NH_2)_2] + 1\frac{1}{2}(O_2) = (CO_2) + (N_2) + 2H_2O \quad \Delta\sum\nu_{i(\text{gas})} = 2 - 1\frac{1}{2} = +\frac{1}{2}$
i.e. $\Delta H^C = -151{,}900 + 0{\cdot}5 \times 1{\cdot}987 \times 298 = -151{,}600$ cal/mole

(6) $[C_5H_4O_3N_4] + 4\frac{1}{2}(O_2) = 5(CO_2) + 2(N_2) + 2H_2O \quad \Delta\sum_{i(\text{gas})} = 7 - 4\frac{1}{2} = +2\frac{1}{2}$
i.e. $\Delta H^C = -460{,}880 + 2{\cdot}5 \times 1{\cdot}987 \times 298 = -459{,}400$ cal/mole.

*Exercise 85

The enthalpy of combustion of benzoic acid, $C_6H_5COOH^*_{\text{solid}}$, at 25 °C is $\Delta H^C = -772{,}200$ cal/mole. Calculate the heat of formation at constant pressure (enthalpy of formation) ΔH^F and the heat of formation at constant volume ΔU^F (energy of formation).

Enthalpy of formation of $CO_{2\,(\text{gas})}$, $\Delta H^F_{CO_2} = -94{,}052$ cal/mole

Enthalpy of formation of $H_2O_{(\text{liq})}$, $\Delta H^F_{H_2O\,(\text{liq})} = -68{,}313$ cal/mole.

Solution 85. The combustion equation is

$$[C_6H_5COOH] + 7\tfrac{1}{2}(O_2) = 7(CO_2) + 3H_2O$$

The enthalpy of formation of benzoic acid is, therefore, from eqn. (145)

$$\Delta H^F_{\text{benz}} = -7 \times 94{,}052 - 3 \times 68{,}313 - (-772{,}200) = -91{,}100 \text{ cal/mole} \quad \ldots\ldots \quad \text{(i)}$$

The following relations are used in order to calculate the heat of formation at constant volume, ΔU^F_{benz}:

$$7[C] + 3(H_2) + (O_2) = [C_6H_5COOH] \quad \Delta\sum\nu_{i(\text{gas})} = 0 - 4 = -4 \quad \ldots\ldots \quad \text{(ii)}$$

* The symbols ( ) and [ ] are generally used to denote gases and solids, respectively. No special markings are used for liquids.

One then has, from eqn. (140)

$$\Delta U = \Delta H - \Delta\sum \nu_{i(\text{gas})} RT \quad T = 273 + 25 = 298\ ^\circ\text{K} \quad \ldots\ldots \text{(iii)}$$

so that, from (i), (ii) and (iii)

$$\Delta U^F_{\text{benz}} = -91{,}100 - (-4 \times 1{\cdot}987 \times 298) = -91{,}100 + 4 \times 592 = -88{,}730 \text{ cal/mole}$$

*Exercise 86

From the enthalpy of combustion of graphite to CO_2 and that of H_2 to H_2O_{liq} at 25 °C, calculate the corresponding values for 18° and 40 °C. The following data are given:

Enthalpy of combustion of graphite = enthalpy of formation of CO_2 at 25 °C, $\Delta H^F_{CO_2} = -94{,}052$ cal/mole

Molar heat of (CO_2), $\bar{c}_p = 9{\cdot}17$ cal/(deg. mole)

Molar heat of (O_2), $\bar{c}_p = 7{\cdot}05$ cal/(deg. mole)

Molar heat of graphite, $\bar{c}_p = 2{\cdot}28$ cal/(deg. mole)

Enthalpy of combustion of H_2 = enthalpy of formation of H_2O at 25 °C, $\Delta H^F_{H_2O} = -68{,}313$ cal/mole

Molar heat of H_2O_{liq}, $\bar{c}_p = 18{\cdot}02$ cal/(deg. mole)

Molar heat of (H_2), $\bar{c}_p = 6{\cdot}92$ cal/(deg. mole).

All molar heats are mean values for the temperature range 0–100 °C.

Solution 86. The temperature dependence of the enthalpy of combustion is calculated from Kirchhoff's Law (150). The temperature coefficient for the molar enthalpy of combustion is, in the case of graphite

$$\left(\frac{\partial \Delta H}{\partial T}\right)_p = c_{p\,(CO_2)} - c_{p\,(\text{graphite})} - c_{p\,(O_2)} \quad \ldots\ldots \text{(i)}$$

and corresponds to the reaction equation: $[C] + (O_2) = (CO_2)$.

Thus $$\left(\frac{\partial \Delta H}{\partial T}\right)_p = 9{\cdot}17 - 2{\cdot}28 - 7{\cdot}05 = 0{\cdot}16 \text{ cal/(deg. mole)} \quad \ldots\ldots \text{(ii)}$$

and hence*

$$\Delta H_{40} = \Delta H_{25} + (40 - 25)\,(-0{\cdot}16) = -94{,}052 - 15 \times 0{\cdot}16 = -94{,}054{\cdot}4 \text{ cal/mole} \quad \ldots\ldots \text{(iii)}$$

and

$$\Delta H_{18} = -94{,}052 + (18 - 25)\,(-0{\cdot}16) = -94{,}052 + 7 \times 0{\cdot}16 = -94{,}050{\cdot}9 \text{ cal/mole}$$

* Mean values for the temperature range 0°–100 °C were given for the molar heats. For the narrow temperature range dealt with in the question, the temperature coefficients can be regarded as constant. Change in enthalpy of combustion can then be obtained by multiplying the temperature coefficients, $(\partial \Delta H/\partial T)_p$, by the temperature difference (relative to 25 °C). For wider temperature ranges, the Kirchhoff equation must be integrated with respect to temperature (see Exercise 88).

The equation for the combustion of H_2 is

$$(H_2) + \tfrac{1}{2}(O_2) = H_2O_{liq} \qquad \ldots. \quad \text{(iv)}$$

so that, using Kirchhoff's law (150), the temperature coefficient is

$$\left(\frac{\partial \Delta H}{\partial T}\right)_p = c_{p\,(H_2O\,liq)} - c_{p\,(H_2)} - \tfrac{1}{2} c_{p\,(O_2)} = 18{\cdot}02 - 6{\cdot}92 - 0{\cdot}5 \times 7{\cdot}05 = 7{\cdot}57 \text{ cal/(deg. mole)} \qquad \ldots. \quad \text{(v)}$$

and hence

$$\Delta H_{40} = -68{,}313 + (40 - 25)\, 7{\cdot}57 = -68{,}200 \text{ cal/mole}$$

and

$$\Delta H_{18} = -68{,}313 + (18 - 25)\, 7{\cdot}57 = -68{,}366 \text{ cal/mole} \qquad \ldots \quad \text{(vi)}$$

It will be noted that the temperature dependence of the heat of formation of CO_2 is so slight that it may virtually be ignored. On the other hand, that of H_2O_{liq} is quite marked.

Note. Conversion of heat of reaction from 18° to 25 °C is often necessary when dealing with equilibria. This is because the enthalpy of formation of inorganic compounds is usually given for 18 °C, whilst the standard entropy is calculated for 25 °C. It will be seen from the above calculation, however, that such small differences can be ignored, unless the highest precision is required.

*Exercise 87

The experimental value of the enthalpy of hydrogenation of ethylene to ethane at 83 °C was found to be $\Delta H_{83}^{hyd} = -33{,}020$ cal/mole. What is the value at 25 °C? The mean molar heats, in cal/(deg. mole), for the temperature range 25–83 °C, are

$$H_2 : \bar{c}_{p\,(H_2)} = 6{\cdot}92 \text{ cal/(deg. mole)} \quad C_2H_6 : \bar{c}_{p\,(C_2H_6)} = 13{\cdot}49 \text{ cal/(deg. mole)}$$

$$C_2H_4 : \bar{c}_{p\,(C_2H_4)} = 11{\cdot}16 \text{ cal/(deg. mole)}.$$

Solution 87. Kirchhoff's law (150) is used to calculate the temperature dependence of the enthalpy of hydrogenation. This gives

$$\left(\frac{\partial \Delta H^{hyd}}{\partial T}\right)_p = c_{p\,(C_2H_6)} - c_{p\,(C_2H_4)} - c_{p\,(H_2)} \qquad \ldots. \quad \text{(i)}$$

corresponding to the reaction equation: $C_2H_4 + H_2 = C_2H_6$.

Substituting the numerical values in (i), we obtain

$$\left(\frac{\partial \Delta H^{hyd}}{\partial T}\right)_p = 13{\cdot}49 - 11{\cdot}16 - 6{\cdot}92 = -4{\cdot}59 \text{ cal/(deg.mole)} \qquad \ldots. \quad \text{(ii)}$$

so that

$$\Delta H_{25}^{hyd} = \Delta H_{83}^{hyd} + (25 - 83)(-4{\cdot}59) = -33{,}020 + 266 = -32{,}754 \text{ cal/mole}.$$

A correction of about $\frac{1}{4}$ kcal mole is therefore required in order to convert the heat of hydrogenation at 83 °C to the value at 25 °C. The amount of heat evolved is, in fact, less at the lower temperature.

8*

Exercise 88

Determine the enthalpy of reaction for the reaction

$$2\,CH_4 + \tfrac{3}{2}O_2 = C_2H_2 + 3\,H_2O_{gas}$$

at 1200 °K. The following enthalpies of formation are given for 25 °C:

$$CH_4 : \Delta H^F_{CH_4} = -17{\cdot}87 \text{ kcal/mole}$$
$$H_2O_{(liq)} : \Delta H^F_{H_2O\,(liq)} = -68{\cdot}31 \text{ kcal/mole}$$
$$C_2H_2 : \Delta H^F_{C_2H_2} = +53{\cdot}9 \text{ kcal/mole}$$

The enthalpy of vaporization of H_2O at 25 °C, $l_{v\,(H_2O)} = 10{\cdot}51$ kcal/mole.
The molar heats are:

$$CH_4 : c_{p\,(CH_4)} = 5{\cdot}34 + 1{\cdot}15 \times 10^{-2}\,T \text{ cal/(deg. mole), between 300 and 1200 °K}$$
$$O_2 : c_{p\,(O_2)} = 7{\cdot}0 + 0{\cdot}105 \times 10^{-2}\,T \text{ cal/(deg. mole), between 300 and 2000 °K}$$
$$H_2O_{gas} : c_{p\,H_2O\,(gas)} = 7{\cdot}42 + 0{\cdot}24 \times 10^{-2}\,T \text{ cal/(deg. mole), between 300 and 2000 °K}$$

No such temperature relationship is given for the molar heat of C_2H_2. The following values (in cal/deg. mole) are taken from tables:

°K	273	298	373	473	573	673	773	873	973	1073	1173	1273	1400
$c_{p\,(C_2H_2)}$	10·25	10·70	11·81	12·88	13·72	14·39	15·01	15·55	16·04	16·49	16·90	17·26	17·63

These values are to be used (*a*) for plotting the $c_p \rightarrow T$ curve and graphical integration by measuring the area beneath the curve between 298 and 1200 °K, and (*b*) in order to develop a temperature relationship by interpolation between 300 and 1200 °K and using a third point on the curve (650 °K, the point of maximum deviation from a linear junction). The function $c_p = +AT - BT^{-2} + C$ is suitably used.

Solution 88. According to eqn. (146), the enthalpy of reaction at 25 °C (= 298 °K) is equal to the difference between the enthalpies of formation of the final products and those of the initial reactants, note being made of the fact that water exists as vapour in the final state.

Thus

$$\Delta H_{298} = +53{\cdot}9 + 3\,(-68{\cdot}31 + 10{\cdot}51) - 2\,(-17{\cdot}87) = -83{\cdot}76 \text{ kcal/mole} \quad \ldots. \quad \text{(i)}$$

From Kirchhoff's law (150), the temperature dependence of the enthalpy of reaction is

$$\left(\frac{\partial \Delta H}{\partial T}\right)_p = 3\,c_{p\,(H_2O)} + c_{p\,(C_2H_2)} - 2\,c_{p\,(CH_4)} - \frac{3}{2}\,c_{p\,(O_2)} \quad \ldots. \quad \text{(ii)}$$

or

$$\Delta H_{1200} = \Delta H_{298} + \int_{298}^{1200} \left[3\,c_{p\,(H_2O)} - 2\,c_{p\,(CH_4)} - \frac{3}{2}\,c_{p\,(O_2)}\right] \mathrm{d}T + \int_{298}^{1200} [c_{p\,(C_2H_2)}]\,\mathrm{d}T \quad \ldots. \quad \text{(iii)}$$

The first integral can be evaluated directly, i.e.

$$\begin{aligned} I_1 &= \int_{298}^{1200} [3 \times 7{\cdot}42 - 2 \times 5{\cdot}34 - 1{\cdot}5 \times 7{\cdot}0 + (3 \times 0{\cdot}24 - 2 \times 1{\cdot}15 - 1{\cdot}5 \\ &\qquad \times 0{\cdot}105)\, 10^{-2}\, T]\, \mathrm{d}T \\ &= \int_{298}^{1200} (1{\cdot}08 - 1{\cdot}738 \times 10^{-2}\, T)\, \mathrm{d}T = 1{\cdot}08\,(1200 - 298) - \frac{1{\cdot}738 \times 10^{-2}}{2} \\ &\qquad \times (1200^2 - 298^2) \\ &= 974 - 11{,}734 = -10{,}760 \text{ cal/mole} = -10{\cdot}76 \text{ kcal/mole} \end{aligned} \quad \ldots \text{(iv)}$$

The second integral I_2 in (iii) may be evaluated graphically by plotting the $c_{p\,(C_2H_2)}$ data as a function of T. It is convenient to use millimetre paper and a scale of 2 cm per 100° and 2 cm per 1 cal/(deg. mole), see *Figure 14.* The value of the second integral

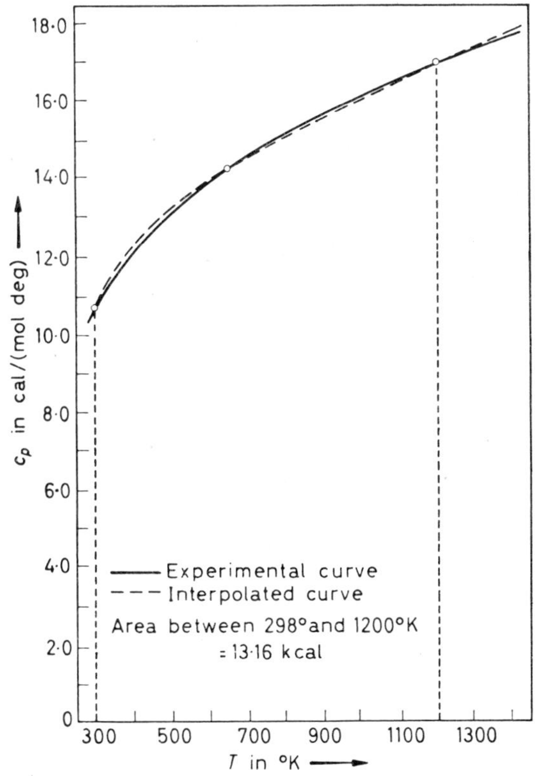

Figure 14. Interpolation and graphical integration of a molar heat temperature function

is then equal to the area between the curve and the x-axis and between the limits $T = 298$ and $T = 1200$ °K. By counting the squares, the area is found to be 526·32 cm². Using the above scale, $2 \times 2 = 4$ cm² is equivalent to $100 \times 1 = 100$ cal/mole, i.e.

1 cm² ≙ 25 cal/mole. The value of the second integral therefore is $I_2 = 526{\cdot}32 \times 25 = 13{\cdot}16$ kcal/mole. .... (v)

The integral can also be evaluated by using a suitable temperature function based on the given data. A power law of the form $c_p = AT - BT^{-2} + C$ may be taken, where the asymptotic nature of the right-hand portion of the curve may be noted, i.e. due to its progressively decreasing curvature. In order to determine the constants A, B and C, three points are selected as data, i.e. two points at the temperature limits of 300 °K and 1200 °K and a third corresponding to the point of maximum deviation of the curve (at 650 °K).

Thus one has the following three pairs of values* from which to determine A, B and C:

$$T_1 = 300 \qquad c_{p_1} = 10{\cdot}75$$
$$T_2 = 650 \qquad c_{p_2} = 14{\cdot}25$$
$$T_3 = 1200 \qquad c_{p_3} = 17{\cdot}00$$

For the sake of convenience, these values of c_p are read from the best curve (*Figure 14*) drawn through the experimental values. The resulting set of equations, with the three unknowns A, B and C:

$$\left.\begin{aligned} AT_1 - BT_1^{-2} + C &= c_{p_1} \\ AT_2 - BT_2^{-2} + C &= c_{p_2} \\ AT_3 - BT_3^{-2} + C &= c_{p_3} \end{aligned}\right\} \quad .. \text{(vi)}$$

is solved in the usual manner (see also Exercise 67).
This gives:

$$\left.\begin{aligned} A &= \frac{(c_{p_2} - c_{p_1})(T_1^{-2} - T_3^{-2}) - (c_{p_3} - c_{p_1})(T_1^{-2} - T_2^{-2})}{(T_2 - T_1)(T_1^{-2} - T_3^{-2}) - (T_3 - T_1)(T_1^{-2} - T_2^{-2})} = \frac{3{\cdot}646 - 5{\cdot}465}{364{\cdot}6 - 787{\cdot}0} \\ &= 0{\cdot}4306 \times 10^{-2} \end{aligned}\right\} \quad .. \text{(vii)}$$

$$\left.\begin{aligned} B &= \frac{(T_2 - T_1)(c_{p_3} - c_{p_1}) - (T_3 - T_1)(c_{p_2} - c_{p_1})}{(T_2 - T_1)(T_1^{-2} - T_3^{-2})(T_3 - T_1)(T_1^{-2} - T_2^{-2})} = \frac{2187{\cdot}5 - 3150}{(364{\cdot}6 - 787{\cdot}0) \times 10^{-5}} \\ &= 2{\cdot}279 \times 10^5 \end{aligned}\right\} \quad .. \text{(viii)}$$

C is found by substituting the values of A and B in any of the three equations at (vi), e.g. using the first

$$C = 10{\cdot}75 - 0{\cdot}4306 \times 10^{-2} \times 300 + 2{\cdot}279 \times 10^5/300^2 = 11{\cdot}99$$

This gives the following expression for $c_{p(C_2H_2)}$ as a function of temperature and valid for the range 273–1300 °K:

$$c_{p(C_2H_2)} = 11{\cdot}99 + 0{\cdot}4306 \times 10^{-2}\,T - 2{\cdot}279 \times 10^5\,T^{-2} \text{ in cal/(deg. mole)} \quad .... \text{(ix)}$$

This function is also plotted in *Figure 14*.

* No dimensions are shown in the ensuing numerical calculation.

It follows that the second integral at (iii) can now be evaluated as

$$\left.\begin{aligned} I_2 &= \int_{298}^{1200} c_{p\,(C_2H_2)}\,dT = \int_{298}^{1200} [11{\cdot}99 + 0{\cdot}4306 \times 10^{-2}T - 2{\cdot}279 \times 10^5 T^{-2}]\,dT \\ &= 11{\cdot}99\,(1200 - 298) + 0{\cdot}4306/2 \times 10^{-2}\,(1200^2 - 298^2) \\ &\qquad + 2{\cdot}279 \times 10^5\,(1/1200 - 1/298) \\ &= 10{,}815 + 2909 - 575 = 13{,}149 = 13{\cdot}15\ \text{kcal/mole} \end{aligned}\right\} \quad .. \quad (x)$$

in comparison with the value of 13·16 kcal/mole previously obtained by measuring the area under the graph [see (v)]. Adding the two integrals at (iii), i.e. (iv) + (v) or (x), therefore gives $-10{\cdot}76 + 13{\cdot}16 = 2{\cdot}40$ kcal/mole and, from (iii) and (i), the enthalpy of reaction at 1200 °K is

$$\Delta H_{1200} = -83{\cdot}76 + 2{\cdot}40 = -81{\cdot}36\ \text{kcal/mole} \quad .... \quad (xi)$$

Note. It will be seen that, in the above example, variation of the enthalpy of reaction with temperature is relatively small. In the case of the formation of ammonia, which features as an example in textbooks, one has $N_2 + 3H_2 = 2NH_3$ and $\Delta H_{298} = -22{\cdot}08$ kcal/mole, and the enthalpy of reaction at 1000 °K is $\Delta H_{1000} = -26{\cdot}47$ kcal/mole, i.e. a difference of 4·39 kcal/mole is observed.

*Exercise 89

Calculate the gross calorific value H_G [see eqn. (147)] and the net calorific value H_N [see eqn. (148)] of methyl alcohol, ethyl alcohol, hexane, benzene and naphthalene, in kcal/kg. Make a similar calculation for methane, ethane and propane, in terms of kcal/Nm³.

Net calorific value is of significance when no condensation of the water in the final products takes place, e.g. during fuel combustion in engines.

The following values are given for the enthalpies of combustion:

Methyl alcohol, CH_3OH	$M = 32{\cdot}04$	$\Delta H^C = -173{\cdot}65$ kcal/mole
Ethyl alcohol, C_2H_5OH	$M = 46{\cdot}1$	$\Delta H^C = -326{\cdot}48$ kcal/mole
Hexane, C_6H_{14}	$M = 86{\cdot}2$	$\Delta H^C = -992$ kcal/mole
Benzene, C_6H_6	$M = 78{\cdot}1$	$\Delta H^C = -782{\cdot}2$ kcal/mole
Naphthalene, $C_{10}H_8$	$M = 128{\cdot}2$	$\Delta H^C = -1231{\cdot}9$ kcal/mole
Methane, CH_4	molar vol. $v = 22{\cdot}36$ l./mole	$\Delta H^C = -212{\cdot}79$ kcal/mole
Ethane, C_2H_6	molar vol. $v = 22{\cdot}16$ l./mole	$\Delta H^C = -372{\cdot}81$ kcal/mole
Propane, C_3H_8	molar vol. $v = 21{\cdot}82$ l./mole	$\Delta H^C = -530{\cdot}5$ kcal/mole

The heat of vaporization of H_2O is $l_v = +10{\cdot}51$ kcal/mole. All values refer to 25 °C.

Solution 89. The gross calorific value H_G is obtained by dividing the enthalpy of combustion by the molecular weight and then multiplying by 1000. In order to determine the net calorific value H_N, it is necessary to calculate the enthalpy of combustion to CO_2 and water vapour, taking the heat of vaporization of water into account, and then to multiply the result by $1000/M$. A similar procedure is adopted when the calorific value is expressed in terms of kcal/Nm³, but the multiplication factor in this case is $1000/v$.

Methyl alcohol contains 4 hydrogen atoms and therefore yields $2\,H_2O$ when burnt. Thus

$$H_G = 173{\cdot}65 \times 1000/32{\cdot}04 = 5420 \text{ kcal/kg} \qquad H_N = (173{\cdot}65 - 2 \times 10{\cdot}51)\,1000/32{\cdot}04 = 4760 \text{ kcal/kg}$$

Similarly, for ethyl alcohol:

$$H_G = 326{\cdot}48 \times 1000/46{\cdot}1 = 7090 \text{ kcal/kg} \qquad H_N = (326{\cdot}48 - 3 \times 10{\cdot}51)\,1000/46{\cdot}1 = 6400 \text{ kcal/kg}$$

for hexane:

$$H_G = 992 \times 1000/86{\cdot}2 = 11{,}500 \text{ kcal/kg} \qquad H_N = (992 - 7 \times 10{\cdot}51)\,1000/86{\cdot}2 = 10{,}640 \text{ kcal/kg}$$

for benzene:

$$H_G = 782{\cdot}2 \times 1000/78{\cdot}1 = 10{,}020 \text{ kcal/kg} \qquad H_N = (782{\cdot}2 - 3 \times 10{\cdot}51)\,1000/78{\cdot}1 = 9620 \text{ kcal/kg}$$

for naphthalene:

$$H_G = 1231{\cdot}9 \times 1000/128{\cdot}2 = 9610 \text{ kcal/kg} \qquad H_N = (1231{\cdot}9 - 4 \times 10{\cdot}51)\,1000/128{\cdot}2 = 9280 \text{ kcal/kg}$$

for methane:

$$H_G = 212{\cdot}79 \times 1000/22{\cdot}36 = 9520 \text{ kcal/Nm}^3 \qquad H_N = (212{\cdot}79 - 2 \times 10{\cdot}51)\,1000/22{\cdot}36 = 8570 \text{ kcal/Nm}^3$$

for ethane:

$$H_G = 372{\cdot}81 \times 1000/22{\cdot}16 = 16{,}820 \text{ kcal/Nm}^3 \qquad H_N = (372{\cdot}81 - 3 \times 10{\cdot}51)\,1000/22{\cdot}16 = 15{,}400 \text{ kcal/Nm}^3$$

for propane:

$$H_G = 530{\cdot}5 \times 1000/21{\cdot}82 = 24{,}320 \text{ kcal/Nm}^3 \qquad H_N = (530{\cdot}5 - 4 \times 10{\cdot}51)\,1000/21{\cdot}82 = 22{,}380 \text{ kcal/Nm}^3$$

Note. The molar volumes quoted in the above example differ from the figure of 22·415 l./mol. [eqn. (4)] for the ideal gas state. This is due to the non-ideal behaviour of the compounds in question.

Gross and net calorific values will, by definition, be identical in the case of the combustion of hydrogen-free compounds such as carbon monoxide, CO.

10

CHEMICAL EQUILIBRIUM AT CONSTANT TEMPERATURE LAW OF MASS ACTION. DISTRIBUTION LAW. GAS SOLUBILITY

(1) Consider the reaction equation

$$\nu_A A + \nu_B B + \cdots = \nu_E E + \nu_F F + \cdots$$

for a homogeneous system (ideal dilute gas mixtures and ideal dilute solutions) where ν_A, ν_B and ν_E, ν_F are the stoichiometric mole numbers (stoichiometric proportions or reaction numbers) of the substances A, B (initial reactants) and E, F (final products). The law of mass action (LMA) may then be written as:

$$\frac{c_E^{\nu_E} c_F^{\nu_F} \ldots}{c_A^{\nu_A} c_B^{\nu_B} \ldots}{}^{*} = K_c \quad \text{or} \quad \frac{[E]^{\nu_E} [F]^{\nu_F} \ldots}{[A]^{\nu_A} [B]^{\nu_B} \ldots} = K_c \qquad \ldots . (151)$$

where $c_A = [A] = n_A/V$ is the molarity (molar concentration in moles/l.) [see eqn. (58)] of substance A; n_A = molar quantity, V = total volume, and K_c is the equilibrium constant. The latter is temperature-dependent but, at a given temperature, can be taken as constant in the case of sufficiently dilute solutions.

(2) In the case of gas mixtures, the partial pressures p_A, $p_B \cdots p_E$, $p_F \cdots$ (in atm) are often used in place of concentrations. In instances where the ideal gas eqn. (8) applies, ($p_i V = n_i RT$), it is found that

$$p_i = \frac{n_i RT}{V} = c_i RT \qquad \ldots . (152)$$

and, from Dalton's law [eqn. (6)], the total pressure p for an ideal gas mixture is

$$p = \Sigma p_i = p_A + p_B + \cdots p_E + p_F + \cdots \qquad \ldots . (153)$$

---

* The generalized and strictly thermodynamic form of the LMA (i.e. not merely for ideal dilute gas mixtures and solutions) is

$$\frac{a_E^{\nu_E} a_F^{\nu_F} \ldots}{a_A^{\nu_A} a_B^{\nu_B} \ldots} = K$$

where K is the thermodynamic equilibrium constant and a_i the activities. In gas reactions, fugacity, $p^\star$, is used in place of activity; see also eqns. (194), (231), (241) and (245).

Substituting eqn. (152) in (151), it follows that

$$\frac{p_{\mathrm{E}}^{\nu_{\mathrm{E}}}\, p_{\mathrm{F}}^{\nu_{\mathrm{F}}} \ldots}{p_{\mathrm{A}}^{\nu_{\mathrm{A}}}\, p_{\mathrm{B}}^{\nu_{\mathrm{B}}} \ldots}^{*} = K_p = K_{\mathrm{c}}(RT)^{\nu_{\mathrm{E}}+\nu_{\mathrm{F}}-\nu_{\mathrm{A}}-\nu_{\mathrm{B}}} = K_{\mathrm{c}}(RT)^{\Delta\Sigma\nu_i} \quad \ldots . (154)$$

[Gas constant $R = 0{\cdot}08206$ l. atm/(deg. mole), see eqn. (4)]

$\Delta\sum\nu_i = \nu_{\mathrm{E}} + \nu_{\mathrm{F}} - \nu_{\mathrm{A}} - \nu_{\mathrm{B}}$ in eqn. (154) represents the difference between the stoichiometric mole numbers on the right-hand side of the reaction equation (final products) and those on the left-hand side (initial reactants). $\Delta\sum\nu_i$ will be referred to as the reaction index. K_p is the equilibrium constant when partial pressures are used instead of concentrations.

(3) By making use of mole fractions $x_i = n_i/\sum n_i = p_i/p$ [see eqn. (10)], it is found that

(a) for gas mixtures, from eqn. (154) with eqn. (152) and (153):

$$\frac{x_{\mathrm{E}}^{\nu_{\mathrm{E}}}\, x_{\mathrm{F}}^{\nu_{\mathrm{F}}} \ldots}{x_{\mathrm{A}}^{\nu_{\mathrm{A}}}\, x_{\mathrm{B}}^{\nu_{\mathrm{B}}} \ldots} = K_x = K_p\, p^{-\Delta\Sigma\nu_i} = K_{\mathrm{c}}\left(\frac{RT}{p}\right)^{\Delta\Sigma\nu_i} = K_{\mathrm{c}}\, c^{-\Delta\Sigma\nu}\left(c = \frac{\Sigma n_i}{V}\right) \quad \ldots . (155)$$

(b) for dilute solutions from eqn. (151) with eqn. (60):

$$x_i = \frac{c_i M_{\mathrm{solv}}}{1000 \times \varrho} \qquad K_x = K_{\mathrm{c}}\left(\frac{M_{\mathrm{solv}}}{1000 \times \varrho}\right)^{\Delta\Sigma\nu_i} \quad \ldots . (156)$$

(4) It should be noted when writing the LMA that the product of the final concentrations (right-hand side of the reaction equation) is always in the numerator. The product of the initial concentrations (left-hand side of the reaction equation) is, of course, always in the denominator.

For reactions which take place without any change in stoichiometric mole numbers

$$\Delta\sum\nu_i = 0, \quad \text{so that} \quad K_x = K_p = K_{\mathrm{c}} \quad \ldots . (157)$$

(5) In the case of reactions which give rise to heterogeneous systems, the partial pressures and concentrations of any substances present as pure solid phase are always constant; these are not, therefore, taken into account when applying the law of mass action. .... (158)

(6) Breakdown of the type $\mathrm{C} = \nu_{\mathrm{A}}\mathrm{A} + \nu_{\mathrm{B}}\mathrm{B}$ is a commonly occurring reaction. This is characterized by the degree of dissociation α, i.e. by the fraction (or percentage) of C which breaks down into A and B. Let the concentration of C before breakdown be taken as $[\mathrm{C}]_0 = n_{0\mathrm{C}}/V = c_0$ (this is also known as the gross or total concentration); the equilibrium concentrations of C, A and B then are

$$\left.\begin{aligned} [\mathrm{C}] &= [\mathrm{C}]_0\,(1-\alpha) \\ [\mathrm{A}] &= [\mathrm{C}]_0\,\alpha\nu_{\mathrm{A}} \\ [\mathrm{B}] &= [\mathrm{C}]_0\,\alpha\nu_{\mathrm{B}} \end{aligned}\right\} \quad \ldots (159)$$

* See footnote p. 121.

Substituting this in the LMA [eqn. (151)], gives

$$\frac{\alpha^{\nu_A+\nu_B}}{1-\alpha}\,\nu_A^{\nu_A}\nu_B^{\nu_B}\,[C]_0^{\nu_A+\nu_B-1} = K_c \qquad \ldots. (160)$$

The partial pressures of C, A and B are

$$\left.\begin{aligned} p_C &= [C]_0(1-\alpha)\,RT = \frac{p(1-\alpha)}{1+\alpha(\nu_A+\nu_B-1)} \\ p_A &= [C]_0\,\nu_A\,\alpha\,RT = \frac{p\,\nu_A\,\alpha}{1+\alpha(\nu_A+\nu_B-1)} \\ p_B &= [C]_0\,\nu_B\,\alpha\,RT = \frac{p\,\nu_B\,\alpha}{1+\alpha(\nu_A+\nu_B-1)} \end{aligned}\right\} \qquad \ldots (161)$$

so that the total pressure $p = p_C + p_A + p_B$ is

$$p = [C]_0\,[1+\alpha\,(\nu_A+\nu_B-1)]\,RT \qquad \ldots. (162)$$

for the total molar quantity n, where

$$n = n_{0C}\,[1+\alpha\,(\nu_A+\nu_B-1)] \qquad \ldots. (163)$$

From eqns. (160) and (162), or from eqns. (154) and (161)

$$\frac{\alpha^{\nu_A+\nu_B}}{1-\alpha}\,\nu_A^{\nu_A}\nu_B^{\nu_B}\left[\frac{p}{1+\alpha(\nu_A+\nu_B-1)}\right]^{\nu_A+\nu_B-1} = K_p \qquad \ldots. (164)$$

(7) In dealing with gas solubility, Henry's law [see eqn. (79)] may be used in the case of dilute solutions in order to define the equilibrium between a gas mixture and a chemically inert solvent:

$$p_i = x_{Li}k_i$$

where k_i = Henry's constant (atm), which is temperature-dependent.
This may be rewritten as

$$x_{Li} = p_i \times 1/k_i \qquad \ldots. (165)$$

In the above equation, $1/k_i$ is in the nature of a solubility coefficient. Its numerical value depends on the concentration units for the liquid and vapour phases. In practice, the following are more particularly used:

(*a*) The Bunsen absorption coefficient, α^{Bu}. This is the volume of gas v_S (reduced to s.t.p., i.e. 0 °C and 1 atm) absorbed by unit volume of solvent when the partial pressure p_i of the gas is 1 atm. Thus

$$v_{Si} = \alpha_i^{Bu}\,p_i \qquad \ldots. (166)$$

(p_i in atm, v_{Si} non-dimensional)

In the case of the molar volume at s.t.p., $v_0 = RT_0/p_0 = 0{\cdot}08206 \times 273/1$ l. atm/(deg. × mole) × deg./atm = 22·4 l./mole [see eqn. (4)], the concentration c_{Li} of gas in the liquid will be

$$c_{Li} = v_{Si}/22{\cdot}4 \text{ (moles/l.)} \qquad \ldots. (167)$$

Since, in the case of dilute solutions, $c_{Li} = x_{Li} \times 1000\,\varrho/M_{solv}$ [from eqn. (60)], it follows that

$$v_{Si} = x_{Li} \times 22{\cdot}4 \times 1000\,\varrho_{solv}/M_{solv} \quad \text{(non-dimensional)} \qquad \ldots. (168)$$

or, with eqns. (165) and (166):

$$\alpha_i^{\mathrm{Bu}} = \frac{1}{k_i} \times \frac{22{\cdot}4 \times 1000\,\varrho_{\mathrm{solv}}}{M_{\mathrm{solv}}}\ (\mathrm{atm}^{-1}) \qquad \ldots.(169)$$

where ϱ_{solv} = density of solution ≈ density of solvent (g cm^{-3})
M_{solv} = molecular weight of solvent

(*b*) The Ostwald solubility coefficient, α^{Os}, is the ratio of the concentration of gas in the liquid, $c_{\mathrm{L}i}$, to that of the gas in the vapour phase, c_{Vi}; thus

$$c_{\mathrm{L}i} = \alpha_i^{\mathrm{Os}} c_{Vi} \quad (\alpha_i^{\mathrm{Os}} \text{ is non-dimensional}) \qquad \ldots.(170)$$

Since, from eqns. (167) and (152), respectively, $c_{\mathrm{L}i} = v_{Si}/22{\cdot}4$ and $c_{Vi} = p_i/RT$, it follows that $v_{Si} = \alpha_i^{\mathrm{Bu}} p_i = 22{\cdot}4\,\alpha_i^{\mathrm{Os}} p_i/RT$ or

$$\alpha_i^{\mathrm{Bu}} = \alpha_i^{\mathrm{Os}} \times \frac{22{\cdot}4}{RT} = \alpha_i^{\mathrm{Os}} \times \frac{273}{T} \qquad \ldots.(171)$$

(8) Distribution of a substance between two solvents. Consider the case of two liquids of limited mutual solubility, existing together as two phases in equilibrium. If a soluble third substance is present (as a dilute solution), it will be distributed between the liquids such that the ratio of its concentrations ($c_{\mathrm{I}i}$ and $c_{\mathrm{II}i}$) in the two phases I and II is constant at a given temperature. This assumes, of course, that the molecular state of the third substance is identical in both phases. If the latter is not the case, then the following law holds only for that fraction of the third substance which is distributed in the same molecular state. Thus

$$\frac{c_{\mathrm{I}i}}{c_{\mathrm{II}i}} = C \quad \text{(Nernst's distribution law)} \qquad \ldots.(172)$$

where C is called the distribution coefficient.

In cases where the third substance shows marked association, of the type $\nu\mathrm{A} = \mathrm{A}_\nu$, in the second solvent, the LMA for phase II becomes

$$\frac{[\mathrm{A}_{\nu\,\mathrm{II}}]}{[\mathrm{A}_{\mathrm{II}}]^\nu} = K_c \quad \text{or} \quad [\mathrm{A}_{\mathrm{II}}] = \sqrt[\nu]{[\mathrm{A}_{\nu\,\mathrm{II}}]/K_c}$$

If this expression is introduced into the distribution equation (172), $\dfrac{[\mathrm{A}_{\mathrm{I}}]}{[\mathrm{A}_{\mathrm{II}}]} = C$, one then has, in the case of association in phase II:

$$\frac{[\mathrm{A}_{\mathrm{I}}]}{\sqrt[\nu]{[\mathrm{A}_{\nu\,\mathrm{II}}]}} = C/\sqrt[\nu]{K_c} = C_{\mathrm{ass}} \qquad \ldots.(173)$$

If the third substance is partly dissociated in the second solvent, the state of the latter is defined by a LMA equation similar to eqn. (160). For example, in the case of dissociation of the type A = B + S, where only A, and not B and S, is appreciably soluble in the first solvent [such as may occur in ionic equilibria between water (II) and a non-aqueous solvent (I)], it follows that

$$\frac{[\mathrm{B}]\,[\mathrm{S}]}{[\mathrm{A}_{\mathrm{II}}]} = K_c$$

In this case, the distribution law $\dfrac{[\mathrm{A}_{\mathrm{I}}]}{[\mathrm{A}_{\mathrm{II}}]} = C$ holds only for $[\mathrm{A}_{\mathrm{II}}] = (1 - \alpha)[\mathrm{A}_{\mathrm{II}}]_0$, see eqn. (159), $[\mathrm{A}_{\mathrm{II}}]_0$ = total concentration of A in phase II.

Hence

$$\frac{[A_I]}{(1-\alpha)\,[A_{II}]_0} = C \qquad \ldots (173\,a)$$

where α may be calculated from the appropriate LMA equation (160), so that

$$\frac{\alpha^2}{1-\alpha}[A_{II}]_0 = K_c$$

The law for the solubility of gases [eqns. (79) and (165)] is only a special case of the distribution law (liquid and vapour phases). The relationships given for association and dissociation (chemical effect of solvent on solute) are, of course, also applicable in the case of solubility of gases.

(9) The phase rule is $P + F = C + 2$, or number of phases + degrees of freedom = number of independently-variable constituents (components) + 2 .... (174)
This is known as Gibbs' phase rule.

Each independent variable of state in a system constitutes one degree of freedom. Temperature, pressure, volume and concentration are examples of variables of state.

A phase is any homogeneous part of a system which, at a given temperature, is separated from other homogeneous parts by a definite boundary surface (discontinuity). Examples are: vapour phase, liquid phases, solid phases and solutions.

The number of components of a system is the smallest number of independently variable constituents by which the composition of each phase present can be expressed either directly or in the form of a chemical equation. Thus, for example, the water system, H_2O_{solid}, H_2O_{liq} and H_2O_{gas} comprises only one component, since the H and O are not independent. On the other hand, in the system $CaCO_3 = CaO + CO_2$, the number of components is two, since CaO and CO_2 may be separated and exist independently, while the third substance, $CaCO_3$, can be formed in any desired quantity from these two independent constituents.

A generalization of the phase rule is often true, i.e. number of phases + number of degrees of freedom = number of constituents minus the number of independent equilibrium constants + 2, or

$$P + F = C^{\star} - K + 2 \qquad \ldots . (174a)$$

where $C^{\star}$ refers to the total number of different types of molecule present, i.e.

$$C = C^{\star} - K$$

For example, in the $CaCO_3 = CaO + CO_2$ system, $C^{\star} = 3$, but the number of equilibrium constants for the system is $K = 1\,(p_{CO_2})$, so that $C = 3 - 1 = 2$.

*Exercise 90

A gas mixture containing 45 vol. per cent CO, 35 vol. per cent H_2 and 20 vol. per cent H_2O is heated to 1400 °K. What is the composition of the mixture after the water–gas equilibrium

$$CO_2 + H_2 \rightleftharpoons CO + H_2O$$

has been established, and when the equilibrium constant $K\ (= K_c = K_p = K_x) = 2{\cdot}21$ at 1400 °K?

Solution 90. Since the reaction index is equal to $\Delta\sum\nu_i = 1 + 1 - (1 + 1) = 0$, the reaction takes place independently of concentration and pressure and $K_p = K_c = K_x$ is non-dimensional. In the ideal gas state, volume per cent and mole per cent, or volume and mole fractions, are identical.

Thus for the initial composition of the gas

$$x_{0\,CO} = 0{\cdot}45 \qquad x_{0\,H_2O} = 0{\cdot}20$$

$$x_{0H_2} = 0{\cdot}35 \qquad x_{0\,CO_2} = 0{\cdot}00$$

Let x be the mole fraction of CO_2 formed. The equilibrium composition then is, in mole fractions:

$$\text{for CO:} \quad x_{0\,CO} - x \qquad \text{for } CO_2\text{:} \quad x$$

$$H_2O\text{:} \quad x_{0\,H_2O} - x \qquad H_2\text{:} \quad x_{0\,H_2} + x \qquad \ldots . \quad \text{(i)}$$

The LMA, in the form of eqn. (155) will, therefore, be

$$\frac{(x_{0\,CO} - x)\,(x_{0\,H_2O} - x)}{(x_{0\,H_2} + x)\,x} = K = 2{\cdot}21 \qquad \ldots . \quad \text{(ii)}$$

which on rearrangement gives

$$(K - 1)\,x^2 + (K\,x_{0\,H_2} + x_{0\,H_2O} + x_{0\,CO})\,x - x_{0\,CO}\,x_{0\,H_2O} = 0 \qquad \ldots . \quad \text{(iii)}$$

Substituting the numerical values, this becomes

$$1{\cdot}21\,x^2 + 1{\cdot}4235\,x - 0{\cdot}09 = 0 \quad x = 0{\cdot}06015 \approx 0{\cdot}060 \qquad \ldots . \quad \text{(iv)}$$

The second value of x is negative and may be ignored. By substituting the value found for x in (i), the equilibrium composition of the gas mixture is found to be

CO: 45 − 6 = 39 per cent by volume

H_2O: 20 − 6 = 14 per cent by volume

H_2: 35 + 6 = 41 per cent by volume

CO_2: 0 + 6 = 6 per cent by volume

*Exercise 91

A mixture of HI ($p_{0\,HI} = 120$ torr), H_2 ($p_{0\,H_2} = 500$ torr) and I_2 ($p_{0\,I_2} = 140$ torr) is heated to 600 °K. The equilibrium constant for the decomposition of $HI = \frac{1}{2}H_2 + \frac{1}{2}I_2$ at 600 °K is $K = (K_p = K_c = K_x) = 0{\cdot}120$.
How much HI decomposes (measured in torr) before equilibrium is established and what is the mixture composition at equilibrium?

Solution 91. The reaction index $\Delta\sum\nu_i = \frac{1}{2} + \frac{1}{2} - 1 = 0$, so that $K(= K_p = K_c = K_x)$ is non-dimensional and independent of pressure. If the partial pressure of HI decrases by x torr to reach equilibrium, the LMA, valid at equilibrium will be, from eqn. (154)

$$\frac{p_{H_2}^{1/2}\,p_{I_2}^{1/2}}{p_{HI}} = K = 0{\cdot}120 \qquad \ldots . \quad \text{(i)}$$

where

$$p_{\mathrm{HI}} = p_{0\,\mathrm{HI}} - x \quad p_{\mathrm{H_2}} = p_{0\,\mathrm{H_2}} + x/2 \quad p_{\mathrm{I_2}} = p_{0\,\mathrm{I_2}} + x/2 \qquad \dots . \quad \text{(ii)}$$

Substituting in (i) gives

$$\frac{(500 + x/2)(140 + x/2)}{(120 - x)^2} = (0{\cdot}120)^2 = 0{\cdot}0144 \qquad \dots . \quad \text{(iii)}$$

or

$$0{\cdot}9424\,x^2 + 1293{\cdot}82\,x + 279{,}171 = 0$$

The solutions to this equation are $x_1 = -1105$ torr, $x_2 = -268$ torr. The solution x_1 is not applicable, since it would lead to negative partial pressures for H_2 and I_2.

The negative value $x = -268$ torr shows that, in order to establish equilibrium, HI must be formed, not decomposed, i.e. so that its partial pressure is increased by 268 torr to a value of 388 torr. At the same time, the partial pressure of H_2 ($p_{0\,\mathrm{H_2}} = 500$ torr) falls by $268/2 = 134$ torr to a figure of 366 torr. Similarly, that of I_2 ($p_{0\,\mathrm{I_2}} = 140$ torr) also falls, by $268/2 = 134$ torr to 6 torr. It follows that almost all the I_2 is converted to HI and the required composition is given by

$$p_{\mathrm{HI}} = 388 \text{ torr} \quad p_{\mathrm{H_2}} = 366 \text{ torr} \quad p_{\mathrm{I_2}} = 6 \text{ torr}$$

*Exercise 92

Calculate the degree of dissociation of ammonia at:

(*a*) 600 °C and 10 atm (*b*) 600 °C and 100 atm

(*c*) 400 °C and 10 atm (*d*) 400 °C and 100 atm.

Also calculate the percentage (mole per cent or volume per cent) of ammonia at equilibrium, given the equilibrium constant for the reaction $NH_3 = \frac{1}{2}N_2 + \frac{3}{2}H_2$ as $K_p = 660{\cdot}7$ atm at 600 °C and $K_p = 77{\cdot}6$ atm at 400 °C. Make a comparison of the results.

Solution 92. Taking $\nu_A = \frac{1}{2}$ and $\nu_B = \frac{3}{2}$, the problem can be dealt with by the direct application of eqn. (164). This gives

$$\frac{\alpha^2}{1-\alpha}\left(\frac{1}{2}\right)^{1/2}\left(\frac{3}{2}\right)^{3/2}\frac{p}{1+\alpha} = K_p = \frac{\alpha^2}{1-\alpha^2} \times \frac{3\sqrt{3}\,p}{4} \qquad \dots . \quad \text{(i)}$$

or

$$\alpha = \sqrt{\frac{4K_p}{3\sqrt{3}\,p + 4K_p}} \qquad \dots . \quad \text{(ii)}$$

For a degree of dissociation α for NH_3, it follows from eqn. (161) that the mole fraction $x_i = p_i/p$ will be

$$x_{\mathrm{NH_3}} = \frac{p_{\mathrm{NH_3}}}{p} = \frac{1-\alpha}{1+\alpha}$$

so that the mole per cent of

$$\mathrm{NH_3} = \frac{100(1-\alpha)}{(1+\alpha)} \qquad \dots . \quad \text{(iii)}$$

Equations (164) and (161) will not generally be directly available. In such a case (i) is derived from the law of mass action, as shown below.

If n_0 is the molar quantity of NH_3 before dissociation, then, for a degree of dissociation α, the number of NH_3 moles after dissociation will be $n_0(1-\alpha)$. It follows from the reaction equation that

$$\frac{1}{2} n_0 \alpha \text{ mole } N_2 \quad \text{and} \quad \frac{3}{2} n_0 \alpha \text{ mole } H_2$$

will be formed by the dissociation of n_0 moles of NH_3. At equilibrium the total quantity of moles will, therefore, be

$$\left(1 - \alpha + \frac{1}{2}\alpha + \frac{3}{2}\alpha\right) n_0 = (1 + \alpha)\, n_0$$

Since the partial pressures will be proportional to the mole quantities, one has (where $p = \sum p_i$ = total pressure):

$$p_{NH_3} : p = n_{NH_3} : \sum n_i = n_0(1-\alpha) : n_0(1+\alpha) \quad \ldots. \quad \text{(iv)}$$

or

$$p_{NH_3} = \frac{1-\alpha}{1+\alpha} p \qquad p_{H_2} = \frac{3}{2} \times \frac{\alpha}{1+\alpha} p \qquad p_{N_2} = \frac{1}{2} \times \frac{\alpha}{1+\alpha} p \quad \ldots. \quad \text{(v)}$$

In accordance with eqn. (154), the law of mass action, for the given reaction equation for the decomposition of ammonia, will be

$$\frac{p_{N_2}^{1/2}\, p_{H_2}^{3/2}}{p_{NH_3}} = K_p \quad \ldots. \quad \text{(vi)}$$

Substituting the values at (v) in (vi), one obtains

$$\frac{p^{1/2}\left(\frac{1}{2}\right)^{1/2}\left(\frac{\alpha}{1+\alpha}\right)^{1/2}\left(\frac{3}{2}\right)^{3/2}\left(\frac{\alpha}{1+\alpha}\right)^{3/2} p^{3/2}}{\frac{1-\alpha}{1+\alpha} p} = K_p = \frac{\alpha^2}{(1-\alpha)(1+\alpha)}\left(\frac{1}{2}\right)^{1/2}\left(\frac{3}{2}\right)^{3/2} p \quad \ldots. \quad \text{(vii)}$$

as an expression identical with (i). The expression for (iii) follows in a similar manner from (v).

Substituting the numerical values in (ii) and (iii) gives

(*a*) for 600 °C and 10 atm:

$$\alpha = \sqrt{\frac{4 \times 660{\cdot}7}{3\sqrt{3} \times 10 + 4 \times 660{\cdot}7}} = \sqrt{\frac{2642{\cdot}8}{51{\cdot}96 + 2642{\cdot}8}} = 0{\cdot}9903$$

$$100\,\frac{1 - 0{\cdot}9903}{1 + 0{\cdot}9903} = 0{\cdot}488 \text{ mole per cent } NH_3 \quad \ldots. \quad \text{(viii)}$$

(*b*) for 600 °C and 100 atm:

$$\alpha = \sqrt{\frac{2642{\cdot}8}{519{\cdot}6 + 2642{\cdot}8}} = 0{\cdot}9142 \text{ and } 4{\cdot}48 \text{ mole per cent } NH_3 \quad \ldots. \quad \text{(ix)}$$

(*c*) for 400 °C and 10 atm:

$$\alpha = \sqrt{\frac{4 \times 77{\cdot}6}{3\sqrt{3} \times 10 + 4 \times 77{\cdot}6}} = \sqrt{\frac{310{\cdot}5}{51{\cdot}96 + 310{\cdot}5}} = 0{\cdot}9255 \text{ and } 3{\cdot}86 \text{ mole per cent } NH_3 \quad \ldots. \quad \text{(x)}$$

(*d*) for 400 °C and 100 atm:

$$\alpha = \sqrt{\frac{310{\cdot}5}{519{\cdot}6 + 310{\cdot}5}} = 0{\cdot}6116 \text{ and } 24{\cdot}10 \text{ mole per cent } NH_3 \quad \ldots\ldots \quad \text{(xi)}$$

The highest concentration of NH_3 is obtained in the equilibrium mixture at 400 °C and 100 atm, i.e. at low temperatures and high pressures.

Note. In setting out the equation for the law of mass action, it is necessary to ascertain

(a) which equilibrium constant K will be used, K_c, K_p or K_x

(b) to which reaction equation the equilibrium constant applies. If, for example, the equation $\frac{1}{2} N_2 + \frac{3}{2} H_2 = NH_3$ is given, then it is reciprocal to the one used above, whereas it will be its square for the equation $2NH_3 = N_2 + 3H_2$;

(c) finally, when applying eqn. (151) for the equilibrium constant, it is necessary to check that the concentrations, partial pressures or mole fractions of the final products (those on the right-hand side of the reaction equation) feature in the numerator of the law of mass action. This procedure is not universally adopted in textbooks, so that reciprocal constants may be given.

The result in the above exercise, i.e. that the highest concentration of NH_3 is obtained at low temperatures and high pressures, is due to the fact that the formation of NH_3 from N_2 and H_2 involves an exothermic reaction, i.e. it is associated with loss of energy by the system (12·7 kcal/mole NH_3 at 500 °C). The reaction equation also shows that reduction of volume will promote the formation of ammonia (Le Chatelier's principle of least constraint). Even in the presence of catalysts, there will, of course, be a limit to the extent to which the temperature can be decreased. This arises from the marked decrease in the rate at which equilibrium will be established as the temperature is lowered.

The increasing deviation of gases from the ideal state as the pressure is raised, results in the equilibrium constant K_p being noticeably pressure-dependent above 100 atm. Its value will depend on the constants of the equations of state for the gases taking part in the reaction. For further details, see Eucken and Jakob, *Chemie-Ingenieur*, vol. III_1 pp. 15—21. In the case of the above example dealing with the calculation of NH_3 in the equilibrium mixture, the influence of pressure is such that, at 600 °C and 100 atm, 4·52 mole per cent NH_3 is formed instead of 4·48 and, at 400 °C and 100 atm, the figure is 25·12 instead of 24·10, i.e. an increased yield results in both cases.

*Exercise 93

In the presence of catalysts, such as camphor and activated charcoal, sulphuryl chloride partially dissociates according to the equation

$$SO_2Cl_2 = SO_2 + Cl_2$$

The molecular weight of SO_2Cl_2 is $M_0 = 134{\cdot}97$. An investigation showed that, at 30 °C and a total pressure of $p = 64{\cdot}9$ torr, the apparent molecular weight was $\overline{M} = 89{\cdot}7$. For a pressure of $p = 291{\cdot}1$ torr, $\overline{M}$ was found to be equal to 106·9. Calculate the degree of dissociation α and also K_p (atm) for both conditions of pressure. Take the arithmetic mean as a final value for K_p (atm) at 30 °C.

Solution 93. It will be seen from Chapter 2, and in particular eqn. (18), that the apparent molecular weight is given by

$$\overline{M} = \frac{M_0}{1 + (\nu - 1)\,\alpha}$$

and, in this case, the number of fragments is $\nu = 2$, so that

$$\bar{M} = \frac{M_0}{1 + \alpha} \qquad \ldots . \quad \text{(i)}$$

It follows that

$$\alpha = \frac{M_0}{\bar{M}} - 1 \quad \text{[see also eqn. (19)]} \qquad \ldots . \quad \text{(ii)}$$

For $\nu_A = 1$ and $\nu_B = 1$, the law of mass action [eqn. (164)] will be

$$\frac{\alpha^2 p}{1 - \alpha^2} = K_p \quad \text{(atm)} \qquad \ldots . \quad \text{(iii)}$$

Substituting numerical values in (ii), one has, for the first experiment:

$$\alpha_1 = \frac{134{\cdot}97}{89{\cdot}7} - 1 = 0{\cdot}5047 \qquad \ldots . \quad \text{(iv)}$$

$$K_p\,\text{(atm)} = \frac{(0{\cdot}5047)^2 \times 64{\cdot}9}{[1 - (0{\cdot}5047)^2]\,760} = 0{\cdot}0292\ \text{atm} \qquad \ldots . \quad \text{(v)}$$

and for the second case:

$$\alpha_2 = \frac{134{\cdot}97}{106{\cdot}9} - 1 = 0{\cdot}2626 \qquad \ldots . \quad \text{(vi)}$$

$$K_p\,\text{(atm)} = \frac{(0{\cdot}2626)^2 \times 291{\cdot}1}{[1 - (0{\cdot}2626)^2]\,760} = 0{\cdot}0284\ \text{atm} \qquad \ldots . \quad \text{(vii)}$$

The required arithmetic mean is

$$K_p\ (\text{at } 30\,°\text{C}) = \frac{0{\cdot}0292 + 0{\cdot}0284}{2} = 0{\cdot}0288\ \text{atm} \qquad \ldots . \quad \text{(viii)}$$

Note. The general definition of mean molecular weight is, according to eqn. (9): $\bar{M} = x_1 M_1 + x_2 M_2 + x_3 M_3 + \cdots$ This is exactly the same as eqn. (18) in the case of a dissociation equilibrium of the type $C = \nu_A A + \nu_B B + \cdots$, where $\nu_A + \nu_B + \cdots = \nu$ is the total number of fragments formed during dissociation. It will be seen from eqns. (15) and (16) that, in such a case, the total quantity of moles is $n_0(1 - \alpha) + n_0(\nu_A + \nu_B + \cdots)\alpha = n_0[1 + (\nu - 1)\alpha]$. The mole fractions will, therefore, be as follows:

$$\text{for C:} \quad x_1 = \frac{1 - \alpha}{1 + (\nu - 1)\alpha}$$

$$\text{for A:} \quad x_2 = \frac{\nu_A \alpha}{1 + (\nu - 1)\alpha}$$

$$\text{for B:} \quad x_3 = \frac{\nu_B \alpha}{1 + (\nu - 1)\alpha} \quad \text{etc.}$$

Bearing in mind that $\nu_A M_2 + \nu_B M_3$, the total weight of the fragments, is equal to the initial molecular weight $M_1 = M_0$, substitution of the mol. fractions x_1, x_2, x_3 in eqn. (9) gives eqn. (18).

*Exercise 94

Nitrogen tetroxide partially dissociates into nitrogen dioxide according to the equation

$$N_2O_4 = 2NO_2$$

Measurements show that $G = 42{\cdot}0\,\text{g}\ N_2O_4$ has a volume $V = 18{\cdot}35$ l. at temperature $\theta = 50$ °C and pressure $p = 710$ torr. Calculate the degree of dissociation and the equilibrium constant K_p (atm.).

Solution 94. If the degree of dissociation of n_0 moles N_2O_4 is α, then the quantity of undissociated moles is $n_{N_2O_4} = n_0(1 - \alpha)$ and $n_{NO_2} = n_0 2\alpha$ is the number of moles of NO_2 formed. The total quantity of moles at equilibrium is then $\sum n_i = n_0(1 + \alpha)$; see also eqn. (163). Thus, the gas equation is

$$pV = \sum n_i RT = n_0 (1 + \alpha) RT = \frac{G}{M} (1 + \alpha) RT \qquad \ldots . \quad \text{(i)}$$

[see eqn. (17)]. Since the partial pressures are proportional to mole quantities, one also has

$$\frac{p_{N_2O_4}}{p} = \frac{1 - \alpha}{1 + \alpha} \quad \text{and} \quad \frac{p_{NO_2}}{p} = \frac{2\alpha}{1 + \alpha} \quad \text{[see also eqn. (161)]}$$

Thus, from the law of mass action, eqn. (154):

$$\frac{p^2_{NO_2}}{p_{N_2O_4}} = K_p \text{ and, by substitution, } \frac{4\alpha^2 p}{1 - \alpha^2} = K_p \qquad \ldots . \quad \text{(ii)}$$

see also eqn. (164) where $\nu_A = 2$, $\nu_B = 0$.

Substituting the numerical values in (i), and where $R = 0{\cdot}08206$ l. atm/(deg. mole) [see eqn. (4)] and $M_{N_2O_4} = 92$ g/mole, gives

$$\frac{710}{760} \times 18{\cdot}35 = \frac{42{\cdot}0}{92} (1 + \alpha) \times 0{\cdot}08206\,(273 + 50)$$

$$1 + \alpha = 1{\cdot}417$$

$$\alpha = 0{\cdot}417 \qquad \ldots . \quad \text{(iii)}$$

Substituting this value of α in (ii) gives

$$\frac{4 \times 0{\cdot}417^2 \times 710}{(1 - 0{\cdot}417^2) \times 760} = K_p = 0{\cdot}787 \text{ atm} \qquad \ldots . \quad \text{(iv)}$$

Exercise 95

Phosphorus pentachloride, PCl_5, and antimony pentachloride, $SbCl_5$, dissociate into the trichlorides and chlorine according to the equations

$$PCl_5 = PCl_3 + Cl_2$$

$$SbCl_5 = SbCl_3 + Cl_2$$

A determination of the molecular weight of PCl_5 ($M_0 = 208{\cdot}26$) shows the apparent molecular weight to be $\overline{M} = 145$ at 212 °C and $p = 814{\cdot}7$ torr. For $SbCl_5$ ($M_0 = 299{\cdot}04$) at 212 °C and $p = 48{\cdot}4$ torr, $\overline{M}$ is found to be 156. What is the degree of dissociation α of PCl_5 and $SbCl_5$ at 212 °C under a pressure of $p = 0{\cdot}5$ atm, and what are the partial pressures of the mixture components, (*a*) if PCl_5 and $SbCl_5$ are considered separately and (*b*) if they are mixed in the mole ratio $r = [SbCl_5]:[PCl_5] = 2:1$?

Solution 95. Since the number of fragments on dissociation is given by $\nu = 2$, then, as in Exercise 93, the apparent molecular weight is, from eqn. (18):

$$\overline{M} = \frac{M_0}{1+\alpha} \quad \text{i.e.} \quad \alpha = \frac{M_0 - \overline{M}}{\overline{M}} \qquad \ldots . \quad \text{(i)}$$

and the law of mass action [eqn. (164)] will be, again as in Exercise 93 (iii):

$$\frac{\alpha^2 p}{1-\alpha^2} = K_p \qquad \ldots . \quad \text{(ii)}$$

Since it is not required to calculate α for the temperatures and pressures given as data, the dissociation constant K_p can be obtained directly from these data by substituting (i) in (ii). This gives

$$K_p = \frac{(M_0 - \overline{M})^2 p}{M_0 (2\overline{M} - M_0)} \qquad \ldots . \quad \text{(iii)}$$

so that, at 212 °C

$$K_p \text{ for } PCl_5 = K_1 = \frac{(208{\cdot}26 - 145)^2 \times 814{\cdot}7}{208{\cdot}26\,(2 \times 145 - 208{\cdot}26)\,760} = 0{\cdot}252 \text{ atm} \qquad \ldots . \quad \text{(iv)}$$

and

$$K_p \text{ for } SbCl_5 = K_2 = \frac{(299{\cdot}04 - 156)^2 \times 48{\cdot}4}{299{\cdot}04\,(2 \times 156 - 299{\cdot}04)\,760} = 0{\cdot}338 \text{ atm} \qquad \ldots . \quad \text{(v)}$$

It follows from (ii) that:

$$\alpha = \sqrt{\frac{K_p}{p + K_p}} \qquad \ldots . \quad \text{(vi)}$$

By substituting K_1 in (vi) for a pressure of $p = 0{\cdot}5$ atm, one finds the degree of dissociation of PCl_5 (by itself) at 0·5 atm:

$$\alpha_{01} = \sqrt{\frac{0{\cdot}252}{0{\cdot}5 + 0{\cdot}252}} = 0{\cdot}579 \qquad \ldots . \quad \text{(vii)}$$

with partial pressures [from eqn. (161), and similarly to Exercise 94] of

$$\left.\begin{aligned} p_{PCl_5} &= p\,\frac{1-\alpha}{1+\alpha} = \frac{0{\cdot}5\,(1 - 0{\cdot}579)}{1 + 0{\cdot}579} = 0{\cdot}1332 \text{ atm} \\ p_{PCl_3} = p_{Cl_2} &= \frac{p\,\alpha}{1+\alpha} = \frac{0{\cdot}5 \times 0{\cdot}579}{1 + 0{\cdot}579} = 0{\cdot}1834 \text{ atm} \end{aligned}\right\} \quad \ldots \text{(viii)}$$

Similarly for $SbCl_5$, by substituting K_2 in (vi):

$$\alpha_{02} = \sqrt{\frac{0{\cdot}338}{0{\cdot}5 + 0{\cdot}338}} = 0{\cdot}635 \qquad \ldots . \quad \text{(ix)}$$

with

$$\left.\begin{aligned} p_{SbCl_5} &= \frac{0{\cdot}5\,(1 - 0{\cdot}635)}{1 + 0{\cdot}635} = 0{\cdot}1112 \text{ atm} \\ p_{SbCl_3} = p_{Cl_2} &= \frac{0{\cdot}5 \times 0{\cdot}635}{1 + 0{\cdot}635} = 0{\cdot}1942 \text{ atm} \end{aligned}\right\} \quad \ldots \text{(x)}$$

Considering a mixture of PCl_5 and $SbCl_5$ in the molar mixture ratio $[SbCl_5]:[PCl_5] = n_{02}:n_{01} = r$, and where α_1 and α_2 represent the degree of dissociation of PCl_5 and $SbCl_5$, respectively, the following expressions show the molar quantities present at equilibrium:

$$\left.\begin{array}{lll} n_{PCl_5} = n_{01}(1-\alpha_1) & \left.\begin{array}{l} n_{PCl_3} = n_{01}\alpha_1 \\ n_{SbCl_3} = n_{02}\alpha_2 \end{array}\right\} & n_{Cl_2} = n_{01}\alpha_1 + n_{02}\alpha_2 \\ n_{SbCl_5} = n_{02}(1-\alpha_2) & & \\ \text{and the total molar quantity} & \sum n_i = n_{01}(1+\alpha_1) + n_{02}(1+\alpha_2) & \end{array}\right\} \quad .. \text{(xi)}$$

Since the molar quantities are proportional to the partial pressures,

$$\frac{n_i}{\sum n_i} = \frac{p_i}{p} \quad \text{[eqn. (10)]} \qquad .... \text{(xii)}$$

and it follows from (xi) and (xii) that

$$p_{PCl_5} = \frac{n_{01}(1-\alpha_1)\,p}{n_{01}(1+\alpha_1) + n_{02}(1+\alpha_2)} \qquad .... \text{(xiii)}$$

or, where $n_{02}/n_{01} = r$

$$p_{PCl_5} = \frac{(1-\alpha_1)\,p}{(1+\alpha_1) + r(1+\alpha_2)}$$

Similarly,

$$\left.\begin{array}{l} p_{PCl_3} = \dfrac{n_{01}\,p\,\alpha_1}{n_{01}(1+\alpha_1) + n_{02}(1+\alpha_2)} = \dfrac{\alpha_1\,p}{(1+\alpha_1) + r(1+\alpha_2)} \\ p_{SbCl_5} = \dfrac{r(1-\alpha_2)\,p}{(1+\alpha_1) + r(1+\alpha_2)} \\ p_{SbCl_3} = \dfrac{r\,\alpha_2\,p}{(1+\alpha_1) + r(1+\alpha_2)} \\ p_{Cl_2} = \dfrac{(n_{01}\alpha_1 + n_{02}\alpha_2)\,p}{n_{01}(1+\alpha_1) + n_{02}(1+\alpha_2)} = \dfrac{(\alpha_1 + r\,\alpha_2)\,p}{(1+\alpha_1) + r(1+\alpha_2)} \end{array}\right\} \quad .. \text{(xiv)}$$

Thus the LMA [eqn. (154)] for PCl_5 is

$$\frac{\alpha_1(\alpha_1 + r\,\alpha_2)\,p}{(1-\alpha_1)\,[(1+\alpha_1) + r(1+\alpha_2)]} = K_1 \qquad .... \text{(xv)}$$

and for $SbCl_5$

$$\frac{\alpha_2(\alpha_1 + r\,\alpha_2)\,p}{(1-\alpha_2)\,[(1+\alpha_1) + r(1+\alpha_2)]} = K_2 \qquad .... \text{(xvi)}$$

Dividing (xv) by (xvi) gives

$$\frac{\alpha_1(1-\alpha_2)}{\alpha_2(1-\alpha_1)} = \frac{K_1}{K_2}$$

which may be rewritten as

$$\alpha_1\alpha_2(K_2 - K_1) - \alpha_1 K_2 + \alpha_2 K_1 = 0 \quad \text{or} \quad \frac{1}{\alpha_2} = \frac{K_1}{K_2\alpha_1} + \frac{K_2 - K_1}{K_2} \qquad .... \text{(xvii)}$$

(xv), rewritten, is

$$\alpha_1^2(p + K_1) + r(p + K_1)a_1\alpha_2 + rK_1\alpha_1 - rK_1\alpha_2 - K_1(1 + \mathrm{r}) = 0 \qquad .... \text{(xviii)}$$

(xvii) and (xviii) are, therefore, a pair of quadratic equations containing the two unknowns α_1 and α_2.

Algebraic solution by substituting α_2 from (xvii) in (xviii) leads to a cubic equation, with three possible roots, which would prove lengthy and tedious to solve. It is, therefore, more convenient to solve the equations by a graphical method. The point of intersection of the two curves obtained by plotting α_2 as a function of α_1 in the range between $\alpha = 0$ and $\alpha = 1$ will be the required solution. In the present case, where one is concerned with the application of the law of mass action to two similar systems having very similar equilibrium constants, solution will depend on finding a clear pair of values (α_1, α_2) close to those of α_{01} and α_{02} determined in (vii) and (ix). Thus, if no discussion is required regarding the influence of variation of the quantities K_1, K_2, p and r in (xvii) and (xviii), the complete curves need not be plotted; the graph may be confined to the region in the vicinity of α_{01} and α_{02}, i.e. somewhere between 0·5 and 0·7.

After substituting the numerical values of the parameters K_1, K_2, p and r in eqn. (vii), we find that

$$\frac{1}{\alpha_2} = \frac{0{\cdot}252}{0{\cdot}338\,\alpha_1} + \frac{0{\cdot}338 - 0{\cdot}252}{0{\cdot}338} \quad \text{or} \quad \frac{1}{\alpha_2} = \frac{0{\cdot}74555}{\alpha_1} + 0{\cdot}25445 \qquad \text{....(xvii}'\text{)}$$

Similarly, from (xviii)

$$\alpha_1^2(0{\cdot}5 + 0{\cdot}252) + \alpha_1\alpha_2 \times 2(0{\cdot}5 + 0{\cdot}252) + 2 \times 0{\cdot}252(\alpha_1 - \alpha_2) - 0{\cdot}252 \times 3 = 0$$

or

$$\alpha_1^2 + 2\alpha_1\alpha_2 + 0{\cdot}67021\alpha_1 - 0{\cdot}67021\alpha_2 - 1{\cdot}00531 = 0 \qquad \text{....(xviii}'\text{)}$$

Taking, by way of bracketing, $\alpha_1 = 0{\cdot}5$ and $0{\cdot}6$, we have

from (xvii′)	$\alpha_1 = 0{\cdot}5$	$\alpha_2 = 0{\cdot}573$
	$\alpha_1 = 0{\cdot}6$	$\alpha_2 = 0{\cdot}669$
and from (xviii′)	$\alpha_1 = 0{\cdot}5$	$\alpha_2 = 1{\cdot}273$
	$\alpha_1 = 0{\cdot}6$	$\alpha_2 = 0{\cdot}458$

Graphical representation of these values gives, to a first approximation, the point of intersection of the straight lines drawn through them (linear interpolation) as $\alpha_1 = 0{\cdot}575$, $\alpha_2 = 0{\cdot}645$ (see *Figure 15*). A closer approximation to the correct solution

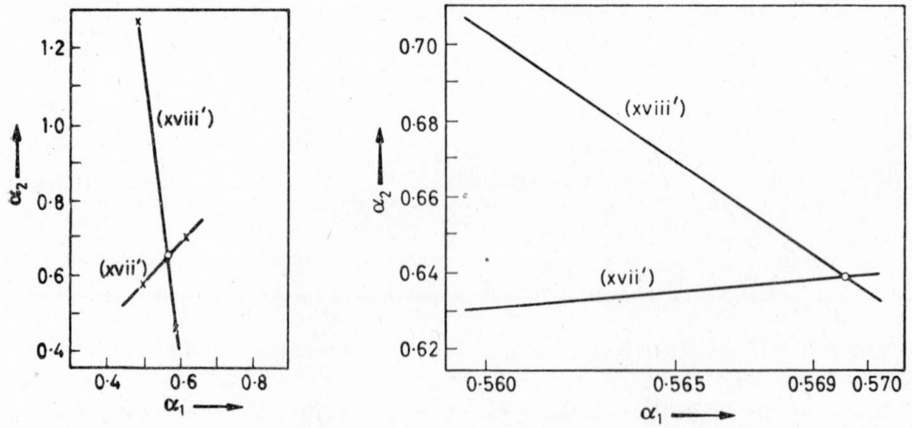

Figures 15 and 16. Graphical solution of two quadratic equations with two unknowns: first and second approximation

is now made by taking values of 0·58, 0·57 and 0·56 for α_1. This gives

from (xviii′)	$\alpha_1 = 0{\cdot}56$	$\alpha_2 = 0{\cdot}631$	from (xviii′)	$\alpha_1 = 0{\cdot}56$	$\alpha_2 = 0{\cdot}703$
	$\alpha_1 = 0{\cdot}57$	$\alpha_2 = 0{\cdot}640$		$\alpha_1 = 0{\cdot}57$	$\alpha_2 = 0{\cdot}636$
	$\alpha_1 = 0{\cdot}58$	$\alpha_2 = 0{\cdot}649$		$\alpha_1 = 0{\cdot}58$	$\alpha_2 = 0{\cdot}572$

The point of intersection of the straight lines drawn through these pairs of values is (see *Figure 16*)

$$\alpha_1 = 0{\cdot}5694 \quad \alpha_2 = 0{\cdot}6395 \qquad \ldots \text{(xix)}$$

Comparison of these values with $\alpha_{01} = 0{\cdot}579$ and $\alpha_{02} = 0{\cdot}635$ [see (vii) and (ix)] shows that the effect of mixing is to reduce the degree of dissociation of PCl_5 (which has the smaller dissociation constant, $K_1 = 0{\cdot}252$), whereas that of $SbCl_5$ is increased ($K_2 = 0{\cdot}338$).

The partial pressures in the mixture are found by substituting the numerical values in (xiv):

$$\left.\begin{aligned} p_{PCl_5} &= \frac{(1 - 0{\cdot}5694)\,0{\cdot}5}{1 + 0{\cdot}5694 + 2\,(1 + 0{\cdot}6395)} = \frac{0{\cdot}2153}{4{\cdot}8484} = 0{\cdot}0444 \text{ atm} \\ p_{PCl_3} &= \frac{0{\cdot}5694 \times 0{\cdot}5}{4{\cdot}8484} = 0{\cdot}0587 \text{ atm} \\ p_{SbCl_5} &= \frac{2\,(1 - 0{\cdot}6395)\,0{\cdot}5}{4{\cdot}8484} = 0{\cdot}0744 \text{ atm} \\ p_{SbCl_3} &= \frac{2 \times 0{\cdot}6395 \times 0{\cdot}5}{4{\cdot}8484} = 0{\cdot}1319 \text{ atm} \\ p_{Cl_2} &= \frac{(0{\cdot}5694 + 2 \times 0{\cdot}6395)\,0{\cdot}5}{4{\cdot}8484} = 0{\cdot}1906 \text{ atm} \\ \text{Total} &= 0{\cdot}5000 \text{ atm} \end{aligned}\right\} \ldots \text{(xx)}$$

It is often helpful, before proceeding with a numerical solution of the final equations [in this case (xvii′) and (xviii′)], to obtain some idea of the way in which the functions vary. This may be done by analytical consideration of the curves, especially when several solutions are possible and when a survey of the dependence of the solutions on the values of the coefficients in the equations (i.e. the parameters) is also required.

It is not proposed to go deeply into the analytical geometry which applies to the present case. Discussion and construction of the curves will merely be quickly illustrated by reference to *Figure 17*.

Curve (xviii) or (xviii′) represents a rectangular hyperbola whose asymptotes are parallel to the coordinate axes and correspond to the lines

$$\alpha_{m1} = -\frac{K_1}{K_2 - K_1} = -\,2{\cdot}93$$

$$\alpha_{m2} = +\frac{K_2}{K_2 - K_1} = +\,3{\cdot}93$$

The length of the transverse axis is

$$a = b = \frac{\sqrt{2\,K_1 K_2}}{K_1 - K_2} = 4{\cdot}80$$

All curves of the family with varying parameter K_1 and K_2 pass through the points

$\alpha_1 = 0$, $\alpha_2 = 0$ and $\alpha_1 = 1$, $\alpha_2 = 1$. The radius of curvature at the vertex is $\varrho = 4{\cdot}80$. These data are sufficient for discussion and construction.

(xviii) or (xviii′) represents a hyperbola whose centre point and point of intersection of the asymptotes lies at

$$\alpha_{m1} = +\frac{K_1}{K_1 + p} = 0{\cdot}335 \qquad \alpha_{m2} = -\frac{r+2}{r}\,\frac{K_1}{K_1 + p} = -0{\cdot}670$$

The angle δ of the transverse axis to the x-axis is determined from the relation $\tan 2\delta = r$, i.e. $\delta = 31°45'$. One asymptote is always parallel to the y-axis, the other has a slope of $\tan \varepsilon = -1/r = -1/2$. The lengths of the transverse axes are given by

$$\sqrt{\frac{(1+r)\,K_1 p}{(K_1 + p)^2\,\lambda}} \qquad \text{where } \lambda = +\frac{1 \pm \sqrt{1 + r^2}}{2}$$

The negative value of λ (taken as absolute) is used to determine the transverse axis b (absolute value). Thus, $a = \sqrt{\dfrac{1{\cdot}337}{3{\cdot}236}} = 0{\cdot}643$ and $b = \sqrt{\dfrac{1{\cdot}337}{1{\cdot}236}} = 1{\cdot}040$ and the radius of curvature at the vertex is $\varrho = \dfrac{b^2}{a} = 1{\cdot}682$. These data are sufficient for discussion and construction. Having the data to hand for the parameters r, K_1, K_2 and p which feature in the hyperbolas, it is now possible to consider the way in which the points of intersection of the curves vary when these parameters are varied.

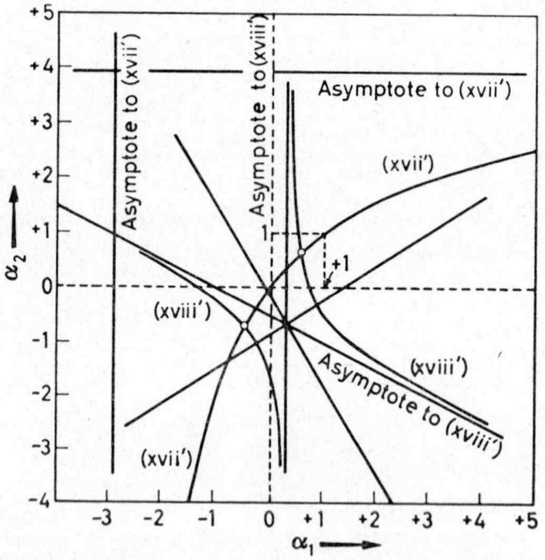

Figure 17. Analytical consideration of the curves for a system of two quadratic equations with two unknowns

Figure 17 shows a point of intersection of the two hyperbolas lying within the range of interest in the present problem, i.e. in the square between the co-ordinate axes and the points α_1 and $\alpha_2 = +1$. The scale of the diagram is relatively small but readings of $\alpha_1 = 0{\cdot}57$ and $\alpha_2 = 0{\cdot}64$ may be taken, as a first approximation, for the co-ordinates of the point of intersection. A second point of intersection, having algebraic but no chemical significance, is seen to lie at $\alpha_1 = -0{\cdot}45$, $\alpha_2 = -0{\cdot}71$. A third point of intersection exists, as may be seen by a glance at the figure. It is the point of intersection of the left-hand extension of the lower branch of the hyperbola (xviii′) with that of the upper hyperbola (xvii′), which is not shown because of the scale of the figure. The point lies, however, at $\alpha_1 = -11{\cdot}55$, $\alpha_2 = +5{\cdot}25$.

Note. The above treatment is, of course, generally valid for a combined equilibrium for two systems:

$$\mathrm{AC} = \mathrm{A} + \mathrm{C} \text{ with equilibrium constant } K_p'$$

and $\mathrm{BC} = \mathrm{B} + \mathrm{C}$ with equilibrium constant K_p''

having a total pressure p and a mixture ratio $\dfrac{[\mathrm{BC}]_0}{[\mathrm{AC}]_0} = r$.

A model example, especially clear both in calculation and plotting and in discussing the curves and their points of intersection, is obtained by taking $K_p' = 1$, $K_p'' = 2$, $p = 1$, $r = 2$. *Solution:* $\alpha_1 = 0{\cdot}70$, $\alpha_2 = 0{\cdot}80$. The other points of intersection lie at $\alpha_1 = -0{\cdot}33$, $\alpha_2 = -1{\cdot}03$ and $\alpha_1 = -6{\cdot}30$, $\alpha_2 = +2{\cdot}33$.

This problem, or a modification of it, arises when oxidation or splitting-off of oxygen from a mixture of compounds is considered, or when the latter are subjected to hydrogenation or dehydrogenation.

Exercise 96

H_2O and CO_2 dissociate progressively at high temperatures according to the equations

$$H_2O = H_2 + \tfrac{1}{2}O_2 \; (K_{p1})$$
$$CO_2 = CO + \tfrac{1}{2}O_2 \; (K_{p2})$$

Calculate the degree of dissociation α_1 of H_2O and α_2 of CO_2 in a mixture containing equal molar fractions of H_2O and CO_2 at 2000 °K and under a total pressure of 1 atm. Also calculate the mixture composition in mole per cent if the equilibrium constant for the dissociation of H_2O at 2000 °K is $K_{p1} = 2{\cdot}96 \times 10^{-4}$ atm$^{1/2}$ and that for CO_2 $= K_{p2} = 1{\cdot}37 \times 10^{-3}$ atm$^{1/2}$. The dissociation of water into OH, H and O will not be considered here.

Solution 96. The problem will be dealt with in a manner similar to the one in Exercise 95.

When the original molar quantities are taken as equal, i.e. $n_{0\,H_2O} = n_{0\,CO_2} = n_0$, the molar quantities in equilibrium are:

$$\left.\begin{aligned} n_{H_2O} &= n_0(1-\alpha_1) & n_{CO_2} &= n_0(1-\alpha_2) \\ n_{H_2} &= n_0\alpha_1 & n_{CO} &= n_0\alpha_2 \\ n_{O_2} &= n_0\left(\frac{\alpha_1+\alpha_2}{2}\right) \end{aligned}\right\} \quad \ldots \quad \text{(i)}$$

The total quantity of moles $\sum n_i = n_0\left(1 - \alpha_1 + 1 - \alpha_2 + \alpha_1 + \alpha_2 + \dfrac{\alpha_1+\alpha_2}{2}\right)$

$$= \frac{n_0}{2}(4 + \alpha_1 + \alpha_2)$$

The partial pressures p_i may be calculated from the relation $p_i : p = n_i : \sum n$. Thus

$$\left.\begin{aligned} p_{H_2O} &= \frac{2p(1-\alpha_1)}{4+\alpha_1+\alpha_2} \qquad & p_{H_2} &= \frac{2p\alpha_1}{4+\alpha_1+\alpha_2} \\ p_{CO_2} &= \frac{2p(1-\alpha_2)}{4+\alpha_1+\alpha_2} \qquad & p_{CO} &= \frac{2p\alpha_2}{4+\alpha_1+\alpha_2} \\ p_{O_2} &= \frac{p(\alpha_1+\alpha_2)}{4+\alpha_1+\alpha_2} \end{aligned}\right\} \quad \ldots \quad \text{(ii)}$$

The law of mass action equations are

$$\frac{p_{H_2} p_{O_2}^{1/2}}{p_{H_2O}} = K_1 \quad \text{and} \quad \frac{p_{CO} p_{O_2}^{1/2}}{p_{CO_2}} = K_2 \quad \ldots\ldots \quad \text{(iii)}$$

Substituting (ii) in (iii) (after squaring) gives

$$\frac{\alpha_1^2(\alpha_1+\alpha_2)p}{(1-\alpha_1)^2(4+\alpha_1+\alpha_2)} = K_1^2 \qquad \frac{\alpha_2^2(\alpha_1+\alpha_2)p}{(1-\alpha_2)^2(4+\alpha_1+\alpha_2)} = K_2^2 \quad \ldots\ldots \quad \text{(iv)}$$

Dividing the two equations gives

$$\frac{\alpha_1(1-\alpha_2)}{(1-\alpha_1)\alpha_2} = \frac{K_1}{K_2} \quad \ldots\ldots \quad \text{(v)}$$

which may be rewritten as

$$\alpha_1\alpha_2(K_2-K_1) - \alpha_1 K_2 + \alpha_2 K_1 = 0 \quad \text{or} \quad \frac{1}{\alpha_2} = \frac{K_1}{K_2\alpha_1} + \frac{K_2-K_1}{K_2} \quad \ldots\ldots \quad \text{(vi)}$$

Before dealing with one of the equations at (iv), e.g. the first, it should be noted that the constants K, and also α_1 and α_2, are small in comparison with unity ($\alpha \ll 1$). When multiplying out, therefore, square and cubic terms of α in the denominator at (iv) may be ignored, as being negligible in comparison with the number 4. The denominator then becomes $4+\alpha_1+\alpha_2-4\times 2\alpha_1 = 4-7\alpha_1+\alpha_2$. Thus, when $p = 1$, the first eqn. (iv) now becomes

$$\alpha_1^3 + \alpha_1^2\alpha_2 + 7K_1^2\alpha_1 - K_1^2\alpha_2 - 4K_1^2 = 0 \quad \ldots\ldots \quad \text{(vii)}$$

The pair of equations, (vi) and (vii), with two unknowns, are best solved graphically. They represent two curves, $\alpha_2 = f(\alpha_1)$, and the solution is obtained by determining the point of intersection of these curves lying in the range between 0 and 1 (i.e. as in Exercise 95, *Figure 15* and *16*).

In order to avoid having to determine too many points on the curve, a start is made (as in Exercise 95) by finding the degree of dissociation (α_{01} and α_{02}) for the two components considered separately, i.e. in the unmixed condition (zero approximation). This may be done with the help of eqn. (164), using the following expressions:

$$\frac{\alpha_1^{3/2} \times 1^1 \left(\frac{1}{2}\right)^{1/2} p^{1/2}}{(1-\alpha_1)(1+\alpha_1/2)} = K_1 \quad \text{or} \quad \frac{2\alpha_1^3 p}{(1-\alpha_1)^2(2+\alpha_1)^2} = K_1^2 \quad \ldots\ldots \quad \text{(viii)}$$

When K is small, α is also small compared with unity, and may, therefore, be neglected in the denominator. Thus, when $p = 1$ atm, $\alpha_1^3/2 \approx K_1^2$. It follows that

$$\alpha_{01} \approx \sqrt[3]{2K_1^2} \quad \text{and} \quad \alpha_{02} \approx \sqrt[3]{2K_2^2} \quad \ldots\ldots \quad \text{(ix)}$$

Substituting for K_1 and K_2 in (ix) gives

$$\alpha_{01} \approx \sqrt[3]{2\,(2{\cdot}96 \times 10^{-4})^2} = 0{\cdot}0056 \qquad \alpha_{02} \approx \sqrt[3]{2(1{\cdot}37 \times 10^{-3})^2} = 0{\cdot}0155 \quad \ldots\ldots \quad \text{(x)}$$

Comparison with Exercise 95 shows that the degree of dissociation of the less strongly dissociated component is reduced by mixing, and that of the more fully dissociated component is increased. As a first attempt to bracket the point of intersection, values of 0·004 and 0·005 will, therefore,be taken for α_1. Substituting these in eqns. (vi) and (vii) gives:

from (vi) for $\alpha_1 = 4 \times 10^{-3}$

$$\frac{1}{\alpha_2} = \frac{0{\cdot}296 \times 10^{-3}}{1{\cdot}37 \times 10^{-3} \times 4 \times 10^{-3}} + \frac{1{\cdot}37 - 0{\cdot}296}{1{\cdot}37} \quad \ldots\ldots \quad \text{(xi)}$$

$$\alpha_2 = 1{\cdot}8255 \times 10^{-2}$$

and for $\alpha_1 = 5 \times 10^{-3}$

$$\alpha_2 = 2{\cdot}274 \times 10^{-2}$$

from (vii) for $\alpha_1 = 4 \times 10^{-3}$

$$64 \times 10^{-9} + 16 \times 10^{-6}\,\alpha_2 + 7\,(0{\cdot}296 \times 10^{-3})^2 \times 4 \times 10^{-3}$$
$$-(0{\cdot}296 \times 10^{-3})^2 \times \alpha_2 - 4(0{\cdot}296 \times 10^{-3})^2 = 0$$

$$\alpha_2 = 1{\cdot}784 \times 10^{-2} \quad \ldots\ldots \quad \text{(xii)}$$

and for $\alpha_1 = 5 \times 10^{-3}$

$$\alpha_2 = 0{\cdot}8925 \times 10^{-2}$$

Similarly to the case in *Figure 15*, the point of intersection of the two straight lines drawn through the two pairs of points (vi) and (vii) is found to lie at

$$\left.\begin{aligned} \alpha_1 &= 3{\cdot}97 \times 10^{-3} \\ \alpha_2 &= 1{\cdot}81 \times 10^{-2} \end{aligned} \quad \text{(first approximation)} \right\} \quad \ldots \quad \text{(xiii)}$$

It will be seen that this point lies just outside the trial values of 4×10^{-3} and 5×10^{-3} taken for α_1, so that a slight extrapolation, rather than interpolation, is actually involved.

As a second approximation, the additional value of $\alpha_1 = 3{\cdot}95 \times 10^{-3}$ is, therefore, taken. Substituting this value in (vi) gives $\alpha_2 = 1{\cdot}805 \times 10^{-2}$; substitution in (vii) gives $\alpha_2 = 1{\cdot}849 \times 10^{-2}$.

Combining these latter values of α_1 with those when $\alpha_1 = 4 \times 10^{-3}$ [as calculated at (xi) and (xii)], the pairs of values to be used as a second approximation are found to be

for (vi):
$$\left.\begin{aligned} \alpha_1 &= 3{\cdot}95 \times 10^{-3} \qquad & \alpha_2 &= 1{\cdot}805 \times 10^{-2} \\ \alpha_1 &= 4 \times 10^{-3} \qquad & \alpha_2 &= 1{\cdot}8255 \times 10^{-2} \end{aligned}\right\} \quad \ldots \quad \text{(xiv)}$$

for (vii):
$$\left.\begin{aligned} \alpha_1 &= 3{\cdot}95 \times 10^{-3} \qquad & \alpha_2 &= 1{\cdot}849 \times 10^{-2} \\ \alpha_1 &= 4 \times 10^{-3} \qquad & \alpha_2 &= 1{\cdot}784 \times 10^{-2} \end{aligned}\right\} \quad \ldots \quad \text{(xv)}$$

The point of intersection so obtained (similarly to the case of *Figure 16*) is thus found to lie at

$$\alpha_1 = 3{\cdot}976 \times 10^{-3} \qquad \alpha_2 = 1{\cdot}8154 \times 10^{-2} \qquad \ldots . \text{(xvi)}$$

Thus, the degree of dissociation in the H_2O—CO_2 mixture at 2000 °K and when $p = 1$ atm is obtained as

$$\left.\begin{aligned} \alpha_1 &= 0{\cdot}00398 \text{ for } H_2O \\ \alpha_2 &= 0{\cdot}01815 \text{ for } CO_2 \end{aligned}\right\} \quad ..\text{(xvii)}$$

Substituting these values in (ii) gives the partial pressures and since $p_i/p = x_i$ represents mole fraction, the mole per cent is found for $p = 1$ atm. by multiplying the partial pressure by 100. It, therefore, follows from (ii):

$$p_{H_2O} = \frac{2(1 - 0{\cdot}00398)}{4 + 0{\cdot}00398 + 0{\cdot}01815} = \frac{1{\cdot}99204}{4{\cdot}02213} = 0{\cdot}4953 \text{ atm, i. e. } 49{\cdot}53 \text{ mole per cent } H_2O$$

$$p_{H_2} = \frac{2 \times 0{\cdot}00398}{4{\cdot}02213} = 0{\cdot}0020 \text{ atm, i. e. } 0{\cdot}20 \text{ mole per cent } H_2$$

$$p_{CO_2} = \frac{2(1 - 0{\cdot}01815)}{4{\cdot}02213} = 0{\cdot}4882 \text{ atm, i. e. } 48{\cdot}82 \text{ mole per cent } CO_2$$

$$p_{CO} = \frac{2 \times 0{\cdot}01815}{4{\cdot}02213} = 0{\cdot}0090 \text{ atm, i. e. } 0{\cdot}90 \text{ mole per cent } CO$$

$$p_{O_2} = \frac{0{\cdot}00398 + 0{\cdot}01815}{4{\cdot}02213} = 0{\cdot}0055 \text{ atm, i. e. } 0{\cdot}55 \text{ mole per cent } O_2$$

$$\text{Total: } = 1{\cdot}0000 \text{ atm, i. e. } 100{\cdot}00 \text{ mole per cent}$$

*Exercise 97

The equilibrium constant for the dissociation reaction $PCl_5 = PCl_3 + Cl_2$ at 212 °C is $K_p = 0{\cdot}252$ atm; calculate K_c. Also determine the degree of dissociation and the total pressure p of PCl_5 when $G = 9{\cdot}65$ g PCl_5 are heated to 212 °C in a closed vessel of volume $V = 2{\cdot}46$ litres.

Solution 97. In the case of the above reaction ν_A and ν_B are both equal to 1. Thus, the reaction index $\Delta\sum\nu_i = 1 + 1 - 1 = 1$, so that, from eqn. (154):

$$K_c = K_p/RT \quad \text{where} \quad R = 0{\cdot}08206 \text{ l.atm/(deg. mole)} \qquad \ldots . \text{(i)}$$

The LMA [from eqn. (160)] is

$$\frac{\alpha^2}{1-\alpha}[C]_0 = K_c \qquad \ldots . \text{(ii)}$$

where $[C]_0 = G/MV$ represents the total molar concentration of PCl_5.
From (ii)

$$\alpha^2 + \frac{K_c}{[C]_0}\alpha - \frac{K_c}{[C]_0} = 0 \quad \text{or} \quad \alpha = \frac{1}{2}\left(-\frac{K_c}{[C]_0} + \sqrt{\left(\frac{K_c}{[C]_0}\right)^2 + \frac{4K_c}{[C_0]}}\right) \qquad \ldots . \text{(iii)}$$

p is calculated from eqn. (17) as

$$p = (1 + \alpha)\frac{G}{M} \times \frac{RT}{V} \quad \text{where} \quad M_{PCl_5} = 208{\cdot}3 \qquad \ldots . \text{(iv)}$$

Substituting the numerical values in (i), (ii), (iii) and (iv) gives:

$$K_c = \frac{0{\cdot}252}{0{\cdot}08206\,(273 + 212)} = 6{\cdot}33 \times 10^{-3}\,(\text{mole/l.}) \quad \ldots. \quad (v)$$

$$[C]_0 = \frac{9{\cdot}65}{208{\cdot}3 \times 2{\cdot}46} = 1{\cdot}884 \times 10^{-2}\,(\text{mole/l.}) \quad \ldots. \quad (vi)$$

$$K_c/[C]_0 = 0{\cdot}3362 \quad \ldots. \quad (vii)$$

$$\alpha = \frac{-0{\cdot}3362 + \sqrt{0{\cdot}1130 + 1{\cdot}3448}}{2} = 0{\cdot}4356 \quad \ldots. \quad (viii)$$

$$p = \frac{1{\cdot}4356 \times 9{\cdot}65 \times 0{\cdot}08206 \times 485}{208{\cdot}3 \times 2{\cdot}46} = 1{\cdot}076 \text{ atm} \quad \ldots. \quad (ix)$$

*Exercise 98

A vessel, which can be closed, is filled with phosgene at a barometer reading of $p_1 = 710$ mm Hg and at a temperature of $\theta_1 = 17$ °C. The gas is virtually undissociated at this temperature. On heating the vessel to $\theta_2 = 500$ °C, the pressure rises to $p_2 = 2007$ mm Hg. Calculate the degree of dissociation α and the equilibrium constants K_p and K_c for dissociation of phosgene into CO and Cl_2 at 500 °C.

Solution 98. It follows from the gas equation [see eqn. (152)] that the total molar concentration $[C]_0$ of phosgene must be

$$\frac{n_0}{V} = [C]_0 = p_1/RT_1 \quad \text{where} \quad T_1 = 273 + \theta_1 \quad \ldots. \quad (i)$$

Thus, the gas equation at temperature $T_2 = 273 + \theta_2$, owing to dissociation of phosgene ($COCl_2 = CO + Cl_2$) is, from eqn. (17) and where the number of breakdown products $\nu = 2$

$$p_2 = \frac{n_0}{V}(1 + \alpha)\,RT_2 = \frac{p_1}{RT_1}(1 + \alpha)\,RT_2$$

or

$$1 + \alpha = \frac{p_2 T_1}{p_1 T_2} \quad \ldots. \quad (ii)$$

where α is the degree of dissociation of phosgene in accordance with the reaction

$$COCl_2 = CO + Cl_2$$

Thus, from eqn. (164) when $\nu_A = \nu_B = 1$:

$$K_p = \frac{\alpha^2}{1 - \alpha^2}\,p_2 \quad \ldots. \quad (iii)$$

and from eqns. (154) or (160):

$$K_c = \frac{\alpha^2}{1 - \alpha^2}\,\frac{p_2}{RT_2} = \frac{\alpha^2}{1 - \alpha}\,\frac{p_1}{RT_1} \quad \ldots. \quad (iv)$$

In all these expressions p should be taken in atm, and R as 0·08206 l. atm/(deg.mole).

Substituting the numerical values gives

$$1 + \alpha = \frac{2007 \times 290}{710 \times 773} = 1{\cdot}0604 \qquad \alpha = 0{\cdot}0604 \quad \ldots\ldots \quad \text{(v)}$$

$$K_p = \frac{0{\cdot}003648}{0{\cdot}996352} \times \frac{2007}{760} = 9{\cdot}68 \times 10^{-3}\ \text{atm.} \quad \ldots\ldots \quad \text{(vi)}$$

$$K_c = \frac{9{\cdot}68 \times 10^{-3}}{0{\cdot}08206 \times 773} = 1{\cdot}525 \times 10^{-4}\ \text{mole/l.} \quad \ldots\ldots \quad \text{(vii)}$$

*Exercise 99

A vessel, which can be closed, has a volume $V = 3{\cdot}64$ l. It is filled with chlorine at a temperature of $\theta_1 = 20$ °C and at a barometer reading of $p_1 = 720$ mm Hg. The vessel also contains $G = 19{\cdot}5$ g of solid antimony pentachloride. What is the total pressure p if the closed vessel is heated to a temperature $\theta_2 = 212$ °C? At this temperature, as was found in Exercise 95 (v), the equilibrium constant for the decomposition of $SbCl_5$ into $SbCl_3$ and Cl_2 is given by $K_p = 0{\cdot}338$ atm.

Solution 99. For equilibrium in the decomposition reaction $SbCl_5 = SbCl_3 + Cl_2$, where $\nu_A = \nu_B = 1$, the LMA is [from eqn. (154)]:

$$\frac{p_{SbCl_3} p_{Cl_2}}{p_{SbCl_5}} = K_p \quad \ldots\ldots \quad \text{(i)}$$

From the gas equation [see eqns. (1), (17) and (161)], the partial pressures, at a degree of dissociation α, will be

$$\left.\begin{aligned} p_{SbCl_5} &= (1 - \alpha) RT_2 [C]_0 \\ p_{SbCl_3} &= \alpha RT_2 [C]_0 \\ p_{Cl_2} &= \alpha RT_2 [C]_0 + \frac{p_1 T_2}{T_1} \end{aligned}\right\} \quad \ldots \quad \text{(ii)}$$

The pressure is measured in atm and R is taken as 0·08206 l. atm/(deg. mole). The total molar concentration of $SbCl_5$ will be $[C]_0 = G/MV$ where $M = 299$ g/mole. The partial pressure of Cl_2 is made up from the chlorine dissociation pressure of $SbCl_5$ and from the chlorine gas initially charged into the vessel. The latter must be adjusted from $T_1 = 273 + \theta_1$, to $T_2 = 273 + \theta_2$ by using the gas equation (1), which is

$$\frac{p_2 V}{T_2} = \frac{p_1 V}{T_1} \quad \text{i.e.} \quad p_2 = \frac{p_1 T_2}{T_1}$$

The total pressure p, the sum of the partial pressures at (ii), will be

$$p = (1 + \alpha) RT_2 \frac{G}{MV} + \frac{p_1 T_2}{T_1} \quad \ldots\ldots \quad \text{(iii)}$$

Substituting (ii) in (i) gives

$$K_p = \frac{\alpha}{1 - \alpha} \left(\alpha RT_2 \frac{G}{MV} + \frac{p_1 T_2}{T_1} \right) \quad \ldots\ldots \quad \text{(iv)}$$

Rearrangement of (iv) gives the equation

$$\alpha^2 + \alpha \left(\frac{p_1}{T_1} + \frac{K_p}{T_2} \right) \frac{MV}{GR} - \frac{K_p MV}{T_2 GR} = 0 \quad \ldots\ldots \quad \text{(v)}$$

The numerical values are

$$
\begin{aligned}
V &= 3{\cdot}64\ \text{l.}\\
M &= 299\ \text{g/mole}\\
G &= 19{\cdot}5\ \text{g}\\
p_1 &= 720/760\ \text{atm}\\
T_1 &= 273 + 20 = 293\ {}^\circ\text{K}\\
T_2 &= 273 + 212 = 485\ {}^\circ\text{K}\\
K_p &= 0{\cdot}338\ \text{atm}\\
R &= 0{\cdot}80206\ \text{l. atm/(deg. mole)}
\end{aligned}
$$

From which follows

$$
\left.
\begin{aligned}
p_1/T_1 &= \frac{720}{760 \times 293} = 3{\cdot}2333 \times 10^{-3}\ \text{atm/deg.}\\
K_p/T_2 &= \frac{0{\cdot}338}{485} = 0{\cdot}6969 \times 10^{-3}\ \text{atm/deg.}\\
\frac{MV}{GR} &= \frac{299 \times 3{\cdot}64}{19{\cdot}5 \times 0{\cdot}08206} = 680{\cdot}16\ \text{deg./atm}
\end{aligned}
\right\} \quad \ldots \text{(vi)}
$$

Substituting the numerical values at (vi) in eqn. (v), one obtains

$$\alpha^2 + \alpha(3{\cdot}2333 \times 10^{-3} + 0{\cdot}6969 \times 10^{-3})\,680{\cdot}16 - 0{\cdot}6969 \times 10^{-3} \times 680{\cdot}16 = 0$$

or

$$\alpha^2 + 2{\cdot}6731\alpha - 0{\cdot}47401 = 0 \qquad \ldots\ldots \text{(vii)}$$

Thus

$$\alpha = \frac{-2{\cdot}6731 + \sqrt{2{\cdot}6731^2 + 4 \times 0{\cdot}47401}}{2} = 0{\cdot}1669 \qquad \ldots\ldots \text{(viii)}$$

Substituting this value of α in (iii), the total pressure at 212 °C is seen to be

$$
\left.
\begin{aligned}
p &= 485\left(\frac{1{\cdot}1669}{680{\cdot}16} + 3{\cdot}2333 \times 10^{-3}\right) = 2{\cdot}400\ \text{atm}\\
\text{or} \quad & 2{\cdot}400 \times 760 = 1824\ \text{mm Hg}
\end{aligned}
\right\} \quad \ldots \text{(ix)}
$$

Exercise 100

In order to synthesize methyl alcohol, a mixture of CO and H_2 is passed over activated zinc oxide at 320 °C and at a pressure of $p = 200$ atm. The equilibrium constant for the reaction $CO + 2H_2 = CH_3OH$ is given by $K_p = 6{\cdot}7 \times 10^{-5}\ \text{atm}^{-2}$ at 320 °C.

What volume fraction (or mole fraction) of the original CO–H_2 mixture is converted into methyl alcohol? What are the volume fractions of methyl alcohol and other components in the equilibrium mixture if the composition of the initial mixture is

(*a*) 60 vol. per cent CO: 40 vol. per cent H_2

(*b*) 33·3 vol. per cent CO: 66·7 vol. per cent H_2 (stoichiometric proportions)

(*c*) 10 vol. per cent CO: 90 vol. per cent H_2?

Compare the yield of methyl alcohol in the three cases.

Solution 100. The method of solution is analogous to that used in Exercise 90. In this case, however, it must be remembered that, instead of zero, the reaction index is $\Delta\sum\nu_i = 1 - (1 + 2) = -2$. This results in a decrease in the number of moles and a decrease in volume during reaction at constant pressure; these facts must be borne in mind when calculating the mole fractions, concentrations, partial pressures, etc., associated with the law of mass action. Volume per cent and mole per cent, volume and mole fractions will be taken as being identical, i.e. as for the ideal gas state. In case (*a*) one then has the mole or volume fractions as

$$x_{0\,CO} = 0{\cdot}60 \qquad x_{0\,H_2} = 0{\cdot}40 \quad \ldots\ldots \quad \text{(i)}$$

If, in order to establish equilibrium, a volume or mole fraction y of CO of the original mixture (or $3\,y$ of the total mixture) is converted into methyl alcohol, then y moles or parts by volume of the latter will be formed and $x_{0\,CO} - y$ and $x_{0\,H_2} - 2\,y$ will represent the amounts of CO and H_2 still remaining. The initial total volume or mole fraction of $x_{0\,CO} + x_{0\,H_2} = 1$ will, therefore, be reduced to $x_{0\,CO} - y + x_{0\,H_2} - 2\,y + y = x_{0\,CO} + x_{0\,H_2} - 2\,y = 1 - 2\,y$. Thus, in comparison with the initial mixture, the volume and mole fractions, concentrations, etc. are increased in the ratio $1 : (1 - 2\,y)$ and the mole or volume fractions in the equilibrium mixture itself will be:

$$x_{CO} = \frac{x_{0\,CO} - y}{1 - 2\,y} \qquad x_{H_2} = \frac{x_{0\,H_2} - 2\,y}{1 - 2\,y} \qquad x_{CH_3OH} = \frac{y}{1 - 2\,y} \quad \ldots\ldots \quad \text{(ii)}$$

Since the partial pressures are given by $p_i = x_i p$ [see eqn. (10) and also (155)], those in the equilibrium mixture will be:

$$p_{CO} = \frac{x_{0\,CO} - y}{1 - 2\,y}\,p \qquad p_{H_2} = \frac{x_{0\,H_2} - 2\,y}{1 - 2\,y}\,p \qquad p_{CH_3OH} = \frac{y}{1 - 2\,y}\,p \quad \ldots\ldots \quad \text{(iii)}$$

where p is the total pressure which, in this case, is 200 atm.

The law of mass action for the methyl alcohol reaction is $p_{CH_3OH}/(p_{CO} \times p_{H_2}^2) = K_p$ or, after substituting (iii) and simplifying:

$$\frac{y\,(1 - 2\,y)^2}{p^2\,(x_{0\,CO} - y)\,(x_{0\,H_2} - 2\,y)^2} = K_p \quad \ldots\ldots \quad \text{(iv)}$$

Multiplying out gives the following cubic equation for y:

$$y^3 - y^2 + \underbrace{\frac{p^2 K_p\, x_{0\,H_2}\,(4\,x_{0\,CO} + x_{0\,H_2}) + 1}{4\,(p^2 K_p + 1)}}_{A}\,y - \underbrace{\frac{p^2 K_p\, x_{0\,CO}\, x_{0\,H_2}^2}{4\,(p^2 K_p + 1)}}_{B} = 0 \quad \ldots\ldots \quad \text{(v)}$$

This cubic equation is solved by a graphical method after substituting the numerical values and putting the left-hand side of (v) equal to z and plotting the curve $z = f(y)$ on millimetre paper (with y as abscissa and z as ordinate). The point of intersection y_0 with the abscissa axis then represents the required solution. The latter may also be obtained to any desired degree of accuracy by the method of successive approximation, i.e. by calculating the values of z over an ever-decreasing range y_1 to y_2 on either side of y_0 and determining the latter by graphical or mathematical interpolation (*regula falsi* method). Since graphical interpolation was described in detail in Exercise 95 (*Figures 15* and *16*), only the numerical values will be calculated here and will be given without an explanatory diagram.

One can also start with eqn. (iv) in order to determine y. This is done by taking a suitable number of values of y and plotting the differences between the left-hand side and right-hand side of the equation. The solution y_0 is obtained when the difference is zero. The convenience of one or the other method merely depends on the nature of the numerical values. The first method will be chosen here.

Case (a). Substituting the numerical values gives

$p = 200$ atm $\quad K_p = 6{\cdot}7 \times 10^{-5}\,\text{atm}^{-2} \quad x_{0\,CO} = 0{\cdot}60 \quad x_{0\,H_2} = 0{\cdot}40$

$$p^2 K_p = 200 \times 200 \times 6{\cdot}7 \times 10^{-5} = 2{\cdot}68$$

$$4(p^2 K_p + 1) = 4(2{\cdot}68 + 1) = 14{\cdot}72$$

$$p^2 K_p x_{0\,CO} x^2_{0\,H_2} = 2{\cdot}68 \times 0{\cdot}60 \times 0{\cdot}40 \times 0{\cdot}40 = 0{\cdot}2573$$

$$p^2 K_p x_{0\,H_2}(4x_{0\,CO} + x_{0\,H_2}) + 1 = 2{\cdot}68 \times 0{\cdot}40(4 \times 0{\cdot}60 + 0{\cdot}40) + 1 = 4{\cdot}0016$$

Thus A in (v) is

$$\text{A} = \frac{4{\cdot}0016}{14{\cdot}72} = 0{\cdot}27185$$

and the term B:

$$\text{B} = \frac{0{\cdot}2573}{14{\cdot}72} = 0{\cdot}017480$$

Equation (v) then reads

$$y^3 - y^2 + 27{\cdot}185 \times 10^{-2} y - 1{\cdot}7480 \times 10^{-2} = 0 \qquad \ldots . \text{(vi)}$$

A glance at (iv) shows that a useful, positive value of y can only lie between 0 and $x_{0\,H_2}/2 = 0{\cdot}20$. Otherwise $x_{0\,H_2} - 2y$, and hence the mole fraction of H_2, would be negative.

When $y = 0$, the right-hand side of (vi) is $z = -1{\cdot}7480 \times 10^{-2}$

for $\quad y = 0{\cdot}1 \quad z = +0{\cdot}0705 \times 10^{-2}$

for $\quad y = 0{\cdot}2 \quad z = +0{\cdot}4890 \times 10^{-2}$

Plotting these values shows that $z = 0$ when y lies between 0·09 and 0·1. Using the *regula falsi* method one also has

$$\left.\begin{aligned} y = y_1 - (y_2 - y_1)\frac{f(y_1)}{f(y_2) - f(y_1)} &= 0 - \frac{(0{\cdot}1 - 0)(-1{\cdot}7480 \times 10^{-2})}{0{\cdot}0707 \times 10^{-2} - (-1{\cdot}7480 \times 10^{-2})} \\ &= \frac{0{\cdot}17480}{1{\cdot}8185} = 0{\cdot}096 \end{aligned}\right\} \quad .. \text{(vii)}$$

The zero value may, therefore, be more closely bracketed by taking the z value, $z = 0{\cdot}0385 \times 10^{-2}$ when $y = 0{\cdot}09$. Plotting on graph paper, or use of the method illustrated at (vii), thus gives $z = 0$ when y lies between 0·093 and 0·094. Still closer bracketing, using the values $y = 0{\cdot}093$ and $0{\cdot}094$ in (vi), then gives:

$y = 0{\cdot}093 \quad z = -0{\cdot}00422 \times 10^{-2}$

$y = 0{\cdot}094 \quad z = +0{\cdot}00600 \times 10^{-2}$

Finally, by plotting, or using the method at (vii), one obtains

$$z = 0 \quad \text{when} \quad y = 0{\cdot}0934 \qquad \ldots . \text{(viii)}$$

Thus, from an initial mixture of 60 vol. per cent CO and 40 vol. per cent H_2,

9·34 vol. per cent CO or 3 × 9·34 = 28·02 vol. per cent of the total

mixture is converted in order to establish equilibrium.

The composition of the equilibrium mixture is, from (ii)

$$\left.\begin{aligned} x_{\mathrm{CO}} &= \frac{0{\cdot}60 - 0{\cdot}0934}{1 - 2 \times 0{\cdot}0934} = \frac{0{\cdot}5066}{0{\cdot}8132} = 0{\cdot}6230 \quad \text{or} \quad 62{\cdot}30 \text{ vol. per cent CO} \\ x_{\mathrm{H_2}} &= \frac{0{\cdot}40 - 2 \times 0{\cdot}0934}{0{\cdot}8132} = 0{\cdot}2622 \quad \text{or} \quad 26{\cdot}22 \text{ vol. per cent } \mathrm{H_2} \\ x_{\mathrm{CH_3OH}} &= \frac{0{\cdot}0934}{0{\cdot}8132} = 0{\cdot}1148 \quad \text{or} \quad 11{\cdot}48 \text{ vol. per cent } \mathrm{CH_3OH} \end{aligned}\right\} \quad .. \quad \text{(ix)}$$

Case (*b*). Calculation using the same methods as above and taking $x_{0\,\mathrm{CO}} = 0{\cdot}333 = {}^1/_3$, $x_{0\,\mathrm{H_2}} = 0{\cdot}667 = {}^2/_3$ gives the equation

$$y^3 - y^2 + 31{\cdot}07 \times 10^{-2} y - 2{\cdot}696 \times 10^{-2} = 0 \quad .... \quad \text{(x)}$$

Referring to eqn. (iv), y must lie between 0 and $\frac{1}{3}$ if all mole fractions are to remain positive. Successive approximation by bracketing gives the value $y = 0{\cdot}1436$. Thus 14·36 vol. per cent CO of the initial mixture or $3 \times 14{\cdot}36 = 43{\cdot}08$ vol. per cent of the total mixture is converted.

The composition of the equilibrium mixture is, from (ii)

$$\left.\begin{aligned} x_{\mathrm{CO}} &= \frac{0{\cdot}3333 - 0{\cdot}1436}{1 - 2 \times 0{\cdot}1436} = 0{\cdot}2662 \quad \text{or} \quad 26{\cdot}62 \text{ vol. per cent CO} \\ x_{\mathrm{H_2}} &= \frac{0{\cdot}6667 - 2 \times 0{\cdot}1436}{1 - 2 \times 0{\cdot}1436} = 2\,x_{\mathrm{CO}} = 0{\cdot}5324 \quad \text{or} \quad 53{\cdot}24 \text{ vol. per cent } \mathrm{H_2} \\ x_{\mathrm{CH_3OH}} &= \frac{0{\cdot}1436}{1 - 2 \times 0{\cdot}1436} = 0{\cdot}2014 \quad \text{or} \quad 20{\cdot}14 \text{ vol. per cent } \mathrm{CH_3OH} \end{aligned}\right\} \quad .. \quad \text{(xi)}$$

Case (*c*). When $x_{0\,\mathrm{CO}} = 0{\cdot}10$ and $x_{0\,\mathrm{H_2}} = 0{\cdot}90$, the same methods of calculation give the following equation for y

$$y^3 - y^2 + 28{\cdot}095 \times 10^{-2} y - 1{\cdot}4747 \times 10^{-2} = 0 \quad .... \quad \text{(xii)}$$

Referring to eqn. (iv), y must lie between 0 and 0·1 if all mole fractions are to remain positive. Successive approximation gives, in this case, $y = 0{\cdot}0678$. Thus 6·78 vol. per cent CO of the initial mixture or $3 \times 6{\cdot}78 = 20{\cdot}34$ vol. per cent of the total mixture is converted.

The composition of the equilibrium mixture is, from (ii)

$$\left.\begin{aligned} x_{\mathrm{CO}} &= \frac{0{\cdot}1 - 0{\cdot}0678}{1 - 2 \times 0{\cdot}0678} = 0{\cdot}0373 \quad \text{or} \quad 3{\cdot}73 \text{ vol. per cent CO} \\ x_{\mathrm{H_2}} &= \frac{0{\cdot}9 - 2 \times 0{\cdot}0678}{1 - 2 \times 0{\cdot}0678} = 0{\cdot}8842 \quad \text{or} \quad 88{\cdot}42 \text{ vol. per cent } \mathrm{H_2} \\ x_{\mathrm{CH_3OH}} &= \frac{0{\cdot}0678}{1 - 2 \times 0{\cdot}0678} = 0{\cdot}0785 \quad \text{or} \quad 7{\cdot}85 \text{ vol. per cent } \mathrm{CH_3OH} \end{aligned}\right\} \quad .. \quad \text{(xiii)}$$

A plot of y values, i.e. of vol. per cent CH_3OH against vol. per cent of CO in the initial mixture, shows that y (the yield of methyl alcohol) is a maximum if the composition of the initial mixture is exactly in the stoichiometric proportions given by the reaction equation.

Note. Textbooks (see, for example, EUCKEN and JAKOB, *Der Chemieingenieur*, Vol. III, p. 10) show that, at equilibrium, the mole fraction of end product produced is always a maximum when the initial mixture is of stoichiometric composition. This, then, is obviously the best way to ensure maximum yield, provided there is little to choose between the costs of the various initial reactants.

In cases where one of the initial reactants is considerably more costly than the others, the yield must be assessed on the basis of the amount of expensive substance converted. It is well known, and follows from the law of mass action, that the yield can be improved by adding the less valuable initial reactants in large excess, for example, O_2 in the reaction $2\,SO_2 + O_2 = 2\,SO_3$, where an SO_2–air mixture is passed over a suitable contact material. The efficiency of this particular reaction is assessed on the basis of the amount of SO_2 converted. To what extent individual components should be added in excess, and whether, after reaction, they should be recirculated via the initial mixture, are largely commercial questions. Many factors enter into consideration; they include the increased volume of gas mixture to be handled, increase in tube surface area, heating capacity, etc. See also note to Exercise 103.

*Exercise 101

Sulphur trioxide, SO_3, is prepared from sulphur dioxide and oxygen by a contact process. A mixture of SO_2 and O_2, in stoichiometric proportions (66·7 vol. per cent SO_2, 33·3 vol. per cent O_2) is passed through a reaction furnace filled with iron oxide and heated to 600 °C. The volumetric rate of flow of mixture entering the furnace is $\dot{V}_a = 6{\cdot}54$ l./h, the temperature $\theta = 18$ °C and the pressure $p = 1$ atm. The conditions are such that true equilibrium for 600 °C is established during passage through the furnace. After leaving the reaction zone, the equilibrium mixture is passed through acidified $BaCl_2$ solution (through capillaries), so rapidly that the equilibrium remains undisturbed. It is found that $G = 81{\cdot}3$ g $BaSO_4$ are precipitated during the course of $2\frac{1}{2}$ hours. What is the relative yield, $\eta = [SO_3]/[SO_2]$, of SO_3 and what is the value of the equilibrium constant K_p for the reaction $SO_2 + \frac{1}{2}\,O_2 = SO_3$?

Solution 101. The proportion of SO_2 converted, i.e. the yield η, may be calculated from the data given. We have:

$$p = 1 \text{ atm} \qquad R = 0{\cdot}08206\,\frac{\text{l. atm}}{\text{deg. mole}}$$

$$T = 273 + 18 = 291\ °\text{K} \qquad G = 81{\cdot}3 \text{ g}$$

$$M_{BaSO_4} = 233{\cdot}4 \text{ g/mole} \qquad x_{0\,O_2} = 0{\cdot}333 = {}^1/_3$$

$$x_{0\,SO_2} = 0{\cdot}667 = {}^2/_3$$

The total volume of gas mixture entering the reaction furnace is $V_a = \dot{V}_a t = 6{\cdot}54 \times 2{\cdot}5$ l.; the partial pressure, $p_{SO_2} = p\,x_{0\,SO_2} = 1 \times {}^2/_3$ atm. .... (i)

The total quantity of moles of SO_2 introduced is, from gas equation (2):

$$p_{SO_2} V_a = n_{SO_2} \times RT = p\,x_{0\,SO_2}\,\dot{V}_a t \qquad n_{SO_2} = \frac{p\,x_{SO_2}\dot{V}_a t}{RT} \quad \ldots. \quad \text{(ii)}$$

and the total quantity of moles of SO_2 converted, i.e. n_{SO_3} of SO_3 formed, is

$$n_{SO_3} = \frac{G}{M_{BaSO_4}} \quad \ldots. \quad \text{(iii)}$$

Thus the yield $\eta = \dfrac{n_{SO_3}}{n_{SO_2}}$ is

$$\eta = \frac{G\,R\,T}{M_{BaSO_4}\,p\,x_{0\,SO_2}\dot{V}_a t} = \frac{81{\cdot}3 \times 0{\cdot}08206 \times 291 \times 3}{233{\cdot}4 \times 1 \times 6{\cdot}54 \times 2{\cdot}5 \times 2} = 0{\cdot}763 \quad \text{or} \quad 76{\cdot}3 \text{ per cent} \quad \ldots. \quad \text{(iv)}$$

Since the yield η represents the fraction of SO_2 converted, the mole fraction of the latter, or that of SO_3 produced, is equal to $\eta\,x_{0\,SO_2}$. The mole fraction of residual SO_2 is $x_{0\,SO_2}(1-\eta)$ and that for residual oxygen is $x_{0\,O_2} - x_{0SO_2}\,\eta/2$. All fractions refer to the original molar quantity of SO_2—O_2 mixture ($x_{0SO_2} + x_{0\,O_2} = 1$). During reaction a decrease in the number of moles and in volume takes place. This effect, expressed as a ratio, is

$$[x_{0\,SO_2}(1-\eta) + x_{0\,O_2} - x_{0\,SO_2}\eta/2 + \eta\, x_{0\,SO_2}] : [x_{0\,SO_2} + x_{0\,O_2}]$$

or $(1 - x_{0\,SO_2}\eta/2):1$. The mole fractions in the equilibrium mixture are, therefore, as follows:

$$x_{SO_3} = \frac{x_{0\,SO_2}\,\eta}{1 - x_{0\,SO_2}\eta/2} \qquad x_{O_2} = \frac{x_{0\,O_2} - x_{0\,SO_2}\eta/2}{1 - x_{0\,SO_2}\eta/2} \qquad x_{SO_2} = \frac{x_{0\,SO_2}(1-\eta)}{1 - x_{0\,SO_2}\eta/2} \quad \ldots . \quad \text{(v)}$$

According to eqn. (155) and with $\Delta\sum \nu_i = 1 - (1 + {}^1/_2) = -{}^1/_2$, the LMA is

$$\frac{x_{SO_3}}{x_{SO_2}\sqrt{x_{O_2}}\sqrt{p}} = K_p \quad \ldots . \quad \text{(vi)}$$

Substituting the expressions at (v) in (vi), cancelling and dividing by $x_{0\,SO_2}$, gives

$$\frac{\eta}{1-\eta} \times \frac{\sqrt{1/x_{0\,SO_2} - \eta/2}}{\sqrt{x_{0\,O_2}/x_{0\,SO_2} - \eta/2} \times \sqrt{p}} = K_p$$

$$= \frac{0{\cdot}763}{1 - 0{\cdot}763} \times \frac{\sqrt{3 - 0{\cdot}763}}{\sqrt{1 - 0{\cdot}763}\sqrt{1}} = 9{\cdot}89 \text{ atm}^{-1/2} \text{ at } 600\,°\text{C} \quad \ldots . \quad \text{(vii)}$$

Exercise 102

The equilibrium constant for the reaction $SO_2 + \frac{1}{2}O_2 = SO_3$ at 600 °C is $K = 9{\cdot}89$ atm$^{-1/2}$ (see Exercise 101).

(*a*) What is the yield $\eta = [SO_3]/[SO_2]$ of SO_3, i.e. in relation to SO_2 employed, if gas having the composition 84·85 vol. per cent N_2, 10·10 vol. per cent SO_2 and 5·05 vol. per cent O_2 is passed over an iron oxide contact bed at 600 °C and at a pressure of 1 atm? It may be assumed that the residence time is sufficiently long for equilibrium to be established.

(*b*) How is the yield affected if, before reaction, the feed gas is mixed with four times its volume of air? Oxygen content of air = 20·9 vol. per cent.

Solution 102. The yield η, which represents the fraction of SO_2 converted, depends on the magnitude of the mole fractions of the initial reactants and on the equilibrium constant K_p, i.e. in accordance with eqn. (155) for the LMA. The expressions determining the solution are given by (v), (vi) and (vii) in Exercise 101. The fact that, in the present Exercise, the gas mixture is diluted with N_2 is unimportant. The decrease in volume and in number of moles is given by the ratio $[x_{0\,SO_2}(1-\eta) + x_{0\,O_2} - x_{0\,SO_2}\eta/2 + \eta\, x_{0\,SO_2} + x_{0\,N_2}] : (x_{0\,SO_2} + x_{0\,O_2} + x_{0\,N_2})$ or (taking $x_{0\,SO_2} + x_{0\,O_2} + x_{0\,N_2} = 1$) by $1 - x_{0\,SO_2}\eta/2 : 1$, as in Exercise 101. Thus the mole fractions (v) and therefore the expressions at (vi) and (vii) in Exercise 101 still apply in the present case. Equation (vii) again provides a basis from which η may be calculated.

Case (*a*). Substituting the values $x_{0\,O_2} = 5{\cdot}05/100$, $x_{0\,SO_2} = 10{\cdot}10/100 = 2\,x_{O_2}$, $p = 1$ atm and $K_p = 9{\cdot}89$ atm$^{-1/2}$ in eqn. (vii), one has

$$\frac{\eta}{1-\eta}\frac{\sqrt{1/x_{0\,O_2} - \eta}}{\sqrt{1-\eta}} = K_p \quad \text{or} \quad \frac{\eta^2}{(1-\eta)^3}\left(\frac{100}{5{\cdot}05} - \eta\right) = (9{\cdot}89)^2 \quad \ldots . \quad \text{(i)}$$

and finally

$$\frac{\eta^2}{(1-\eta)^3}(19{\cdot}802-\eta)-97{\cdot}812=0 \qquad \ldots\ldots \quad \text{(ii)}$$

as the equation for η. This cubic equation is either solved graphically or by successive approximation and interpolation (*regula falsi*). The left-hand side is put equal to y and the curve $y = f(\eta)$ is plotted. The solution is given by the point of intersection of the curve with the abscissa axis, the plot being made by selecting various values of η lying between 0 and 1. Rough calculation shows that η must lie between 0·55 and 0·6, when one obtains the following corresponding values:

$$\eta_1 = 0{\cdot}55 \qquad y_1 = -33{\cdot}902$$
$$\eta_2 = 0{\cdot}60 \qquad y_2 = +10{\cdot}198$$

Drawing the line connecting these two points on the curve gives a closer approximation for the point of intersection with the abscissa axis, the value being $\eta \approx 0{\cdot}588$. The *regula falsi* method [see Exercise 100 (vii)] also gives

$$\eta = 0{\cdot}55-(0{\cdot}60-0{\cdot}55)\times\frac{(-33{\cdot}902)}{10{\cdot}198-(-33{\cdot}902)} = 0{\cdot}5885$$

A second approximation is obtained by taking the point $\eta_3 = 0{\cdot}59$. Substituting this value in (ii) gives $y_3 = -0{\cdot}78$. Plotting, or using the regula falsi method, between $\eta_2 = 0{\cdot}60$ and $\eta_3 = 0{\cdot}59$, gives a sufficiently accurate answer for case (*a*) of

$$\eta = 0{\cdot}5907 \quad \text{or} \quad 59{\cdot}07 \text{ per cent yield of } SO_3 \qquad \ldots\ldots \quad \text{(iii)}$$

Case (*b*). Here one must bear in mind that the oxygen content of air is 20·9 vol. per cent. The composition of the feed gas when mixed with four times its volume of air is obtained by means of the following expression [see eqns. (64) and (65)]:

$$x_{0\,\mathrm{m}}(V_1+V_2) = x_{0\,1}V_1 + x_{0\,2}V_2 \qquad \ldots\ldots \quad \text{(iv)}$$

Thus, for O_2 $\qquad x_{0\,O_2}(1+4) = 5{\cdot}05\times 1 + 20{\cdot}9\times 4$

i.e. $\qquad x_{0\,O_2} = 17{\cdot}73$ vol. per cent or 0·1773

for SO_2 $\qquad x_{0\,SO_2}(1+4) = 10{\cdot}10\times 1$

i.e. $\qquad x_{0\,SO_2} = 2{\cdot}02$ vol. per cent or 0·0202 $\qquad \ldots\ldots$ (v)

Since $1/x_{0\,SO_2} = 1/0{\cdot}0202 = 49{\cdot}505$ and $x_{0\,O_2}/x_{0\,SO_2} = 0{\cdot}1773/0{\cdot}0202 = 8{\cdot}777$, one obtains, by substituting in (vii) at Exercise 101 and squaring:

$$\frac{\eta^2}{1-\eta^2}\times\frac{(49{\cdot}505-\eta/2)}{(8{\cdot}777-\eta/2)} - 97{\cdot}812 = 0\,(=y) \qquad \ldots\ldots \quad \text{(vi)}$$

This cubic equation is solved graphically, as for Case (*a*).

Rough calculation shows that η is about 0·8; when $\eta_1 = 0{\cdot}80$, $y_1 = -4{\cdot}023$ [by substituting in (vi)] and when $\eta_2 = 0{\cdot}85$, $y_2 = +91$. Interpolation then gives a first approximate value of $\eta \approx 0{\cdot}802$. Now, taking $\eta_3 = 0{\cdot}804$, it is found that $y_3 = +0{\cdot}845$. Combining η_3 with η_1 gives a solution of sufficient accuracy of $\eta = 0{\cdot}8033$ or 80·33 per cent as the yield of SO_3 for Case (*b*). It will be seen that dilution of the feed gas with four times its volume of air leads to an increased yield of SO_3, i.e. an improvement from 59·07 per cent to 80·33 per cent, based on the amount of SO_2 introduced.

*EXERCISE 103

The equilibrium constant K_p for the reaction $SO_2 + \frac{1}{2}O_2 = SO_3$ at 600 °C was found to be $K_p = 9{\cdot}89$ atm$^{-1/2}$. What is the composition of the equilibrium mixture leaving the reaction zone if pure SO_3 is fed into the furnace at 600 °C and 710 mm Hg pressure?

Solution 103. It follows from the law of mass action that the equilibrium constant for the decomposition reaction $SO_3 = SO_2 + \frac{1}{2}O_2$ must be $K'_p = 1/K_p = 1/9{\cdot}89$ atm$^{1/2}$. The degree of dissociation α for SO_3 may be obtained from eqn. (164), so that, by determining the mole fractions $x_i = p_i/p$, the composition is calculated from eqn. (161).

In eqn. (164), one has $\nu_A = \nu_{SO_2} = 1$, $\nu_B = \nu_{O_2} = \frac{1}{2}$, $p = 710/760$ atm. Substituting and squaring gives

$$\frac{\alpha^3}{(1-\alpha)^2} \times \frac{1}{2}\left(\frac{710}{760} \times \frac{1}{1+\alpha/2}\right) = \frac{1}{9{\cdot}89^2} \quad \text{or} \quad \frac{\alpha^3}{(1-\alpha)^2(2-\alpha)} = \frac{760}{710 \times 9{\cdot}89^2}$$

or finally

$$\frac{(1-\alpha)^2(2+\alpha)}{\alpha^3} - 91{\cdot}378 = 0\,(= y) \qquad \ldots\ldots \quad \text{(i)}$$

This cubic equation is solved graphically by putting the left-hand side equal to y, interpolating between any close pair of numerical values for α lying between 0 and 1 and finally determining the value of α for which $y = 0$.

Rough calculation shows that α must lie between 0·25 and 0·20. When $\alpha_1 = 0{\cdot}25$, (i) gives $-10{\cdot}4$ for y_1 and when $\alpha_2 = 0{\cdot}20$, $y_2 = +84{\cdot}6$. Plotting the point of intersection, of the line joining the two points (α_1, y_1) (α_2, y_2), with the abscissa axis $(y = 0)$, gives a first approximate value of $\alpha \approx 0{\cdot}245$. Taking $\alpha_3 = 0{\cdot}240$ and $\alpha_4 = 0{\cdot}245$, for the purpose of more accurate interpolation, and substituting in (i) gives

$$\alpha_3 = 0{\cdot}240 \qquad y_3 = +2{\cdot}215$$
$$\alpha_4 = 0{\cdot}245 \qquad y_4 = -4{\cdot}362$$

Graphic interpolation then gives a sufficiently accurate value of $\alpha = 0{\cdot}2417$. Using the regula falsi method [see Exercise 100 (vii)], we find that

$$\alpha = 0{\cdot}240 - (0{\cdot}245 - 0{\cdot}240) \times \frac{(+\,2{\cdot}215)}{(-\,4{\cdot}362 - 2{\cdot}215)} = 0{\cdot}24169$$

Thus the degree of dissociation of SO_3 under the given conditions is

$$\alpha_{SO_3} = 0{\cdot}2417 \quad \text{or} \quad 24{\cdot}17 \text{ per cent} \qquad \ldots\ldots \quad \text{(ii)}$$

The mole fractions in the equilibrium mixture are obtained from eqn. (161) as

$$\left.\begin{aligned} x_{SO_3} &= p_{SO_3}/p = \frac{1-\alpha}{1+\alpha/2} = \frac{1-0{\cdot}2417}{1+0{\cdot}12085} = 0{\cdot}6766 \quad \text{or} \quad 67{\cdot}66 \text{ vol. per cent} \\ x_{SO_2} &= p_{SO_2}/p = \frac{\alpha}{1+\alpha/2} = \frac{0{\cdot}2417}{1+0{\cdot}12085} = 0{\cdot}2156 \quad \text{or} \quad 21{\cdot}56 \text{ vol. per cent} \\ x_{O_2} &= p_{O_2}/p = \frac{\alpha/2}{1+\alpha/2} = \frac{0{\cdot}2417}{2+0{\cdot}2417} = 0{\cdot}1078 \quad \text{or} \quad 10{\cdot}78 \text{ vol. per cent} \end{aligned}\right\} \quad \ldots \quad \text{(iii)}$$

Note to Exercises 101-103 (see also note to Exercise 100). The reaction $SO_2 + \frac{1}{2} O_2 = SO_3$ with a reaction index $\Delta\Sigma_{\nu i} = 1 - (1 + \frac{1}{2}) = -\frac{1}{2}$ leads to a decrease in volume (paralleled by an increase for the reverse reaction). This effect must be taken into account when calculating mole fractions, concentrations and partial pressures for the purpose of applying the law of mass action [see Exercise 101 (v) and 100 (iii)]. Incorrect results are often obtained if this consideration is ignored.

The reaction $SO_2 + \frac{1}{2} O_2 = SO_3$ is a typical case where the yield of product SO_3 is referred to the amount of more expensive initial reactant (SO_2) employed. The cost of the admixed air can be ignored. In such a case, the yield is expressed in terms of the fraction of SO_2 converted, i.e. $\eta = [SO_3]/[SO_2]$. For a straight-forward type of reaction (as in the present case), the yield of the process (or chemical efficiency) may also be expressed as

$$\eta = \frac{\dot{V}_a c_{ia} - \dot{V}_e c_{ie}}{\dot{V}_a c_{ia}} \quad \ldots \quad \text{(iv)}$$

where $\dot{V}_a$ is the volumetric rate of flow of initial reactants fed into the reaction chamber and c_{ia} is the molar concentration of the component X_i in the initial mixture. $\dot{V}_e$ and c_{ie} are the volumetric rate of flow and molar concentration, respectively, of the final product leaving the reaction vessel. The product $\dot{V}_a c_{ia}$ represents the throughput* of component X_i (rate of feed in unit time = production). The difference $\dot{V}_a c_{ia} - \dot{V}_e c_{ie}$ represents the quantity of X_i converted in unit time or the output capacity* of the plant. From (iv) we get the important expression

$$\text{Output} = \text{yield} \times \text{troughput} \quad \ldots \quad \text{(v)}$$

Plant operating time × output determines the amount of substance produced. It also determines overhead charges such as cost of plant, which, as opposed to operating costs, must be met whether the plant is operating or idle. It will be appreciated therefore that operating time, yield and throughput are important factors to be reckoned with. It is often advantageous to accept a slight drop in yield but to increase the output by raising the rate of feed. After separating the reaction product, the unconverted portion of the mixture can then be recirculated through the reaction furnace. This is done in the case of ammonia synthesis or when carrying out catalytic hydrogenation (fuel synthesis).

Exercise 102 shows the effect of the presence of an excess component (air) in promoting an increased yield, in comparison with (vii) in Exercise 101. With this example to hand, it should be pointed out that an *ad lib.* increase in the amount of excess component will not result in the yield asymptotically approaching the limiting value of 1. It will, in fact, result in a lower limiting value, determined mainly by the reaction index. With a progressive increase in the amount of excess O_2 (either pure oxygen or in mixture with air) there will be a decrease in $x_{0\,SO_2}$, asymptotically approaching a limiting value of 0; (vii) then becomes

$$\lim_{x_{0\,SO_2}\to 0} \frac{\eta}{1-\eta} \times \frac{\sqrt{1/x_{0\,SO_2} - \eta/2}}{\sqrt{x_{0\,O_2}/x_{0\,SO_2} - \eta/2}\,\sqrt{p}} = \frac{\eta}{1-\eta} \times \frac{1}{\sqrt{x_{0\,O_2}\,p}} = K_p$$

or

$$\lim_{x_{0\,SO_2}\to 0} \eta = \frac{K_p\sqrt{x_{0\,O_2}\,p}}{1 + K_p\sqrt{x_{0\,O_2}\,p}} \quad \ldots \quad \text{(vi)}$$

For the conditions in Exercise 102, $p = 1$ atm, $K_p = 9{\cdot}89\ \text{atm}^{-1/2}$ at 600 °C, and when an unlimited amount of pure oxygen is added (i.e. $\lim x_{0\,O_2} = 1$), the limiting value for the yield will be

$$\lim_{x_{0\,O_2}\to 1} \eta = \frac{K_p}{1 + K_p} = \frac{9{\cdot}89}{1 + 9{\cdot}89} = 90{\cdot}8 \text{ per cent}$$

* In practice, throughput and output are usually referred to unit volume of reaction space or catalyst, rather than to the total volume V_R of the reaction chamber; i.e. troughput $= \dot{V}_a c_{ia}/V_R$ and the output (in this case, also referred to as yield per unit volume and time) $= (\dot{V}_a c_{ia} - \dot{V}_e c_{ie})/V_R$.

and when unlimited oxygen is added in the form of air (i.e. $\lim x_{0\,O_2} = 0{\cdot}209$), it follows that

$$\lim_{x_{0\,O_2} \to 0{\cdot}209} \eta = \frac{9{\cdot}89\sqrt{0{\cdot}209}}{1 + 9{\cdot}89\sqrt{0{\cdot}209}} = 81{\cdot}9 \text{ per cent}$$

The relation between the residence time t_r during which a component remains in the reaction furnace (referred to in Exercise 102), and the reaction volume V_R and the volumetric rate of flow $\dot{V}$ (volume velocity), is

$$t_r = V_R/\dot{V} \qquad \ldots\ldots \quad \text{(vii)}$$

This relation is important when considering the question of establishment of equilibrium or the progress of ambiguous reactions. In English-speaking countries the reciprocal expression $\dot{V}/V_R$(volume–space velocity) is preferred, i.e. the volume of feed (under standard conditions) is referred to unit time and unit volume of reaction space or catalyst.

Exercise 104

If solid NH_4I is rapidly heated to 357 °C it shows a vapour pressure $p_0 = 275$ torr. At this temperature, however, NH_4I is virtually completely dissociated into NH_3 and HI, so that the observed vapour pressure must be equal to the sum of the partial pressures $p_{0\,NH_3}$ and $p_{0\,HI}$. If the temperature is held constant over a period of time, the pressure over the solid NH_4I phase rises as HI dissociates according to the equation $HI = \frac{1}{2}H_2 + \frac{1}{2}I_2$, for which the equilibrium constant $K_p = 0{\cdot}127$ at 357 °C. What is the final pressure p_e over the solid NH_4I after equilibrium has been established?

Solution 104. The state of the system is essentially determined by two equilibria. For the first, $NH_4I = NH_3 + HI$, the LMA gives

$$\frac{p_{NH_3}\,p_{HI}}{p_{NH_4I}} = K'_p \qquad \ldots\ldots \quad \text{(i)}$$

Because NH_4I is present as solid phase, its vapour pressure p_{NH_4I} is constant at constant temperature; thus the term p_{NH_4I} can be transferred to the right-hand side of (i) and combined with K'_p to give a new constant K''_p. It follows that, when applying the LMA to this heterogeneous system, p_{NH_4I} can be ignored and (i) now becomes

$$p_{NH_3} \times p_{HI} = K''_p \qquad \ldots\ldots \quad \text{(ii)}$$

Since, when NH_4I is heated rapidly, the observed vapour pressure p_0 is virtually only the sum of the (equal) partial pressures of the dissociation products NH_3 and HI, one may write

$$p_0 = p_{0\,NH_3} + p_{0\,HI} \quad \text{where } p_{0\,NH_3} = p_{0\,HI} \text{ and, therefore,}$$

$$p_{0\,NH_3} = p_{0\,HI} = \frac{p_0}{2} \qquad \ldots\ldots \quad \text{(iii)}$$

It is now possible to calculate the unknown K''_p. From (ii) and (iii), one has

$$p_{0\,NH_3}\,p_{0\,HI} = \frac{p_0}{2} \times \frac{p_0}{2} = \frac{p_0^2}{4} = K''_p \qquad \ldots\ldots \quad \text{(iv)}$$

and

$$p_{NH_3}\,p_{HI} = \frac{p_0^2}{4} \qquad \ldots\ldots \quad \text{(v)}$$

In the case of the second equilibrium, $HI = \frac{1}{2}H_2 + \frac{1}{2}I_2$, the LMA gives

$$\frac{p_{H_2}^{1/2}\, p_{I_2}^{1/2}}{p_{HI}} = K_p \qquad \ldots\ldots \text{(vi)}$$

If, during the second stage of the experiment, the HI formed up to the time when equilibrium is established, then dissociates according to (vi), the dissociation equilibrium of NH_4I at (v) must simultaneously adjust itself. The following equations then hold good:

(1) $$p_e = p_{e\,NH_3} + p_{e\,HI} + p_{e\,H_2} + p_{e\,I_2}$$

i.e. the total final pressure is equal to the sum of the partial pressures after final equilibrium has been reached.

(2) $$p_{e\,H_2} = p_{e\,I_2}$$

because HI dissociates into equal parts of H_2 and I_2.

(3) $$p_{e\,NH_3} = p_{e\,HI} + p_{e\,H_2} + p_{e\,I_2}$$

NH_4I first dissociates into equal parts of NH_3 and HI, so that, in the first place, $p_{NH_3} = p_{HI}$ [see (iii)]. If the HI now dissociates into $\frac{1}{2}I_2 + \frac{1}{2}H_2$, the pressure for this part of the system remains unchanged because each mole of HI gives rise to half-mole quantities of H_2 and I_2. It follows that the number of moles also remains the same (reaction index = 0). Thus, the partial pressure of NH_3 must always equal the sum of the partial pressures of HI and its dissociation products, H_2 and I_2, as stated at (3)*.

(4) $$p_{e\,NH_3}\, p_{e\,HI} = \frac{p_0^2}{4} \qquad \text{[see (v)]}$$

(5) $$(p_{e\,H_2}\, p_{e\,I_2})^{1/2} = K_p\, p_{e\,HI} \qquad \text{[see (vi)]}$$

One therefore has a set of five equations with five unknowns. By way of solution, one obtains, from (3) and (2)

$$p_{e\,NH_3} = p_{e\,HI} + 2\,p_{e\,H_2} \qquad \ldots\ldots \text{(vii)}$$

and, from (5) and (2)

$$p_{e\,H_2} = K_p\, p_{e\,HI} \qquad \ldots\ldots \text{(viii)}$$

from (vii) and (viii)

$$p_{e\,NH_3} = p_{e\,HI}(1 + 2\,K_p) \qquad \ldots\ldots \text{(ix)}$$

Elimination of $p_{e\,HI}$ from (ix) and (4) gives

$$p_{e\,NH_3} = \frac{p_0}{2}\sqrt{1 + 2\,K_p} \qquad \ldots\ldots \text{(x)}$$

and, since from (1) and (3)

$$p_e = 2\,p_{e\,NH_3} \qquad \ldots\ldots \text{(xi)}$$

it follows that

$$p_e = p_0\sqrt{1 + 2\,K_p} \qquad \ldots\ldots \text{(xii)}$$

* The literature previously, and incorrectly, gave the equation $p_{e\,NH_3} = p_{e\,HI} + \frac{p_{e\,H_2} + p_{e\,I_2}}{2}$ for this problem. This led to incorrect final formulae.

Substituting the numerical values in (xii) gives the total, final, stable equilibrium pressure of the system as

$$p_e = 275\sqrt{1 + 2 \times 0{\cdot}127} = 308{\cdot}0 \text{ torr} \qquad \ldots . \text{(xiii)}$$

Exercise 105

The vapour pressure p_0 over solid ammonium chloride, NH_4Cl, at 46 °C is approximately 0·1 torr. Since, at this temperature, the vapour is virtually completely dissociated according to the equation

$$NH_4Cl = NH_3 + HCl$$

the vapour pressure is essentially the sum of the partial pressures $p_{0\,NH_3}$ and $p_{0\,HCl}$. If powdered lead oxide, PbO, is mixed with the ammonium chloride and the temperature remains constant, the pressure of the system increases to about 1 atm. This is due to the fact that the PbO reacts with HCl gas to form basic lead chloride, $PbCl_2 . Pb(OH)_2$, in accordance with the equation

$$2\,PbO + 2\,HCl = PbCl_2 \,.\, Pb(OH)_2$$

Calculate the vapour pressure of HCl, $p_{e\,HCl}$ (dissociation pressure), over $PbCl_2$. $Pb(OH)_2$ at 46 °C.

Solution 105. Since, in the case of heterogeneous equilibria where solid phases are present, the partial pressures of the latter may be ignored for the purpose of the LMA [see (158)], the law of mass action for the dissociation equilibrium of ammonium chloride will be

$$p_{NH_3}\, p_{HCl} = K'_p \qquad \ldots . \text{(i)}$$

The vapour pressure of solid ammonium chloride is

$$p_0 = p_{0\,NH_3} + p_{0\,HCl} \qquad \ldots . \text{(ii)}$$

and

$$p_{0\,NH_3} = p_{0\,HCl} \qquad \ldots . \text{(iii)}$$

so that

$$p_{0\,NH_3} = p_{0\,HCl} = \frac{p_0}{2} \qquad \ldots . \text{(iv)}$$

K'_p is obtained by substituting (iv) in (i):

$$K'_p = \frac{p_0^2}{4} \qquad \ldots . \text{(v)}$$

Bearing in mind that the PbO and $PbCl_2$. $Pb(OH)_2$ are present as solid phases and that their vapour pressures do not, therefore, enter into the LMA, one has for the reaction between PbO and HCl

$$p_{e\,HCl} = K''_p \qquad \ldots . \text{(vi)}$$

i.e. $p_{e\,HCl}$ remains constant as long as PbO and $PbCl_2$. $Pb(OH)_2$ are present as solid phases.

The total pressure over the mixture of NH_4Cl, PbO and $PbCl_2 . Pb(OH)_2$ is

$$p_e = p_{e\,HCl} + p_{e\,NH_3} \quad \ldots. \quad (vii)$$

Eliminating $p_{e\,NH_3}$ and K'_p by using (i) and (v), one obtains from (vii)

$$p_e = p_{e\,HCl} + \frac{p_0^2}{4}\,\frac{1}{p_{e\,HCl}} \quad \text{or} \quad p^2_{e\,HCl} - p_e\,p_{e\,HCl} + \frac{p_0^2}{4} = 0 \quad \ldots. \quad (viii)$$

Substituting the numerical values in (vii) gives

$$p^2_{e\,HCl} - 760\,p_{e\,HCl} + \frac{0{\cdot}01}{4} = 0 \qquad p_{e\,HCl} \approx \frac{0{\cdot}01}{4{\cdot}760} = 3{\cdot}3 \times 10^{-6}\ \text{torr} \quad \ldots. \quad (ix)$$

The HCl dissociation pressure over the basic lead chloride is thus so small that virtually all the HCl produced by dissociation of the ammonium chloride becomes absorbed by the PbO.

Note (to Exercises 104 and 105). Exercise 105 is a standard example of the mathematical treatment for the 'expulsion' of a weak base (NH_3) from a solid salt (NH_4Cl) arising from mechanical admixture with a stronger solid base (PbO). The NH_3 pressure during displacement is virtually a measure of the relative strength of the base. In practice — as is well known — slaked lime, $Ca(OH)_2$, is used as a stronger (and cheaper) base for displacing NH_3 from ammonium salts (and also for detecting the presence of NH_4 groups in qualitative analysis). A similar mathematical treatment may be adopted for the case of displacement of a weak acid from a solid salt, e.g. $(NH_4)_2CO_3$, by mixing it with a solid acid (or acid anhydride, e.g. phosphorus pentoxide).

The treatment in Exercises 104 and 105 is very similar. In Exercise 104 one dissociation product (HI) is removed from the system on account of its own dissociation. In Exercise 105 the HCl is removed by absorption. The essential procedure in both exercises is the combination of two equilibria.

*Exercise 106

Calculate the equilibrium constants K_p for the pair of composite reactions

(I) $$3H_2 + SO_2 = 2H_2O + H_2S \qquad (K_p^{I})$$

(II) $$3S_2 + 4H_2O = 4H_2S + 2SO_2 \qquad (K_p^{II})$$

at 1200 °K, i.e. by combining the equilibrium constants for the following basic reactions (at the same temperature):

(III) $$H_2O = H_2 + \tfrac{1}{2}O_2 \qquad K_p^{III} = 1{\cdot}28 \times 10^{-8}\ \text{atm}^{1/2}$$

(IV) $$SO_2 = \tfrac{1}{2}S_2 + O_2 \qquad K_p^{IV} = 1{\cdot}12 \times 10^{-12}\ \text{atm}^{1/2}$$

(V) $$H_2S = H_2 + \tfrac{1}{2}S_2 \qquad K_p^{V} = 4{\cdot}35 \times 10^{-2}\ \text{atm}^{1/2}$$

Solution 106. On the basis of the data given, the following equations may be written for the LMA:

(III) $$\frac{p_{H_2}\,p_{O_2}^{1/2}}{p_{H_2O}} = K_p^{III} \quad \ldots. \quad (i)$$

(IV) $$\frac{p_{S_2}^{1/2}\,p_{O_2}}{p_{SO_2}} = K_p^{IV} \quad \ldots. \quad (ii)$$

(V) $$\frac{p_{H_2}\,p_{S_2}^{1/2}}{p_{H_2S}} = K_p^{V} \quad \ldots. \quad (iii)$$

On the other hand, the LMA equations for the composite reactions are

(I) $$\frac{p^2_{H_2O}\,p_{H_2S}}{p^3_{H_2}\,p_{SO_2}} = K_p^{I} \quad \ldots\ldots \text{(iv)}$$

(II) $$\frac{p^4_{H_2S}\,p^2_{SO_2}}{p^3_{S_2}\,p_{H_2O}} = K_p^{II} \quad \ldots\ldots \text{(v)}$$

The LMA equations for compound reactions may be obtained by combining the basic reaction equations in a number of different ways. At times, this can easily be done if each individual reactant is thought of as being formed from the molecules of its constituent elements. The appropriate LMA equations are then established by writing a series of expanded fractions; this procedure will be made clear by considering the following practical example:

$$K_p^{I} = \frac{p^2_{H_2O}\,p_{H_2S}}{p^3_{H_2}\,p_{SO_2}} = \frac{\dfrac{p^2_{H_2O}\,p_{H_2S}}{p^2_{H_2}\,p_{O_2}\,p_{H_2}\,p^{1/2}_{S_2}}}{\dfrac{p^3_{H_2}\,p_{SO_2}}{p^{1/2}_{S_2}\,p_{O_2}}}\;\frac{p^2_{H_2}\,p_{O_2}\,p_{H_2}\,p^{1/2}_{S_2}}{p^{1/2}_{S_2}\,p_{O_2}} = \frac{(1/K_p^{III})^2\,(1/K_p^{V})}{(1/K_p^{IV})} = K_p^{I} \quad \ldots\ldots \text{(vi)}$$

The extension fraction cancels to unity with the term $p^3_{H_2}$ featuring in the denominator of the first part of the fraction on the right-hand side at (vi).

Substituting numerical values in (vi) gives

$$K_p^{I} = \frac{1/(1{\cdot}28 \times 10^{-8})^2 \times 1/(4{\cdot}35 \times 10^{-2})}{1/(1{\cdot}12 \times 10^{-12})} = 1{\cdot}57 \times 10^5\ \text{atm}^{-1} \quad \ldots\ldots \text{(vii)}$$

K_p^{II} is calculated in a similar way:

$$K_p^{II} = \frac{p^4_{H_2S}\,p^2_{SO_2}}{p^3_{S_2}\,p^4_{H_2O}} = \frac{\dfrac{p^4_{H_2S}\,p^2_{SO_2}}{p^4_{H_2}\,p^2_{S_2}\,p_{S_2}\,p^2_{O_2}}}{\dfrac{p^3_{S_2}\,p^4_{H_2O}}{p^4_{H_2}\,p^2_{O_2}}}\;\frac{p^4_{H_2}\,p^2_{S_2}\,p_{S_2}\,p^2_{O_2}}{p^4_{H_2}\,p^2_{O_2}} = \frac{(1/K_p^{V})^4\,(1/K_p^{IV})^2}{(1/K_p^{III})^4} = K_p^{II} \quad \ldots\ldots \text{(viii)}$$

The extension fraction cancels to unity with the term $p^3_{S_2}$ featuring in the denominator of the first part of the fraction on the right-hand side (viii).

Substituting numerical values in (viii) gives, after rearranging

$$K_p^{II} = \frac{(1{\cdot}28 \times 10^{-8})^4}{(4{\cdot}35 \times 10^{-2})^4\,(1{\cdot}12 \times 10^{-12})^2} = 5{\cdot}98 \times 10^{-3}\ \text{atm}^{-1} \quad \ldots\ldots \text{(ix)}$$

Note. The equilibrium constants for a large number of industrially important reactions may be determined in this way. The following are commonly featured in textbooks.

(*a*) The water-gas reaction, $CO + H_2O = CO_2 + H_2$, where

$$K_p^{wgr} = \frac{p_{H_2}\,p_{CO_2}}{p_{H_2O}\,p_{CO}}$$

K_p^{wgr} may be calculated by combining the reactions for the dissociation of H_2O (see III) and the dissociation of carbon dioxide, $CO_2 = CO + \frac{1}{2}\,O_2$, where

$$K_p^{CO_2} = \frac{p_{CO}\,p^{1/2}_{O_2}}{p_{CO_2}}$$

This gives

$$K_p^{wgr} = \frac{\dfrac{p_{H_2} p_{CO_2}}{p_{CO} p_{O_2}^{1/2}}}{\dfrac{p_{H_2O} p_{CO}}{p_{H_2} p_{O_2}^{1/2}}} \frac{p_{CO} p_{O_2}^{1/2}}{p_{H_2} p_{O_2}^{1/2}} = \frac{1/K_p^{CO_2}}{1/K_p^{III}} = \frac{K_p^{III}}{K_p^{CO_2}}$$

(*b*) The generator process (Boudouard reaction) for the formation of temper carbon from carbon monoxide

$$CO = \tfrac{1}{2}\,C_{solid} + \tfrac{1}{2}\,CO_2 \qquad \text{where} \qquad K_p^{Boud} = \frac{p_{CO_2}^{1/2}}{p_{CO}}$$

K_p^{Boud} may calculated by combining the dissociation reactions

$$CO_2 = CO + \tfrac{1}{2}\,O_2 \qquad \text{where} \qquad K'_p = \frac{p_{CO} p_{O_2}^{1/2}}{p_{CO_2}}$$

and

$$CO_2 = C_{solid} + O_2 \qquad \text{where} \qquad K''_p = \frac{p_{O_2}}{p_{CO_2}}$$

It will be readily seen that

$$K_p^{Boud} = \frac{K_p''^{\,1/2}}{K'_p}$$

(*c*) The Deacon process for the production of chlorine, $2\,HCl + \frac{1}{2}\,O_2 = H_2O + Cl_2$, where clay spheres impregnated with $CuCl_2$ are used as catalyst and where

$$K_p^{Deac} = \frac{p_{Cl_2} p_{H_2O}}{p_{HCl}^2 p_{O_2}^{1/2}}$$

K_p^{Deac} may be calculated by combining the H_2O dissociation equation III and the dissociation equation for HCl:

$$HCl = \tfrac{1}{2}\,H_2 + \tfrac{1}{2}\,Cl_2 \qquad \text{where} \qquad K_p^{HCl} = \frac{p_{H_2}^{1/2} p_{Cl_2}^{1/2}}{p_{HCl}}$$

This gives

$$K_p^{Deac} = \frac{\dfrac{p_{H_2O}}{p_{H_2} p_{O_2}^{1/2}}}{\dfrac{p_{HCl}^2}{p_{H_2} p_{Cl_2}}} \frac{p_{Cl_2} p_{H_2} p_{O_2}^{1/2}}{p_{Cl_2} p_{H_2} p_{O_2}^{1/2}} = \frac{1/K_p^{III}}{(1/K_p^{HCl})^2} = \frac{(K_p^{HCl})^2}{K_p^{III}}$$

Conversely, one may also deduce data for simple reactions which may be difficult to measure experimentally, by using composite reactions amenable to experimental study. For example, the action of steam on iron

$$Fe_{solid} + H_2O = FeO_{solid} + H_2 \qquad \text{where} \qquad K_p = \frac{p_{H_2}}{p_{H_2O}}$$

may be combined with the H_2O dissociation equation III to give the O_2 dissociation pressure of FeO:

$$FeO_{solid} = Fe_{solid} + \tfrac{1}{2}\,O_2 \qquad \text{where} \qquad p_{O_2} = K_p^{FeO}$$

It is easily seen that

$$K_p^{FeO} = p_{O_2} = (K_p^{III}/K_p)^2$$

The method used in this Exercise is of special importance for determining the equilibrium constants of rather complicated inorganic chemical reactions, by making use of a number of known simple reactions.

*EXERCISE 107

What is the oxygen content of the air dissolved in water when the latter is saturated with CO_2-free air at 0 °C? How many cubic centimetres of oxygen and nitrogen (containing argon) are contained in 5 l. of water at 0 °C under a dry air pressure of 710 mm Hg?

The oxygen content of atmospheric air is 20·9 vol. per cent. The Bunsen absorption coefficient of oxygen in water at 0 °C is $\alpha^{Bu}_{O_2} = 0{\cdot}04889$ atm^{-1}; for N_2 (containing 1·185 per cent Ar) the value is $\alpha^{Bu}_{N_2} = 0{\cdot}02354$ atm^{-1}.

Solution 107. The volumes of oxygen and nitrogen dissolved in the given volume of water are, from eqn. (166):

$$V_{O_2} = 0{\cdot}04889 \times 20{\cdot}9 \times \frac{710 \times 5000}{760 \times 100}\ \text{cm}^3 = 47{\cdot}8\ \text{cm}^3 \quad \ldots\ldots \quad \text{(i)}$$

$$V_{N_2} = 0{\cdot}02354 \times 79{\cdot}1 \times \frac{710 \times 5000}{760 \times 100}\ \text{cm}^3 = 87{\cdot}0\ \text{cm}^3 \quad \ldots\ldots \quad \text{(ii)}$$

Thus, the oxygen content of the dissolved air is, from (i) and (ii)

$$\frac{V_{O_2}}{V_{O_2} + V_{N_2}} = \frac{0{\cdot}04889 \times 20{\cdot}9}{0{\cdot}04889 \times 20{\cdot}9 + 0{\cdot}02354 \times 79{\cdot}1} = \frac{1{\cdot}022}{1{\cdot}022 + 1{\cdot}861} = 35{\cdot}5\ \text{vol. per cent}\ O_2 \quad \ldots\ldots \quad \text{(iii)}$$

*EXERCISE 108

Two litres of water are shaken with 8 litres of carbon dioxide at 10 °C until saturation equilibrium is established, the initial CO_2 pressure being $p_{0\,CO_2} = 700$ mm Hg. The Bunsen absorption coefficient for CO_2 at 10 °C is $\alpha^{Bu}_{CO_2} = 1{\cdot}194$ atm^{-1}. What is the equilibrium pressure of CO_2, p_{CO_2} (mm), and how many cm³, V_{CO_2}, of CO_2 are dissolved by the water?

Solution 108. From eqn. (166)

$$V_{CO_2} = \frac{1{\cdot}194}{760}\, p_{CO_2} \times 2000\ \text{cm}^3 \quad \ldots\ldots \quad \text{(i)}$$

Since, by definition, V_{CO_2} represents the volume at s.t.p., the pressure, p'_{CO_2}, for 8000 cm³ at 10 °C will be, from gas equation (1)

$$\frac{V_{CO_2} \times 760}{273} = \frac{8000\, p'_{CO_2}}{283} \quad \ldots\ldots \quad \text{(ii)}$$

Eliminating V_{CO_2} by substituting (ii) in (i) and remembering that $p_{CO_2} + p'_{CO_2}$ must be equal to $p_{0\,CO_2}$ (sum of the partial pressures), one obtains

$$\frac{8000}{760}\, p'_{CO_2} \times \frac{273}{283} = \frac{1{\cdot}194}{760} \times 2000\, p_{CO_2}$$

or, with $p'_{CO_2} = 700 - p_{CO_2}$

$$p_{CO_2}\left(1 + \frac{8000 \times 273}{2000 \times 283 \times 1{\cdot}194}\right) = \frac{8000 \times 273 \times 700}{1{\cdot}194 \times 2000 \times 283}$$

$$p_{CO_2} = 535\ \text{mm} \quad \ldots\ldots \quad \text{(iii)}$$

The number of cubic centimetres of carbon dioxide dissolved in the water (and reduced to s.t.p.) is obtained by substituting (iii) in (i):

$$V_{CO_2} = \frac{1{\cdot}194 \times 2000 \times 535}{760} = 1681 \text{ cm}^3 \qquad \ldots\ldots \quad \text{(iv)}$$

It will be seen that, if the above volume of CO_2 is adjusted from s.t.p. to 10 °C and 8000 cm³ by means of the gas equation, the resulting pressure is, in fact:

$$p'_{CO_2} = \frac{1681 \times 283 \times 760}{8000 \times 273} = 165 \text{ mm} \qquad \ldots\ldots \quad \text{(v)}$$

which, together with the equilibrium pressure $p_{CO_2} = 535$ mm, gives the initial pressure $p_{0\,CO_2} = 700$ mm. This additional calculation serves as a check on the accuracy of the arithmetic.

Exercise 109

Water is shaken, in a closed vessel, with twice its volume ($\gamma = 2{:}1$) of a gas mixture containing 60 per cent hydrogen, 30 per cent carbon monoxide and 10 per cent hydrogen sulphide, until equilibrium is established at 8°C. The initial total pressure is $p_0 = 740$ mm Hg. Calculate the total pressure after equilibrium has been established, the composition of the dissolved gas mixture and that of the residual (dry) gas. The vapour pressure of water at 8 °C is $p_{H_2O} = 8$ mm; any variation caused by the dissolved gases should be ignored. The Bunsen absorption coefficients in water at 8 °C are:

$$\alpha^{Bu}_{H_2} = 0{\cdot}01989 \text{ atm}^{-1} \qquad \alpha^{Bu}_{CO} = 0{\cdot}02942 \text{ atm}^{-1}$$

$$\alpha^{Bu}_{H_2S} = 3{\cdot}616 \text{ atm}^{-1} \quad \text{(gas-washing principle)}$$

Solution 109. Each mixture component X_i establishes its own equilibrium independently of the others and, according to eqn. (166)

$$v_{si} = \alpha^{Bu}_i p_i (p_i \text{ in atm}) \quad \text{or} \quad v_{si} = \alpha^{Bu}_i \frac{p_i}{760} (p_i \text{ in mm Hg}) \qquad \ldots\ldots \quad \text{(i)}$$

The initial partial pressure of the gas mixture $p_0 - p_{H_2O}$ is obtained by subtracting the vapour pressure of water p_{H_2O} from the initial total pressure p_0. By multiplying by the fraction x_{0i} of component X_i in the initial mixture, one has the initial partial pressure of this component as $p_{0i} = (p_0 - p_{H_2O})\, x_{0i}$.

The equilibrium partial pressure p_i is obtained by subtracting the partial pressure p'_i for that fraction of component X_i which has gone into solution; thus

$$p_i = (p_0 - p_{H_2O})\, x_{0i} - p'_i \qquad \ldots\ldots \quad \text{(ii)}$$

The volume of this same fraction, i.e. v_{si} at s.t.p. per unit volume of water, exhibited a partial pressure p'_i in the gas space before solution in the water. This pressure can be calculated from the gas equation:

$$\frac{v_{si} \times 760}{273} = \frac{\gamma p'_i}{273 + 8}$$

where $\gamma = 2{:}1$ is the ratio of the volumes of gas to water. From this

$$p'_i = 760 \times \frac{281}{273} \times \frac{v_{si}}{\gamma} \quad \text{(in mm Hg)} \qquad \ldots\ldots \quad \text{(iii)}$$

By substituting (i) and (ii) in (iii), i.e. in order to eliminate p_i' and v_{si}, one obtains an equation for p_i (in mm Hg):

$$(p_0 - p_{H_2O})\, x_{0\,i} - p_i = 760 \times \frac{281}{273} \times \frac{\alpha_i^{Bu}}{\gamma} \times \frac{p_i}{760} \quad \text{or} \quad p_i = \frac{(p_0 - p_{H_2O})\, x_{0\,i}}{1 + \dfrac{281\,\alpha_i^{Bu}}{273\,\gamma}} \quad \text{(in mm Hg)} \qquad \ldots . \quad \text{(iv)}$$

as the equilibrium pressure of component X_i.

The total pressure at equilibrium will be

$$p = \sum p_i + p_{H_2O} \qquad \ldots . \quad \text{(v)}$$

The fraction of component X_i remaining as undissolved (dry) gas, $x_{g\,i}$, is

$$x_{g\,i} = \frac{p_i}{\Sigma p_i} \qquad \ldots . \quad \text{(vi)}$$

The fraction of component X_i in the dissolved (dry) gases, $x_{s\,i}$, is

$$x_{s\,i} = \frac{v_{s\,i}}{\Sigma v_{s\,i}} = \frac{\alpha_i^{Bu}\, p_i}{\Sigma \alpha^{Bu}\, p_i} \qquad \ldots . \quad \text{(vii)}$$

Substituting the numerical values, one obtains from (iv) and (i):

$$p_{H_2} = \frac{(740 - 8)\, 0{\cdot}60}{1 + \dfrac{281 \times 0{\cdot}01989}{273 \times 2}} = 435{\cdot}0 \text{ mm} \qquad v_{s(H_2)} = 0{\cdot}01989 \times 435{\cdot}0/760 = 8{\cdot}65/760$$

$$p_{CO} = \frac{(740 - 8)\, 0{\cdot}30}{1 + \dfrac{281 \times 0{\cdot}02942}{273 \times 2}} = 216{\cdot}4 \text{ mm} \qquad v_{s(CO)} = 0{\cdot}02942 \times 216{\cdot}4/760 = 6{\cdot}37/760$$

$$p_{H_2S} = \frac{(740 - 8)\, 0{\cdot}10}{1 \times \dfrac{281 \times 3{\cdot}616}{273 \times 2}} = 25{\cdot}6 \text{ mm} \qquad v_{s(H_2S)} = 3{\cdot}616 \times 25{\cdot}6/760 = 92{\cdot}50/760$$

The total pressure is, from (v)

$$p = 435{\cdot}0 + 216{\cdot}4 + 25{\cdot}6 + 8 = 677 + 8 = 685 \text{ mm}$$

The composition of the residual (dry) gas is obtained from (vi):

$$x_{g(H_2)} = \frac{435}{677} = 0{\cdot}643 = 64{\cdot}3 \text{ vol. per cent}$$

$$x_{g(CO)} = \frac{216{\cdot}4}{677} = 0{\cdot}319 = 31{\cdot}9 \text{ vol. per cent}$$

$$x_{g(H_2S)} = \frac{25{\cdot}6}{677} = 0{\cdot}038 = 3{\cdot}8 \text{ vol. per cent}$$

The composition of the dissolved gas mixture is calculated from (vii):

$$x_{s(H_2)} = \frac{8{\cdot}65}{107{\cdot}52} = 8{\cdot}1 \text{ vol. per cent} \qquad \left(\sum v_{s\,i} = \frac{8{\cdot}65 + 6{\cdot}37 + 92{\cdot}50}{760} = \frac{107{\cdot}52}{760}\right)$$

$$x_{s(CO)} = \frac{6{\cdot}37}{107{\cdot}52} = 5{\cdot}9 \text{ vol. per cent}$$

$$x_{s(H_2S)} = \frac{92{\cdot}50}{107{\cdot}52} = 86{\cdot}0 \text{ vol. per cent}$$

It will be seen that washing this gas mixture with water removes a large proportion of the H_2S.

The expression (iii) can be used to check the accuracy of the calculation. One has for $\sum p_i'$:

$$\sum p_i' = \frac{760 \times 281}{273 \cdot 2} \times \frac{107 \cdot 52}{760 \times 2} = 55 \cdot 3 \text{ mm}$$

as the decrease in pressure, while the value calculated above was 740 − 685 = 55 mm; i.e. the two values agree within the limit of error to be expected.

*Exercise 110

A solution of 0·035 g sulphur in 10 cm³ benzene is in equilibrium at 25 °C with 0·0655 g sulphur dissolved in 25 cm³ carbon tetrachloride. (*a*) What is the value of the carbon tetrachloride–benzene distribution coefficient? (*b*) How much sulphur must be dissolved in 20 cm³ CCl_4 in order that it shall be in equilibrium with 1·000 g sulphur dissolved in 100 cm³ benzene? (*c*) What is the solubility of sulphur in CCl_4 at 25 °C if its solubility in benzene at the same temperature is 17·93 g/l.? Sulphur exists as S_8 molecules in both solvents.

Solution 110. The distribution coefficient is, from eqn. (172)

$$C_s = \frac{c_{CCl_4}}{c_{C_6H_6}}$$

it being convenient to express the concentrations as g/l. of solution.

(*a*) One then has for C_s

$$C_s = \frac{0 \cdot 0655/0 \cdot 025}{0 \cdot 035/0 \cdot 010} = 0 \cdot 749 \quad \ldots \quad \text{(i)}$$

(*b*) A similar expression to (i) is used to calculate the quantity of sulphur [S]

$$\frac{[S]/0 \cdot 020}{1 \cdot 000/0 \cdot 100} = 0 \cdot 749 \qquad [S] = 0 \cdot 1498 \text{ g} \quad \ldots \quad \text{(ii)}$$

(*c*) It must now be remembered that a saturated solution in a given solvent can only be in equilibrium with the saturated solution in a second solvent. It follows that the ratio of the solubilities in both solvents is equal to the distribution coefficient, as far as this particular law applies, i.e. for dilute solutions and the same molecular state for the solute in either solvent. One then has

$$\frac{\text{solubility of sulphur in } CCl_4}{\text{solubility of sulphur in } C_6H_6} = C_s = 0 \cdot 749$$

or, solubility of

$$\text{S in } CCl_4 = 0 \cdot 749 \times 17 \cdot 93 = 13 \cdot 43 \text{ g/l.} \quad \ldots \quad \text{(iii)}$$

Note. If the saturation concentrations have high values, the calculation is approximate only. It must also be remembered that the solvents are, to some extent, mutually soluble. It follows that the saturation concentrations when the solvents are in contact are only approximately equal to those when the separate pure solvents are considered.

*EXERCISE 111

The Bunsen absorption coefficients for the solution of chlorine in carbon tetrachloride are $\alpha_{Cl_2}^{Bu} = 97{\cdot}7\ atm^{-1}$ at 0 °C, $54{\cdot}8\ atm^{-1}$ at 19 °C and $34{\cdot}2\ atm^{-1}$ at 40 °C. What would the Bunsen absorption coefficients at these temperatures be if Raoult's law were valid? The vapour pressure of pure chlorine is 3·59 atm at 0 °C, 6·40 atm at 19 °C and 11·2 atm at 40 °C. The density of Cl_2 is $\varrho = 1{\cdot}5985\ g/cm^3$. Compare the measured absorption coefficients with those obtained assuming the validity of Raoult's law, i.e. by calculating the corresponding ratios.

Solution 111. If Raoult's law holds, the constant k_i in Henry's law [eqn. (79)] will be equal to the vapour pressure of pure chlorine ($p_{0\,Cl_2}$) at this temperature [see eqn. (66)]. This value of k_i is used in eqn. (169) in order to calculate $\alpha_{Cl_2}^{Bu}$ (Raoult). With $M_{CCl_4} = 153{\cdot}8$ g/mole, one has

$$\text{at } 0\,°C \qquad \alpha_{Cl_2}^{Bu}\,(\text{Raoult}) = \frac{22{\cdot}4 \times 1000 \times 1{\cdot}5985}{153{\cdot}8} \times \frac{1}{3{\cdot}59} = 64{\cdot}8\ atm^{-1}$$

$$\text{at } 19\,°C \qquad \alpha_{Cl_2}^{Bu}\,(\text{Raoult}) = \frac{22{\cdot}4 \times 1000 \times 1{\cdot}5985}{153{\cdot}8} \times \frac{1}{6{\cdot}40} = 36{\cdot}4\ atm^{-1}$$

$$\text{at } 40\,°C \qquad \alpha_{Cl_2}^{Bu}\,(\text{Raoult}) = \frac{22{\cdot}4 \times 1000 \times 1{\cdot}5985}{153{\cdot}8} \times \frac{1}{11{\cdot}2} = 20{\cdot}8\ atm^{-1}$$

The ratios of the measured coefficients to those calculated, on the assumption that. Raoult's law is valid, are

$$\text{for } 0\,°C = 97{\cdot}7/64{\cdot}8 = 1{\cdot}51$$

$$\text{for } 19\,°C = 54{\cdot}8/36{\cdot}4 = 1{\cdot}51$$

$$\text{for } 40\,°C = 34{\cdot}2/20{\cdot}8 = 1{\cdot}64$$

The solubility of chlorine is, therefore, greater than that for ideal mixtures, by a factor of about 1·5. It follows that attractive forces between the Cl_2 and CCl_4 molecules must exist.

*EXERCISE 112

At 15 °C and 1 atm total pressure, 1 volume of acetone dissolves 25 volumes of acetylene (reduced to s.t.p.). What is the value of the Bunsen absorption coefficient if the vapour pressure of pure acetone at 15 °C is $p_{0\,acetone} = 141{\cdot}5$ mm Hg? The lowering of the vapour pressure of the acetone, when acetylene is dissolved in it, must be taken into account. The density of acetone, CH_3COCH_3, is $\varrho = 0{\cdot}796\ g/cm^3$; mol. wt. $M = 58{\cdot}1$. What would the Bunsen absorption coefficient be if Raoult's law were valid for the solubility of acetone? The vapour pressure of acetylene at 15 °C is $p_{0\,C_2H_2} = 38{\cdot}5$ atm.

Solution 112. The lowering of the vapour pressure of the solvent may be calculated from eqn. (97):

$$\frac{p_0 - p}{p_0} = \frac{n_{C_2H_2}}{n_{acetone}} \qquad \ldots . \quad (i)$$

From the data given

$$n_{C_2H_2} = 25/22{\cdot}4 \text{ mole and } n_{acetone} = \frac{1000 \times 0{\cdot}796}{58{\cdot}1} \text{ mole}$$

so that

$$p_0 - p = 141{\cdot}5 \frac{25 \times 58{\cdot}1}{22{\cdot}4 \times 1000 \times 0{\cdot}796} = 11{\cdot}5 \text{ mm} \qquad \ldots. \quad \text{(ii)}$$

The vapour pressure of acetone over the solution is, therefore, $141{\cdot}5 - 11{\cdot}5 = 130$ mm .... (iii)

It follows that the partial pressure of acetylene must be

$$760 - 130 = 630 \text{ mm}$$

and the Bunsen absorption coefficient is, according to eqn. (166)

$$25 = \alpha^{Bu}_{C_2H_2} \times \frac{630}{760} \quad \text{or} \quad \alpha^{Bu}_{C_2H_2} = \frac{25 \times 760}{630} = 30{\cdot}2 \text{ atm}^{-1} \qquad \ldots. \quad \text{(iv)}$$

In the case when Raoult's law applies, the Bunsen absorption coefficient is calculated from eqn. (169) and k_i is equal to the vapour pressure of pure acetylene at 15 °C, $p_{0C_2H_2} = 38{\cdot}5$ atm [see eqn. (66)]. This gives

$$\alpha^{Bu}_{C_2H_2} = \frac{22{\cdot}4 \times 1000 \times 0{\cdot}796}{58{\cdot}1} \times \frac{1}{38{\cdot}5} = 7{\cdot}98 \text{ atm}^{-1} \text{ (according to Raoult)}$$

obviously a much smaller value.

*Exercise 113

The distribution coefficient for hydrogen peroxide, H_2O_2, between water and amyl alcohol is 7·01. 300 cm³ of a solution of 4·5 g H_2O_2 per litre of amyl alcohol are extracted by shaking, until equilibrium is established, (*a*) once with 100 cm³ water, (*b*) 10 times with 10 cm³ water. What is the final concentration of H_2O_2 in the amyl alcohol in both cases? H_2O_2 shows its normal molecular weight in both water and amyl alcohol.

Solution 113. Case (*a*). Let the final concentration of hydrogen peroxide in amyl alcohol be x (g/l.). It follows that $300/1000\,(4{\cdot}5 - x)$ g H_2O_2 must have been extracted by the water and the concentration of H_2O_2 in the water will be

$$\frac{300}{1000} \times \frac{(4{\cdot}5 - x)\,1000}{100} \text{ g/l.}$$

The distribution law [eqn. (172)] then gives

$$\frac{\dfrac{300\,(4{\cdot}5 - x)\,1000}{1000 \times 100}}{x} = 7{\cdot}01 \quad \text{or} \quad x = \frac{4{\cdot}5 \times 3}{7{\cdot}01 + 3} = 1{\cdot}349 \text{ g/l. of } H_2O_2 \text{ remaining in the amyl alcohol} \qquad \ldots. \quad \text{(i)}$$

Case (*b*). Let the concentration of H_2O_2 in the amyl alcohol after the first extraction be x_1 g/l. It follows that $\dfrac{300\,(4{\cdot}5 - x_1)}{1000}$ g H_2O must have been extracted by the water. The concentration of H_2O_2 in the water is therefore

$$\frac{300\,(4{\cdot}5 - x_1)}{1000} \times \frac{1000}{10} \text{ g/l.}$$

The distribution law then gives

$$\frac{\dfrac{3000\,(4{\cdot}5 - x_1)\,1000}{1000 \times 10}}{x_1} = 7{\cdot}01 \quad \text{or} \quad x_1 = \frac{4{\cdot}5 \times 30}{7{\cdot}01 + 30}\,\text{g/l.} \qquad \ldots . \quad \text{(ii)}$$

After ten similar extractions, the concentration will be

$$x_{10} = 4{\cdot}5\left(\frac{30}{7{\cdot}01 + 30}\right)^{10} = 4{\cdot}5 \times 0{\cdot}1227 = 0{\cdot}552\ \text{g/l. of } H_2O_2 \text{ remaining in the amyl alcohol} \qquad \ldots . \quad \text{(iii)}$$

Note. The above results are in agreement with the well-known fact that, for a given quantity of wash liquid, more efficient extraction is obtained by making a number of extractions using small quantities of the wash liquid each time. See Exercise 44.

*Exercise 114

In a series of experiments carried out at 25 °C, regarding the distribution of acetic acid between water and carbon tetrachloride, the following equilibrium concentrations, moles/l. acetic acid in H_2O and CCl_4, were observed:

	I	II	III	IV	V	VI
In water	1·69	3·16	4·47	5·42	7·98	9·69
In CCl_4	0·045	0·135	0·251	0·363	0·725	1·07

If acetic acid displays a normal molecular weight in water and, under the given conditions, is virtually undissociated into ions, what is the state of association in carbon tetrachloride?

Solution 114. According to eqn. (173), the following expression may be used to define the acetic acid concentration [A] in CCl_4, when ν molecules are associated:

$$[A_{H_2O}] = C_{ass}\sqrt[\nu]{[A_{CCl_4}]} \quad \text{or} \quad \log\{[A_{CCl_4}]\} = \nu \log\{[A_{H_2O}]\} - \nu \log\{C_{ass}\} \quad \ldots . \quad \text{(i)}$$

It follows from this that a linear relationship is obtained if the logarithm of the acetic acid concentration in water is plotted against the corresponding values in CCl_4. The slope of the line is equal to ν. In actual fact, the numerical values given do give a straight-line relationship.

The slope of the line may either be read directly from the graph or calculated by dividing the logarithmic increments for CCl_4 against the corresponding increments for water. The errors are kept to a minimum if points as widely separated as possible are combined, e.g. VI and III, V and II, IV and I.

Taking the logs of the given concentrations, we find that

for VI and III

$$\frac{0{\cdot}02938 - (0{\cdot}39967 - 1)}{0{\cdot}98632 - 0{\cdot}65031} = 1{\cdot}87$$

for V and II

$$\frac{(0{\cdot}86034 - 1) - (0{\cdot}13033 - 1)}{0{\cdot}90200 - 0{\cdot}49969} = 1{\cdot}82$$

for IV and I

$$\frac{(0{\cdot}55991 - 1) - (0{\cdot}65321 - 2)}{0{\cdot}73400 - 0{\cdot}22789} = 1{\cdot}79 \qquad \ldots \quad \text{(ii)}$$

Thus $\nu \approx 1{\cdot}8$, i.e. in carbon tetrachloride, acetic acid exists essentially as double molecules. The value of ν increases, as would be expected, as the concentration increases.

*Exercise 115

Benzoic acid (mol wt. $M = 122{\cdot}1$) dissolves in water without molecular association taking place. It is, however, partially electrolytically dissociated ($HA = H^+ + A^-$). The dissociation constant at 25 °C is $K_1 = 6{\cdot}46 \times 10^{-5}$ mole/l. (concentrations in mole/l.). In toluene, benzoic acid does not dissociate and is largely present as double molecules. The distribution coefficient for monomolecular benzoic acid in water/toluene is $C = 0{\cdot}65$ at 25 °C. Calculate the dissociation constant K_2 at 25 °C for dissociation of the double molecules into single molecules ($B_2 = 2B$) in toluene solution. Use the following experimental results, obtained for the distribution equilibrium of benzoic acid between water and toluene, as a basis for the calculation.

The aqueous layer is found to contain a total of $G_1 = 0{\cdot}054$ g benzoic acid in $V_1 = 300$ cm³ of solution. The corresponding figure for the toluene layer is $G_2 = 26{\cdot}20$ g in $V_2 = 200$ cm³ of solution.

Solution 115. The total concentration of benzoic acid (in mole/l.) in the aqueous layer is

$$c_w = \frac{G_1}{MV_1} = \frac{0{\cdot}054}{122{\cdot}1 \times 0{\cdot}300} = 1{\cdot}474 \times 10^{-3} \text{ mole/l.} \quad \ldots\ldots \quad \text{(i)}$$

The degree of dissociation α_1 in the aqueous layer may be calculated from eqn. (160) by using (i) above and the dissociation constant K_1:

$$\frac{\alpha_1^2 c_w}{1-\alpha_1} = K_1 \quad \text{or} \quad \alpha_1 = \frac{-K_1 + \sqrt{K_1^2 + 4K_1 c_w}}{2c_w} \quad \ldots\ldots \quad \text{(ii)}$$

so that

$$\alpha_1 = \frac{-6{\cdot}46 \times 10^{-5} + \sqrt{41{\cdot}75 \times 10^{-10} + 38{\cdot}1 \times 10^{-8}}}{2{\cdot}948 \times 10^{-3}} = 0{\cdot}1886 \quad \ldots\ldots \quad \text{(iii)}$$

The concentration of undissociated benzoic acid in the aqueous layer, therefore, is

$$c_{w\,(\text{undis})} = c_w(1-\alpha_1) = 1{\cdot}474 \times 10^{-3} \times 0{\cdot}8114 \text{ mole/l.} \quad \ldots\ldots \quad \text{(iv)}$$

The distribution law, eqn. (172), gives the following expression for the concentration of monomolecular benzoic acid in toluene $[B_{1(T)}]$:

$$\frac{c_{w\,(\text{undis})}}{[B_{1(T)}]} = C = 0{\cdot}65$$

so that, with (iv):

$$[B_{1(T)}] = \frac{c_w(1-\alpha_1)}{C} = \frac{1{\cdot}474 \times 10^{-3} \times 0{\cdot}8114}{0{\cdot}65} = 1{\cdot}840 \times 10^{-3} \text{ mole/l.} \quad \ldots\ldots \quad \text{(v)}$$

The law of mass action, for the equation (benzoic acid)$_2$ = 2 benzoic acid ($B_{2(T)} = 2B_{1(T)}$), is

$$\frac{[B_{1(T)}]^2}{[B_{2(T)}]} = K_2 \quad \ldots\ldots \quad \text{(vi)}$$

If the total concentration of benzoic acid in the toluene, expressed in moles of monomolecular acid per litre, is $[B_{total(T)}]$, then one must have

$$[B_{total(T)}] = [B_{1(T)}] + 2[B_{2(T)}] \qquad \ldots\ldots \text{(vii)}$$

since 1 mole of $B_{2(T)}$ is made up from 2 moles of $B_{1(T)}$.

Eliminating $[B_{2(T)}]$ from (vi) and (vii) gives

$$\frac{2[B_{1(T)}]^2}{[B_{total(T)}] - [B_{1(T)}]} = K_2 \qquad \ldots\ldots \text{(viii)}$$

$$[B_{total(T)}] = \frac{G_2}{V_2 M} = \frac{26{\cdot}20}{0{\cdot}200 \times 122{\cdot}2} = 1{\cdot}072 \text{ mole/l.} \qquad \ldots\ldots \text{(ix)}$$

Substituting (v) and (ix) in (viii) gives K_2 as

$$K_2 = \frac{2(1{\cdot}840 \times 10^{-3})^2}{(1{\cdot}072 - 1{\cdot}840 \times 10^{-3})} = 6{\cdot}33 \times 10^{-6} \text{ mole/l.} \qquad \ldots\ldots \text{(x)}$$

11

TEMPERATURE DEPENDENCE OF CHEMICAL EQUILIBRIA. ABSOLUTE CALCULATION OF CHEMICAL EQUILIBRIUM

(1) The temperature dependence of the equilibrium constants K_p, K_x and K_c is given by

$$\frac{\partial \ln K_p}{\partial T} = \frac{\Delta H}{RT^2} = \frac{-\mathfrak{Q}_p}{RT^2} = \frac{\partial \ln K_x}{\partial T} \qquad \frac{\partial \ln K_c}{\partial T} = \frac{\Delta U}{RT^2} = \frac{-\mathfrak{Q}_v}{RT^2} \quad \ldots . (175)$$

K_p, K_x and K_c are defined in eqns. (154), (155) and (151) and H, U, $\mathfrak{Q}_p$ and $\mathfrak{Q}_v$ in eqns. (128), (125), (126) and (139). ΔH and ΔU are the heats of reaction, positive when the system absorbs heat, at constant pressure and constant volume, respectively. They are the heats of reaction which apply to the state of equilibrium and relate to the quantitative changes as defined by the reaction equation (i.e. molar formula conversion).

$$\left. \begin{aligned} &K_p \text{ is independent of pressure } \left(\frac{\partial K_p}{\partial p} = 0\right) \\ &\frac{\partial \ln K_x}{\partial p} = -\Delta \sum \nu_i / p \quad \text{[from eqn. (155)]} \end{aligned} \right\} \quad \ldots (176)$$

(2) There are corresponding equations for other constants which characterize an equilibrium:

(*a*) for the solubility of a substance X_i in a solvent $c_i^{\star}$, where the asterisk denotes a state of equilibrium

$$\frac{\partial \ln c_i^{\star}}{\partial T} = \frac{{}^{d}l_i^{\star}}{RT^2} \quad \ldots . (177)$$

${}^{d}l_i^{\star}$ is the so-called 'final heat of solution', i.e. the energy change when 1 mole of X_i is dissolved in a very large quantity of a practically saturated solution of X_i;

(*b*) for the solubility coefficient relating to gas solubility, eqn. (165): $x_{Li}/p_i = 1/k_i$ and, correspondingly, for the Bunsen absorption coefficient, α_i^{Bu}, eqn. (169):

$$\frac{\partial \ln \alpha_i^{Bu}}{\partial T} = \frac{\partial \ln (1/k_i)}{\partial T} = \frac{{}^{d}l_i^{\star}}{RT^2} \quad \ldots . (178)$$

(*c*) for the distribution coefficient C, eqn. (172):

$$\frac{\partial \ln C}{\partial T} = \frac{{}^{d}l_{12}^{\star}}{RT^2} \quad \ldots . (179)$$

In this case, ${}^{d}l_{12}^{\star}$ represents the heat of transition from phase I to phase II, i.e. the energy (enthalpy) change which occurs when 1 mole of solute is transferred from a very large quantity of saturated phase I to a very large quantity of practically saturated phase II.

In practice, eqns. (177)–(179) are usually applied to the behaviour of dilute solutions (sparingly soluble substances). In such a case, the final heats of solution (differential heats of solution) may be replaced by, and are equal to, the ordinary (integral) heats of solution.

(3) Over small intervals of temperature ΔH and ΔU may be taken either as constant or a mean value assigned to them. It is then possible to integrate eqn. (175) and the corresponding eqns. (177)–(179). One then obtains expressions analogous to eqns. (103) and (104):

$$\log K_{p\,1} - \log K_{p\,2} = \frac{-\Delta H}{4 \cdot 574}(1/T_1 - 1/T_2) \quad \ldots\ldots (180)$$

where

$$\Delta H = 4 \cdot 574 \frac{T_1 T_2}{T_1 - T_2} \log (K_{p\,1}/K_{p\,2}) \quad \text{(cal)} \quad \ldots\ldots (181)$$

(4) The following relations are an extension of the thermodynamic equations and definitions given in eqns. (125)–(150).

The thermodynamic potential (free enthalpy; Gibbs free energy) is

$$G \equiv H - TS = U - TS + pV \quad \ldots\ldots (182)$$

where $H \equiv U + pV$ is the enthalpy and S the entropy.

The entropy of a substance at temperature T (p = const. = 1 atm) is defined by

$$S_T^{(p)} = \int_0^T \frac{C_p}{T} \, \mathrm{d}T + S_0^{(p)} \quad \ldots (183)$$

The zero-point entropy $S_0^{(p)} = 0$ in the case of homogeneous ideal solids (Nernst's heat theorem; M. Planck; A. Eucken). ....(183a)

The following expression relates to a substance having an enthalpy of transition L_t at its transition point T_t, and when change of entropy with pressure (gases) must be taken into account:

$$S_T^{(p)} = \int_0^T \frac{C_p}{T} \, \mathrm{d}T^* + \frac{L_t}{T_t} - \int_1^p \left(\frac{\partial V}{\partial T}\right)_p \mathrm{d}p + S_0^{(p)} \quad \ldots\ldots (184)$$

($L_t/n = l_t$ = enthalpy of transition per mole)

Entropy is measured in cal/deg. or Clausius (Cl). Standard entropy $S_{0\,298}$ refers to the entropy per mole of substance at 25 °C and 1 atm, hence

$$S_{0\,298} + \int_0^{298 \cdot 1} \frac{c_p}{T} \, \mathrm{d}T \left[+ \sum \frac{l_{t\,i}}{T_{t\,i}} \right] \quad \text{(Cl/mole) or [cal/(deg. mole)]} \quad \ldots\ldots (185)$$

* More accurately, $\int_0^{T_t} \frac{C_{p\,1}}{T} \, \mathrm{d}T + \int_{T_t}^{T} \frac{C_{p\,2}}{T} \, \mathrm{d}T$ because, in general, $C_{p\,1}$, relating to phase I before transition, does not have the same temperature dependence as that of $C_{p\,2}$, which relates to phase II after the transition point.

The isothermal or isobaric change in thermodynamic potential per mole, $\Delta G = \Delta H - T\Delta S$, during the course of a chemical reaction, is known as the maximum useful work (reaction work, cal/mole) at constant pressure, and this important conception is given a special symbol by many authors. A reaction can proceed spontaneously in the direction for which the maximum work ΔG is negative, i.e. work from the reacting system is lost to its surroundings. Equilibrium exists when $\Delta G = 0$. Chemical affinity is defined by $(-\Delta G)$.

The symbol Δ signifies the differences between the variables of state and the reaction numbers for substances on the right-hand side of the reaction equation (positive terms) and the corresponding values for substances on the left-hand side (negative terms). The variation of ΔG with temperature at (constant pressure) is given by

$$\left(\frac{\partial \Delta G}{\partial T}\right)_p = -\Delta S^{(p)} = \frac{\Delta G - \Delta H}{T} \qquad \Delta H = \Delta G - T\left(\frac{\partial \Delta G}{\partial T}\right)_p$$

or

$$\left[\frac{\partial\left(\frac{\Delta G}{T}\right)}{\partial T}\right]_p = \frac{-\Delta H}{T^2} \qquad \ldots (186\text{a})$$

the Gibbs–Helmholtz equation at constant pressure.

The variation of ΔG with pressure is

$$\left(\frac{\partial \Delta G}{\partial p}\right)_T = \Delta V \qquad \ldots . (187)$$

For the temperature dependence of ΔS, we find that

$$\left(\frac{\partial \Delta S}{\partial T}\right)_p = \frac{\Delta \sum \nu_i c_{p\,i}}{T} \qquad \ldots . (188)$$

where ν_i represents the reaction numbers (stoichiometric mole numbers); see eqns. (151) and (154).

The variation of ΔH with temperature [see eqns. (150) and (151)] is given by

$$\left(\frac{\partial \Delta H}{\partial T}\right)_p = \Delta \sum \nu_i c_{p\,i} \qquad \ldots . (189)$$

The relation between maximum work ΔG and the equilibrium constant K_p [eqn. (154)] is

$$\Delta G = RT \ln \frac{p'^{\nu_E}_E\, p'^{\nu_F}_F \ldots}{p'^{\nu_A}_A\, p'^{\nu_B}_B \ldots} - RT \ln K_p \qquad \ldots . (190)$$

where p'_i represents the initial and final pressures of the components (i.e. not the equilibrium pressures).

If unit pressure (usually 1 atm) is taken for all values of p'_i, the standard maximum work will be

$$\Delta G_0 = \Delta H_{0T} - T\Delta S_{0T} = -RT \ln K_p \text{ (cal/mole)}; \quad (p = 1 \text{ atm}) \qquad \ldots . (191)$$

so that K_p becomes

$$\log K_p = -\frac{\Delta H_{0T}}{4{\cdot}574\, T} + \frac{\Delta S_{0T}}{4{\cdot}574} \quad (p = 1 \text{ atm}) \qquad \ldots . (192)$$

In the case of solutions, one has the following relation between the maximum work ΔG and the equilibrium constant $K_{c(sol)}$ [eqn. (151)]:

$$\Delta G = RT \ln \frac{c'^{\nu_E}_E \, c'^{\nu_F}_F \ldots}{c'^{\nu_A}_A \, c'^{\nu_B}_B \ldots} - RT \ln K_{c(sol)} \quad \ldots . (193)$$

where c'_i represents the initial and final concentrations or, in the case of concentrated solutions, the initial or final activities.

If all substances are present in initial and final concentrations of $c'_i = 1$ mole/l., the standard reaction work will be

$$\Delta G_0 = -RT \ln K_{c(sol)} \, (\text{cal/mole}) \quad \ldots . (194)$$

(5) The absolute value of the equilibrium constant K_p may be determined to various degrees of accuracy by using eqn. (192). The following description is essentially the same as that given by H. ULICH.

The standard entropies, $S_{0\,298}$ at 25 °C and $p = 1$ atm, of a large number of substances are calculated from eqn. (185). For greater detail, see LAVROV *et al.*, *The Thermodynamics of Gasification and Gas-synthesis Reactions*, London (Pergamon) 1963, where tabulated results are given.

It follows from eqn. (189) that, when considering the molar enthalpy of transition l_{ti} of a substance X_i at a transition temperature T_{ti} above 298 °K (= 25 °C), it is possible to use the following expression for ΔH_{0T}

$$\Delta H_{0T} = \Delta H_{0\,298} + \int_{298}^{T} \Delta \sum \nu_i c_{pi} \, dT \, (+ \Delta \sum \nu_i l_{ti}) \quad (\text{cal/mole}) \quad \ldots . (195)$$

where $\Delta H_{0\,298}$ = standard reaction enthalpy at $p = 1$ atm and $T = 298$ °K (= 25 °C),

$\Delta \sum \nu_i c_{pi}$ = difference in specific heats

$\Delta \sum \nu_i l_{ti}$ = difference in transition enthalpies.

Similarly, from eqn. (188), and when considering the molar entropy of transition l_{ti}/T_{ti} of a substance X_i at a transition temperature T_{ti} above 298 °K (= 25 °C), one has for ΔS_{0T}

$$\Delta S_{0T} = \Delta S_{0\,298} + \int_{298}^{T} \frac{\Delta \sum \nu_i c_{pi}}{T} \, dT \left[+ \frac{\Delta \sum \nu_i l_{ti}}{T_{ti}} \right] \quad \ldots . (196)$$

In this equation $\Delta S_{0\,298} = \Delta \sum \nu_i S_{0\,298\,i}$, the standard reaction entropy, is equal to the difference between the standard entropies of the components X_i in the final state (right-hand side of the reaction equation) and the corresponding values in the initial state (left-hand side of the reaction equation). See also eqn. (185).

Approximation 1. If one takes $\Delta \sum \nu_i c_{pi} = 0$ as a first approximation, which is necessary if the specific heats of one or more of the reactants are unknown, then eqn. (192) may be combined with eqns. (195) and (196) to give

$$\log K_p = -\frac{\Delta H_{0\,298} [+ \Delta \sum \nu_i l_{ti}]}{4 \cdot 574 \, T} + \frac{\Delta S_{0\,298}}{4 \cdot 574} \left[+ \frac{1}{4 \cdot 574} \Delta \sum \frac{\nu_i l_{ti}}{T_{ti}} \right] \quad \ldots . (197)$$

Approximation 2. If the specific heats of the reactants at 25 °C or their mean values between 20 °C and 100 °C are known, one may write $\Delta\sum \nu_i c_{pi} = a$ (where a is a constant). Appropriate integration of eqns. (195) and (196) then gives

$$\log K_p = -\frac{\Delta H_{0\,298}\,[+\,\Delta\sum \nu_i l_{ti}]}{4{\cdot}574\,T} + \frac{\Delta S_{0\,298}}{4{\cdot}574}\left[+\frac{1}{4{\cdot}574}\Delta\sum\frac{\nu_i l_{ti}}{T_{ti}}\right] + \frac{a}{4{\cdot}574} f\left(\frac{T}{298}\right) \quad \ldots . (198)$$

where $^*f\left(\frac{T}{298}\right) = \ln\left(\frac{T}{298{\cdot}15}\right) + \frac{298{\cdot}15}{T} - 1$ and is listed in the tables, already calculated. For temperatures up to 1600 °C, a close approximation is obtained by taking $f\left(\frac{T}{298}\right) \approx 0{\cdot}0007\,T - 0{\cdot}20$.

In the case of a completely condensed system where no gaseous components are present, eqn. (158) shows that there will be no equilibrium constant. In order to study the equilibrium one must, therefore, consider the change in free enthalpy ΔG_0, i.e. the reaction work at constant pressure; see eqn. (191). ΔG_0 is then obtained by multiplying eqn. (198) by $-2{\cdot}3\,RT = -4{\cdot}574\,T$ (cal/mole):

$$\Delta G_0 = \Delta H_{0\,298}\,[+\,\Delta\sum \nu_i l_{ti}] - T\Delta S_{0\,298}\left[-\,T\Delta\sum\frac{\nu_i l_{ti}}{T_{ti}}\right] - Ta\,f\left(\frac{T}{298}\right) \quad \ldots . (199)$$

The system is in equilibrium when $\Delta G_0 = 0$. If ΔG_0 is negative, the reaction proceeds towards the right; towards the left when ΔG_0 is positive. .... (200)

ΔG_0 is valid when $p = 1$ atm; see eqn. (191). The variation of ΔG with pressure is given by eqn. (187).

Approximation 3. If $\Delta\sum \nu_i c_{pi}$ has a marked temperature dependence, and the latter is known, eqn. (198) may still be used, provided suitable mean values for $a = \Delta\sum \nu_i c_{pi}$ are adopted.

One usually takes mean values of $\Delta\sum \nu_i c_{pi}$ for the following temperature ranges:

(1) $\overline{\Delta\sum \nu_i c_{pi}}^{300,\,600}$ from room temperature to 600° K

(2) $\overline{\Delta\sum \nu_i c_{pi}}^{600,\,1200}$ from 600° to 1200 °K

(3) $\overline{\Delta\sum \nu_i c_{pi}}^{1200,\,2400}$ from 1200° to 2400° K

When the c_p-curves are continuous, the mean value is given by the arithmetic mean of the two border values for $\Delta\sum \nu_i c_{pi}$, i.e. for the lower and upper end of the temperature range considered. This mean value will be indicated by

$$\overline{\Delta\sum \nu_i c_{pi}}^{300,\,600\,\text{(border)}}$$

Alternatively, the values of $\Delta\sum \nu_i c_{pi}$ for the middle of the temperature ranges may be used, i.e. for the temperatures 450°, 900° and 1800 °K. Better still, the mean of the values at 900 ° and 1800 °K may be taken. One can also assess the mean value, especially when the c_p curves are discontinuous, by plotting values of $\Delta\sum \nu_i c_{pi}$ against T.

* $f(x)$ means 'function of x'.

The following values of a are obtained from these mean values:

$$a_{300,\,600} = \overline{\Delta \sum \nu_i c_{p\,i}}^{\,300,\,600}$$

$$a_{300,\,1200} = \frac{1}{2}\left(\overline{\Delta \sum \nu_i c_{p\,i}}^{\,300,\,600} + \overline{\Delta \sum \nu_i c_{p\,i}}^{\,600,\,1200}\right)$$

$$a_{300,\,2400} = \frac{1}{3}\left(\overline{\Delta \sum \nu_i c_{p\,i}}^{\,300,\,600} + \overline{\Delta \sum \nu_i c_{p\,i}}^{\,600,\,1200} + \overline{\Delta \sum \nu_i c_{p\,i}}^{\,1200,\,2400}\right)$$

The following values of a are used in eqn. (198), depending on the temperature T at which the reaction takes place:

for $T =$ 300 ° to 450 °K: $a_{300} = \Delta \sum \nu_i c_{pi}$ at room temperature

for $T =$ 450 ° to 550 °K: the mean value of a_{300} and $a_{300,\,600}$

for $T =$ 550 ° to 1100 °K: $a_{300,\,600}$

for $T =$ 1100 ° to 1500 °K: the mean value of $a_{300,\,600}$ and $a_{300,\,1200}$

for $T =$ 1500 ° to 2600 °K: $a_{300,\,1200}$

for $T =$ 2600 ° to 3400 °K: the mean value of $a_{300,\,1200}$ and $a_{300,\,2400}$

for $T = >$ 3400 °K: $a_{300,\,2400}$

Approximation 4. When the variations of the molar heats at temperatures above room temperature are well known, EUCKEN shows that more accurate results can be obtained by using eqn. (202, below) rather than (198). The c_{pi} values for temperatures above 300 °K will be expressed by an interpolation formula

$$c_{pi} = c_{p\,0\,i} + \beta_i/T - \gamma_i T^{-2} \quad \ldots . \text{(201)}$$

$$4{\cdot}574 \log K_p = -\frac{\Delta H_0'}{T} + B + 2{\cdot}303\, \Delta \sum \nu_i c_{p\,0\,i} \log T + \frac{T}{2} \Delta \sum \nu_i \beta_i - \frac{1}{2\,T^2} \Delta \sum \nu_i \gamma_i \quad \ldots . \text{(202)}$$

where

$$\Delta H_0' = \Delta H_{0\,298} - 298\, \Delta \sum \nu_i c_{p\,0\,i} - \frac{298^2}{2} \Delta \sum \nu_i \beta_i - \frac{1}{298} \Delta \sum \nu_i \gamma_i \quad \ldots . \text{(203)}$$

$$\left.\begin{aligned} B = \Delta \sum \nu_i S_{0\,298\,i} - \underbrace{(1 + 2{\cdot}303 \log 298)}_{6{\cdot}699} \Delta \sum \nu_i c_{p\,0\,i} - 298\, \Delta \sum \nu_i \beta_i \\ - \frac{1}{2 \times 298^2} \Delta \sum \nu_i \gamma_i [+ \Delta \sum \nu_i l_{ti} (1/T_{ti} - 1/T)] \end{aligned}\right\} \quad \ldots \text{(204)}$$

Data on the variation of molar heats with temperature may be found in JUSTI. Data on the constants $c_{p\,0}$, β_i and γ_i are given by EUCKEN, *Chemieingenieur*, Vol. III, pp. 102, 103.

At the approximations 1 to 4 above, terms having the form $\Delta \sum \nu_i l_{ti} (1/T_{ti} - 1/T)$ are given in square brackets. These terms must be taken into account if, for any of the components X_i, any phase changes (melting, vaporization, transitions) occur between room temperature and the equilibrium temperature, i.e. changes accompanied by molar heats of transition l_{ti} at the transition temperatures T_{ti}.

The exact formula applicable for $\log K_{p0}$ is, in general, not used when the standard entropy values $S_{i\,298}$ are known. It reads

$$\log K_p = -\frac{\Delta H_0}{4{\cdot}574\,T} + \frac{\log T}{1{\cdot}986}\Delta\sum_{\text{gas}} \nu_i c_{p\,0\,i} + \frac{1}{4{\cdot}574}\int_0^T \frac{\mathrm{d}\,T}{T^2}\int_0^T \Delta\sum_{\text{gas}} \nu_i c_{p\,T\,i\,(\text{gas})}\,\mathrm{d}\,T$$

$$+\frac{1}{4{\cdot}574}\int_0^T \frac{\mathrm{d}\,T}{T^2}\int_0^T \Delta\sum_{(\text{cond})} \nu_i c_{p\,i\,(\text{cond})}\,\mathrm{d}\,T + \Delta\sum \nu_i j_i$$

$$\left[+\frac{1}{4{\cdot}574}\Delta\sum \nu_i l_{ti}(1/T_{ti} - 1/\mathrm{T})\right] \qquad \ldots\ldots (205)$$

In the above expression, ΔH_0 is the reaction enthalpy at $T = 0$ °K in cal/mole:

$$\Delta H_0 = \Delta H_{0\,298} - \int_0^{298} \Delta\sum \nu_i c_{p\,i}\,\mathrm{d}\,T \qquad \ldots\ldots (206)$$

$c_{p\,0\,i}$ and $c_{pTi\,(\text{gas})}$ are the temperature-independent and temperature-dependent parts of the specific heats of the gaseous components; $c_{pTi\,(\text{cond})}$ are the specific heats for condensed phases; j_i are the so-called chemical constants. For further information regarding this equation and its use, see EUCKEN and JAKOB, *Chemieingenieur*, Vol. III.

*EXERCISE 116

Experimental studies give the following values for the equilibrium constant K_p in the case of the ammonia equilibrium $N_2 + 3H_2 = 2NH_3$:

at 500 °C, $\log K_p/\text{atm}^{-2} = -4{\cdot}80$

at 600 °C, $\log K_p/\text{atm}^{-2} = -5{\cdot}64$

(*a*) What is the heat of reaction, ΔH, in this temperature range? (*b*) What is the value of the equilibrium constant at 530 °C?

Solution 116. The heat of reaction is calculated from eqn. (181). Substitution gives

$$\Delta H = 4{\cdot}574 \times \frac{873 \times 773}{873 - 773}[-5{\cdot}64 - (-4{\cdot}80)] = -25{,}930 \text{ cal/mole} \qquad \ldots\ldots \text{(i)}$$

The reaction is therefore exothermic.

Using the value found for ΔH, the equilibrium constant for 530 °C = 803 °K can be obtained from eqn. (180):

$$\log K_{803}/\text{atm}^{-2} = -4{\cdot}80 - \frac{(-25\,930)}{4{\cdot}574}(1/803 - 1/773)$$

$$= -4{\cdot}80 - 0{\cdot}274 = -5{\cdot}074 = 0{\cdot}926 - 6$$

or $$K_p \text{ (at 530 °C)} = 8{\cdot}433 \times 10^{-6} \text{ atm}^{-2} \qquad \ldots\ldots \text{(ii)}$$

Note. If ΔH is not required, an intermediate value for $\log K_p$ can usually be obtained more rapidly by graphical interpolation of the $\log K_p$ versus $1/T$ curve. In the preceding example, the points $-5{\cdot}64$ (ordinate), $1/873 = 1{\cdot}1455 \times 10^{-3}$ (abscissa) and $-4{\cdot}80$, $1/773 = 1{\cdot}2937 \times 10^{-3}$ on the curve would be joined. This gives an ordinate value of $-5{\cdot}075$ for a point $1/803 = 1{\cdot}2453 \times 10^{-3}$ on the abscissa.

*Exercise 117

The degree of formation x (in volume or mole per cent) of NO from air (20·93 vol. per cent O_2, 78·10 vol. per cent N_2) for the reaction $\frac{1}{2}N_2 + \frac{1}{2}O_2 = NO$ was found to be

$$\text{at } T = 1811\ °K \qquad x_1 = 0{\cdot}37 \text{ per cent}$$

$$\text{at } T = 2195\ °K \qquad x_2 = 0{\cdot}97 \text{ per cent}$$

$$\text{at } T = 2695\ °K \qquad x_3 = 2{\cdot}23 \text{ per cent}$$

Calculate the molar heat of formation of NO, ΔH^F_{NO}, in this temperature range.

Solution 117. The equilibrium is independent of pressure, since the sum of the reaction numbers $\Delta\sum \nu_i = 1 - \frac{1}{2} - \frac{1}{2} = 0$. It follows that $K_p = K_c = K_x$. If, under these conditions and for the sake of simplicity, the concentrations are measured in mole or vol. per cent, the following may be taken for application of the law of mass action:

	Initial percentage	*Percentage at equilibrium*
NO	0·0	x
O_2	20·93	$20{\cdot}93 - x/2$
N_2	78·10	$78{\cdot}10 - x/2$

Thus

$$K_p = \frac{x}{(20{\cdot}93 - x/2)^{1/2} \times (78{\cdot}10 - x/2)^{1/2}}$$

and

$$\log K_p = \log x - \tfrac{1}{2}\log(20{\cdot}93 - x/2) - \tfrac{1}{2}\log(78{\cdot}10 - x/2) \quad \ldots\ldots \quad \text{(i)}$$

Substituting the numerical values, one obtains for (i):

$$\left.\begin{array}{lll} x_1 = 0{\cdot}37 & \log K_{p(1811)} = 0{\cdot}9639 - 3 & 1/T = 1/1811 = 5{\cdot}522 \times 10^{-4} \\ x_2 = 0{\cdot}97 & \log K_{p(2195)} = 0{\cdot}3865 - 2 & 1/T = 1/2195 = 4{\cdot}556 \times 10^{-4} \\ x_3 = 2{\cdot}23 & \log K_{p(2695)} = 0{\cdot}7566 - 2 & 1/T = 1/2695 = 3{\cdot}711 \times 10^{-4} \end{array}\right\} \quad \ldots \quad \text{(ii)}$$

Substituting the values in eqn. (181) gives by combining x_2 and x_1

$$\Delta H^F_{NO} = \frac{4{\cdot}574\,[0{\cdot}3865 - 2 - (0{\cdot}9639 - 3)]}{(5{\cdot}522 - 4{\cdot}566)\,10^{-4}} = +\,20{\cdot}01 \text{ kcal/mole} \quad \ldots\ldots \quad \text{(iii)}$$

by combining x_3 and x_2

$$\Delta H^F_{NO} = \frac{4{\cdot}574\,(0{\cdot}7566 - 0{\cdot}3865)}{(4{\cdot}566 - 3{\cdot}711)10^{-4}} = +20{\cdot}05 \text{ kcal/mole} \quad \ldots\ldots \quad \text{(iv)}$$

Thus the heat of formation of NO in the temperature range 1800 – 2700 °K is $\Delta H^F_{NO} = +20$ kcal/mole and the reaction is endothermic.

Note. The heat of formation under standard conditions (25 °C) is $\Delta H^F_{NO} = +\,21{\cdot}6$ kcal/mole.

*Exercise 118

The solubility of benzoic acid in 100 g of water is 0·21 g at 10 °C, 0·29 g at 20 °C and 0·41 g at 30 °C. Calculate the molar heat of solution at 20 °C. Benzoic acid is practically undissociated in water.

Solution 118. One uses the integrated form of eqn. (177) which is analogous to eqn. (181). The units in which the concentration is measured are not important, since only concentration ratios feature in eqn. (181).

For the temperature range 10 to 20 °C, we find that

$$ {}^{\mathrm{d}}l^{\star} = \frac{4{\cdot}574 \log (0{\cdot}29/0{\cdot}21)}{(1/273 - 1/283)} = \frac{4{\cdot}574 \times 0{\cdot}1402}{0{\cdot}121 \times 10^{-3}} = +5{\cdot}3 \text{ kcal/mole} \quad \ldots . \quad \text{(i)} $$

and for the temperature range 20° to 30 °C

$$ {}^{\mathrm{d}}l^{\star} = \frac{4{\cdot}574 \log (0{\cdot}41/0{\cdot}29)}{1/283 - 1/293} = \frac{4{\cdot}574 \times 0{\cdot}1504}{0{\cdot}113 \times 10^{-3}} = +6{\cdot}1 \text{ kcal/mole} \quad \ldots . \quad \text{(ii)} $$

The mean value for the heat of solution at 20 °C is, therefore $\frac{5{\cdot}3 + 6{\cdot}1}{2}$ = 5·7 kcal/mole. .... (iii)

The experimental value is about 6·5 kcal/mole.

Exercise 119

Calculate the molar heats of solution of mercuric chloride, $HgCl_2$, and thallous chloride, TlCl, from the variation of solubility with temperature, given in the following table.

	Solubility in g/100 g H_2O	
	at 0 °C	*at* 20 °C
$HgCl_2$	4·29	6·6
TlCl	0·17	0·32

Both substances are sparingly soluble. $HgCl_2$ is practically undissociated in aqueous solution. On the other hand, TlCl is almost completely dissociated into ions, and the equilibrium constant should be calculated for the case when a solid phase is present [see (158)], i.e. the so-called solubility product, K_s, should be calculated.

Solution 119. For the undissociated solution of $HgCl_2$ the integrated form of eqn. (177), analogous to eqn. (181), should be used, as in Exercise 118. This gives

$$ {}^{\mathrm{d}}l^{\star}_{\mathrm{HgCl_2}} = \frac{4{\cdot}574 \log (6{\cdot}6/4{\cdot}29)}{1/273 - 1/293} = \frac{4{\cdot}574 \times 0{\cdot}1871}{0{\cdot}25 \times 10^{-3}} = +3420 \text{ cal/mole} \quad \ldots . \quad \text{(i)} $$

An experimental value of +3520 cal/mole was found.

In the case of the saturated TlCl solution, which contains TlCl as solid phase, the law of mass action takes the form $c_{\mathrm{Tl^+}} \times c_{\mathrm{Cl^-}} = K_s$ = solubility product. Since TlCl is practically completely dissociated, it follows that $c_{\mathrm{Tl^+}} = c_{\mathrm{Cl^-}} = c^{\star}_{\mathrm{TlCl\,(total)}}$.

Thus $K_s = c^{\star 2}_{\text{TlCl (total)}}$ and, from eqn. (175):

$$\frac{\partial \ln K_s}{\partial T} = \frac{2\,\partial \ln c^{\star}_{\text{TlCl}}}{\partial T} = \frac{\Delta U}{RT^2} \quad \text{or} \quad \frac{\partial \ln c^{\star}_{\text{TlCl}}}{\partial T} = \frac{\frac{\Delta U}{2}}{RT^2} \qquad \ldots\ldots \text{(ii)}$$

i.e. in this case, neither the normal temperature coefficient of solubility [eqn. (177)] nor the integrated form analogous to eqn. (181) gives the full value for the molar heat of solution of one mole of solid substance (TlCl) to an aqueous solution of Tl^+ and Cl^- ions. It gives only half the value. The units of measurement of concentration are not important, since only the ratios K_1/K_2 or $c_1^{\star}/c_2^{\star}$ feature. One has

$$\Delta U = {}^{\text{d}}l^{\star}_{\text{TlCl}} = 2 \times 4{\cdot}574\,\frac{\log(0{\cdot}32/0{\cdot}17)}{1/273 - 1/293} = \frac{2 \times 4{\cdot}574 \times 0{\cdot}2747}{0{\cdot}25 \times 10^{-3}} = 10{,}100 \text{ cal/mole} \qquad \ldots\ldots \text{(iii)}$$

The experimental value is 10,300 cal/mole.

*Exercise 120

Determine the equilibrium constants ($\log K_p/\text{atm}^{-1}$) for the Deacon process, $4\,HCl + O_2 = 2\,Cl_2 + 2\,H_2O$ at 450 °C and 650 °C.

The following numerical values are found from tables (see p. 103):

	Heat of formation ΔH^F (kcal/mole)	*Standard entropy* $S_{0\,298}$ [cal/(deg.mole)]	*Molar heat* c_p [cal/(deg. mole)]	
			at 300 °K	*at* 450 °K
HCl	−21·9	44·66	6·96	7·00
O_2	—	49·02	7·02	7·31
Cl_2	—	53·32	8·07	8·50
$H_2O_{(gas)}$	−57·80	45·14	8·00	8·26

Make the calculation using approximations 1, 2 and 3 in turn.

Solution 120. The heat of reaction at 298 °K, $\Delta H_{0\,298}$, may be calculated from the heats of formation by using eqn. (146):

$$\Delta H_{0\,298} = 2\,\Delta H^F_{H_2O\,(gas)} - 4\,\Delta H^F_{HCl} = 2(-57{\cdot}80) - 4(-21{\cdot}9) = -28{\cdot}0 \text{ kcal/mole} \qquad \ldots\ldots \text{(i)}$$

The entropy of reaction $\Delta S_{0\,298}$ is obtained in a similar way from the standard entropies:

$$\Delta S_{0\,298} = 2 \times 53{\cdot}32 + 2 \times 45{\cdot}14 - 4 \times 44{\cdot}66 - 49{\cdot}02 = -30{\cdot}74 \text{ cal/(deg. mole)} \qquad \ldots\ldots \text{(ii)}$$

Thus, for *approximation 1*, from eqn. (197):

for 450 °C: $T = 723$ °K

$$\log K_p/\text{atm}^{-1} = \frac{-(-28\,000)}{4{\cdot}574 \times 723} + \frac{(-30{\cdot}74)}{4{\cdot}574} = +1{\cdot}744 \qquad \ldots\ldots \text{(iii)}$$

for 650 °C: $T = 923\ °K$

$$\log K_p/\text{atm}^{-1} = \frac{-(-28\,000)}{4{\cdot}574 \times 923} + \frac{(-30{\cdot}74)}{4{\cdot}574} = -0{\cdot}091 \quad \ldots . \quad \text{(iv)}$$

Approximation 2. One has from eqn. (198) that $a = \Delta\sum \nu_i c_{pi}$, and $f\left(\frac{T}{298}\right)$ must be calculated. Using the values of c_{pi} at 300 °K, one obtains

$$a = 2\,c_{p(\text{Cl}_2)} + 2\,c_{p\,(\text{H}_2\text{O})} - 4\,c_{p\,(\text{HCl})} - c_{p\,(\text{O}_2)}$$
$$= 16{\cdot}14 + 16{\cdot}00 - 27{\cdot}84 - 7{\cdot}02 = -2{\cdot}72 \quad \ldots . \quad \text{(v)}$$

$$\frac{f\left(\frac{723}{298}\right)}{4{\cdot}574} = 0{\cdot}0650 \qquad \frac{f\left(\frac{923}{298}\right)}{4{\cdot}574} = 0{\cdot}0990 \quad \ldots . \quad \text{(vi)}$$

so that, from eqn. (198) and using the results at approximation 1

for 450 °C:

$$\log K_p/\text{atm}^{-1} = +1{\cdot}744 + (-2{\cdot}72)\,0{\cdot}0650 = +1{\cdot}567 \quad \ldots . \quad \text{(vii)}$$

for 650 °C:

$$\log K_p/\text{atm}^{-1} = -0{\cdot}091 + (-2{\cdot}72)\,0{\cdot}0990 = -0{\cdot}361 \quad \ldots . \quad \text{(viii)}$$

Approximation 3. The mean value $\overline{\Delta\sum \nu_i c_{pi}}^{300,\,600}$ may be replaced by the value for 450 °K, so that

$$\Delta\sum \nu_i c_{pi}^{450} = 2 \times 8{\cdot}50 + 2 \times 8{\cdot}26 - 4 \times 7{\cdot}00 - 7{\cdot}31 = -1{\cdot}79 = a_{300,\,600} \quad \ldots . \quad \text{(ix)}$$

In the temperature range 550° to 1100 °K, this is the value of a which must be substituted in eqn. (198). Thus

for 450 °C:

$$\log K_p/\text{atm}^{-1} = +1{\cdot}744 + (-1{\cdot}79)\,0{\cdot}0650 = +1{\cdot}628 \quad \ldots . \quad \text{(x)}$$

for 650 °C:

$$\log K_p/\text{atm}^{-1} = -0{\cdot}091 + (-1{\cdot}79)\,0{\cdot}0990 = -0{\cdot}268 \quad \ldots . \quad \text{(xi)}$$

Note. The observed values of log K_p/atm^{-1} for the Deacon process are $+1{\cdot}41$ and $-0{\cdot}40$ for temperatures 450° and 650 °C, respectively.

*Exercise 121

Calculate, as accurately as possible, the oxygen decomposition pressure of ferric oxide, Fe_2O_3, at 1200 °C.

At high temperatures, Fe_2O_3 decomposes to give Fe_3O_4 in accordance with the equation

$$\underset{\text{(solid)}}{6\,Fe_2O_3} = \underset{\text{(solid)}}{4\,Fe_3O_4} + O_2$$

Fe_2O_3 has a transition point at 675 °C (hexagonal → regular); heat of transition, $l_t = +0{\cdot}10$ kcal/mole.

β-Fe_3O_4 has a transition point at 750 °C ($\beta \to \alpha$); heat of transition, $l_t = +0{\cdot}10$ kcal/mole.

The following values are obtained from tables (see p. 103) for use in the calculation:

	Heat of formation at 25 °C, ΔH^F (kcal/mole)	*Standard entropy at 25 °C, 1 atm* $S_{0\,298}$[cal/(deg.mole)]	*Molar heat, c_p [cal/(deg. mole)]*				
			300 °K	450 °K	600 °K	900 °K	1200 °K
Fe_2O_3	− 196·9	21·5	24·3	29·7	33·7	37·9	38·0
β-Fe_3O_4	− 266·9	35·0	35·0	43·9	50·7	57·4	58·0
O_2	—	49·02	7·02	7·31	7·68	8·22	8·53

Solution 121. Since oxygen is the only gaseous product and the rest of the reactants are solids, the law of mass action takes the form

$$p_{O_2} = K_p\,[\text{atm}] \quad \text{or} \quad \log p_{O_2} = \log K_p \qquad \ldots . \quad \text{(i)}$$

where $\log K_p$ is calculated from eqn. (198). Thus

$$\left.\begin{aligned}\log p_{O_2}/\text{atm} &= \log K_p/\text{atm}\\ &= -\frac{\Delta H_{0\,298} + \Delta\sum \nu_i l_{ti}}{4\cdot 574\, T} + \frac{\Delta S_{0\,298}}{4\cdot 574} + \frac{1}{4\cdot 574}\Delta\sum\frac{\nu_i l_{ti}}{T_{ti}} + \frac{a f\left(\frac{T}{298}\right)}{4\cdot 574}\end{aligned}\right\} \qquad \ldots \quad \text{(ii)}$$

$$\Delta H_{0\,298} = 4(-266\cdot 9) - 6(-196\cdot 9) = +113\cdot 8\,\text{kcal/mole} \quad [\text{from eqn. (146)}] \quad \ldots . \quad \text{(iii)}$$

$$\Delta\sum \nu_i l_{ti} = 4(+0\cdot 10) - 6\,(+0\cdot 10) = -0\cdot 2\,\text{kcal/mole} \qquad \ldots . \quad \text{(iv)}$$

$$T = 1200 + 273 = 1473\ \text{°K} \qquad \ldots . \quad \text{(v)}$$

$$\Delta S_{0\,298} = 4 \times 35\cdot 0 + 49\cdot 02 - 6 \times 21\cdot 5 = 60\cdot 02\ \text{cal/(deg. mole)} \qquad \ldots . \quad \text{(vi)}$$

$$\Delta\sum\frac{\nu_i l_{ti}}{T_{ti}} = \frac{4 \times 100}{1023} - \frac{6 \times 100}{984} = -0\cdot 24\ \text{cal/(deg. mole)} \qquad \ldots . \quad \text{(vii)}$$

The heats of transition of both components are $l_t = +0\cdot 1$ kcal/mole $= 100$ cal/mole. The transition temperatures are $T_t = 750 + 273 = 1023$ °K for Fe_3O_4 and $T_t = 675 + 273 = 948$ °K for Fe_2O_3. The kilocalories must be converted to calories.

$$f\left(\frac{1473}{298}\right)\Big/ 4\cdot 574 = 0\cdot 175 \qquad \ldots . \quad \text{(viii)}$$

In order to determine the factor a [cal/(deg. mole)] a number of mean values must be calculated:

$a_{300,\,600}$ as the mean value of $\Delta\sum \nu_i c_{pi}^{450}$ and $\Delta\sum \nu_i \overline{c_{pi}}^{\,300,\,600\ \text{(border)}}$ i.e. the mean value of the two values corresponding to the borders of the temperature range under consideration, viz. $\Delta\sum \nu_i c_{pi}^{600}$ and $\Delta\sum \nu_i c_{pi}^{300}$.

$$\Delta\sum \nu_i c_{pi}^{450} = 4 \times 43\cdot 9 + 7\cdot 31 - 6 \times 29\cdot 7 = 4\cdot 71$$

$$\left.\begin{aligned}\Delta\sum \nu_i c_{pi}^{600} &= 4 \times 50\cdot 7 + 7\cdot 68 - 6 \times 33\cdot 7 = 8\cdot 28\\ \Delta\sum \nu_i c_{pi}^{300} &= 4 \times 35 \ \ + 7\cdot 02 - 6 \times 24\cdot 3 = 1\cdot 22\end{aligned}\right\} \text{mean} = 4\cdot 75 = \Delta\sum \nu_i \overline{c_{pi}}^{\,300,\,600\ \text{(border)}}$$

$$\text{Mean:}\ \frac{4\cdot 71 + 4\cdot 75}{2} = 4\cdot 73 = a_{300,\,600} \qquad \ldots . \quad \text{(ix)}$$

$a_{300,\,600}$ as mean value of

$$\frac{1}{2}\left(\Delta\sum \nu_i c_{pi}^{450} + \Delta\sum \nu_i c_{pi}^{900}\right) = \frac{1}{2}(4{\cdot}71 + 10{\cdot}42) = 7{\cdot}56$$

and of

$$\frac{1}{2}\left(\overline{\Delta\sum \nu_i c_{pi}}^{300,\,600\,\text{(border)}} + \overline{\Delta\sum \nu_i c_{pi}}^{600,\,1200\,\text{(border)}}\right)$$

$$= \frac{1}{2}\left(4{\cdot}75 + \frac{12{\cdot}53 + 8{\cdot}28}{2}\right) = 7{\cdot}58$$

$$\text{Mean: } \frac{7{\cdot}56 + 7{\cdot}58}{2} = 7{\cdot}57 = a_{300,\,1200} \qquad \ldots. \quad \text{(x)}$$

Thus

$$\Delta\sum \nu_i c_{pi}^{900} = 4 \times 57{\cdot}4 + 8{\cdot}22 - 6 \times 37{\cdot}9 = 10{\cdot}42$$

$$\Delta\sum \nu_i c_{pi}^{1200} = 4 \times 58 + 8{\cdot}53 - 6{\cdot}38 = 12{\cdot}53$$

The mean value of $a_{300,\,600}$ and $a_{300,\,1200}$ should be used for a in the temperature range 1100° to 1500 °K. Thus $a = \frac{4{\cdot}73 + 7{\cdot}57}{2} = 6{\cdot}15$ cal/(deg. mole) .... (xi)

The necessary values for substitution in the expression for $\log p_{O_2}$ have now been determined. Substituting (iii) – (xi) in (ii) gives

$$\log p_{O_2}/\text{atm} = -\frac{(113\,800 - 200)}{4{\cdot}574 \times 1473} + \frac{60{\cdot}02}{4{\cdot}574} + \frac{(-0{\cdot}24)}{4{\cdot}574} + 0{\cdot}175 \times 6{\cdot}15$$

$$= -2{\cdot}716 = 0{\cdot}284 - 3$$

$$p_{O_2} = 1{\cdot}92 \times 10^{-3}\ \text{atm}$$

$$= 1{\cdot}92 \times 10^{-3} \times 760 = 1{\cdot}46\ \text{mm Hg} \qquad \ldots. \quad \text{(xii)}$$

Note. The experimental values for the dissociation pressure of Fe_2O_3 are

at 1150 °C: 0·5 mm Hg

at 1200 °C: 1·0 mm Hg

at 1260 °C: 2·0 mm Hg

*Exercise 122

White tin changes into an allotropic modification, grey crumbly tin, at a temperature somewhat below room temperature. This is a phenomenon referred to as 'tin pest' and destroys tin vessels if they are stored for a long period at low temperatures. Calculate the transition temperature as accurately as possible. The following data have been taken from tables (see p. 103):

	Heat of formation at 25 °C, ΔH^F (cal/mole)	*Standard entropy* $S_{0\,298}$ [cal/(deg. mole)]	*Molar heat c_p at room temp.* [cal/(deg. mole)]
Sn (white)	0·0	12·5	6·25
Sn (grey)	– 525	10·7	6·15

Solution 122. Consider the reaction $Sn_{white} = Sn_{grey}$: here one is dealing with a completely condensed system. Equation (199) is used, and the temperature at which $\Delta G_0 = 0$ is determined. It is found that

$$\Delta G_0 = \Delta H_{0\,298} - T\Delta S_{0\,298} - T a f\left(\frac{T}{278}\right) \quad \ldots \quad \text{(i)}$$

and from (146)

$$\Delta H_0 = -525 - 0 = -525 \text{ cal/mole}$$

$$\Delta S_{0\,298} = 10{\cdot}7 - 12{\cdot}5 = -1{\cdot}8 \text{ cal/(deg. mole)}$$

$$a_{300} = \Delta \sum \nu_i c_{pi} = 6{\cdot}15 - 6{\cdot}25 = 0{\cdot}1 \text{ cal/(deg. mole)}$$

$f(T/298)$ lies between 0·0041 and 0 in the range 0 °C to 25 °C. It follows that the term $-T a f(T/298)$ can have a maximum value of only $273 \times 0{\cdot}1 \times 0{\cdot}0041 = 0{\cdot}11$ cal/mole and can, in this case, be virtually ignored. For the equilibrium condition one then has

$$\Delta G_0 \approx -525 + T \times 1{\cdot}8 = 0 \quad \ldots \quad \text{(ii)}$$

or

$$T \approx \frac{525}{1{\cdot}8} = 292\ ^\circ\text{K} \quad \text{or} \quad 19^\circ\text{C} \quad \ldots \quad \text{(iii)}$$

ΔG_0 will be negative at temperatures below 19 °C, when the reaction will proceed towards the right with formation of grey tin. ΔG_0 is positive at higher temperatures, under which conditions the white metallic modification is stable.

An experimental study showed the transition temperature to be 13·2 °C. The close agreement between the experimental and calculated values should be regarded as accidental since, as can be seen from the above equation, the value is markedly dependent on the change in entropy [$-1{\cdot}8$ cal/(deg. mole)], where the figure after the decimal point is by no means well established.

Exercise 123

Consider the question (*a*) whether a transformation from graphite to diamond ($C_{graphite} = C_{diamond}$) is possible at atmospheric pressure, and (*b*) under what pressures can this transformation be made to occur at room temperature (300 °K), at 327 °C (600 °K), at 727 °C (1000 °K) and at 1227 °C (1500 °K).

The following values have been taken from tables (see p. 103):

	Heat of formation at 25 °C ΔH^F	*Standard entropy* $S_{0\,298}$	*Density*	*Molar heat* c_p [cal/(deg. mole)]				
	(cal/mole)	[cal/(deg. mole)]	(g/cm³)	300 °K	450 °K	600 °K	900 °K	1200 °K
$C_{(graphite)}$	0·0	1·365	2·260	2·09	3·28	4·05	4·89	5·34
$C_{(diamond)}$	+453	0·585	3·513	1·52	3·00	3·92	4·92	5·52

Conversion factor: 1 cm³ atm = 0·02421 cal.

As can be seen, the influence of compressibility may be ignored for a first approximation.

The isothermal compressibility coefficient, $k = -\frac{1}{V}\left(\frac{\mathrm{d}V}{\mathrm{d}p}\right)_T$ is

for diamond: $k = 0{\cdot}165 \times 10^{-6}$ atm^{-1}

for graphite: $k = 3 \times 10^{-6}$ atm^{-1} (approx.)

falling with increase in pressure and temperature but functions are not accurately known.

Solution 123. The reaction $C_{\text{graphite}} = C_{\text{diamond}}$ takes place in a fully condensed system. As in Exercise 122, it is therefore necessary to consider the maximum useful work at constant pressure, ΔG [eqn. (199)]. Again, as in Exercise 122, the following relation holds at atmospheric pressure:

$$\Delta G_0 = \Delta H_{0\,298} - \Delta T S_{0\,298} - Ta f\left(\frac{T}{298}\right) \quad \ldots \quad \text{(i)}$$

If higher pressures are considered, the variation of ΔG with pressure must be taken into account in accordance with eqn. (187):

$$\left(\frac{\partial \Delta G}{\partial p}\right)_T = \Delta V \quad \ldots \quad \text{(ii)}$$

Here, ΔV is the difference between the molar volumes of the reactants, $v_{\text{diamond}} - v_{\text{graphite}}$; molar volume $= \frac{\text{mol. wt.}}{\text{density}}$ (cm^3/mole). Ignoring compressibility, $\Delta V = \Delta V_0$ is a constant independent of pressure, and integration of (ii) gives

$$\left.\begin{aligned}\Delta G - \Delta G_0 &= \int_{1\,\text{atm}}^{p\,\text{atm}} \Delta V\,\mathrm{d}p = \Delta V_0(p-1) \approx \Delta V_0 p \quad \text{at high pressures } p \text{ (in cm}^3\text{ atm/mole)}\\ &= 0{\cdot}02421\,\Delta V_0 p \text{ (in cal/mole)}\end{aligned}\right\} \quad \ldots \quad \text{(iii)}$$

Taking the effect of pressure into account and combining (i) and (iii), one has

$$\Delta G = \Delta H_{0\,298} - T\Delta S_{0\,298} - Ta f\left(\frac{T}{298}\right) + 0{\cdot}02421\,\Delta V_0 p \quad \text{(cal/mole)} \quad \ldots \quad \text{(iv)}$$

The coefficients in eqns. (i) and (iv) must now be calculated:

$$\Delta H_{0\,298} = +453 - 0 = +453 \text{ cal/mole [from (146)]}$$

$$\Delta S_{0\,298} = 0{\cdot}585 - 1{\cdot}365 = -0{\cdot}78 \text{ cal/(deg. mole)}$$

$$\Delta V_0 = \frac{12{\cdot}01}{3{\cdot}513} - \frac{12{\cdot}01}{2{\cdot}260} = 3{\cdot}418 - 5{\cdot}314 = -1{\cdot}896 \text{ cm}^3\text{/mole}$$

(mol. wt. of C = 12·01)

$T = 300$ °K:

$$a = a_{300} = \Delta \sum \nu_i c_{pi}^{300} \text{ for room temperature} = 1{\cdot}52 - 2{\cdot}09 = -0{\cdot}57$$

$$f\left(\frac{T}{298}\right) \approx 0$$

$T = 600$ °K:

$$a_{600} = \Delta\sum \nu_i c_{pi}^{600} = 3{\cdot}92 - 4{\cdot}05 = -0{\cdot}13$$

$$\left.\begin{aligned} a &= a_{300,\,600} = \overline{\Delta\sum \nu_i c_{pi}}^{\,300,\,600\text{ (border)}} = \frac{0{\cdot}13 - 0{\cdot}57}{2} = 0{\cdot}35 \\ a &= \Delta\sum \nu_i c_{pi}^{450} = +3{\cdot}00 - 3{\cdot}28 = -0{\cdot}28 \end{aligned}\right\} \text{mean} = -0{\cdot}315$$

$$T f\left(\frac{T}{298}\right) = 118$$

$T = 1000$ °K:

$$a = a_{300,\,600} = -0{\cdot}315$$

$$T f\left(\frac{T}{298}\right) = 508$$

$T = 1500$ °K:

$$a_{1200} = \Delta\sum \nu_i c_{pi}^{1200} = 5{\cdot}52 - 5{\cdot}34 = 0{\cdot}18$$

$$(1)\; a = a_{300,\,1200} = \frac{1}{2}\left(\overline{\Delta\sum \nu_i c_{pi}}^{\,300,\,600\text{ (border)}} + \overline{\Delta\sum \nu_i c_{pi}}^{\,600,\,1200\text{ (border)}}\right)$$

$$= \frac{1}{2}\left(-0{\cdot}35 + \frac{+0{\cdot}18 - 0{\cdot}13}{2}\right) = \frac{1}{2}(-0{\cdot}35 + 0{\cdot}025) = -0{\cdot}16$$

or

$$a = \frac{1}{2}\left(\Delta\sum \nu_i c_{pi}^{450} + \Delta\sum \nu_i c_{pi}^{900}\right) = \frac{1}{2}(-0{\cdot}28 + 0{\cdot}03) = -0{\cdot}12$$

$$\text{mean} = -0{\cdot}14$$

$$(2)\quad a = \text{mean of } a_{300,\,600} \text{ and } a_{300,\,1200} = \frac{-0{\cdot}315 - 0{\cdot}14}{2} = -0{\cdot}23$$

The mean of (1) and (2) finally gives $a = -0{\cdot}18$ cal/(deg. mole)

$$T f\left(\frac{T}{298}\right) = 1222$$

(*a*) If the calculated values of the coefficients are substituted in (i) for atmospheric pressure, it will be seen that the equation leads to positive values of ΔG_0 at any temperature, for example:

for $T = 300$: $\Delta G_0 = +453 + 300 \times 0{\cdot}78 + 0{\cdot}57 \times 0$ (cal/mole)

for $T = 1500$: $\Delta G_0 = +453 + 1500 \times 0{\cdot}78 + 0{\cdot}18 \times 1222$ (cal/mole)

It follows that, at atmospheric pressure, there is no temperature at which both forms of carbon are in equilibrium. Only the graphite modification is stable. This is monotropy.

Note. The reason for the above is that diamond possesses more energy and has a lower standard entropy than graphite. This lower entropy cannot be sufficiently increased (to permit transition) by raising the temperature since, for the greater part of the temperature range in question, diamond has an appreciably lower molar heat than graphite. On the other hand, diamond has a considerably smaller molar volume than graphite. Under the influence of pressure, therefore, the system reacts against the effect of the external force by decrease in volume, i.e. by transition from graphite into diamond (Le Chatelier's principle of least constraint). The external work done on the system is therefore released to the surroundings as maximum useful work (reaction work), and the free enthalpy of the reacting system becomes more negative. Increasing this negative value still further leads to the possibility of making the whole expression for ΔG equal to zero, or even less, i.e. of converting the graphite by means of external force into diamond with its smaller volume.

(b) The mathematical relationship is again given by (iv). For a transition point at $T = 300$ °K, one has

$$\Delta G = 453 + 300 \times 0{\cdot}78 + 0 - 0{\cdot}02421 \times 1{\cdot}896p = 0$$

so that the equilibrium pressure is

$$p = \frac{453 + 300 \times 0{\cdot}78}{0{\cdot}02421 \times 1{\cdot}896} = 15{,}000 \text{ atm}$$

for $T = 600$ °K: $$p = \frac{453 + 600 \times 0{\cdot}78 + 0{\cdot}315 \times 118}{0{\cdot}02421 \times 1{\cdot}896} = 20{,}900 \text{ atm}$$

for $T = 1000$ °K: $$p = \frac{453 + 1000 \times 0{\cdot}78 + 0{\cdot}315 \times 508}{0{\cdot}02421 \times 1{\cdot}896} = 30{,}400 \text{ atm}$$

for $T = 1500$ °K: $$p = \frac{453 + 1500 \times 0{\cdot}78 + 0{\cdot}18 \times 1222}{0{\cdot}02421 \times 1{\cdot}896} = 40{,}200 \text{ atm}$$

At higher temperatures a large increase in pressure is therefore necessary to effect the transition from graphite to diamond.

Note. The effect of compressibility may be ignored in first approximation; incidentally, it is not accurately known. The effect depends on a decrease of the molar volume from V_0 to V. For the least favourable case, when k does not decrease with increase of temperature or pressure but remains constant, integration of the equation $k = -(\mathrm{d}V/\mathrm{d}p)_T/V$ gives

$$\frac{+\,\mathrm{d}V}{V} = -k\,\mathrm{d}p \quad \text{or} \quad \ln\frac{V}{V_0} = -k(p-1) \approx -kp \quad \text{at high pressures} \qquad \text{(v)}$$

or

$$V = V_0\,\mathrm{e}^{-kp}$$

so that

$$\Delta V + V_{di} - V_{gr} = V_{0\,di}\,\mathrm{e}^{-k_{di}p} - V_{0\,gr}\,\mathrm{e}^{-k_{gr}p} \qquad \text{(vi)}$$

At a pressure of 20,000 atm, kp is $3 \times 10^{-6} \times 2 \times 10^4 = 0{\cdot}06$ for graphite and 0·0033 for diamond.

Since $\mathrm{e}^{-0\cdot06} = 0{\cdot}942$ and $\mathrm{e}^{-0\cdot0033} = 0{\cdot}997$, ΔV will be $3{\cdot}418 \times 0{\cdot}997 - 5{\cdot}314 \times 0{\cdot}942 = 1{\cdot}598$ cm^3/mole instead of $\Delta V_0 = 1{\cdot}896$ cm^3/mole, i.e. by ignoring compressibility and its pressure and temperature dependence, a maximum error of about 15 per cent in ΔV is introduced. In the present case, therefore, ΔV_0 is too great and the calculated pressures will be too low by 15 per cent, or less. The difference may well lie within the limits of accuracy of the calculation. From the physico-chemical standpoint, the pressure correction is significant in that soft graphite eludes the effect of external pressure by contracting and can thus be converted to the diamond form of carbon (which has a smaller molar volume) only under the influence of much higher pressures.

Technically, it is very difficult to produce diamond crystals from graphite because of the high pressures required, and carrying out the process consistently is only a recent development. Temperatures of 1500 °K or higher are required if conversion is to be effected within a reasonable period of time and the applied pressures must, therefore, be very high. On the other hand, in the solidifying magma of volcanoes, for example in the diamond mines of South Africa, geologically favourable conditions may exist.

A recent achievement is the transformation of hexagonal boron nitride (BN), which is isosteric with graphite, into the borazon modification, which has the diamond structure. Borazon is harder than diamond and unaffected by oxygen at temperatures up to 2200 °K.

**Exercise 124

Calculate the maximum flame temperature when carbon monoxide, CO, is burnt in excess air at atmospheric pressure: $CO + \frac{1}{2}O_2 = CO_2$. The excess air value (better referred to as the air ratio) is defined by λ = actual air consumption/air theoretically required. A value of $\lambda = 1{\cdot}2$ will be taken. Air contains 20·9 vol. per cent O_2 and the remainder may be regarded as N_2. The initial temperature of the CO is 100 °C and that of the air, 25 °C. Make the calculation (*a*) by ignoring dissociation of CO_2 ($CO_2 = CO + \frac{1}{2}O_2$) as a first approximation, and (*b*) by taking dissociation into account. The dissociation of oxygen ($O_2 = 2O$) and formation of NO ($\frac{1}{2}N_2 + \frac{1}{2}O_2 = NO$) may be neglected under the conditions given. Tables give the following data.

Heat of formation at 25 °C:

$$\Delta H^F_{CO} = -26{\cdot}64 \text{ kcal/mole}$$

$$\Delta H^F_{CO_2} = -94{\cdot}39 \text{ kcal/mole}$$

Change in heat content between θ °C and 0 °C, ΔH_0 (kcal/mole)

θ °C	$\Delta H_{0\,(CO)}$	$\Delta H_{0\,(CO_2)}$	$\Delta H_{0\,(air)}$	$\Delta H_{0\,(O_2)}$	$\Delta H_{0\,(N_2)}$
0	0·000	0·000	0·000	0·000	0·000
25	0·174	0·219	0·174	0·175	0·174
100	0·697	—	—	—	—
1400	10·93	17·42	—	11·40	10·82
1500	11·78	18·84	—	12·29	11·66
1750	13·93	22·39	—	14·54	13·80
2000	16·11	25·99	—	16·82	15·96
2250	18·31	29·60	—	19·13	18·15
2500	20·53	33·24	—	21·475	20·35

Equilibrium constant K_p for $CO_2 = CO + \frac{1}{2}O_2$: $K_p = \dfrac{p_{CO}\, p_{O_2}^{1/2}}{p_{CO_2}}$

T (°K)	K_p (atm$^{-1/2}$)
1750	$1{\cdot}25 \times 10^{-4}$
2000	$1{\cdot}37 \times 10^{-3}$
2500	$3{\cdot}77 \times 10^{-2}$

Solution 124. (*a*) The heat of reaction for the reaction $CO + \frac{1}{2}O_2 = CO_2$ at 25 °C is given by: $\Delta H_0 = \Delta H^F_{CO_2} - \Delta H^F_{CO} = -94{\cdot}39 - (-26{\cdot}64) = -67{\cdot}75$ kcal/mole [from (146)].

According to the first law of thermodynamics, the heat of reaction ($-\Delta H_0$) plus the change in heat content for the initial substance (above 25 °C) is equal to the change in heat content for the final products (above 25 °C). At equilibrium, therefore:

$$\left.\begin{aligned} &\underset{(100^\circ\,C)}{1 \text{ mole CO}} + \underbrace{\lambda\left(\frac{1}{2}\text{ mole } O_2 + \frac{79{\cdot}1}{20{\cdot}9}\times\frac{1}{2}\text{ mole } N_2\right)}_{\text{air } (25^\circ\,C)} \\ &= \underbrace{1 \text{ mole } CO_2 + \lambda\frac{79{\cdot}1}{20{\cdot}9}\times\frac{1}{2}\text{ mole } N_2 + (\lambda-1)\frac{1}{2}\text{ mole } O_2}_{\text{final gas } (\theta^\circ\,C)} \end{aligned}\right\} \quad \ldots \quad \text{(i)}$$

In the present case

$$\Delta H_{25}^{100}\,(\mathrm{CO}) + 67{\cdot}75\ \mathrm{kcal/mole} = \Delta H_{25}^{\theta}\,(\mathrm{CO}) + \lambda\,\frac{79{\cdot}1}{20{\cdot}9}\times\frac{1}{2}\,\Delta H_{25}^{\theta}\,(\mathrm{N_2})$$
$$+ (\lambda - 1)\,\frac{1}{2}\,\Delta H_{25}^{\theta}\,(\mathrm{O_2}) \quad \ldots\ldots \quad \text{(ii)}$$

The left-hand side of (ii) becomes: $(0{\cdot}697 - 0{\cdot}174) + 67{\cdot}75 = 68{\cdot}27$ kcal/mole.

It is convenient to calculate the value of the right-hand side for several different temperatures. These results are then plotted and a temperature, θ °C, read off where the value agrees accurately with that of the left-hand side. One finds

for $\theta = 1750$ °C:

$$(22{\cdot}39 - 0{\cdot}219) + \frac{79{\cdot}1}{20{\cdot}9}\times\frac{1}{2}\times 1{\cdot}2\,(13{\cdot}80 - 0{\cdot}174) + 0{\cdot}2\times\frac{1}{2}\,(14{\cdot}54 - 0{\cdot}175)$$
$$= 54{\cdot}56\ \mathrm{kcal/mole}$$

for $\theta = 2000$ °C:

$$(25{\cdot}99 - 0{\cdot}219) + \frac{79{\cdot}1}{20{\cdot}9}\times\frac{1}{2}\times 1{\cdot}2\,(15{\cdot}96 - 0{\cdot}174) + 0{\cdot}2\times\frac{1}{2}\,(16{\cdot}82 - 0{\cdot}175)$$
$$= 63{\cdot}30\ \mathrm{kcal/mole}$$

for $\theta = 2250$ °C:

$$(29{\cdot}60 - 0{\cdot}219) + \frac{79{\cdot}1}{20{\cdot}1}\times\frac{1}{2}\times 1{\cdot}2\,(18{\cdot}15 - 0{\cdot}174) + 0{\cdot}2\times\frac{1}{2}\,(19{\cdot}13 - 0{\cdot}175)$$
$$= 72{\cdot}11\ \mathrm{kcal/mole}$$

for $\theta = 2500$ °C:

$$(33{\cdot}24 - 0{\cdot}219) + \frac{79{\cdot}1}{20{\cdot}9}\times\frac{1}{2}\times 1{\cdot}2\,(20{\cdot}35 - 0{\cdot}174) + 0{\cdot}2\times\frac{1}{2}\,(21{\cdot}475 - 0{\cdot}175)$$
$$= 80{\cdot}98\ \mathrm{kcal/mole}$$

If these four temperature-dependent values are plotted, a nearly linear relationship is obtained and a temperature of $\theta = 2141$ °C is read off, as corresponding to the value (68·27 kcal/mole) of the left-hand side. This is the maximum flame temperature.

(*b*) If dissociation of carbon dioxide is taken into account ($CO_2 = CO + \frac{1}{2}O_2$) and α is the degree of dissociation, only $(1 - \alpha)$ moles of CO and $(1 - \alpha)$ moles of CO_2 must be taken and the heat of reaction will be $(1 - \alpha)\,\Delta H_0$, i.e. a heat of reaction of only $(1 - \alpha)$ 67·75 kcal/mole will be generated. For an initial $\lambda/2$ moles of O_2, $\alpha/2 + (\lambda - 1)/2$ moles will be present after reaction. The nitrogen figures remain unaffected. We now have

$$\left.\begin{aligned} &\underset{(100\ ^\circ\mathrm{C})}{1\ \text{mole CO}} + \underbrace{\lambda\left(\frac{1}{2}\ \text{mole O}_2 + \frac{1\times 79{\cdot}1}{2\times 20{\cdot}9}\ \text{mole N}_2\right)}_{\text{air }(25\ ^\circ\mathrm{C})} \\ &= \underbrace{(1-\alpha)\ \text{moles CO}_2 + \alpha\ \text{moles CO} + \frac{\lambda-(1-\alpha)}{2}\ \text{moles O}_2 + \frac{\lambda\times 79{\cdot}1}{2\times 20{\cdot}9}\ \text{moles N}_2}_{\text{final gas }(\theta\ ^\circ\mathrm{C})} \end{aligned}\right\} \quad \ldots \quad \text{(iii)}$$

Thus

$$\left.\begin{aligned} &\Delta H_{25}^{100}\,(\mathrm{CO}) + (1-\alpha)\,67{\cdot}75\ \mathrm{kcal/mole} = (1-\alpha)\,\Delta H_{25}^{\theta}\,(\mathrm{CO_2}) + \alpha\times\Delta H_{25}^{\theta}\,(\mathrm{CO}) \\ &\quad + \frac{\lambda-(1-\alpha)}{2}\,\Delta H_{25}^{\theta}\,(\mathrm{O_2}) + \frac{79{\cdot}1}{20{\cdot}9}\times\frac{\lambda}{2}\times\Delta H_{25}^{\theta}\,(\mathrm{N_2}) \quad \text{where } \lambda = 1{\cdot}2 \end{aligned}\right\} \quad \ldots \quad \text{(iv)}$$

or

$$\text{left-hand side} - \text{right-hand side} = f(\theta)^* = 0 \quad \ldots\ldots \quad \text{(v)}$$

* $f(\theta)$ means 'function of θ'.

It is best to calculate (v) for a number of different temperatures. A plot will then give the temperature for which (v) has a value of 0. But it is necessary first to determine K_p (preferably by a graphical method) and, from it, evaluate α for various temperatures. Intermediate values of K_p are most suitably obtained by plotting $\log K_p$ against $1/T$ in accordance with the note to Exercise 116 (see *Figure 18*, curve 1); α is calculated from K_p by using the law of mass action (see Exercise 92).

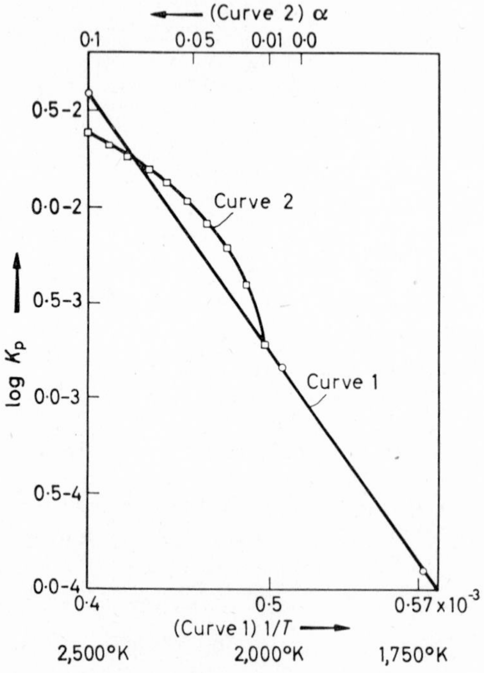

Figure 18. Graphical determination of maximum flame temperature

If n_0 is the total quantity of moles of CO_2 before dissociation, one has at equilibrium:

$$\left.\begin{array}{rll} (1-\alpha)\,n_0 & \text{moles } CO_2 & \text{corresponding to } p_{CO_2} \\ \alpha\, n_0 & \text{moles CO} & \text{corresponding to } p_{CO} \\ \dfrac{\lambda-(1-\alpha)}{2}\,n_0 & \text{moles } O_2 & \text{corresponding to } p_{O_2} \\ \dfrac{79{\cdot}1}{26{\cdot}9}\,\dfrac{\lambda}{2}\,n_0 & \text{moles } N_2 & \text{corresponding to } p_{N_2} \\ \hline \text{Total:}\quad \left[1+\dfrac{\lambda-(1-\alpha)}{2}+\dfrac{79{\cdot}1}{20{\cdot}9}\times\dfrac{\lambda}{2}\right] n_0 & \text{moles, abbreviated} & \end{array}\right\} \quad \ldots \text{(vi)}$$

to $[\;]n_0$, corresponding to a total pressure $p = 1$ atm.

Since the pressures will be in the same ratios as the quantities of moles

$$\left.\begin{aligned} p_{CO_2} &= \frac{1-\alpha}{[\,]} \qquad p_{CO} = \frac{\alpha}{[\,]} \\ p_{O_2} &= \frac{\lambda-(1-\alpha)}{2[\,]} \end{aligned}\right\} \quad \ldots \text{(vii)}$$

so that, from the law of mass action for $CO_2 = CO + \frac{1}{2}O_2$:

$$K_p = \frac{p_{CO}\,p_{O_2}^{1/2}}{p_{CO_2}} = \frac{\alpha\left(\dfrac{\lambda-(1-\alpha)}{2}\right)^{1/2}}{(1-\alpha)[\,]^{1/2}} \quad \text{or} \quad K_p^2 = \frac{\alpha^2[\lambda-(1-\alpha)]}{(1-\alpha)^2\left[2+\lambda-(1-\alpha)+\dfrac{79{\cdot}1}{20{\cdot}9}\lambda\right]} \quad \ldots\ldots \text{(viii)}$$

or, in the present case (where $\lambda = 1{\cdot}2$),

$$\log K_p = \log\alpha - \log(1-\alpha) + \frac{1}{2}[\log(0{\cdot}2+\alpha) - \log(6{\cdot}745+\alpha)] \quad \ldots\ldots \text{(ix)}$$

It is convenient to plot $\log K_p$ both as a function of α (*Figure 18*, curve 2) and as a function of $1/T$ (*Figure 18*, curve 1) on the same paper, so that a relevant reading of α may be taken for any particular temperature.

One then evaluates (v) for several temperatures and reads off the temperature for which the right-hand side is equal to 0:

$$\theta = 2000\ °C,\quad T = 2273\ °K,\quad 1/T = 0{\cdot}4399 \times 10^{-3}\,\text{deg.}^{-1}$$

Using *Figure 18*, the value of $\log K_p$ corresponding to $1/T = 0{\cdot}4399 \times 10^{-3}$ is found. Moving horizontally across the paper to the curve for $\log K_p$ versus α, a reading on the abscissa axis is then taken for the corresponding value of α. This value is found to be 0·0497, so that (v) becomes

$$+(0{\cdot}697 - 0{\cdot}174) + 0{\cdot}9503 \times 67{\cdot}75 - 0{\cdot}9503(25{\cdot}99 - 0{\cdot}219) - 0{\cdot}0497\,(16{\cdot}11 - 0{\cdot}174)$$
$$-\frac{1{\cdot}2 - 0{\cdot}9503}{2}(16{\cdot}82 - 0{\cdot}175) - \frac{1{\cdot}2 \times 79{\cdot}1}{2 \times 20{\cdot}9}(15{\cdot}96 - 0{\cdot}174) = +0{\cdot}68\,\text{kcal/mole}$$

This value is still somewhat too high and the calculation must, therefore, be repeated using a slightly higher temperature:

$\theta = 2050$ °C $\quad T = 2323$ °K $\quad 1/T = 0{\cdot}4305 \times 10^{-3}$ deg.$^{-1}$. In this case $\alpha = 0{\cdot}0651$.

The changes in heat content for 2050 °C are obtained from the given data by means of interpolation:

$$\left.\begin{aligned} \Delta H_{0\,(CO)} &= 16{\cdot}55 \quad & \Delta H_{0\,(CO_2)} &= 26{\cdot}71 \\ \Delta H_{0\,(O_2)} &= 17{\cdot}28 \quad & \Delta H_{0\,(N_2)} &= 16{\cdot}395 \end{aligned}\right\}\ \text{kcal/mole}$$

(v) now becomes:

$$+(0{\cdot}697 - 0{\cdot}174) + 0{\cdot}9349 \times 67{\cdot}75 - 0{\cdot}9349(26{\cdot}71 - 0{\cdot}219) - 0{\cdot}0651(16{\cdot}55 - 0{\cdot}174)$$
$$-\frac{1{\cdot}2 - 0{\cdot}9349}{2}(17{\cdot}28 - 0{\cdot}175) - \frac{1{\cdot}2 \times 79{\cdot}1}{2 \times 20{\cdot}9}(16{\cdot}395 - 0{\cdot}174) = -1{\cdot}06\,\text{kcal/mole}$$

The zero value has now been closely bracketed and can be obtained by interpolation. Linear interpolation or use of the regula falsi method [see Exercise 100 (vii)] gives the following value

$$\theta = 2000 + 50 \times \frac{0{\cdot}68}{0{\cdot}68 - (-1{\cdot}06)} \quad \text{i.e.} \quad \theta = 2020\,°\mathrm{C}$$

as the maximum flame temperature when dissociation of CO_2 is taken into account. The degree of dissociation of CO_2 at this temperature is given by $\alpha = 0{\cdot}0555$.

Note. Dissociation of oxygen ($O_2 = 2\,O$) and formation of NO ($\frac{1}{2}\,N_2 + \frac{1}{2}\,O_2 = NO$) were not considered in this calculation. For the temperature in question, it is quite reasonable to ignore the dissociation of oxygen, since $K_p = 10^{-5}$ atm and the degree of dissociation α is less than 1 per thousand. On the other hand, when making accurate calculations, the formation of NO must be considered. K_p for this reaction is $3{\cdot}5 \times 10^{-2}$ and the degree of association $(1 - \beta)$ can be shown, by means of rough calculation using the law of mass action, to be about 8 per thousand under the given partial pressures. The heat of formation of NO is only + 21·6 kcal/mole, so that the extra term to eqn. (v) would only amount to some $-0{\cdot}008 \times \frac{1{\cdot}2}{2} \times \frac{79{\cdot}1}{20{\cdot}9} \times 21{\cdot}6 \approx -0{\cdot}4$ kcal/mole. The maximum flame temperature would therefore be about 10 °C lower, a difference which is close to the limits of accuracy of the calculation.

In order to take NO formation accurately into account, its degree of dissociation α must be included in eqns. (iv) and (v) and α and β calculated from the law of mass action equations for the dissociation of both CO_2 and NO (two equations with two unknowns).

The dissociation equilibria of the combustion products play an important part when flame temperatures higher than 2500 °C are being calculated. A stoichiometric mixture of methane and oxygen should give a maximum flame temperature of 5000 °C on the assumption that H_2O and CO_2 are the products of combustion. In fact, a temperature of only 2700 °C is reached because the combustion products are largely dissociated into CO, H_2 and O_2 and into the radicals and atoms OH, O and H. On the other hand, a mixture of cyanogen and oxygen forms CO and N_2 when burnt and produces the hottest known flame, despite a moderate heat of reaction. The temperature of this flame has almost the theoretical value of 4600 °C because CO and N_2 are not appreciably dissociated below 3700 °C. Other very hot flames are given by fluorine and hydrogen (4500 °C), aluminium and oxygen (3500 °C) and beryllium and oxygen (4500 °C). Very stable combustion products are formed in these cases also. See Porter, G., *Endeavour* 16 (1957) 224.

12

ELECTROCHEMISTRY: IONIC THEORY AND IONIC EQUILIBRIA

DEFINITIONS and fundamental equations are

$$I = \frac{E}{R} = EC \quad \text{(Ohm's law)} \qquad \ldots . (207)$$

I = current (ampere, A) = quantity of electricity (coulomb)/sec
U = voltage, terminal voltage, cell voltage (volt, V)
R = resistance (ohm, Ω)
C = conductivity (mho $1/\Omega$) = $1/R$

$$C = \frac{q}{d}\varkappa \qquad R = \frac{d}{q}\sigma \qquad \ldots . (208)$$

$\varkappa$ = specific conductivity, i.e. conductivity of a cylinder of length $d = 1$ cm and cross-section $q = 1\ \text{cm}^2$. The dimensions of $\varkappa$ are ($1/\Omega$ cm); $\sigma = 1/\varkappa$ = specific resistance (Ω cm)

$$c_{\text{eq}} = n_e c_{\text{mol}} \qquad \ldots . (209)$$

$n_e \equiv \nu_+ z_+ = \nu_- |z_-|$ = electrochemical valency of an electrolyte which dissociates into ν_+ cations with a charge z_+ and ν_- anions with a charge z_-; see also pp. 191, 229.

z = ionic charge, with sign; number of elementary charges, e (ionic charge number, ionic valency, electrovalency)

c_{mol} = electrolyte concentration in moles/l.

$c_{\text{eq}} = c_{\text{mol}} \times n_e$ = electrolyte concentration in equivalents, l.

$$1/c_{\text{mol}} = v_{\text{mol}} = \text{molar volume in l./mole} \qquad \ldots . (210)$$

$$1/c_{\text{eq}} = v_{\text{eq}} = v_{\text{mol}}/n_e = \text{equivalent volume in l./equiv.} \qquad \ldots . (211)$$

$$\Lambda_{c\,(\text{mol})} = \frac{\varkappa \times 1000}{c_{\text{mol}}} = \varkappa \times 1000\, v_{\text{mol}} \quad (\text{mho cm}^2/\text{mole}) \qquad \ldots (212)$$

= molar conductivity of an elelctrolyte solution of concentration c_{mol} (mole/l.) or $c_{\text{mol}}/1000$ (mole/cm^3) or 1 mole in v_{mol} (l.) or 1 mole in $1000\, v_{\text{mol}}$ (cm^3)

$$\Lambda_{c\,(\text{eq})} = \frac{\varkappa \times 1000}{c_{\text{mol}} \times n_e} = \frac{\varkappa \times 1000}{c_{\text{eq}}} = \varkappa \times 1000\, v_{\text{eq}} \qquad \ldots (213)$$

$= \Lambda_{c\,(\text{mol})}/n_e$ (mho cm^2/equiv.) = equivalent conductivity

The molar conductivity is equal to the conductivity of a cylinder of 1 cm^2 cross-section and 1 cm length in which 1 mole of electrolyte is dissolved. It is also equal to the conductivity when 1 mole of electrolyte diluted to the molar volume is placed between two electrodes 1 cm apart. .... (214)

The equivalent conductivity is equal to the conductivity of a cylinder of 1 cm^2 cross-section and 1 cm length in which 1 equivalent of electrolyte is dissolved. It is also equal to the conductivity when one equivalent of electrolyte, diluted to the equivalent volume, is placed between two electrodes 1 cm apart. .... (215)

$\Lambda_{0\,(\mathrm{eq})}$ = limiting value of the equivalent conductivity at infinite dilution ($c_{\mathrm{eq}} = 0$), when dissociation of the electrolyte into ions is complete. Thus

$$\frac{\Lambda_{c\,(\mathrm{eq})}}{\Lambda_{0\,(\mathrm{eq})}} = \alpha \quad (\text{or } f_\lambda) \qquad \ldots . (216)$$

α = degree of dissociation of a weak electrolyte

f_λ = conductivity coefficient of a strong electrolyte

For the dissociation of a weak electrolyte according to the equation $AB = A^+ + B^-$, the law of mass action equation will be

$$\frac{[A^+][B^-]}{[AB]} = \frac{c\alpha^2}{1-\alpha} = \frac{c\Lambda_c^2}{(\Lambda_0 - \Lambda_c)\Lambda_0} = K_{c\,(\mathrm{soln})} \qquad \ldots . (217)$$

If $[A^+] = [B^-]$

$$[A^+]^2 = K_{c\,(\mathrm{soln})}\,[AB] \qquad \ldots . (218)$$

and when $K_{c\,(\mathrm{soln})}$ is small, $1 - \alpha \approx 1$ and $[AB] \approx c$ = total concentration of AB, so that

$$\alpha \approx \sqrt{\frac{K_{c\,(\mathrm{soln})}}{c}} \quad \text{and} \quad [A^+] = \alpha c \approx \sqrt{K_{c\,(\mathrm{soln})}\,c} \qquad \ldots . (219)$$

$\Lambda_{0\,(\mathrm{eq})}$ is equal to the sum of $\Lambda_{\mathrm{K}\,(\mathrm{eq})}$ and $\Lambda_{\mathrm{A}\,(\mathrm{eq})}$, the ionic equivalent conductivities of the cations and anions:

$$\Lambda_{0\,(\mathrm{eq})} = \Lambda_{\mathrm{K}\,(\mathrm{eq})} + \Lambda_{\mathrm{A}\,(\mathrm{eq})} \qquad \ldots . (220)$$

The absolute migration velocity of an ion, u_{K} or u_{A}, in a solution under the influence of a field of 1 V/cm, called ionic mobility, is equal to $\Lambda_{\mathrm{K}\,(\mathrm{eq})}$ or $\Lambda_{\mathrm{A}\,(\mathrm{eq})}$ divided by F = 96,495·1 coulomb/equiv. = Faraday's constant (1 faraday) .... (221)

$$u_{\mathrm{K}} = \frac{\Lambda_{\mathrm{K}\,(\mathrm{eq})}}{F}$$

$$u_{\mathrm{A}} = \frac{\Lambda_{\mathrm{A}\,(\mathrm{eq})}}{F}\left(\frac{\text{mho cm}^2}{\text{equiv.}}\,\frac{\text{equiv.}}{\text{coulomb}}\right) = \left(\frac{\text{cm}}{\text{sec}}\Big/\frac{\text{volt}}{\text{cm}}\right) \qquad \ldots . (222)$$

The fraction of the total current carried by a particular ion species is called its transport number

$$\left.\begin{aligned} n_{\mathrm{K}} &= \frac{\Lambda_{\mathrm{K}\,(\mathrm{eq})}}{\Lambda_{0\,(\mathrm{eq})}} = \frac{\Lambda_{\mathrm{K}\,(\mathrm{eq})}}{\Lambda_{\mathrm{K}\,(\mathrm{eq})} + \Lambda_{\mathrm{A}\,(\mathrm{eq})}} = \frac{u_{\mathrm{K}}}{u_{\mathrm{K}} + u_{\mathrm{A}}} \\ n_{\mathrm{A}} &= \frac{\Lambda_{\mathrm{A}\,(\mathrm{eq})}}{\Lambda_{0\,(\mathrm{eq})}} = \frac{\Lambda_{\mathrm{A}\,(\mathrm{eq})}}{\Lambda_{\mathrm{K}\,(\mathrm{eq})} + \Lambda_{\mathrm{A}\,(\mathrm{eq})}} = \frac{u_{\mathrm{A}}}{u_{\mathrm{K}} + u_{\mathrm{A}}} \end{aligned}\right\} \quad \ldots (223)$$

The following expressions are also derived from the various formulae:

$$\varkappa = (u_K + u_A) F \alpha n_e c_{mol}/1000 \qquad \ldots . (224)$$

$$I = \frac{U q}{d} (u_K + u_A) F \alpha n_e c_{mol}/1000 \qquad \ldots . (225)$$

When a current I (amp) is passed for time t (sec), the quantity G (grammes) of any substance deposited or dissolved at an electrode [or $n_e n$ (equiv.) or volume of gas V (l.)] is given by Faraday's law of equivalents:

$$\frac{It}{F} = n n_e = \frac{G n_e}{M} = \frac{p V n_e}{RT} = \frac{p V n_e}{22{\cdot}41} \times \frac{273}{T} \qquad \ldots . (226)$$

I = current, in amps
F = 1 faraday = 96495·1 coulomb/equivalent, Faraday's constant
n = quantity of moles
$n_e = \nu_+ z_+ = \nu_- |z_-|$ = ionic charge transported for each separated molecule; reaction cell charge; see also pp. 189, 229
$n n_e$ = quantity of substance, in equivalents (equiv.)
G = mass, in grammes
M = mol. weight or atomic weight of the substance separated
$\frac{M}{n_e}$ = equivalent weight of the substance separated
p = pressure, in atmospheres
V = volume of gas separated, in litres
T = absolute temperature (°K)
R = gas constant = 0·08206 l. atm/(deg. mole)
RT_0 = 0·08206 × 273·15 = 22·415 l./mole at 1 atm (molar volume)
t = time, in seconds

$$f_0 = \frac{E'_f}{\nu E_f} \qquad \ldots . (227)$$

E'_f = observed depression of freezing point for 1 mole of electrolyte per 1000 g of solvent
νE_f = theoretical depression of freezing point for 1 mole of electrolyte decomposed into ν ions per 1000 g of solvent
f_0 = osmotic coefficient; see also eqns. (94) and (100)
f_λ = conductivity coefficient; see also pp. 74–75 and eqn. (216)

$$f_0 = f_\lambda + \frac{1 - f_\lambda}{\nu} \qquad f_\lambda = \frac{\nu f_0 - 1}{\nu - 1} \qquad \ldots . (228)$$

In the case of an equilibrium $AB_{solid} = A^+ + B^-$ between a solid phase and ions in solution, one has, from the law of mass action:

$$c_{A^+} c_{B^-} = c_{AB} K_{c(soln)} = K_s \qquad \ldots . (229)$$

K_s = solubility product or ionic product

When the law of mass action is applied to concentrated solutions, ionic activity is used instead of ionic concentration: $a = fc$ .... (230)

f = activity coefficient; see also p. 75.
The law of mass action then reads

$$\frac{a_{A^+} \times a_{B^-}}{c_{AB}} = K_a = \frac{c_{A^+}\, c_{B^-}\, f_+ f_-}{c_{AB}} = K_{c\,(\mathrm{soln})}\,(f_\pm)^2 \quad \text{where} \quad f_\pm = \sqrt{f_+ f_-} \qquad \ldots. (231)$$

and the activity coefficient f_{AB} of the undissociated molecule AB is taken as 1.
f_+ and f_- are the activity coefficients of the individual ions.
$f_\pm$ is the mean activity coefficient of the electrolyte AB.

When an electrolyte dissociates into $\nu = \nu_+ + \nu_-$ ions, the following expressions are obtained for its mean activity coefficient $f_\pm$ and mean ionic activity $a_\pm$:

$$f_\pm^{\nu} = f_+^{\nu_+} f_-^{\nu_-} \quad \text{and} \quad a_\pm^{\nu} = a_+^{\nu_+} a_-^{\nu_-} \qquad \ldots. (232)$$

$$-\log f_+ = A\,z_+^2 \sqrt{J} \qquad -\log f_- = A\,z_-^2 \sqrt{J}$$

$$\nu_+ z_+ = \nu_- |z_+| \equiv n_e \text{ (see eqn. 209)} \qquad \ldots. (233)$$

It follows that, for ions which may be considered as points, the limiting law at great dilution is

$$-\log f_\pm = \frac{1}{\nu}(\nu_+ z_+^2 + \nu_- z_-^2)\,\mathrm{A}\sqrt{J} = |z_+ z_-|\,\mathrm{A}\sqrt{J} \qquad \ldots. (234)$$

A = 0·5092 (l./mole)$^{1/2}$, B = 0·3286 × 10^8 (l./mole)$^{1/2}$/cm for water at 25 °C
$J = \frac{1}{2}(z_+^2 c_+ + z^2 c_-)$ = ionic strength* or, generalized, $J = \frac{1}{2}\sum z_i^2 c_i$
c_+, c_- = ionic concentrations in mole/l. (N.B.)
z_+, z_- = ionic charges or ionic valencies.

For a single electrolyte one, therefore, has

$$J = \tfrac{1}{2}(\nu_+ z_+^2 + \nu_- z_-^2)\,c_{\mathrm{mol}} \quad (\text{where } c_+ = \nu_+ c_{\mathrm{mol}} \text{ and } c_- = \nu_- c_{\mathrm{mol}}) \qquad \ldots. (234a)$$

DEBYE and HÜCKEL give the following expressions in the case of ions of radius r (cm) or $10^8 r$ (Ångström units, Å):

$$-\log f_+ = \frac{z_+^2 \mathrm{A}\sqrt{J}}{1 + \mathrm{B}r\sqrt{J}} \qquad -\log f_\pm = \frac{|z_+ z_-|\,\mathrm{A}\sqrt{J}}{1 + \mathrm{B}r\sqrt{J}} \qquad \log f_+ = \frac{\nu z_+^2}{\nu_+ z_+^2 + \nu_- z_-^2}\ln f_\pm \text{ (approximation equation)} \qquad \ldots (235)$$

The negative logarithm† of the hydrogen ion activity pH = $-\log a_{H^+}$/(mole/l.) ≈ $-\log c_{H^+}$/(mole/l.) when

$$c_{H^+}{}^{**} < 0{\cdot}1 \text{ mole/l.} \qquad \ldots. (236)$$

* Many authors prefer the ionic concentration $\Gamma = z_+^2 c_+ + z^2 c_-$, i.e. without the factor $\frac{1}{2}$; A = 0·3601 (l./mole)$^{1/2}$, B = 0·2324 × 10^8 (l./mole)$^{1/2}$/cm. In particular, English-speaking authors define the ionic strength of a single electrolyte by $J^\star = \frac{1}{2}(z_+^2 m_+ + z_-^2 m_-)$ or $\frac{1}{2}(\nu_+ z_+^2 + \nu_- z_-^2)\,m_{\mathrm{mol}}$, where m is the molality, see eqn. (59); A = 0·5085 (kg/mole)$^{1/2}$; B = 0·3281 × 10^8 (kg/mole)$^{1/2}$/cm.

† Dimensions are not usually shown when using logarithms; see p. 1.

** Strictly speaking, one should use $a_{H_3O^+}$ and $c_{H_3O^+}$ here. For the sake of simplicity, however, H^+ will be used in place of H_3O^+. Regarding the determination of pH, see note to Exercise 163.

*Exercise 125

What current is required in order to deposit 4·5 kg of aluminium in $2\frac{1}{4}$ h?

Solution 125. The atomic weight of Al is 26·97. The electrovalency (ionic charge number) $z_+ = 3$; the equivalent number, $n_e = \nu_+ z_+ = 1 \times 3 = 3$. From eqn. (226)

$$I = \frac{2{\cdot}25 \times 3600}{96\,495} = \frac{4500 \times 3}{26{\cdot}97} \qquad I = 5960 \text{ amp}$$

*Exercise 126

What is the mean value of the current required to liberate 120 cm³ of detonating gas in a coulometer (explosive mixture of hydrogen and oxygen) in a period of 14 min, at a pressure of 712 torr and 18 °C?

Solution 126. At the negative electrode $2H^+$ ions will combine to liberate H_2. Thus the equivalent number per molecule, H_2, will be $n_e = \nu_+ z_+ = 2 \times 1 = 2$. For each mole of H_2 formed, $\frac{1}{2}$ mole O_2 will be liberated. The total volume of gas produced in the coulometer is therefore $1\frac{1}{2}$ times the volume of hydrogen liberated. Hence, from eqn. (226)

$$\frac{I \times 14 \times 60}{96{,}495} = \frac{712}{760} \times \frac{0{\cdot}120 \times 2}{1{\cdot}5 \times 291 \times 0{\cdot}08206} = \frac{712 \times 0{\cdot}120 \times 2 \times 273}{760 \times 1{\cdot}5 \times 22{\cdot}41 \times 291}$$

$$I = 0{\cdot}721 \text{ amp}$$

*Exercise 127

A current of 0·854 amp is passed for 2·5 h through cells connected in series, and containing (*a*) $AgNO_3$ solution, (*b*) $CuSO_4$ solution, (*c*) $AuCl_3$ solution and (*d*) dilute sulphuric acid. Temperature, $\theta = 17$ °C, pressure $p = 715$ mm Hg. How many grammes of silver, copper and gold, and how many litres of hydrogen are obtained during the electrolysis?

Solution 127. Using Faraday's law of equivalents [eqn. (226)] in the case of $AgNO_3$ gives

$$I = 0{\cdot}854 \text{ amp},\ t = 2{\cdot}5 \text{ h} = 9000 \text{ sec},\ n_e = \nu_+ z_+ = 1 \times 1 = 1,\ M = 107{\cdot}88$$

for $CuSO_4$: $n_e = 1 \times 2 = 2$, $M = 63{\cdot}57$

for $AuCl_3$: $n_e = 1 \times 3 = 3$, $M = 197{\cdot}2$

for H_2SO_4: $n_e = 2 \times 1 = 2$, $T = 273 + 17 = 290$ °K, $p = \frac{715}{760}$ atm

so that

(*a*) $$G_{Ag} = \frac{107{\cdot}88 \times 0{\cdot}854 \times 9000}{97{,}495 \times 1} = 8{\cdot}61 \text{ g Ag}$$

(*b*) $$G_{Cu} = \frac{63{\cdot}57 \times 0{\cdot}854 \times 9000}{96{,}495 \times 2} = 2{\cdot}535 \text{ g Cu}$$

(c) $$G_{Au} = \frac{197{\cdot}2 \times 0{\cdot}854 \times 9000}{96{,}495 \times 3} = 5{\cdot}235 \text{ g Au}$$

(d) $$V_{H_2} = \frac{0{\cdot}08206 \times 290 \times 0{\cdot}854 \times 9000 \times 760}{96{,}495 \times 2 \times 715} = 1{\cdot}009 \text{ l. } H_2$$

*Exercise 128

A copper coulometer is connected to the anode and chromate is formed during the electrolysis of 400 cm³ of chrome alum solution, [$KCr(SO_4)_2 \cdot 12H_2O$]. At the completion of the reaction, 12·8 g of Cu are deposited in the coulometer and titration shows the chromate concentration to be 0·185 mole/l. CrO_3 (or CrO_4^{2-}). Express the actual yield as a percentage of the theoretical value.

Solution 128. The anodic oxidation, ζ, can be written as

$$Cr^{3+} - 3e^- \text{ (electrons)} + 4H_2O = CrO_4^{2-} + 8H^+$$

It follows [see (226)] that 3F (cell reaction number $|n_\zeta| = 3$) are required for the formation of 1 mole CrO_4^{2-} or CrO_3 (reaction number of CrO_4^{2-}, $\nu_E = 1$).

The copper coulometer shows that a total of $(12{\cdot}8 \times 2)/63{\cdot}57 = 0{\cdot}404$ equivalents of Cu were sent through the reaction vessel, i.e. since $M_{Cu} = 63{\cdot}57$ and $z_{Cu} = 2$, the equivalent weight of Cu is 63·57/2 and the quantity of equivalents of copper is given by 12·8/(63·57/2) equivalents. Titration gives the quantity of the final product E (chromate) as

$$n_E = \frac{0{\cdot}185 \times 400}{1000} \text{ mol.} \quad \text{or} \quad \frac{n_E}{\nu_E} \times |n_\zeta| = \frac{0{\cdot}185 \times 400 \times 3}{1000 \times 1} = 0{\cdot}2215 \text{ actual equiv.}$$

Thus, the yield is $$\frac{0{\cdot}2215}{0{\cdot}404} 100 = 55{\cdot}1 \text{ per cent}$$

*Exercise 129

The specific conductivity of an acetic acid solution of concentration $c_1 = 0{\cdot}05$ mole/l. was found to be $\varkappa_1 = 3{\cdot}18 \times 10^{-4}$ mho/cm at 18 °C. That of a strongly diluted solution of sodium acetate of concentration $c_2 = 1{\cdot}24 \times 10^{-3}$ mole/l. was $\varkappa_2 = 0{\cdot}961 \times 10^{-4}$ mho/cm (at 18 °C); this solution may be regarded as virtually completely dissociated. Taking the equivalent conductivities of the H^+ and Na^+ ions at 18 °C as $\Lambda_{H^+} = 315$ mho cm²/equiv. and 43·5 mho cm²/equiv., calculate the dissociation constant for acetic acid at this temperature.

Solution 129. The molar and equivalent conductivity for sodium acetate solution ($n_e = \nu_+ z_+ = 1 \times 1 = 1$) is, from eqns. (212) and (213)

$$\Lambda_{0\,(eq)\,(Na\bar{A})} = \frac{0{\cdot}916 \times 10^{-4} \times 1000}{1{\cdot}24 \times 10^{-3}} = 77{\cdot}5 \text{ mho cm}^2\text{/equiv.}$$

The equivalent conductivity of the acetate ion is obtained from eqn. (220):

$$\Lambda_{eq\,(\bar{A}^-)} = \Lambda_{0\,(eq)\,(Na\bar{A})} - \Lambda_{Na^+} = 77{\cdot}5 - 43{\cdot}5 = 34 \text{ mho cm}^2\text{/equiv.}$$

Thus $$\Lambda_{0\,(eq)\,(H\bar{A})} = 315 + 34 = 349 \text{ mho cm}^2\text{/equiv.}$$

while $$\Lambda_{c\,(eq)\,(H\bar{A})} = \frac{3{\cdot}18 \times 10^{-4} \times 1000}{0{\cdot}05} = 6{\cdot}36 \text{ mho cm}^2\text{/equiv.}$$

One then has from eqn (216), for the degree of dissociation α of acetic acid, under the given conditions:

$$\alpha = \frac{\Lambda_{c\,(\text{eq})}}{\Lambda_{0\,(\text{eq})}} = \frac{6{\cdot}63}{349} = 1{\cdot}823 \times 10^{-2}$$

Finally, $K_{c(\text{Ac})}$ is obtained from eqn. (217) as

$$K_{c(\text{Ac})} = \frac{(1{\cdot}823 \times 10^{-2})^2 \times 0{\cdot}05}{1 - 1{\cdot}823 \times 10^{-2}} = 1{\cdot}693 \times 10^{-5}\ \text{mole/l.}$$

*Exercise 130

What is the pH of (*a*) 0·01 N HCl at 25 °C, (*b*) 0·01 N NaOH at 25 °C, (*c*) 1·253 N/1000 HCl at 37 °C, (*d*) 2·815 N/1000 NaOH at 37 °C, (*e*) water at 0 °C, 18 °C, 24 °C, 25 °C, 37 °C and 50 °C? The ionic product of water k_{H_2O} (mole/l.)^2 is

Temp. °C	k_{H_2O} (mole/l.)^2	*Temp.* °C	k_{H_2O}(mole/l.)^2
0	$1{\cdot}16 \times 10^{-15} = 10^{-14{\cdot}94}$	25	$1{\cdot}10 \times 10^{-14} = 10^{-13{\cdot}96}$
18	$0{\cdot}61 \times 10^{-14} = 10^{-14{\cdot}21}$	37	$2{\cdot}75 \times 10^{-14} = 10^{-13{\cdot}56}$
20	$0{\cdot}72 \times 10^{-14} = 10^{-14{\cdot}14}$	50	$6{\cdot}10 \times 10^{-14} = 10^{-13{\cdot}22}$
24	$1{\cdot}00 \times 10^{-14}$		

HCl and NaOH may be regarded as being virtually completely dissociated.

Solution 130. From eqn. (236), $\text{pH} = -\log c_{H^+}/(\text{mole l.}^{-1})$, from eqn. (229)$c_{H^+}\, c_{OH^-} = k_{H_2O}$.

(*a*) $c_{H^+} = 0{\cdot}01\ \text{mol. l.}^{-1}$, $-\log c_{H^+}/(\text{mol. l.}^{-1}) = \text{pH} = -(-2) = 2$

(*b*) $c_{OH^-} = 0{\cdot}01$*, $c_{H^+}\, c_{OH^-} = 10^{-13{\cdot}96}$, $\log c_{H^+} + \log c_{OH^-} = -13{\cdot}96$, $\log c_{OH^-} = -2$, $-\log c_{OH^-}\ (= \text{pOH}) = 2$, $-\log c_{H^+} - \log c_{OH^-} = 13{\cdot}96$

or $\text{pH} + \text{pOH} = 13{\cdot}96 = -\log k_{H_2O}$,

$\text{pH} = 13{\cdot}96 - 2 = 11{\cdot}96$

(*c*) $c_{H^+} = 1{\cdot}253 \times 10^{-3}$

$-\log c_{H^+} = \text{pH} = -(0{\cdot}098 - 3) = 2{\cdot}902$

(*d*) $c_{OH^-} = 2{\cdot}815 \times 10^{-3}$, $-\log c_{OH^-} = \text{pOH} = -(0{\cdot}449 - 3)$

$\text{pH} = 13{\cdot}56 - \text{pOH}\,(\text{at } 37°\,\text{C}) = 13{\cdot}56 + 0{\cdot}449 - 3 = 11{\cdot}01$

(*e*) In water, $c_{H^+} = c_{OH^-}$ or $\text{pH} = \text{pOH}$, so that $2\,\text{pH} = -\log k_{H_2O}$.

Temp. °C	2 pH	pH
0	14·94	7·47
18	14·21	7·105
24	14·00	7·00
25	13·96	6·98
37	13·56	6·78
50	13·22	6·61

* Dimensions are omitted from (*b*) to (*e*).

*Exercise 131

From the temperature dependence of the ionic product of water (see data in Exercise 130), calculate the mean value of the heat of dissociation of water, or heat of neutralization, between 0 °C and 25 °C.

Solution 131. The ionic products differ from the dissociation constants $K_{c\,(\mathrm{sol})}$ of water only by a constant factor (c_{H_2O}), so that, for $H_2O = H^+ + OH^-$, one has

$$K_{c\,(\mathrm{sol})} = \frac{[H^+]\,[OH^-]}{[H_2O]}$$

or $[H^+][OH^-] = k_{H_2O} = K_{c\,(\mathrm{sol})}[H_2O]$, if concentrations are indicated by [ ]. The relation between heat of dissociation and the temperature dependence of the equilibrium constant is given by the expressions in eqns. (175) or (181). Thus, in the present case:

$$\Delta U = 4{\cdot}574\,\frac{T_1\,T_2}{T_1 - T_2}\log\,(K_{c\,(\mathrm{sol})\,1}/K_{c\,(\mathrm{sol})\,2})\ \text{(cal/mole)} \qquad \ldots. \quad \text{(i)}$$

It will be seen that the ionic products k_{H_2O} may also be used here, instead of $K_{c\,(\mathrm{sol})}$, since the constant factor c_{H_2O} cancels out.

Substituting the numerical values for 25 °C = 298 °K and for 0 °C = 273 °K, gives

$$\Delta U = 4{\cdot}574\,\frac{298 \times 273}{25}\,[-13{\cdot}96 - (-14{\cdot}94)] = +14{\cdot}6\ \text{kcal/mole}$$

Note. More accurate values of the heat of dissociation of water, or heat of neutralization, are found by calorimetric methods. These give $\Delta U = 13{\cdot}7$ kcal/mole.

Exercise 132

Determine the pH of a mixed solution which, with respect to iso-butyric acid and sodium iso-butyrate, is (*a*) 0·1 N and (*b*) 0·01 N. The dissociation constant of iso-butyric acid is $K_{c\,(\mathrm{Ac})} = 1{\cdot}44 \times 10^{-5}$ mole/l. As a first approximation, sodium iso-butyrate may be regarded as being completely dissociated, and the activity coefficient ignored.

Solution 132. The dissociation equilibrium for a weak acid is, from the law of mass action

$$\frac{[H^+]\,[A^-]}{[HA]} = K_{c\,(\mathrm{Ac})} \qquad \ldots. \quad \text{(i)}$$

where $[H^+]$ indicates the concentration of H^+ ions, $[A^-]$ that of the acid anions and [HA] the concentration of undissociated acid, in mole/l.

[HA] is obtained from the total concentration of acid [Ac] put in, by deducting the dissociated fraction, for which $[H^+]$ may be taken; thus

$$[HA] = [Ac] - [H^+] \qquad \ldots. \quad \text{(ii)}$$

$[A^-]$ is the sum of the dissociated fraction of the acid, corresponding to $[H^+]$, and the total concentration of the salt of the same acid (sodium iso-butyrate) [salt]; i.e.

$$[A^-] = [\text{salt}] + [H^+] \qquad \ldots. \quad \text{(iii)}$$

Hence, by substituting (ii) and (iii) in (i)

$$\frac{[H^+]([\text{salt}] + [H^+])}{[\text{Ac}] - [H^+]} = K_{c\,(\text{Ac})} \quad \text{or} \quad [H^+] = K_{c\,(\text{Ac})} \frac{[\text{Ac}] - [H^+]}{[\text{salt}] + [H^+]} \qquad \ldots\ldots \quad \text{(iv)}$$

In general, by solving for $[H^+]$, (iv) leads to the quadratic equation

$$[H^+]^2 + [H^+]([\text{salt}] + K_{c\,(\text{Ac})}) - K_{c\,(\text{Ac})}\,[\text{Ac}] = 0 \qquad \ldots\ldots \quad \text{(v)}$$

which may be solved by conventional methods.

If, however, as in the present case, the dissociation constant $K_{c\,(\text{Ac})}$ has a very small value (so that $[H^+]$ is also very small) then (iv) simplifies, as a first approximation, to

$$[H^+] = K_{c\,(\text{Ac})} \frac{[\text{Ac}]}{[\text{salt}]} \qquad \ldots\ldots \quad \text{(vi)}$$

or

$$-\log [H^+] = \text{pH} = -\log K_{c\,(\text{Ac})} + \log \frac{[\text{salt}]}{[\text{Ac}]} \qquad \ldots\ldots \quad \text{(vii)}$$

It therefore follows from (vii), as a first approximation, that the pH of the mixed solution is independent of absolute concentration or dilution and depends only on the mixture ratio salt/acid. In the present case therefore

$$\begin{aligned} \text{pH} &= -\log [1{\cdot}44 \times 10^{-5}] + \log \frac{0{\cdot}1}{0{\cdot}1} \quad \text{or} \quad -\log [1{\cdot}44 \times 10^{-5}] + \log \frac{0{\cdot}01}{0{\cdot}01} \\ &= -\log [1{\cdot}44 \times 10^{-5}] + 0 \\ &= -(0{\cdot}158 - 5) = 4{\cdot}84 \end{aligned}$$

Note. For a weak base, with the dissociation constant

$$K_{c\,(\text{base})} = \frac{[B^+][OH^-]}{[\text{BOH}]}$$

where [B] is the total concentration of the base and [salt] is that of the salt of the base, one has the following expression, analogous to (vi):

$$[OH^-] = K_{c\,(\text{base})} \frac{[\text{base}]}{[\text{salt}]} \qquad \ldots\ldots \quad \text{(viii)}$$

or, where

$$[OH^-] = \frac{k_{H_2O}}{[H^+]} \qquad \ldots\ldots \quad \text{(ix)}$$

(see Exercises 130—131),

$$[H^+] = \frac{k_{H_2O}}{K_{c\,(\text{base})}} \times \frac{[\text{salt}]}{[\text{base}]} \qquad \ldots\ldots \quad \text{(x)}$$

$$-\log [H^+] = \text{pH} = \log K_{c\,(\text{base})} - \log k_{H_2O} + \log \frac{[\text{base}]}{[\text{salt}]} \qquad \ldots\ldots \quad \text{(xi)}$$

The fact that the pH of mixtures of weak acids or bases and their salts is very largely independent of the dilution (see Exercise 133) and is not easily changed by the addition of acid or alkali, has led to these systems being called buffer solutions. They are of great importance in biology and medicine.

Calculation of a second approximation for (iv) or (v) gives the answer to the question as to over what range of dilution does the pH remain constant, within the limits of error. Substituting the first approximation (vi) in (iv), one obtains

$$[H^+] = K_{c(Ac)} \frac{[Ac] - K_{c(Ac)}\dfrac{[Ac]}{[salt]}}{[salt] + K_{c(Ac)}\dfrac{[Ac]}{[salt]}} = K_{c(Ac)} \frac{[Ac]}{[salt]} \frac{1 - \dfrac{K_{c(Ac)}}{[salt]}}{1 + \dfrac{K_{c(Ac)}[Ac]}{[salt]^2}}$$

$$\approx K_{c(Ac)} \frac{[Ac]}{[salt]} \left(1 - \frac{K_{c(Ac)}}{[salt]}\right)\left(1 - \frac{K_{c(Ac)}[Ac]}{[salt]^2}\right)$$

so that, neglecting terms of higher order

$$[H^+] \approx K_{c(Ac)} \frac{[Ac]}{[salt]} \left[1 - \frac{K_{c(Ac)}}{[salt]}\left(1 + \frac{[Ac]}{[salt]}\right)\right] \quad \ldots. \quad \text{(xii)}$$

The same result may be obtained by expanding the quadratic eqn. (v) as a series.
It follows from (xii) that

$$pH = -\log K_{c(Ac)} + \log \frac{[salt]}{[Ac]} - \log \left[1 - \frac{K_{c(Ac)}}{[salt]}\left(1 + \frac{[Ac]}{[salt]}\right)\right] \quad \ldots. \quad \text{(xiii)}$$

and, since $\log(1 - x) \approx -0{\cdot}4343\,x$ when $x \ll 1$,

$$pH = -\log K_{c(Ac)} + \log \frac{[salt]}{[Ac]} + \frac{0{\cdot}4343\,K_{c(Ac)}}{[salt]}\left(1 + \frac{[Ac]}{[salt]}\right) \quad \ldots. \quad \text{(xiv)}$$

In the case under consideration, therefore, a correction of the pH formula at (vii) only arises when the total concentration of salt is less than about $100K_{c(Ac)}$, i.e. if the limit of error for the pH is set at 1 per cent.

For a more accurate approach, activity rather than concentration must be used in the law of mass action [see eqns. (230) to (235)]. This is because $K_{a(Ac)} = K_{a(Ac)}(f_\pm)^2$ is the true constant, not $K_{c(Ac)}$ [see eqn. (231)]. This means that $K_{a(Ac)}/(f_\pm)^2$ should be used in place of $K_{c(Ac)}$ in (vii). Similarly, incomplete dissociation of the salt should be allowed for by introducing its degree of dissociation, α_{salt}; i.e. α_{salt} [salt] should be substituted for [salt].

If this is done, (vii) becomes

$$pH = -\log K_{a(Ac)} + 2\log f_\pm + \log \alpha_{salt} + \log \frac{[salt]}{[Ac]} \quad \ldots. \quad \text{(xv)}$$

where $\log f_\pm$ is dependent on the total ionic concentration (or ion strength), in accordance with eqns. (234) or (235) and (231).

Exercise 133

Determine the change in pH when (*a*) 1/1000 mole of HCl and (*b*) 1/1000 mole of NaOH are added to a buffer mixture containing equal mole fractions of iso-butyric acid and sodium iso-butyrate. Consider two cases: (*i*) when the number of moles of salt and of acid is 0·1, and (*ii*) when the number of moles is 0·01; (*c*) compare this change in pH with that obtained when 1/1000 mole of HCl is added to 1 l. of HCl having the same pH as the buffer solution. The dissociation constant of iso-butyric acid is $K_{c(Ac)} = 1{\cdot}44 \times 10^{-5}$ mole/l. See also explanations in Exercise 132, especially eqn. (vii).

Solution 133. The following is obtained from eqn. (vii) in Exercise 132:

$$pH = -K_{c(Ac)} + \log \frac{[salt]}{[Ac]} \qquad \begin{array}{l}[salt] = \text{total salt}\\ [Ac] = \text{total acid}\end{array} \quad \ldots. \quad \text{(i)}$$

(*a*) (*i*) The addition of 1/1000 mole of HCl reduces the 0·1 mole of salt by 0·001 mole to 0·099 mole and increases the 0·1 mole of acid to 0·101 mole. This is because the H^+ ions of the fully-dissociated HCl combine with the iso-butyrate ions to form undissociated iso-butyric acid. Thus

$$\left.\begin{aligned} pH &= -\log 1{\cdot}44 \times 10^{-5} + \log \frac{0{\cdot}099}{0{\cdot}101} \\ pH &= 4{\cdot}842 - 0{\cdot}009 = 4{\cdot}83 \end{aligned}\right\} \quad .. \quad \text{(ii)}$$

or an increase in hydrogen ion concentration of 101/99 = 1·02-fold, i.e. 2 per cent.

In case (*ii*), the buffer solution contains 0·01 mole of salt and of acid, and the second summand in (ii) becomes log 0·009/0·011 = −0·087; hence, pH = 4·842 − 0·087 = 4·75, or an increase in hydrogen ion concentration of 11/9 = 1·22-fold, i.e. 22 per cent.

(*b*) Conversely, the addition of 1/1000 mole of NaOH increases the amount of salt but reduces the amount of acid. It follows that the decreases in pH correspond to the increases observed in the two cases above.

(*c*) One litre of HCl solution with a hydrogen ion concentration of $K_{c\,(Ac)} = 1{\cdot}44 \times 10^{-5}$ mole/l. (pH = 4·84) will, by the addition of 1/1000 mole of HCl, then have a hydrogen ion concentration of $101{\cdot}44 \times 10^{-5}$ mol./l. or a pH of −(0·006 − 3) = 2·99. The buffer effect in the case of the mixed solution of iso-butyric acid and iso-butyrate is obvious.

Note. The question may now be posed as to what is the best ratio of total salt to total acid, [salt]/[Ac], so that the buffer action against the addition of a strong acid or base is most effective. The change in pH per unit quantity of added alkali (or acid), i.e.

$$d\,pH/d[alk] \qquad ([alk] = \text{concentration of alkali, in mole/l.})$$

may be taken as a measure of the buffer action. The problem is then limited to finding when dpH/d[alk] is a minimum in relation to [alk]. From (i), for an acid-salt buffer, we have:

$$\left.\begin{aligned} pH &= -\log K_{c\,(Ac)} + \log \frac{[salt] + [alk]}{[Ac] - [alk]} \\ \frac{d\,pH}{d\,[alk]} &= 0{\cdot}4343 \left(\frac{1}{[salt] + [alk]} + \frac{1}{[Ac] - [alk]} \right) \end{aligned}\right\} \quad .. \quad \text{(iii)}$$

As is well known in the determination of minima, the differential coefficient of the expression dpH/d[alk] must be taken as being equal to zero, i.e.

$$\frac{d^2\,pH}{(d\,[alk])^2} = -0{\cdot}4343 \left[\left(\frac{1}{[salt] + [alk]} \right)^2 - \left(\frac{1}{[Ac] - [alk]} \right)^2 \right] = 0$$

or

$$[salt] + [alk] = [Ac] - [alk] \quad .... \quad \text{(iv)}$$

It follows that the most effective buffer action is obtained when equal quantities of salt and acid are present in the mixture after the addition of the alkali.

When [salt] = 0, eqn. (iii) represents the titration curve obtained when a weak acid is titrated with alkali.

The corresponding expression holds for the titration of a weak base with a strong acid [according to (xi) in Exercise 132]. It will be seen that, in the neutralization of alkali by the addition of acid, the quantity of alkali is reduced by an amount corresponding to the increase in the quantity of salt:

$$pH = +\log K_{c\,(base)} - \log k_{H_2O} + \log \frac{[alk] - [Ac]}{[salt] + [Ac]} \quad .... \quad \text{(v)}$$

The titration curve (iii) (pH as ordinate, [alk] as abscissa) rises steeply at small values of [alk] and reaches, when [alk] = [Ac]/2, a flat point of inflection where

$$\text{pH} = -\log K_{c\,(\text{Ac})} \qquad \ldots\ldots \quad \text{(vi)}$$

since $\dfrac{d^2\text{pH}}{d\,[\text{alk}]^2} = 0$ indicates a point of inflection on the titration curve (iii), and eqn. (iv), valid for this condition, gives, when [salt] = 0: [alk] = [Ac] − [alk] or [alk] = [Ac]/2; substitution of (iv) in (iii) gives (vi). The titration curve again rises steeply when [alk] lies close to [Ac], the neutral point — the final pH values indicate just the excess of pure alkali. In the titration o weak bases with acids, the corresponding point of inflection is at [Ac] = [alk]/2

$$\text{pH} = -\log k_{H_2O} + \log K_{c\,(\text{base})} \qquad \ldots\ldots \quad \text{(vii)}$$

The closely similar ~-shaped curve segments for weak acids lie higher the weaker the acid. (For the application of buffer equations, see Exercise 140; see also note to Exercise 199.)

Exercise 134

A mixed solution contains 0·2 mole/l. acetic acid with (*a*) 0·1 mole/l. lactic acid, and (*b*) 0·1 mole/l. HCl. Determine the degrees of dissociation, ε_m and μ_m, of the acetic acid and the lactic acid in the mixture and compare the values obtained with those (ε and μ) for the pure acids at the same concentration.

$K_{c\,(\text{sol})}$ for acetic acid is: $K_A = 1{\cdot}76 \times 10^{-5}$ mole/l.; $K_{c\,(\text{soln})}$ for lactic acid is: $K_L = 1{\cdot}38 \times 10^{-4}$ mole/l. (at 25 °C). HCl may be regarded as being virtually fully dissociated.

Solution 134. Since acetic and lactic acids are weak acids with a small degree of dissociation, it is possible to simplify the dissociation eqn. (217)

$$K_{c\,(\text{soln})} = \frac{c\,\alpha^2}{1-\alpha} \text{ to } K_{c\,(\text{soln})} = c\,\alpha^2 \quad \text{or} \quad \alpha = \sqrt{\frac{K_{c\,(\text{soln})}}{c}} \qquad \ldots\ldots \quad \text{(i)}$$

[see eqn. (219)].
The degree of dissociation of the acetic acid is then

$$\varepsilon = \sqrt{\frac{1{\cdot}76 \times 10^{-5}}{0{\cdot}2}} = 0{\cdot}938 \times 10^{-2} = \sqrt{\frac{K_A}{c_A}} \qquad \ldots\ldots \quad \text{(ii)}$$

and for the lactic acid

$$\mu = \sqrt{\frac{1{\cdot}38 \times 10^{-4}}{0{\cdot}1}} = 3{\cdot}72 \times 10^{-2} = \sqrt{\frac{K_L}{c_L}} \qquad \ldots\ldots \quad \text{(iii)}$$

(*a*) In the mixed solution (of acetic and lactic acids), the concentration of acetate ions is $\varepsilon_m c_A$, of undissociated acetic acid $(1-\varepsilon_m)c_A$, of lactate ions $\mu_m c_L$, of undissociated lactic acid $(1-\mu_m)c_L$ and of hydrogen ions $(\varepsilon_m c_A + \mu_m c_L)$. The law of mass action then gives for the acetic acid:

$$K_A = \frac{\varepsilon_m c_A (\varepsilon_m c_A + \mu_m c_L)}{(1-\varepsilon_m)\,c_A} \quad \text{or, where } \varepsilon_m \ll 1, \text{ and from (i)}$$

$$K_A \approx \varepsilon^2 c_A \approx \varepsilon_m (\varepsilon_m c_A + \mu_m c_L) \qquad \ldots\ldots \quad \text{(iv)}$$

for the lactic acid:

$$K_L = \frac{\mu_m c_L (\varepsilon_m c_A + \mu_m c_L)}{(1-\mu_m)\,c_L} \quad \text{or, where } \mu_m \ll 1, \text{ and from (ii)}$$

$$K_L \approx \mu^2 c_L \approx \mu_m (\varepsilon_m c_A + \mu_m c_L) \qquad \ldots\ldots \quad \text{(v)}$$

Dividing (iv) by (v) gives

$$\frac{K_A}{K_L} \approx \frac{\varepsilon_m}{\mu_m} \quad \ldots\ldots \text{(vi)}$$

Eliminating μ_m from (iv) and (vi) gives

$$\varepsilon^2 c_A \approx \varepsilon_m \left(\varepsilon_m c_A + \varepsilon_m \frac{K_L c_L}{K_A}\right) \quad \text{and} \quad \varepsilon_m \approx \frac{\varepsilon}{\sqrt{1 + \dfrac{K_L c_L}{K_A c_A}}} \quad \ldots\ldots \text{(vii)}$$

Similarly, eliminating ε_m from (v) and (vi):

$$\mu_m \approx \frac{\mu}{\sqrt{1 + \dfrac{K_A c_A}{K_L c_L}}} \quad \ldots\ldots \text{(viii)}$$

Substitution of numerical values gives

$$\varepsilon_m = \frac{0{\cdot}938 \times 10^{-2}}{\sqrt{1 + \dfrac{1{\cdot}38 \times 10^{-4} \times 0{\cdot}1}{1{\cdot}76 \times 10^{-5} \times 0{\cdot}2}}} = 0{\cdot}938 \times 10^{-2}/2{\cdot}22 = 0{\cdot}42 \times 10^{-2} \quad \ldots\ldots \text{(ix)}$$

The degree of dissociation of the weaker acetic acid therefore drops to less than one-half.

$$\mu_m = \frac{3{\cdot}72 \times 10^{-2}}{\sqrt{1 + 0{\cdot}255}} = 3{\cdot}72 \times 10^{-2}/1{\cdot}12 = 3{\cdot}32 \times 10^{-2} \quad \ldots\ldots \text{(x)}$$

The degree of dissociation of the stronger acid is therefore only reduced by some 12 per cent.

(*b*) In this case, $\varepsilon_m \ll 1$ but, on the other hand, $\mu_m \approx 1$ (HCl). Hence (iv) becomes

$$K_A = \varepsilon_m \frac{(\varepsilon_m c_A + c_L)}{1 - \varepsilon_m} \approx \varepsilon_m c_L \quad \text{or} \quad \varepsilon_m = \frac{K_A}{c_L} \quad \ldots\ldots \text{(xi)}$$

Substituting gives

$$\varepsilon_m = \frac{1{\cdot}76 \times 10^{-5}}{0{\cdot}1} = 1{\cdot}76 \times 10^{-4} \quad \ldots\ldots \text{(xii)}$$

Thus the degree of dissociation of the acetic acid falls from $0{\cdot}938 \times 10^{-2}$ to $1{\cdot}76 \times 10^{-4}$.

Note. It will be seen from this example and from eqns. (vii), (viii) and (xi) that, in a mixture of two weak acids or of a weak and a strong acid, the degree of dissociation of the weaker acid is greatly reduced, but that of the stronger acid is only slightly affected, if at all.

Exercise 135

Oxalic acid, $(COOH)_2$, is a dibasic acid. At 25 °C, the dissociation constant for the first stage is $K_1 = 5{\cdot}9 \times 10^{-2}$ mole/l.; for the second stage, $K_2 = 6{\cdot}4 \times 10^{-5}$ mole/l. Determine the degree of dissociation, α and β, for both stages, for $c = 1, 10^{-1}, 10^{-2}, 10^{-3}, 10^{-4}$ and 10^{-5} mole/l. Compare the values with the degrees of dissociation, $\alpha^\star$ and $\beta^\star$, of monobasic acids having the dissociation constants K_1 and K_2. Suitable approximations should be used where applicable.

Solution 135. The equation for the first stage is $H_2C_2O_4 = H^+ + HC_2O_4^-$; that for the second is $HC_2O_4^- = H^+ + C_2O_4^{2-}$.

The concentrations of the reactants are:

$$[H_2C_4O_4] = (1-\alpha)c \qquad [C_2O_4^{2-}] = \alpha c\beta$$

$$[HC_2O_4^-] = \alpha c(1-\beta) \qquad [H^+] = \alpha c + \alpha c\beta = \alpha(1+\beta)c$$

c = total concentration of oxalic acid added, in mole/l.

as illustrated by the scheme

$$\begin{array}{llll} \text{I} & & \text{II} & \\ H_2C_4O_4 \longrightarrow & HC_2O_4 & HC_2O_4^- \longrightarrow & C_2O_4^{2-} \\ (1-\alpha)\,c & \alpha\,c & \alpha\,c\,(1-\beta) & \alpha\,c\,\beta \\ H^+ & & H^+ & \\ \alpha\,c & & \alpha\,c\,\beta & \end{array}$$
$$\underbrace{\qquad\qquad\qquad\qquad\qquad}_{\alpha\,c\,(1+\beta)}$$

Thus, from the law of mass action, for the first stage

$$\frac{\alpha(1+\beta)\,c\,\alpha\,c\,(1-\beta)}{(1-\alpha)\,c} = K_1 \quad \text{or} \quad \frac{\alpha^2(1+\beta)(1-\beta)}{1-\alpha} = \frac{K_1}{c} \qquad \ldots. \quad \text{(i)}$$

and for the second stage

$$\frac{\alpha\,(1+\beta)\,c\,\alpha\,\beta\,c}{\alpha\,c\,(1-\beta)} = K_2 \quad \text{or} \quad \frac{\alpha\,\beta\,(1+\beta)}{1-\beta} = \frac{K_2}{c} \qquad \ldots. \quad \text{(ii)}$$

Since the value of K_1 ($= 5{\cdot}9 \times 10^{-2}$ mole/l.) is large in comparison with K_2 ($= 6{\cdot}4 \times 10^{-5}$ mole/l.) and in the absolute sense, it is possible, especially for large values of c in eqn. (i), to neglect β in comparison with 1, i.e. in the terms $(1+\beta)$ and $(1-\beta)$. On the other hand, it is not possible to neglect α in $(1-\alpha)$. One therefore obtains

$$\alpha \approx \frac{-K_1/c + \sqrt{(K_1/c)^2 + 4K_1/c}}{2} \qquad \ldots. \quad \text{(iii)}$$

From (ii), $\alpha = \dfrac{K_2(1-\beta)}{c\,(1+\beta)\,\beta}$ or, when $\beta \ll 1$ and $\dfrac{1-\beta}{1+\beta} \approx 1 - 2\beta$,

$$\alpha \approx \frac{K_2(1-2\beta)}{c\,\beta} \quad \text{or} \quad \beta \approx \frac{K_2/c}{\alpha + 2\,K_2/c} \text{ for small values of } K_2/c \quad \ldots. \quad \text{(iv)}$$

For larger values of K_2/c, (ii) must be solved for β, which gives

$$\beta = \frac{-\left(\alpha + \dfrac{K_2}{c}\right) + \sqrt{\left(\alpha + \dfrac{K_2}{c}\right)^2 + 4\,\alpha\,K_2/c}}{2\,\alpha} \qquad \ldots. \quad \text{(v)}$$

where $\alpha \approx 1$. $\alpha^\star$ and $\beta^\star$ may be determined from the normal dissociation equations, $\dfrac{\alpha^{\star 2}c}{(1-\alpha^\star)} = K_1$ or $\dfrac{\beta^{\star 2}c}{(1-\beta^\star)} = K_2$, by solving for $\alpha^\star$ or $\beta^\star$.

Thus the same formula (iii) is found for $\alpha^\star$ as for α; i.e. α is virtually unaffected by the second stage of dissociation.

For $\beta^\star$, one obtains

$$\beta^\star = \frac{-K_2/c + \sqrt{(K_2/c)^2 + 4K_2/c}}{2} \quad \dots \quad \text{(vi)}$$

Substituting the numerical values gives:

c (mole/l.)	$\frac{K_1}{c}$	$\frac{K_2}{c}$	*from* (iii) $\alpha = \alpha^\star$	*from* (iv) β	*from* (vi) $\beta^\star$
1·0	$5{\cdot}9 \times 10^{-2}$	$6{\cdot}4 \times 10^{-5}$	0·215	$2{\cdot}97 \times 10^{-4}$	$8{\cdot}0 \times 10^{-3}$
0·1	$5{\cdot}9 \times 10^{-1}$	$6{\cdot}4 \times 10^{-4}$	0·528	$1{\cdot}21 \times 10^{-3}$	$2{\cdot}53 \times 10^{-2}$
0·01	5·9	$6{\cdot}4 \times 10^{-3}$	0·8715	$7{\cdot}24 \times 10^{-3}$	$8{\cdot}0 \times 10^{-2}$
0·001	59·0	$6{\cdot}4 \times 10^{-2}$	0·984	0·0575	0·223
0·0001	590	0·64	0·9985	0·326	0·542
0·00001	5900	6·4	1·0	0·782	0·88

It will be seen, especially after plotting the values against log c (see *Figure 19*) that (*a*) the degree of dissociation (α) for the first stage hardly differs from that for a monobasic acid having the same dissociation constant ($\alpha^\star$); (*b*) in comparison with

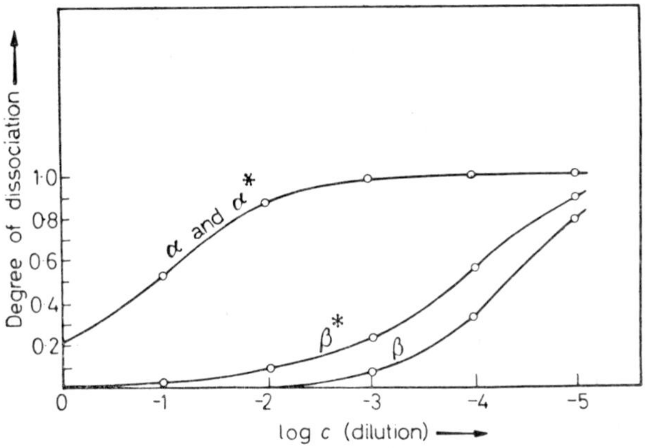

Figure 19. Relation between concentration and degree of dissociation of dibasic oxalic acid

a monobasic having the same dissociation constant, the degree of dissociation (β) for the second stage is strongly suppressed, in such a way that, as will be seen from the figure, the second stage of dissociation hardly commences ($\beta \approx 0$) until the first stage is virtually complete ($\alpha \approx 1$).

Note. With reference to the effect of degree of dissociation, it is seen that a dibasic acid behaves similarly to a mixture of a stronger and a weaker monobasic acid. (See note to Exercise 134). The observation that the second stage of dissociation does not start until the first is almost complete shows that a mixture of a dibasic acid with its alkali metal hydrogen salt (e.g. H_2CO_3 with $NaHCO_3$), or a mixture of the primary salt with the secondary salt of a tribasic acid (e.g. H_2NaPO_4 and HNa_2PO_4), must behave as a buffer solution, i.e. like a weak monobasic acid with its corresponding salt (e.g. acetic acid and sodium acetate). The effect of the second stage of dissociation is negligible over the useful working range of the buffer. Therefore the approximate equation at (vii) in Exercise 132 may be used for such systems.

The observation that the dissociation constant for the second stage is much lower than that for the first is true in general. As a start, it may be estimated that the dissociation constant for the first stage must be at least about 8 times larger, because (*a*) the H^+ ions in the second stage, in the course of their molecular motion, have, a priori, twice the probability of being taken up (two free accommodation positions) and half the probability for dissociation in comparison with the H^+ ions for the first stage (half as many H^+ ions dissociated off); (b) the attractive forces for the H^+ ions in the second stage are at least twice as great, since there are twice as many negatively charged accommodation positions. For more accurate calculation, distance and inductive coupling of charges would have to be taken into account.

Exercise 136

What ratio of primary and secondary sodium phosphates (NaH_2PO_4 and Na_2HPO_4) must be used in a phosphate buffer in order to establish a pH of (*a*) 7·0 and (*b*) 5·5? What absolute concentration (in mole/l.) of the individual salts must be taken if the total salt concentration is to be 0·20 mole/l.?

The dissociation constants of phosphoric acid, H_3PO_4, at 25 °C are

$$K_a^{\mathrm{I}} = 7{\cdot}52 \times 10^{-3} \text{ mole/l.}$$

$$K_a^{\mathrm{II}} = 6{\cdot}23 \times 10^{-8} \text{ mole/l.}$$

$$K_a^{\mathrm{III}} = 1{\cdot}8 \times 10^{-12} \text{ mole/l.}$$

The mean ionic activity coefficient for sodium phosphate in aqueous solution, at a salt concentration of 0·2 mole/l., is $f^{\pm} = 0{\cdot}56$. During calculation, refer to the methods in Exercise 132, especially eqn. (xv), and the note to Exercise 135.

Solution 136. The dissociation constants show that, under the given conditions of concentration, the first stage of dissociation is almost complete, whilst the opposite is true for the third stage. It follows that the behaviour of the system as a buffer is determined only by the equilibrium for the second stage, where NaH_2PO_4 acts as the acid and Na_2HPO_4 as the salt component. Since the given equilibrium constants are based on concentration-independent K_a values, calculated from the activities, the accurate formula (xv) in Exercise 132 may be used for the calculation (degree of dissociation of the salt, $\alpha \approx 1$).

Substituting the numerical values in (xv) of Exercise 132, gives

for case (*a*):

$$7{\cdot}0 = -\log 6{\cdot}23 \times 10^{-8} + 2 \log 0{\cdot}56 + \log \frac{[\text{sec. phos.}]}{[\text{prim. phos.}]}$$

$$\log \frac{[\text{sec. phos.}]}{[\text{prim. phos.}]} = \log \frac{10^7 \times 6{\cdot}23 \times 10^{-8}}{0{\cdot}56^2} = \log 1{\cdot}99$$

$$\frac{[\text{sec. phos.}]}{[\text{prim. phos.}]} = 1{\cdot}99 \approx 2:1 \qquad \ldots \qquad \text{(i)}$$

for case (*b*):

$$\log \frac{[\text{sec. phos.}]}{[\text{prim. phos.}]} = 5{\cdot}5 + \log 6{\cdot}23 \times 10^{-8} - 2 \log 0{\cdot}56 = 0{\cdot}798 - 2$$

$$\frac{[\text{sec. phos.}]}{[\text{prim. phos.}]} = 0{\cdot}0628 \approx 1:16 \qquad \ldots \qquad \text{(ii)}$$

In order to determine the absolute concentrations, the equation

$$[\text{sec. phos.}] + [\text{prim. phos.}] = 0{\cdot}20 \text{ mole/l.} \qquad \ldots . \quad \text{(iii)}$$

must be added to eqns. (i) or (ii).

By elimination, one finds from (i) and (iii):

$$\text{sec. phosphate:} \quad \frac{0{\cdot}2 \times 2}{3} = 0{\cdot}133 \text{ mole/l.}$$

$$\text{prim. phosphate:} \quad 0{\cdot}067 \text{ mole/l.}$$

and from (ii) and (iii):

$$\text{sec. phosphate:} \quad \frac{0{\cdot}2 \times 1}{17} = 0{\cdot}0118 \text{ mole/l.}$$

$$\text{prim. phosphate:} \quad 0{\cdot}1882 \text{ mole/l.}$$

Note. The primary/secondary phosphate system plays a part as a buffer in urine, where the pH usually lies between 6·5 and 5, i.e. in the weakly acid region. Vegetable nutriment, by the liberation of alkali bicarbonate, makes the urine less acid, but meat, on the other hand, renders it more acid. Strongly alkaline urine becomes cloudy owing to the precipitation of calcium carbonate and calcium phosphate; strongly acid urine is also cloudy due to the precipitation of uric acid, which is not readily soluble in acid solution.

Exercise 137

Carbonic acid–sodium bicarbonate, with $NaHCO_3$ as salt, $H_2CO_3 = H^+ + HCO_3^-$, is the most important buffer system in blood. A blood test for total CO_2 (as carbonic acid and bicarbonate) gave a figure of 53·5 cm³ CO_2 per 100 cm³ blood (53·5 vol. per cent CO_2). The amount of free CO_2 is given by the Bunsen absorption coefficient for CO_2 in blood at body temperature as $\alpha^{Bu}_{CO_2} = 0{\cdot}511$ cm³ CO_2/(cm³ atm) blood, and from the partial pressure of CO_2 in the lungs as $p_{CO_2} = 40$ mm Hg. The apparent dissociation constants of H_2CO_3 are $K_a^{I} = 4{\cdot}31 \times 10^{-7}$ mol./l. and $K_a^{II} = 5{\cdot}61 \times 10^{-11}$ mol./l.; these values are apparent because, in the law of mass action, in place of undissociated H_2CO_3 one should substitute the total free CO_2 dissolved in water. Since the total molarity of the dissolved substances in blood is about 0·3 mole/l., one should use the figure of $f_{\pm} = 0{\cdot}74$ as the mean activity coefficient of $NaHCO_3$ (1-1 valent) for 0·3 molar solutions.

Calculate the pH of the blood sample under the given conditions. Note the methods used in Exercise 132, especially formula (xv) and the note to Exercise 135.

Solution 137. The above constants for carbonic acid show that only the first stage of dissociation will be significant as far as buffer action is concerned. The second stage of dissociation is negligible by comparison. Since the given K_a values are independent of concentration, it is possible to use the accurate formula at (xv) in Exercise 132 in order to calculate the pH. In the first stage, $NaHCO_3$ is practically completely dissociated.

From (xv) in Exercise 132 we find that

$$\text{pH} = -\log 4{\cdot}31 \times 10^{-7} + 2 \log 0{\cdot}74 + \log \frac{[NaHCO_3]}{[H_2CO_3]} \qquad \ldots . \quad \text{(i)}$$

The volume of absorbed CO_2 (at s.t.p.) per cm^3 of blood is, from Henry's law [see eqn. (166), p. 123]:

$$v_{s(CO_2)} = \alpha^{Bu}_{CO_2} p_{CO_2} \qquad (p \text{ in atm}) \qquad \ldots . \quad \text{(ii)}$$

Hence, in the above case, for 100 cm^3 of blood:

$V_{CO_2} = 0{\cdot}511 \times 100 \times 40/760 = 2{\cdot}69$ cm^3 CO_2/100 cm^3 blood (= 2·69 vol. per cent free CO_2) .... (iii)

The quantity of bicarbonate is obtained by deducting the free CO_2 from the total CO_2:

$$53{\cdot}5 - 2{\cdot}69 = 50{\cdot}81 \text{ vol. per cent [= mole per cent; see eqn. (11)]} \ldots . \quad \text{(iv)}$$

Hence

$$\log \frac{[NaHCO_3]}{[H_2CO_3]} = \log \frac{53{\cdot}5 - 2{\cdot}69}{2{\cdot}69} = \log \frac{50{\cdot}81}{2{\cdot}69} = 1{\cdot}276 \qquad \ldots . \quad \text{(v)}$$

Thus, from (i)

$$\text{pH} = -(0{\cdot}634 - 7) + 2(0{\cdot}869 - 1) + 1{\cdot}276 = 7{\cdot}38 \qquad \ldots . \quad \text{(vi)}$$

Note. The general buffer equation at (xv) in Exercise 132, applied to the blood system in the form at (i), is known as the Henderson–Hasselbalch formula. Determination of the total CO_2 in blood is carried out by using van Slyke's apparatus, where a volumetric measurement is made of the amount of CO_2 liberated by acid.

Exercise 138

From the pH and the sodium bicarbonate $NaHCO_3$ content (alkali reserve) of blood, estimate its content of calcium ions. The following equation applies:

$$CaCO_{3(solid)} + H^+ = Ca^{2+} + HCO_3^- \qquad \ldots . \quad \text{(i)}$$

$$[\text{or} \quad CaCO_3 + H_2CO_3 = Ca(HCO_3)_2]$$

The values of the pH of blood and its concentration of bicarbonate may be taken from Exercise 137 as pH = 7·38, [bicarbonate] = 50·81 vol. per cent CO_2 at 37 °C. Since the total molarity of the dissolved substances is about 0·3 mole/l. (see Exercise 137), $f_\pm = 0{\cdot}74$ should be taken as the mean activity coefficient for $NaHCO_3$ and $HHCO_3$ (1-1 valent); a value of $f_\pm = 0{\cdot}39$ should be used for $Ca(HCO_3)_2$ (2-1-1 valent).

The equilibrium constant K_a for the equilibrium at (i) may be calculated, as a first approximation, by using eqn. (197). The following values are found from tables (see p. 103):

	Heat of formation, ΔH^F, at 25 °C, 1 atm, 1 mole/l. (kcal/mole)	*Standard entropy, $S_{0\,298}$* cal/(deg. mole)
Ca^{2+}_{aq}	−129·5	−11·4
$HCO_{3\,(aq)}$	−164·6	+22·2
$H^+_{(aq)}$	0·0	0·0*
$CaCO_{3\,(solid)}$	−288·5	+22·2

* The standard entropies for ions at 25 °C and 1 atm, in aqueous solution at a concentration of 1 mole/l., refer to ideal behaviour (activity coefficient $f = 1$). They are given relative to the standard entropy for the H^+ ion [$S_0(H^+_{aq}) = 0{\cdot}0$ cal/(deg. mole)]. The absolute value of the standard entropy for the H^+_{aq} ion is about −5·0 cal/(deg. mole).

Solution 138. Applying the law of mass action to (i), one obtains from eqn. (231)

$$K_a = \frac{[Ca^{2+}] f_{Ca^{2+}} [HCO_3^-] f_{HCO_3^-}}{[H^+] f_{H^+}} \left(\frac{f_{HCO_3^-}}{f_{HCO_3^-}}\right) \quad \ldots\ldots \quad \text{(ii)}$$

where $f_{Ca^{2+}}(f_{HCO_3^-})^2 = f_\pm^3$ for $Ca(HCO_3)_2$ and $f_{H^+} f_{HCO_3^-} = f_\pm^2$ for H_2CO_3 or $NaHCO_3$ (approximately).

From the given data, one has $f_\pm^3$ for $Ca(HCO_3)_2 = 0{\cdot}39^3 = 0{\cdot}05932$ and $f_\pm^2$ for $H_2CO_3 = 0{\cdot}74^2 = 0{\cdot}5476$.

A pH of 7·38 corresponds to a H^+ ion concentration of $4{\cdot}17 \times 10^{-8}$ mol./l. (because $-7{\cdot}38 = 0{\cdot}62 - 8$ and $\log 4{\cdot}17 = 0{\cdot}62$). The concentration of bicarbonate in mol./l. is obtained, from 50·81 vol. per cent CO_2 at 37 °C, as follows:

There are 508·1 cm³ CO_2 at 37 °C in 1000 cm³ blood. The molar volume of a gas at 37 °C or 310 °K is $\frac{22{\cdot}4 \times 310}{273} = 25{\cdot}44$ l./mole, so that there are $\frac{508{\cdot}1}{25{\cdot}44 \times 10^3} = 1{\cdot}998 \times 10^{-2}$ mole/l. of bicarbonate ions. It follows from (ii) that

$$K_a = \frac{[Ca^{2+}]\, 1{\cdot}998 \times 10^{-2} \times 0{\cdot}05932}{4{\cdot}17 \times 10^{-8} \times 0{\cdot}5476} \text{ (mole/l.)} \quad \text{or} \quad [Ca^{2+}] = K_a \times 1{\cdot}926 \times 10^{-5} \text{ (mole/l.)} \quad \ldots\ldots \quad \text{(iii)}$$

K_a is calculated from eqn. (197), using (146):

$$\Delta H_{0\,298} = \Delta H^F_{Ca^{2+}} + \Delta H^F_{HCO_3^-} - \Delta H^F_{H^+} - \Delta H^F_{CaCO_3}$$
$$= -129{\cdot}5 - 164{\cdot}6 - (-288{\cdot}5) = -5{\cdot}6 \text{ kcal/mole} = -5600 \text{ cal/mole}$$

$$\Delta S_{0\,298} = S_{0\,298\,(Ca^{2+})} + S_{0\,298\,(HCO_3^-)} - S_{0\,298\,(H^+)} - S_{0\,298\,(CaCO_3)}$$
$$= -11{\cdot}4 + 22{\cdot}2 - 22{\cdot}2 = -11{\cdot}4 \text{ cal/(deg. mole)}$$

When $T = 310$ °K, eqn. (197) becomes

$$\left.\begin{aligned} \log K_a/(\text{mol./l.}) &= -\frac{\Delta H_{0\,298}}{4{\cdot}574\,T} + \frac{\Delta S_{0\,298}}{4{\cdot}574} = \frac{5600}{4{\cdot}574 \times 310} - \frac{11{\cdot}4}{4{\cdot}574} = 1{\cdot}455 \\ K_a &= 28{\cdot}5/(\text{mole/l.}) \end{aligned}\right\} \quad \ldots \quad \text{(iv)}$$

Substituting this value of K_a in (iii), one obtains

$$[Ca^{2+}] = 1{\cdot}926 \times 10^{-5} \times 28{\cdot}5 = 5{\cdot}49 \times 10^{-4} \text{ mole/l.} = 0{\cdot}549 \text{ millimole/l.}$$

or, with the atomic weight of calcium as 40·08,

$$0{\cdot}549 \times 40{\cdot}08 = 22{\cdot}1 \text{ mg } Ca^{2+} \text{ per litre of blood.}$$

Note. The concentration of calcium ions in blood is difficult to determine experimentally. This is because, of a total calcium content in blood serum and plasma of about 100 mg/l. of blood, about 30 mg is colloidally combined with the protein and can be separated from the residual 70 mg by ultrafiltration. However, a large part of the filtrate is non-ionized in the plasma. A mean experimental figure of 22 mg Ca^{2+}/l. is usually obtained.

Exercise 139

Without taking activity coefficients into account, calculate the pH and the degree of hydrolysis

$$\gamma = \frac{\text{number of undissociated acid or base molecules}}{\text{number of salt molecules taken}}$$

of (*a*) $c = 0{\cdot}1$ mole/l., (*b*) $c = 0{\cdot}2$ mole/l. potassium cyanide (KCN) at 18 °C. At this temperature the ionic product of H_2O is $k_{H_2O} = 0{\cdot}61 \times 10^{-14}$ (mole/l.)^2 and the dissociation constant of HCN is

$$K_{c\,(\mathrm{soln})\,\mathrm{HCN}} = \frac{[\mathrm{H}^+]\,[\mathrm{CN}^-]}{[\mathrm{HCN}]} = 4{\cdot}79 \times 10^{-10}\ \text{mole/l.}$$

Solution 139. The general solution of hydrolysis problems is given in textbooks. In the case under consideration one has the equation

$$\mathrm{CN}^- + \mathrm{H_2O} = \mathrm{HCN} + \mathrm{OH}^- \qquad \ldots\ldots \quad \text{(i)}$$

which represents a combination of the dissociation of water and of hydrocyanic acid, HCN. In general, one has five unknowns, $[K^+]$, $[CN^-]$, $[H^+]$, $[OH^-]$ and [HCN], and five equations:

(1) $$[\mathrm{K}^+] = c \qquad \ldots\ldots \quad \text{(ii)}$$

(2) $$[\mathrm{H}^+][\mathrm{OH}^-] = k_{\mathrm{H_2O}} \qquad \ldots\ldots \quad \text{(iii)}$$

(3) $$\frac{[\mathrm{H}^+]\,[\mathrm{CN}^-]}{[\mathrm{HCN}]} = K_{c\,(\mathrm{soln})\,\mathrm{HCN}} \qquad \ldots\ldots \quad \text{(iv)}$$

(4) $[\mathrm{CN}^-] + [\mathrm{HCN}] = c$ (conservation of the mass of CN^-) .... (v)

(5) $[\mathrm{K}^+] + [\mathrm{H}^+] = [\mathrm{CN}^-] + [\mathrm{OH}^-]$ (conservation of charge; electrical neutrality) .... (vi)

For moderate hydrolysis the problem is simplified [see (i)], in that

$$[\mathrm{HCN}] \approx [\mathrm{OH}^-] \qquad ([\mathrm{H}^+] \ll [\mathrm{OH}^-]) \qquad \ldots\ldots \quad \text{(vi}')$$

and

$$[\mathrm{CN}^-] \approx c \qquad \ldots\ldots \quad \text{(v}')$$

One then has, from (iv), (v), (vi) and (iii):

$$[\mathrm{H}^+] = \frac{K_{c\,(\mathrm{soln})\,\mathrm{HCN}}\,[\mathrm{HCN}]}{[\mathrm{CN}^-]} = \frac{K_{c\,(\mathrm{soln})\,\mathrm{HCN}}\,[\mathrm{OH}^-]}{c} = \frac{K_{c\,(\mathrm{soln})\,\mathrm{HCN}}}{c} \times \frac{k_{\mathrm{H_2O}}}{[\mathrm{H}^+]} \qquad \ldots\ldots \quad \text{(vii)}$$

or

$$[\mathrm{H}^+]^2 = \frac{K_{c\,(\mathrm{soln})\,\mathrm{HCN}}\,k_{\mathrm{H_2O}}}{c} \qquad [\mathrm{H}^+] = \sqrt{\frac{K_{c\,(\mathrm{soln})\,\mathrm{HCN}}\,c_{\mathrm{H_2O}}}{c}} \qquad \ldots\ldots \quad \text{(viii)}$$

The degree of hydrolysis, $\gamma = [\mathrm{HCN}]/c$, is similarly obtained from (v′) and (iv)

$$\gamma = \frac{[\mathrm{HCN}]}{c} = \frac{[\mathrm{HCN}]}{[\mathrm{CN}^-]} = \frac{[\mathrm{H}^+]}{K_{c\,(\mathrm{soln})\,\mathrm{HCN}}}$$

and, with (viii)

$$\gamma = \sqrt{\frac{k_{\mathrm{H_2O}}}{K_{c\,(\mathrm{soln})\,\mathrm{HCN}}\,c}} \qquad \ldots\ldots \quad \text{(ix)}$$

Substituting the numerical values in (viii) and (ix), one obtains for Case (*a*):

$$\left.\begin{aligned} \mathrm{pH} &= -\log[\mathrm{H}^+] = \tfrac{1}{2}(\log c - \log k_{\mathrm{H_2O}} - \log K_{c\,(\mathrm{soln})\,\mathrm{HCN}}) \\ &= \frac{0{\cdot}0 - 1 + 14{\cdot}215 + 9{\cdot}32}{2} = 11{\cdot}27 \end{aligned}\right\} \quad \ldots \quad \text{(x)}$$

$$\gamma = \sqrt{\frac{0{\cdot}61 \times 10^{-14}}{4{\cdot}79 \times 10^{-10} \times 0{\cdot}1}} = 1{\cdot}13 \times 10^{-2} \qquad \ldots\ldots \quad \text{(xi)}$$

Case (*b*):

$$\mathrm{pH} = 11{\cdot}42 \qquad \ldots\ldots \text{(xii)}$$

$$\gamma = 0{\cdot}798 \times 10^{-2} \qquad \ldots\ldots \text{(xiii)}$$

Note. (*a*) Corresponding formulae are applicable for the hydrolysis of salts of weak bases, where the dissociation constant is K_{base} ($BOH = B^+ + OH^-$). In place of $[H^+]$, one has $[OH^-]$ which, by using the relation $[H^+][OH^-] = k_{H_2O}$, can be expressed in terms of $[H^+]$. Thus, in the case of bases, (viii) becomes

$$[OH^-] = \sqrt{\frac{K_{\text{base}}\, k_{H_2O}}{c}} \qquad \ldots\ldots \text{(xiv)}$$

or

$$[H^+] = \sqrt{\frac{k_{H_2O}\, c}{K_{\text{base}}}} \qquad \ldots\ldots \text{(xv)}$$

For the degree of hydrolysis of salts of weak bases, a formula analogous to (ix) for the salts of weak acids is applicable:

$$\gamma = \sqrt{\frac{k_{H_2O}}{K_{\text{base}}\, c}} \qquad \ldots\ldots \text{(xvi)}$$

(*b*) The simplified eqns. (viii), (ix), (xv) and (xvi) hold in the case of moderate hydrolysis, i.e. for degrees of hydrolysis of about 10^{-2} to 10^{-4}. For weaker hydrolysis and when c is very small, the simplification (vi′), that $[HAc] \approx [OH^-]$ or $[BOH] \approx [H^+]$, should be replaced by the exact expression, by substituting (ii) and (v) in (vi),

$$[OH^-] = [HAc] + [H^+] \quad \text{or} \quad [H^+] = [BOH] + [OH^-] \qquad \ldots\ldots \text{(xvii)}$$

i.e. the OH^- or H^+ ions derived from $H_2O = H^+ + OH^-$ can no longer be disregarded; the approximation (v′) is even better

$$[Ac^-] \approx c \quad \text{or} \quad [B^+] \approx c$$

Substituting the expressions (xvii), (v′) and (iii) in (iv), one obtains for salts of weak acids, in place of (viii) and (ix):

$$[H^+] = \frac{K_{ac}}{c}\left([OH^-] - [H^+]\right) = \frac{K_{ac}}{c}\left(\frac{k_{H_2O}}{[H]} - [H^+]\right)$$

or

$$[H^+] = \sqrt{\frac{K_{ac}\, k_{H_2O}}{c + K_{ac}}} \qquad \ldots\ldots \text{(xviii)}$$

and

$$\gamma = \frac{[HAc]}{c} = \frac{[H^+]}{K_{ac}} = \sqrt{\frac{k_{H_2O}}{K_{ac}(c + K_{ac})}} \qquad \ldots\ldots \text{(xix)}$$

Similarly, for salts of weak bases:

$$[OH^-] = \sqrt{\frac{K_{\text{base}}\, k_{H_2O}}{c + K_{\text{base}}}} \qquad [H^+] = \sqrt{\frac{k_{H_2O}(c + K_{\text{base}})}{K_{\text{base}}}} \qquad \ldots\ldots \text{(xx)}$$

and

$$\gamma = \sqrt{\frac{k_{H_2O}}{K_{\text{base}}(c + K_{\text{base}})}} \qquad \ldots\ldots \text{(xxi)}$$

On the other hand, in the case of the stronger hydrolysis of salts of weak acids, the simplification (vi′), that $[HAc] \approx [OH^-]$, is valid. In contrast, the simplification (v′), that $[Ac^-] \approx c$, should be replaced by the exact expression at (v), i.e. $[Ac^-] = c - [HAc]$. We then find

$$[H^+] = \frac{K_{ac}[HAc]}{c - [HAc]} = \frac{K_{ac}[OH^-]}{c - [OH^-]}$$

and, with (iii), where $[H^+][OH^-] = k_{H_2O}$:

$$[H^+]^2 c - [H^+] k_{H_2O} - K_{ac} k_{H_2O} = 0$$

$$[H^+] = \frac{k_{H_2O}}{2c} + \sqrt{\left(\frac{k_{H_2O}}{2c}\right)^2 + \frac{k_{H_2O} K_{ac}}{c}} \quad \text{.... (xxii)}$$

With (vi′)

$$\gamma = \frac{[HAc]}{c} = \frac{[OH^-]}{c}$$

the following expression also holds:

$$\left(\frac{[OH^-]}{c}\right)^2 + \frac{[OH^-]}{c} \times \frac{k_{H_2O}}{K_{ac} c} - \frac{k_{H_2O}}{K_{ac} c} = 0$$

This equation is obtained by substituting (iii) in the above quadratic equation for $[H^+]$ and rearranging. Thus γ becomes:

$$\gamma = \frac{-\frac{k_{H_2O}}{K_{ac} c} + \sqrt{\left(\frac{k_{H_2O}}{K_{ac} c}\right)^2 + \frac{4 k_{H_2O}}{K_{ac} c}}}{2} \quad \text{.... (xxiii)}$$

Similarly, for salts of weak bases:

$$[H^+] = \frac{-k_{H_2O}}{2 K_{base}} + \sqrt{\left(\frac{k_{H_2O}}{2 K_{base}}\right)^2 + \frac{k_{H_2O} c}{K_{base}}} \quad \text{.... (xxiv)}$$

$$\gamma = \frac{-\frac{k_{H_2O}}{K_{base} c} + \sqrt{\left(\frac{k_{H_2O}}{K_{base} c}\right)^2 + \frac{4 k_{H_2O}}{K_{base} c}}}{2} \quad \text{.... (xxv)}$$

(*c*) For the mean degree of hydrolysis when activity is taken into account, one must multiply by the following factors:

for salts of weak acids, γ in (ix) and (xix), by $\dfrac{f_{Ac^-}}{f_{OH^-}}$

for salts of weak bases, γ in (xvi) and (xxi), by $\dfrac{f_{B^+}}{f_{H^+}}$

but, since these activity coefficients are approximately equal, the correction is not appreciable. (See Exercise 142 regarding the hydrolysis of salts of weak acids and weak bases.)

(*d*) See also Exercise 140 (a), (electrometric titration).

**Exercise 140

10 cm³ 0·1 N acid are titrated with 0·1 N alkali. Without taking activities into account, calculate and draw a graph of the approximate dependence of pH on the amount of alkali added (up to 20 cm³). Take the cases of:

(*a*) HCl with NaOH, strong acid – strong base

(*b*) HCN with NaOH, weak acid – strong base

(*c*) HCl with NH_4OH, strong acid – weak base

(*d*) NH_4OH with HCl, weak base – strong acid*

* Properly written $NH_{3\,(aq.)}$ and $NH_3 + H_2O \rightleftharpoons NH_4^+ + OH^-$, with $K_{c\,(NH_3\,aq.)} = \{[NH_4^+] \times [OH^-]\}/[NH_3]$, as no NH_4OH is present in aqueous solution.

The appropriate transition range (pH) for a particular indicator may be read off from the figure.

For the purpose of the calculation and according to the range and conditions, use the ionic product of water, eqn. (229) and Exercise 130, the dissociation equation for weak electrolytes, eqn. (217), the buffer equation [Exercise 133 (iii)] for [salt] = 0 and (v) for [Ac] = 0 or [salt] = 0 and the hydrolysis equation [Exercise 139, (viii) and (xv)].

HCl is practically completely dissociated;

$K_{c\,(\mathrm{soln})\,\mathrm{HCN}} \approx 5 \times 10^{-10}$ mole/l. (dissociation constant of HCN)

$k_{\mathrm{H_2O}} \approx 1 \times 10^{-14}$ (mole/l.)^2 (ionic product of water) $= [\mathrm{H^+}][\mathrm{OH^-}]$

$K_{c\,(\mathrm{soln})\,\mathrm{NH_4OH}} \approx 2 \times 10^{-5}$ mole/l.*

Solution 140. Calculation is simplest for Case (*a*), i.e. for HCl—NaOH. The equivalence point (10 cm³ NaOH) lies at pH = 7 (neutral point).

$$\mathrm{pH} = -\log[\mathrm{H^+}] \qquad \text{for } 0{\cdot}1\ \mathrm{N\ HCl} = 1$$
$$\text{for } 0{\cdot}1\ \mathrm{N\ NaOH} = 14 - 1 = 13$$

The intermediate values are obtained from the logarithms of the particular hydrogen concentrations for the partially neutralized HCl or NaOH. Thus, when 2 cm³ NaOH are added to 10 cm³ N HCl: $[\mathrm{H^+}] = \dfrac{10 - 2}{10 + 2} \times 0{\cdot}1$ mole/l., pH = 1·176.

cm³ NaOH	pH	cm³ NaOH	pH
4	1·37	9	2·28
6	1·60	9·9	3·30
8	1·95	9·99	4·30

The part of the curve on the alkaline side is obtained in a similar manner, using the ionic product of water. It is almost symmetrically disposed in relation to the acid side of the curve, the neutral point being at the centre. One has

$$[\mathrm{H^+}] = \frac{k_{\mathrm{H_2O}}}{[\mathrm{OH^-}]} \qquad \mathrm{pH} = -\log[\mathrm{H^+}] = 14 + \log[\mathrm{OH^-}]$$

i.e. for example, for 16 cm³ NaOH added: $[\mathrm{OH}]^- = \dfrac{16 - 10}{16 + 10} \times 0{\cdot}1$ mole/l., pH = 12·36. Similarly

cm³ NaOH	pH	cm³ NaOH	pH
20	12·52	10·1	10·70
12	11·96	10·01	9·70*
11	11·68		

* See *Figure 20*, curve 1

* See footnote to p. 210.

(*b*) In the case of HCN—NaOH the acid end of the curve is calculated from the dissociation equation for HCN. The branch of the curve on the acid side is obtained from the buffer eqn. (iii) in Exercise 133, where [salt] = 0, and the neutral point from the hydrolysis eqn. (viii) in Exercise 139. The branch of the curve on the alkaline side must be calculated by means of generalization of (ii) to (vi) in Exercise 139. As a first approximation, however, it is sufficient to use the ionic product of water as in Case (*a*) above, because the curve approximates to that obtained on the alkaline side for the HCl—NaOH system.

One has, from eqn. (217), for the addition of 0 cm³ NaOH:

$$K_{c\,(\mathrm{soln})\,\mathrm{HCN}} = 5 \times 10^{-10}\ \mathrm{mole/l.} = \frac{c\,\alpha^2}{1-\alpha} \approx c\,\alpha^2$$

$$[\mathrm{H^+}] = \alpha_c = \sqrt{K_{c\,(\mathrm{soln})\,\mathrm{HCN}}\, c} = \sqrt{0{\cdot}5 \times 10^{-10}}\ \mathrm{mole/l.}$$

$$\mathrm{pH} = -\log[\mathrm{H^+}] = -\tfrac{1}{2}(\log 0{\cdot}5 - 10) = 5{\cdot}15 \quad \ldots. \quad \mathrm{(i)}$$

For the branch of the curve on the acid side and using the buffer eqn. (iii) in Exercise 133, one has

$$\mathrm{pH} = -\log K_{c\,(\mathrm{soln})\,\mathrm{HCN}} + \log \frac{[\mathrm{alkali}]}{[\mathrm{acid}] - [\mathrm{alkali}]} \quad \ldots. \quad \mathrm{(ii)}$$

For 1 cm³ NaOH added:

$$\mathrm{pH} = 9{\cdot}3 + \log \tfrac{1}{9} = 8{\cdot}35$$

Similarly for

cm³ NaOH	pH	cm³ NaOH	pH
0·01	6·30	5	9·3*
0·1	7·30	7	9·67
0·5	8·02	9	10·25
3	8·93	9·5	10·58

* = $-\log K_{c\,(\mathrm{sol})\,\mathrm{HCN}}$ (point of inflection)

The hydrolysis eqn. (viii) in Exercise 139 gives the equivalence point (10 cm³ 0·1 N HCN + 10 cm³ 0·1 N NaOH = 20 cm³ 0·05 N NaCN solution), where $c = 0{\cdot}05$ (*sic*) mole/l.

$$[\mathrm{H^+}] = \sqrt{\frac{K_{c\,(\mathrm{soln})\,\mathrm{HCN}}\, k_{\mathrm{H_2O}}}{c}} = \sqrt{\frac{5 \times 10^{-10} \times 1 \times 10^{-14}}{0{\cdot}05}} = 10^{-11}\ \mathrm{mole/l.} \quad \mathrm{pH} = 11{\cdot}0 \quad \ldots. \quad \mathrm{(iii)}$$

See *Figure 20*, curve 2.

(*c*) As a first approximation, the HCl—NaOH curve may be taken for the acidic side of the curve obtained when HCl is titrated with the weak base NH_4OH (see footnote 210). For accurate calculation it is necessary to use expressions analogous to (ii)–(vi) in Exercise 139. The equivalence point is given by the hydrolysis equation at (xv) in Exercise 139:

$$[\mathrm{H^+}] = \sqrt{\frac{k_{\mathrm{H_2O}}\, c}{K_{\mathrm{base}}}} \quad \ldots. \quad \mathrm{(iv)}$$

The pH at the equivalence point is, therefore

$$[H^+] = \sqrt{\frac{0{\cdot}05 \times 10^{-14}}{2 \times 10^{-5}}} = 5 \times 10^{-6}\ \text{mole/l.} \quad \text{pH} = 5{\cdot}30 \qquad \ldots . \quad \text{(v)}$$

For the branch of the curve on the alkaline side, the buffer equation at (v) in Exercise 133 is used, where [Ac] = 0. This gives

$$\text{pH} = -\log k_{H_2O} + \log K_{c(\text{soln})\,NH_4OH} + \log \frac{[\text{alk}]}{[\text{salt}]} \qquad \ldots . \quad \text{(vi)}$$

In the present case the amount of salt [salt] is constant (10 cm³ NH_4Cl), whereas the amount of alkali [alk] (cm³ 0·1 N NH_4OH) increases on the right-hand side of the

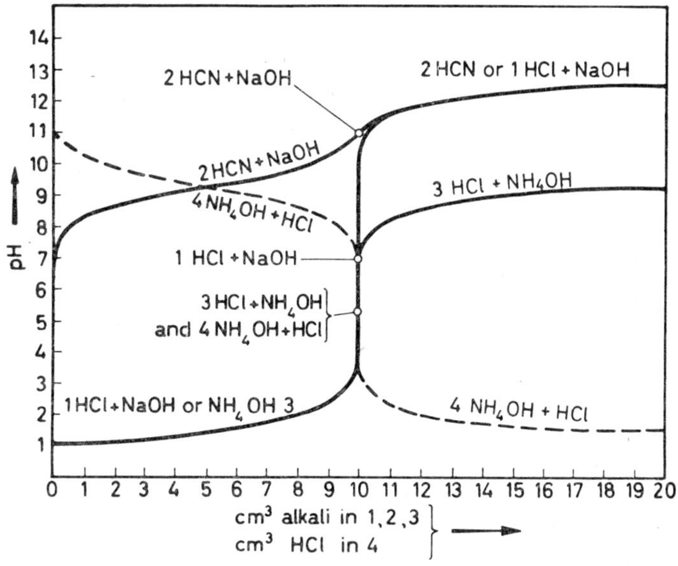

Figure 20. Titration curves (pH curves) for various acids and bases

equivalence point (where [alk] = 0). At a value of 20 cm³ on the abscissa, one has [alk] = 10 cm³; see *Figure 20*. If still more NH_4OH were added, the limit for the pH of pure 0·1 N NH_4OH would be reached; this may be calculated from the dissociation equation for NH_4OH. Numerical evaluation gives:

for 10·01 cm³ NH_4OH([alk] = 0·01 cm³), $\text{pH} = 14 + 0{\cdot}3 - 5 + \log \frac{0{\cdot}01}{10} = 6{\cdot}3$

cm³ NH_4OH	pH	cm³ NH_4OH	pH
10·1	7·3	12	8·6
10·5	8·0	15	9·0
11	8·3	20	9·3*

* See *Figure 20*, curve 3

(*d*) Finally, the titration curve for NH_4OH–HCl (weak base and strong acid) is obtained in a similar manner to that for HCN–NaOH (weak acid and strong base), the relevant formulae being suitably varied. One has, for the addition of 0 cm³ HCl, i.e. for pure NH_4OH solution:

$$[OH^-] = \sqrt{K_{c\,(soln)\,NH_4OH}\,c} \qquad [H^+] = \frac{k_{H_2O}}{\sqrt{K_{c\,(soln)\,NH_4OH}\,c}} = \frac{10^{-14}}{\sqrt{2 \times 10^{-5} \times 0{\cdot}1}} \quad \ldots\ldots \text{(vii)}$$

$$pH = 14 + \tfrac{1}{2}(0{\cdot}3 - 5 - 1) = 11{\cdot}15$$

For the branch of the curve on the alkaline side, the buffer equation at (v) in Exercise 133 applies, where [salt] = 0:

$$pH = -\log k_{H_2O} + \log K_{c\,(soln)\,NH_4OH} + \log \frac{[alk] - [Ac]}{[Ac]} \quad \ldots\ldots \text{(viii)}$$

So that, for 0·5 cm³ HCl, $pH = 14 + 0{\cdot}3 - 5 + \log \frac{9{\cdot}5}{0{\cdot}5} = 10{\cdot}58$

cm³ HCl	pH	cm³ HCl	pH
1	10·25	8	8·70
2	9·9	9	8·35
3	9·67	9·5	8·02
5	9·3*	9·9	7·30
7	8·93	9·99	6·30

* $= -\log K_{H_2O} + \log K_{c\,(soln)\,NH_4OH}$ (point of inflection)

The equivalence point lies at 5·3, as in the case of the system HCl–NH_4OH; see (v).

The residual concentration of H^+ ions may be taken as a first approximation for the acid region; thus

for 10·01 cm³ HCl, $pH = -\log \frac{0{\cdot}01}{10 + 10{\cdot}01} \times 0{\cdot}1 = 4{\cdot}3$

cm³ HCl	pH	cm³ HCl	pH
10·1	3·3	16	1·64
11	2·32	20	1·48*
12	2·04		

* See *Figure 20*, curve 4

It is, of course, a coincidence that the points of inflection of the HCN + NaOH and NH_4OH + HCl systems at 5 cm³ both have a pH value of 9·3. This is seen by comparison of the two buffer eqns. (ii) and (viii), which, by chance, happen to give:

$$K_{c\,(soln)\,HCN}\,K_{c\,(soln)\,NH_4OH} = 5 \times 10^{-10}\,\text{mole/l.} \times 2 \times 10^{-5}\ \text{mole/l.} = 10^{-14}\,(\text{mole/l.})^2 = k_{H_2O}$$

i.e.

$$-\log K_{c\,(soln)\,HCN} = -\log k_{H_2O} + \log K_{c\,(soln)\,NH_4OH}$$

An inspection of *Figure 20*, in which the numerical values are plotted, shows that, for the titrations in question, the indicator should span the following values:

(*a*) HCl + NaOH pH = 5 to 9 (litmus and phenol red)

(*b*) HCN + NaOH pH = 11 (alizarin yellow R*)

(*c*) and (*d*) NH_4OH + HCl pH = 4 to 7 (methyl red)

Note. The questions arising in this Exercise are of great importance regarding acidimetric titrations in analytical chemistry, for pH determinations, especially in biology, and in the theory of indicators. These questions are usually dealt with in detail in textbooks. It may be pointed out that the examples afford an illustration of Ostwald's rule, which is that weak acids may be titrated with strong bases if an indicator is used which has its transition in the alkaline region, while weak bases titrated with strong acids require the use of an indicator having a transition in the acid region (see also Exercise 147). That weak bases cannot be titrated with weak acids is best seen in *Figure 20* by roughly connecting the left branch of curve 2 (for HCN + NaOH) with the right branch of curve 3 (for HCl + NH_4OH), i.e. to define the HCN + NH_4OH system. It will then be seen that such a curve shows no slope, or leap in pH, at the equivalence point — a feature which is essential in titration.

As has already been said in the note to Exercise 133, weak acids and bases show a flat point of inflection in the pH curve at the position where the acid: salt ratio equals 1:1. In the case of acids, this point is in the vicinity of $pH = -\log K_{c\,(Ac)}$; for bases it lies at $pOH = -\log K_{c\,(base)}$, i.e. at $pH = -\log K_{H_2O} + \log K_{c\,(base)}$ [see Exercise 133, eqns. (vi) and (vii), and also note to Exercise 199, p. 307].

Conversely, if the pH is the independent variable and the ratio acid:salt, or base:salt, is the dependent variable, then a marked change in this ratio will be obtained at the point of inflection of pH in the region of the ratio 1:1. This is why coloured weak acids or bases are used as indicators, the salts (or ions) of which have a colour different from that of the undissociated acid or base; the position of marked change of colour of the mixture,i.e. the transition range, corresponds to the ratio salt:acid or salt:base = 1:1. According to the above, the relevant transition of pH is given by $pH_{(transition)} = -\log K_{c\,(coloured\ acid)}$ in the case of coloured acids, and by $pH_{(transition)} = -\log k_{H_2O} + \log K_{c\,(coloured\ base)}$ in the case of coloured bases. Variations due to consideration of the activity of the solution are not dealt with here.

**Exercise 140 (a)

Melamine [2,4,6-triamino-1,3,5-triazine, $C_3N_3(NH_2)_3$; $M = 126{\cdot}1$] is the starting material in the manufacture of melamine–formaldehyde synthetic resins. A very high degree of purity is required. One has the problem of working out an electrometric method of titration for the continuous determination of the melamine content of the raw materials and of the degree of purity of the final products. The problem is based on the fact that melamine is a weak base, like NH_3, and thus reacts in accordance with the equation: $mel + H_2O = (mel)HOH \rightleftharpoons (Mel)H^+ + OH^-$. It is, therefore, possible to titrate melamine with HCl after the pattern in Exercise 140 (iv), i.e. titration of NH_4OH with HCl, and to find the equivalence point on the rise (or leap) of the pH curve, similar to curve 4 in *Figure 20*.

A pH-meter (with an accuracy of $\pm 0{\cdot}01$ units of pH), a glass electrode, a calomel reference electrode and a 5 ml microburette with 0·02 ml graduations are available for the purpose of measurement. Normal HCl is used for the titration.

---

* Phenolphthalein, which has a range of pH from 8 to10, is not suitable, but would be suitable, as may be shown by an appropriate diagram, for the titration of a medium strength acid (e.g. acetic acid) with NaOH.

The theory and practice of pH measurement, using a glass and a calomel reference electrode, are explained in Exercise 165. The treatment in the present problem is, however, connected with Exercises 139 and 140. A knowledge of the electrometric method for determining pH is not necessary in the present context.

Explanation. In order to solve the problem, it is necessary to make an accurate calculation (but not taking activity coefficients into account) of pH as a function of the amount of acid (cm^3 HCl) added to the melamine solution in question. This will be done by setting up expressions similar to those at (i) to (vi) in Exercise 139, using the procedure outlined in Exercise 140 and drawing a curve for discussion of the expression obtained. Since the curve is probably similar to curve 4 in *Figure 20*, the problem will be mainly one of locating the points of inflection; i.e. it will be necessary to calculate and discuss the first and second differential coefficients of the function defining the pH curve. The mean value of later electrometric titrations at 24 °C gave a pH of 3·50 at the equivalence point, when 200 cm^3 of an aqueous solution of 2·00 g/l. of melamine was titrated with normal HCl. The dissociation constant K_{mel} of the (base) melamine may be calculated from this.

Discussion of the curve is made much easier owing to the fact that the numerical coefficients entering into the function defining the pH are, in part, of quite different orders of magnitude. This means that, both in the function and in its differential coefficients certain terms may be neglected without affecting accuracy. The ionic product of water at 24 °C is $k_{H_2O} = 1{\cdot}00 \times 10^{-14}$ (mole/l.)^2; see p. 195.

Solution 140 (a). One has the following which is analogous to (i)–(vi) in Exercise 139:

$$(\text{mel})\text{H}^+ + \text{H}_2\text{O} = (\text{mel})\text{HOH} + \text{H}^+ \qquad \ldots\ldots \quad \text{(i)}$$

Taking $[\text{mel}_{tot}]$ = total concentration of melamine (mole/l.)

$[\text{Ac}_{tot}]$ = total concentration of acid (HCl) (mole/l.)

one has

(*a*) $$[\text{Ac}^-] = [\text{Ac}_{tot}] \quad \text{(complete dissociation)} \qquad \ldots\ldots \quad \text{(ii)}$$

(*b*) $$[\text{H}^+][\text{OH}^-] = k_{H_2O} \qquad \ldots\ldots \quad \text{(iii)}$$

(*c*) $$\frac{[(\text{mel})\,\text{H}^+][\text{OH}^-]}{[(\text{mel})\,\text{HOH}]} = K_{mel} \qquad \ldots\ldots \quad \text{(iv)}$$

(*d*) $$[(\text{mel})\,\text{H}^+] + [(\text{mel})\,\text{HOH}] = [\text{mel}_{tot}] \quad \text{[conservation of mass of (mel)]} \qquad \ldots\ldots \quad \text{(v)}$$

(*e*) $$[\text{Ac}^-] + [\text{OH}^-] = [(\text{mel})\text{H}^+] + [\text{H}^+] \quad \text{(condition for electrical neutrality)} \qquad \ldots\ldots \quad \text{(vi)}$$

Eliminating $[\text{Ac}^-]$, $[\text{OH}^-]$, $[(\text{mel})\text{H}^+]$ and $[(\text{mel})\text{HOH}]$ from (ii)–(vi), the following is obtained after simple rearrangement:

$$[\text{H}^+]^3 + [\text{H}^+]^2 \left\{[\text{mel}_{tot}] - [\text{Ac}_{tot}] + \frac{k_{H_2O}}{K_{mel}}\right\} - [\text{H}^+]\left\{k_{H_2O} + \frac{k_{H_2O}}{K_{mel}}[\text{Ac}_{tot}]\right\} - \frac{k^2_{H_2O}}{K_{mel}} = 0 \qquad \ldots\ldots \quad \text{(vii)}$$

or, solving for $[\text{Ac}_{tot}]$:

$$[\text{Ac}_{tot}] = \frac{[\text{H}^+]^3 + [\text{H}^+]^2\left\{[\text{mel}_{tot}] + \dfrac{k_{H_2O}}{K_{mel}}\right\} - [\text{H}^+]\,k_{H_2O} - \dfrac{k^2_{H_2O}}{K_{mel}}}{[\text{H}^+]^2 + [\text{H}^+]\dfrac{k_{H_2O}}{K_{mel}}} \qquad \ldots\ldots \quad \text{(viii)}$$

At the equivalence point $[\text{mel}_{tot}]_{eq} = [\text{Ac}_{tot}]_{eq}$, so that, from eqn. (vii) and by simple rearrangement:

$$K_{mel} = \frac{k_{H_2O}^2 + [H^+]_{eq}[\text{Ac}_{tot}]_{eq} k_{H_2O} - [H^+]_{eq}^2 k_{H_2O}}{[H^+]_{eq}^3 - [H^+]_{eq} k_{H_2O}} \quad \dots \quad \text{(ix)}$$

It is convenient to take 200 cm³ of the aqueous solution of 2·00 g/l. melamine (where $M = 126{\cdot}1$); this is suited to the use of a 5 ml microburette and is equivalent to $\frac{2{\cdot}00 \times 200}{126{\cdot}1 \times 1000} = 3{\cdot}172 \times 10^{-3}$ moles of melamine, i.e. during titration with normal HCl, 3·17 cm³ of acid solution are required to reach the equivalence point. Under these conditions, the (total) concentration of melamine and that of the (total) added acid at the equivalence point are $[\text{mel}_{tot}]_{eq}$ and $[\text{Ac}_{tot}]_{eq}$, respectively, and one has the relation

$$[\text{mel}_{tot}]_{eq} = [\text{Ac}_{tot}]_{eq} = \frac{3{\cdot}172 \times 10^{-3} \times 1000}{200 + 3{\cdot}17} = 1{\cdot}561 \times 10^{-2} \text{ mole/l.} \quad \dots \quad \text{(x)}$$

Using the fact, originally given, that the pH at the equivalence point is 3·50, it is now possible to calculate the dissociation constant K_{mel} for the melamine base, where $\text{pH} = 3{\cdot}50 = -\log[H^+]$, $[H^+]_{eq} = 3{\cdot}162 \times 10^{-4}$ mole/l., $k_{H_2O} = 1{\cdot}00 \times 10^{-14}$ (mole/l.)². This gives

$$K_{mel} = \frac{(1{\cdot}00 \times 10^{-14})^2 + 3{\cdot}162 \times 10^{-4} \times 1{\cdot}561 \times 10^{-2} \times 1{\cdot}00 \times 10^{-14} - 1{\cdot}00 \times 10^{-7} \times 1{\cdot}00 \times 10^{-14}}{3{\cdot}162 \times 10^{-11} - 3{\cdot}162 \times 10^{-4} \times 1{\cdot}00 \times 10^{-14}}$$

$$= 1{\cdot}53 \times 10^{-9} \text{ mole/l.*} \quad \dots \quad \text{(xi)}$$

The pH of the pure melamine base at the standard concentration used (CO_2-free solution) $[\text{mel}_{tot}]_0 = 2{\cdot}00/126{\cdot}1 = 1{\cdot}586 \times 10^{-2}$ mole/l., may now be calculated.

The degree of dissociation, α, of the melamine base is, from eqn. (219)

$$\alpha = \sqrt{\frac{K_{mel}}{[\text{mel}_{tot}]_0}} \qquad [OH^-] = \alpha[\text{mel}_{tot}] \quad \text{and} \quad [H^+] = \frac{k_{H_2O}}{[OH^-]}$$

so that

$$[H^+] = \frac{k_{H_2O}}{\sqrt{K_{mel}[\text{mel}_{tot}]_0}} = \frac{1{\cdot}00 \times 10^{-14}}{\sqrt{1{\cdot}53 \times 10^{-9} \times 1{\cdot}586 \times 10^{-2}}} = 2{\cdot}03 \times 10^{-9} \text{ mole/l.}$$

$$\text{pH} = 8{\cdot}69 \quad \dots \quad \text{(xii)}$$

Discussion of Curve. The discussion relates to the curve for $\log[H^+] = -\text{pH}$ as a function of $[\text{Ac}_{tot}]$. The following substitutions will be used in order to simplify the writing:

$$[\text{Ac}_{tot}] = x \qquad [H^+] = y \qquad [\text{mel}_{tot} = a]$$

$$k_{H_2O}/K_{mel} = r = 1{\cdot}00 \times 10^{-14}/1{\cdot}53 \times 10^{-9} = 0{\cdot}6536 \times 10^{-5} \text{ mole/l.}$$

$$[\text{mel}_{tot}]_0 = a_0 = 1{\cdot}586 \times 10^{-2} \text{ mole/l.} \qquad [\text{mel}_{tot}]_{eq} = 1{\cdot}561 \times 10^{-2} \text{ mole/l.}$$

Eqn. (viii) then reads

$$x = \frac{y^3 + y^2(a + r) - k(y + r)}{y(y + r)} = y + \frac{a\,y}{y + r} - \frac{k}{y} = y - \frac{a\,r}{y + r} - \frac{k}{y} + a \quad \dots \quad \text{(xiii)}$$

* Since the pH value at the equivalence point is $3{\cdot}50 \pm 0{\cdot}01$, it is only possible to give the dissociation constant of the melamine base as $K_{mel} = 1{\cdot}5 \times 10^{-9}$ mole/l.; further calculations will, however, be made taking the value of K_{mel} as $1{\cdot}53 \times 10^{-9}$ mole/l.

The following are necessary for the discussion:

$$\frac{\mathrm{d}\log y}{\mathrm{d}x} = 0{\cdot}4343\,\frac{\mathrm{d}\ln y}{\mathrm{d}x} \quad \text{and} \quad \frac{\mathrm{d}^2\log y}{\mathrm{d}x^2} = 0{\cdot}4343\,\frac{\mathrm{d}^2\ln y}{\mathrm{d}x^2}$$

The following are of general validity:

$$\frac{\mathrm{d}\ln y}{\mathrm{d}x} = \frac{1}{y}\frac{\mathrm{d}y}{\mathrm{d}x} = \left(y\frac{\mathrm{d}x}{\mathrm{d}y}\right)^{-1} \quad \left(\text{where } \frac{\mathrm{d}y}{\mathrm{d}x} = 1\Big/\frac{\mathrm{d}x}{\mathrm{d}y}\right)$$

$$\frac{\mathrm{d}^2\ln y}{\mathrm{d}x^2} = -\left(y\frac{\mathrm{d}x}{\mathrm{d}y}\right)^{-2}\left(\frac{\mathrm{d}y}{\mathrm{d}x}\frac{\mathrm{d}x}{\mathrm{d}y} + y\frac{\mathrm{d}^2x}{\mathrm{d}y^2}\frac{\mathrm{d}y}{\mathrm{d}x}\right) = -\frac{\dfrac{\mathrm{d}x}{\mathrm{d}y} + y\dfrac{\mathrm{d}^2x}{\mathrm{d}y^2}}{y^2\left(\dfrac{\mathrm{d}x}{\mathrm{d}y}\right)^3}$$

In the present case, from eqn. (xiii)

$$\frac{\mathrm{d}x}{\mathrm{d}y} = 1 + \frac{ar}{(y+r)^2} + \frac{k}{y^2} \qquad \frac{\mathrm{d}^2x}{\mathrm{d}y^2} = -\frac{2ar}{(y+r)^3} - \frac{2k}{y^3}$$

hence

$$\frac{\mathrm{d}\ln y}{\mathrm{d}x} = \left[y\left(1 + \frac{ar}{(y+r)^2} + \frac{k}{y^2}\right)\right]^{-1} \qquad \ldots\ldots (\text{xiv})$$

$$\frac{\mathrm{d}^2\ln y}{\mathrm{d}x^2} = \frac{-1 + \dfrac{(y-r)ar}{(y+r)^3} + \dfrac{k}{y^2}}{\left(1 + \dfrac{ar}{(y+r)^2} + \dfrac{k}{y^2}\right)^3 y^2} \qquad \ldots\ldots (\text{xv})$$

For a point of inflection, $\dfrac{\mathrm{d}^2\ln y}{\mathrm{d}x^2} = 0$; i.e. the numerator of eqn. (xv) is

$$Z = -1 + \frac{(y-r)ar}{(y+r)^3} + \frac{k}{y^2} = 0 \qquad \ldots\ldots (\text{xvi})$$

For pH values between 8 and 6 ($y = [H^+]$ between 10^{-8} and 10^{-6}) Z must be negative throughout; this is easily seen by estimating the order of magnitude.

No discussion of the curve is made for pH values greater than 8, since at pH = 8, eqn. (xiii) gives

$$[\mathrm{Ac_{tot}}] = x = 10^{-8} + \frac{1{\cdot}586 \times 10^{-2} \times 10^{-8}}{10^{-8} \times 0{\cdot}6536 \times 10^{-5}} - \frac{10^{-14}}{10^{-8}} = 2{\cdot}3 \times 10^{-5}\ \mathrm{mol./l.}$$

The smallest quantity measurable in the microburette is 0·02 cm³. The addition of this quantity of N/1 HCl to 200 cm³ of the given solution results in a concentration of $[\mathrm{Ac_{tot}}] = x = 1 \times 0{\cdot}02/200 = 1 \times 10^{-4}$ mole/l. $> 2{\cdot}3 \times 10^{-5}$ mole/l. Thus a point on the curve at pH = 8 is still beyond the limit of error for the method of measurement. The measuring range is only reached when the pH falls to 7·38; this can easily be checked. It therefore remains only to examine the range of pH between 6 and 3 for the occurrence of a point of inflection. In this range, however, the term k/y^2 in Z, at (xvi), may be neglected – this may be shown by an estimation of order of magnitude.

Since Z is negative both at pH = 6 and at pH = 3, there is a possibility that two zero values may be found, i.e. that two points of inflection may exist. *Figure 20* would lead one to expect this.

Multiplying Z in eqn. (xvi) by $(y + r)^3$ gives the relation

$$Z' = -(y+r)^3 + (y-r)ar = -(y+r)^3 + (y+r)ar - 2ar^2 = 0 \qquad \ldots\ldots (\text{xvii})$$

which should be examined for zero values between pH = 6 and pH = 3.

An estimation of orders of magnitude shows that, between pH values of 6 and 5 the term $-(y + r)^3$ in eqn. (xvii) may be neglected without affecting accuracy Eqn. (xvii) then becomes

$$(y-r)ar = 0 \quad \text{or} \quad y = r; \quad -\log y = \text{pH} = -\log r = -\log k_{H_2O} + \log K_{\text{mel}} \quad \ldots \text{(xviii)}$$

and from eqn. (xiii)

$$x = r + \frac{a\,r}{2\,r} - \frac{k}{r} = \frac{a}{2} + r - \frac{k}{r} \approx \frac{a}{2}$$

within the limit of error.

Since, for increasing values of x and y, Z or Z' pass from being negative through a zero value to positive (corresponding to change from negative to positive curvature of the graph), one is dealing with an ⁄-shaped curve and a flat point of inflection. This indicates a position where there is only a small change of pH on addition of acid, i.e. the system is insensitive to the addition of acid and not suitable for titration (buffer action; see also the note to Exercise 133). The point of inflection given by (xviii) is clearly the first point of inflection on curve 4 in *Figure 20*; see also note to Exercise 140.

Accurate solution of the cubic equation at (xvii) gives, when $y + r = z$, and in the range of pH between 5 and 3:

$$z^3 - arz + 2ar^2 = 0 \quad \text{or, where} \quad p = -ar/3 \quad \text{and} \quad q = ar^2$$

$$z^3 + 3pz + 2q = 0$$

whereby

$$p = -1{\cdot}561 \times 10^{-2} \times 0{\cdot}6536 \times 10^{-5}/3$$

$$= 0{\cdot}340 \times 10^{-7}\,(\text{mole/l.})^2$$

$$q = 0{\cdot}667 \times 10^{-12}\,(\text{mole/l.})^3$$

Since $q^2 + p^3 = 0{\cdot}4447 \times 10^{-24} - 0{\cdot}3934 \times 10^{-22} < 0$, one is faced with a *casus irreducibilis*; taking $\cos\varphi = -q/\sqrt{-p^3} = -0{\cdot}667 \times 10^{-12}/0{\cdot}627 \times 10^{-11} = -0{\cdot}1063$; $\varphi = 180° - 83°\,54'$; $\varphi/3 = 32°02'$; $\cos\varphi/3 = 0{\cdot}8477$, one has

$$\left.\begin{aligned} z &= 2\sqrt{-p}\cos\varphi/3 = (2/\sqrt{3})\sqrt{ar}\cos\varphi/3 = 0{\cdot}979\sqrt{ar} \\ y &= z - r = 0{\cdot}979\sqrt{ar} - r = 3{\cdot}06 \times 10^{-4}\,\text{mol./l.} \\ -\log y &= \text{pH} = 3{\cdot}5 \end{aligned}\right\} \quad \ldots \text{(xix)}$$

and with eqn. (xiii):

$$x = 0{\cdot}979\sqrt{ar} - r - \frac{a\,r}{0{\cdot}979\sqrt{ar}} + a - \frac{k}{y} \approx a$$

within the limit of error.

At a pH of 3·5, $x = [\text{Ac}_{\text{tot}}] = a = [\text{mel}_{\text{tot}}]$, i.e. at the equivalence point a transition through zero, from positive to negative values of Z', takes place (corresponding to a change from positive to negative curvature of the graph); thus a rising point of inflection in the ∫-shaped curve occurs in this case. This corresponds to the second point of inflection at the equivalence point in *Figure 20* suitable for titration.

It is usual, as in *Figure 20*, to plot the pH against the number of cubic centimetres of acid added (v_{Ac}) and not against $[Ac_{tot}]$. Taking

$[Ac_{tot}]_0$ = standard concentration (mole/l.) of HCl used (1 mole/l. here),

$[mel_{tot}]_0$ = standard concentration (mole/l.) of melamine solution used ($1{\cdot}586 \times 10^{-2}$ mole/l. here),

$v_{0\,mel}$ = amount of melamine solution in question (200 cm³ here), one then has the relations:

$$\left.\begin{aligned} [Ac_{tot}] = x = [Ac_{tot}]_0 \frac{v_{Ac}}{v_{0\,mel} + v_{Ac}} &\approx \frac{[Ac_{tot}]_0 v_{Ac}}{v_{0\,mel}}\left(1 - \frac{v_{Ac}}{v_{0\,mel}}\right) = \frac{v_{Ac}}{200}\left(1 - \frac{v_{Ac}}{200}\right) \\ [mel_{tot}] = a = [mel_{tot}]_0 \frac{v_{0\,mel}}{v_{0\,mel} + v_{Ac}} &\approx 1{\cdot}586 \times 10^{-2}\left(1 - \frac{v_{Ac}}{200}\right) \end{aligned}\right\} \quad \ldots \text{(xx)}$$

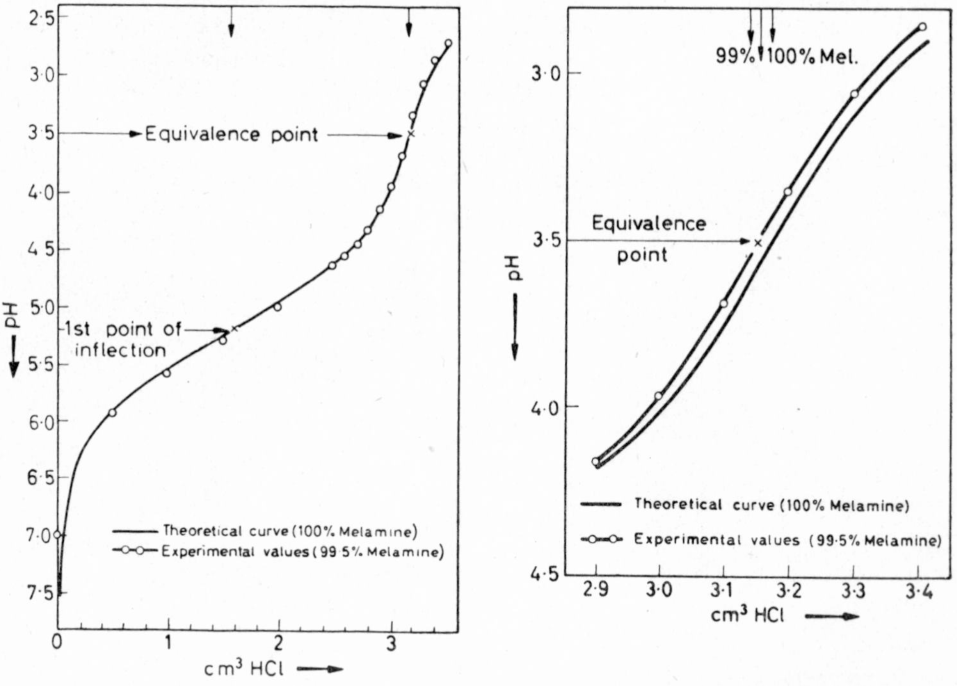

Figures 21 and 22. Titration curve for melamine with HCl *(the latter, enlarged part)*

Since $v_{Ac(eq)} = 3{\cdot}172$ cm³ [see (x)], it follows that $v_{Ac}/200$ lies between 0 and $1{\cdot}586 \times 10^{-2}$, so that $[Ac_{tot}] = x$ is, according to (xx), practically proportional to v_{Ac} and $[mel_{tot}]$ is virtually constant. Discussion of the curve is therefore unaffected if, as above, one replaces v_{Ac} in eqn. (xiii) by $[Ac_{tot}]$; this makes the mathematical treatment more simple. *Figure 21* shows the titration curve as given by (xiii) but calculated, taking the expressions at (xx) into account.

Figure 21 also shows experimental values obtained during the titration of 200 cm³ of a solution of 2 g/l. melamine, where the degree of purity was to be determined.

Figure 22 shows a large-scale plot of the decisive part of the curve in the region of the rising point of inflection. It will be seen that the latter (pH = 3·50) lies at 3·155 cm³ instead of at the theoretical value of 3·172 cm³. The degree of purity of the melamine sample in question is therefore $\frac{3{\cdot}155 \times 100}{3{\cdot}172} = 99{\cdot}5$ per cent.

Figure 23 shows a plot of the differential coefficient of the log [H⁺] (– pH) versus v_{Ac} curve given in *Figure 22*. It relates to the vicinity of the equivalence point and is calculated from eqn. (xiv), taking (xx) into account after multiplying by 0·4343. A correction factor of $(1 - v_{Ac\,(eq)}/200) = 0{\cdot}984$ is used, so that $a = a_{eq} = 1{\cdot}561 \times 10^{-2}$ mol./l., i.e. when $r = 0{\cdot}654 \times 10^{-5}$, $ar = 1{\cdot}020 \times 10^{-5}$ mole/l.

Accordingly

$$\left.\begin{aligned}\frac{\mathrm{d}\log[\mathrm{H}^+]}{\mathrm{d}v_{Ac}} &= 0{\cdot}4343\,\frac{\mathrm{d}\ln y}{\mathrm{d}x} \times \frac{\mathrm{d}x}{\mathrm{d}v_{Ac}} = 0{\cdot}4343 \times \frac{0{\cdot}984}{200} \times \frac{\mathrm{d}\ln y}{\mathrm{d}x} \\ &= 0{\cdot}214 \times 10^{-2}\,\frac{\mathrm{d}\ln y}{\mathrm{d}x}\left[\frac{\text{pH units}}{\text{cm}^3\ \text{HCl soln.}}\right]\end{aligned}\right\} \quad \ldots \text{(xxi)}$$

Comparison of *Figure 22* with *Figure 23* clearly shows that the position of the equivalence point (point of inflection) may be more accurately determined from the maximum in the differential curve.

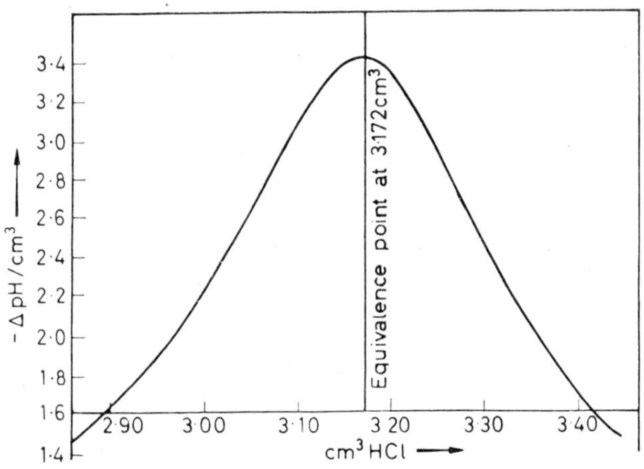

Figure 23. Plot of the first differential coefficient of the titration curve shown in Figure 22

The differential curve also has the distinct advantage of being unaffected by small temperature fluctuations or by electrode influences. As a first approximation, these effects only result in a vertical displacement of the curve of pH versus cm³ HCl, without changing its shape; these features therefore have negligible effect on the differential curve.

On the basis of the above theoretical study of the conditions for the titration of melamine, it is convenient to adopt the following procedure.

Taking 200 cm³ of a solution of 2 g/l. melamine, N/1 HCl is added until the equivalence point is approached, i.e. until a pH of 4·2 is reached. Measured amounts of

0·1 cm^3 of HCl are then added, the resulting pH value being read each time, and the titration taken to 0·3 cm^3 beyond the equivalence point. The differences between the pH values are plotted against the mean values of the corresponding amounts of acid added, using the same scales as shown for the differential curve in *Figure 23* which, for this purpose, may be drawn on translucent paper. The plotted points are now positioned so as to coincide as closely as possible with the superimposed translucent differential curve. The perpendicular line on the latter indicates the point of inflection and, therefore, the amount of HCl solution used in the titration. From this value the melamine content may be calculated (see p. 221).

*Exercise 141

Determine the isoelectric point for glycine, NH_2CH_2COOH, and for *o*-aminobenzoic acid (anthranilic acid) at 25 °C. The isoelectric point is defined as the pH at which an amphoteric electrolyte is dissociated into equal quantities of cations and anions. The dissociation constants are

for glycine $K_{ac} = 1{\cdot}67 \times 10^{-10}$ mole/l. $K_{\text{base}} = 2{\cdot}26 \times 10^{-12}$ mole/l.

for anthranilic acid $K_{ac} = 1{\cdot}5 \times 10^{-5}$ mole/l. $K_{\text{base}} = 1{\cdot}1 \times 10^{-12}$ mole/l.

The ionic product of water, $k_{H_2O} = 1{\cdot}1 \times 10^{-14}$ (mole/l.)^2.

Solution 141. The dissociation equations for an amphoteric electrolyte may be formally written as

$$\frac{[ROH^-][H^+]}{[RH \cdot OH]} = K_{ac} \qquad \frac{[HR^+][OH^-]}{[RH \cdot OH]} = K_{\text{base}} \qquad \ldots\ \text{(i) (ii)}$$

If $[OH^-]$ is substituted in (ii) by using the equation for the ionic product of water, $[OH^-] = k_{H_2O}/[H^+]$, and noting that at the isoelectric point, $[ROH^-] = [HR^+]$, dividing (i) by (ii) then gives:

$$\frac{[H^+_{\text{iso}}]^2}{k_{H_2O}} = \frac{K_{ac}}{K_{\text{base}}} \quad \text{or} \quad [H^+_{\text{iso}}] = \sqrt{\frac{K_{ac}\,k_{H_2O}}{K_{\text{base}}}} \qquad \ldots\ \text{(iii)}$$

$$pH_{(\text{iso})} = \tfrac{1}{2}(\log K_{\text{base}} - \log K_{ac} - \log k_{H_2O}) \qquad \ldots\ \text{(iv)}$$

Substituting the numerical values gives

for glycine

$$pH_{(\text{iso})} = \tfrac{1}{2}(0{\cdot}354 - 12 - 0{\cdot}223 + 10 - 0{\cdot}04 + 14) = 6{\cdot}05$$

for anthranilic acid

$$pH_{(\text{iso})} = \tfrac{1}{2}(0{\cdot}04 - 12 - 0{\cdot}176 + 5 - 0{\cdot}04 + 14) = 3{\cdot}41$$

Note. Textbooks show that at the isoelectric point the sum of the cations and anions of an amphoteric electrolyte has a minimum value, the concentration of the undissociated or neutral ampholyte being at a maximum. In the case of colloidal ampholytes, therefore, coagulation occurs at this point, especially when the substance is lyophobic; a knowledge of this behaviour is important in biology.

Exercise 142

Calculate the pH and degree of hydrolysis of a 0·1 N ammonium acetate solution (weak base + weak acid) at 25 °C. The activity should not be taken into account. The dissociation constant of NH_4OH is $K_{base} = 1{\cdot}79 \times 10^{-5}$ mole/l.; the value for acetic acid is $K_{ac} = 1{\cdot}76 \times 10^{-5}$ mole/l. The ionic product of water is $k_{H_2O} = 1{\cdot}1 \times 10^{-14}$ (mole/l.)^2. See the treatment in Exercise 139.

Solution 142. The hydrolysis equation is

$$NH_4^+ + \bar{A}^- + H_2O \rightleftharpoons NH_4OH + H\bar{A} \qquad K_{hydr} = \frac{[NH_4OH][H\bar{A}]}{[NH_4^+][\bar{A}^-]} \quad \ldots\ldots \quad (i)$$

where

$$K_{base} = \frac{[NH_4^+][OH^-]}{[NH_4OH]} \quad \ldots\ldots \quad (ii)$$

$$K_{ac} = \frac{[H^+][\bar{A}^-]}{[H\bar{A}]} \quad \ldots\ldots \quad (iii)$$

$$k_{H_2O} = [H^+][OH^-]$$

Dividing (iii) by the product of (i) and (ii):

$$K_{hydr} = \frac{k_{H_2O}}{K_{ac}K_{base}} \quad \ldots\ldots \quad (iv)$$

Let c be the concentration of salt taken and let x and y represent the concentrations of undissociated base and undissociated acid present at equilibrium. The concentrations of residual cations and residual anions will therefore be given by $(c - x)$ and $(c - y)$, respectively, and (i) will read

$$K_{hydr} = \frac{x\,y}{(c - x)(c - y)} \quad \ldots\ldots \quad (v)$$

The following relationships must also be true [see (vi) in Exercise 139; conservation of charge and neutrality]:

$$[B^+] + [H^+] = [Ac^-] + [OH^-] \qquad [H^+] - [OH^-] = [Ac^-] - [B^+] \quad \ldots\ldots \quad (vi)$$

and here especially

$$[H^+] - [OH^-] = [A^-] - [NH_4^+]$$

so that

$$[H^+] - [OH^-] = (c - y) - (c - x) = x - y \quad \ldots\ldots \quad (vii)$$

By substitution, (iii) gives

$$[H^+] = K_{ac}\frac{y}{c - y} \quad \ldots\ldots \quad (viii)$$

and (ii)

$$[OH^-] = K_{base} \times \frac{x}{c - x} \quad \ldots\ldots \quad (ix)$$

A second equation is thus obtained for x and y:

$$x - y = K_{ac} \times \frac{y}{c - y} - K_{base} \times \frac{x}{c - x} \quad \ldots\ldots \quad (x)$$

It is best to determine x and y graphically from (v) and (x), i.e. as the point of intersection of the two curves; alternatively one unknown can be eliminated (fourth degree equation).

In view of the degree of hydrolysis under consideration, the approximations at (v′) and (vi′) in Exercise 139 may be used to advantage, i.e. $c - x \approx c$, $c - y \approx c$ and $x \approx y$. From (v) or (viii) we then obtain

$$\frac{y^2}{c^2} = K_{\text{hydr}} \qquad y = [\text{HAc}] = c\sqrt{K_{\text{hydr}}} = c\sqrt{\frac{k_{\text{H}_2\text{O}}}{K_{ac}K_{\text{base}}}} \qquad \ldots\ (\text{xi})$$

$$[\text{H}^+] = \frac{y}{c} \times K_{ac} = \sqrt{\frac{K_{ac}k_{\text{H}_2\text{O}}}{K_{\text{base}}}} \qquad \ldots\ (\text{xii})$$

$$\text{pH} = -\log[\text{H}^+] = \tfrac{1}{2}(\log K_{\text{base}} - \log K_{ac} - \log k_{\text{H}_2\text{O}}) \qquad \ldots\ (\text{xiii})$$

The degree of hydrolysis

$$\gamma = \frac{[\text{HAc}]}{c} = \frac{[\text{BOH}]}{c} = \frac{y}{c} = \sqrt{\frac{k_{\text{H}_2\text{O}}}{K_{ac}K_{\text{base}}}} = \sqrt{K_{\text{hydr}}} \qquad \ldots\ (\text{xiv})$$

Substituting the numerical values gives an expression independent of the concentration, provided the dilution is not too great (limit for the approximation), and

$$\text{pH} = \tfrac{1}{2}(\log 1{\cdot}79 \times 10^{-5} - \log 1{\cdot}76 \times 10^{-5} - \log 1{\cdot}1 \times 10^{-14}) = 6{\cdot}98$$

$$\gamma = \sqrt{\frac{1{\cdot}1 \times 10^{-14}}{1{\cdot}76 \times 10^{-5} \times 1{\cdot}79 \times 10^{-5}}} = 0{\cdot}59 \times 10^{-2}$$

Note. One recognizes a similarity between (xii) above and (iii) in Exercise 141 (isoelectric point), because of the similarity of the treatment. Taking activity into account in the degree of hydrolysis necessitates multiplying (xiv) by $\sqrt{f_{\text{Ac}^-}f_{\text{B}^+}} = f^{\pm}_{\text{salt}}$ (mean activity coefficient of the salt). This is easily recognized in (xiv) if one remembers that calculation of the degree of hydrolysis is, by definition, based on concentrations, while in K_{ac}, K_{base} and $k_{\text{H}_2\text{O}}$ the activities are used. These quantities must accordingly again be reduced to concentrations:

$$y = \sqrt{\frac{\dfrac{k_{\text{H}_2\text{O}}}{f_{\text{H}^+}f_{\text{OH}^-}}}{\dfrac{K_{ac}}{f_{\text{H}^+}f_{ac^-}}\;\dfrac{K_{\text{base}}}{f_{\text{OH}^-}f_{\text{B}^+}}}} = \sqrt{\frac{k_{\text{H}_2\text{O}}}{K_{ac}K_{\text{base}}}}\sqrt{f_{ac^-}f_{\text{B}^+}}$$

In the case of the degree of hydrolysis of salts of weak bases with strong acids, or of weak acids with strong bases, the *quotient* of the activity coefficients is involved [see note (*c*) to Exercise 139]. In the present case, however, the *product* of the activity coefficients enters into the correction factor, and the latter is considerable. Thus, the mean activity coefficient of ammonium acetate, when $c = 0{\cdot}1$ mole/l., is $f_{\pm} = 0{\cdot}75$.

*Exercise 143

What is the concentration of a benzoic acid solution, such that its pH value is the same as that for a 0·03 M solution of butyric acid? The dissociation constant for butyric acid is $K_{\text{Bu}} = 1{\cdot}54 \times 10^{-5}$ mole/l. The figure for benzoic acid is $K_{\text{Be}} = 6{\cdot}45 \times 10^{-5}$ mole/l.

Solution 143. In view of the small values of the dissociation constants, it is possible to use the approximation in eqn. (219) for the dissociation equilibrium:

$$[\text{H}^+] = \sqrt{K_c c} \qquad \ldots\ (\text{i})$$

Thus

$$\sqrt{K_{\text{Bu}}c_{\text{Bu}}} = \sqrt{K_{\text{Be}}c_{\text{Be}}} \quad \text{or} \quad c_{\text{Be}} = c_{\text{Bu}} \times \frac{K_{\text{Bu}}}{K_{\text{Be}}} \qquad \ldots\ (\text{ii})$$

Substitution gives

$$c_{\mathrm{Be}} = 0{\cdot}03 \times \frac{1{\cdot}54 \times 10^{-5}}{6{\cdot}45 \times 10^{-5}} = 0{\cdot}0072\ \mathrm{mole/l.}$$

*Exercise 144

How much fully dissociated sodium propionate must be added to one litre of 0·1 M propionic acid in order to increase the pH value by 1·5 ? (Activity should not be taken into account.) The dissociation constant of propionic acid is $K_{\mathrm{Pr}} = 1{\cdot}32 \times 10^{-5}$ mole/l. See (vii) in Exercise 132.

Solution 144. Using the approximation in eqn. (219), we find that, for the pure propionic acid solution:

$$[\mathrm{H}^+] = \sqrt{K_{\mathrm{Pr}}\, c_{\mathrm{Pr}}} = \sqrt{1{\cdot}32 \times 10^{-5} \times 0{\cdot}1} = 1{\cdot}15 \times 10^{-3}\ \mathrm{mole/l.}$$

so that

$$\mathrm{pH} = -\log 1{\cdot}15 \times 10^{-3} = 2{\cdot}94$$

x[mole/l.] of C_2H_5COONa must now be added to attain a pH of 2·94 + 1·5 = 4·44. The buffer formula at (vii) in Exercise 132 gives

$$4{\cdot}44 = -\log 1{\cdot}32 \times 10^{-5} + \log \frac{x}{0{\cdot}1\ \mathrm{mole/l.}}$$

or

$$x = 0{\cdot}036\ \mathrm{mole/l.}$$

*Exercise 145

0·6 millimoles of morphine chloride are dissolved in 750 cm³ of water at 20 °C. The pH of this partially hydrolysed solution is found to be 5·54. What is the dissociation constant for the alkaloid base, morphine? The ionic product of water at 20 °C is $k_{\mathrm{H_2O}} = 0{\cdot}72 \times 10^{-14}$ (mole/l.)². See note (*a*) to Exercise 139.

Solution 145. The expression at (xv) in Exercise 139 is applicable in the case of the hydrolysis of a weak base with a strong acid. Using the given numerical values, we find

$$c = \frac{0{\cdot}6 \times 10^{-3}}{750 \times 10^{-3}}\ \mathrm{mole/l.}$$

$$5{\cdot}54 = \tfrac{1}{2}(\log K_{\mathrm{base}}/(\mathrm{mole\ l.^{-1}}) - \log 0{\cdot}72 \times 10^{-14} - \log 0{\cdot}6 + \log 750)$$

$$\log K_{\mathrm{base}}/(\mathrm{mole\ l.^{-1}}) = 0{\cdot}842 - 7 \qquad K_{\mathrm{base}} = 6{\cdot}95 \times 10^{-7}\ \mathrm{mole/l.}$$

Exercise 146

A solution, of 1 l. volume, contains approximately 0·05 mole HCl and 0·1 mole glyoxalic acid (dissociation constant = 5·10 × 10⁻⁷ mole/l.). Determine the exact content of both acids by titrating with 0·1 M NaOH. Two indicators, with two different transition ranges, will be required; the first for neutralization of the HCl (pH range of a solution of NaCl + weak acid) and the second for neutralization of the total acid.

For what pH ranges must the two indicators be suitable? See Exercise 140, note to Exercise 134 and Exercise 139.

Solution 146. For the purpose of solving the problem, it is convenient to draw an approximate representation of the titration curve (variation of pH with addition of alkali) in a manner similar to the treatment in Exercise 140 and *Figure 20.* As long as free HCl is present, this will be the determining factor as far as pH is concerned, and the weak glyoxalic acid will be practically undissociated (see note to Exercise 134). When $c_{HCl} \approx 0{\cdot}05$ mole/l., the pH at the start of the titration will be pH $= -\log[H^+]$ $\approx 1{\cdot}3$. After the HCl has been neutralized to NaCl, free glyoxalic acid will still remain and its hydrogen ion concentration may be approximately calculated (ignoring activity) by using eqn. (219):

$$[H^+] = \sqrt{K_c\, c}$$

As a result of the titration with 0·1 M NaOH the concentration of the glyoxalic acid will have fallen to about 0·1 mole in 1·5 l., i.e. to $c \approx 0{\cdot}067$ mole/l. Hence

$$[H^+] = \sqrt{5{\cdot}10 \times 10^{-7} \times 0{\cdot}067} = 1{\cdot}85 \times 10^{-4}\ \text{mole/l.} \qquad \text{pH} \approx 3{\cdot}73$$

Thus the pH at the equivalence point for neutralization of HCl will have risen – steeply towards the end – to pH $\approx 3{\cdot}73$. The continuation of the titration curve now lies in the buffer range of sodium glyoxalate + glyoxalic acid (with features similar to the curve for HCN + NaOH in *Figure 20*). After a further initial steep rise, the titration curve will level out at pH $= -\log K_c = 6{\cdot}29$ (point of inflection; titration of half the glyoxalic acid) and will then climb again more steeply to the equivalence point for NaCl + sodium glyoxalate, which is characterized by the pH for the hydrolysis of sodium glyoxalate.

The hydrolysis equation is given by (viii) in Exercise 139:

$$[H^+] = \sqrt{\frac{K_{ac}\, k_{H_2O}}{c}} \qquad \text{where } k_{H_2O} \approx 10^{-14} \quad (\text{mole/l.})^2$$

The concentration c of sodium glyoxalate at the equivalence point is determined from the fact that the 0·1 mole of glyoxalic acid originally dissolved in 1 l., will have yielded 0·1 mole of glyoxalate in 2·5 l. of solution, i.e. by titration of 0·05 moles of HCl and 0·1 mole of glyoxalic acid, a total of 0·15 mole of acid with 0·1 M NaOH. This means an addition of 1·5 l. of NaOH. Hence $c = 0{\cdot}1/2{\cdot}5 = 0{\cdot}04$ mole/l. It follows that

$$[H^+] = \sqrt{\frac{5{\cdot}10 \times 10^{-7} \times 10^{-14}}{0{\cdot}04}} = 3{\cdot}57 \times 10^{-10}\ \text{mole/l.} \qquad \text{pH} = 9{\cdot}45$$

The titration curve rises once more with continued addition of NaOH, steeply at first but then asymptotically approaching the pH value for pure 0·1 M NaOH (pH = 13).

These considerations, in connection with similar problems in analytical chemistry, permit one to deduce and sketch the shape of the titration curve. The most important feature is the estimation of pH at both equivalence points, i.e. the determination of the pH of the free weak acid and of the hydrolysed sodium salt of the weak acid.

It will be easily seen that the transition range for the first indicator, for the estimation of the HCl, must be pH = 3 to 4·5 (methyl orange); the range for the second indicator, for estimation of the total acid, must be pH = 8·5 to 10·5 (phenolphthalein).

*Exercise 147

How many cubic centimetres of N/10 hydrochloric acid must be added to 25 cm³ of N/5 ammonia solution in order to (*a*) turn phenolphthalein colourless and (*b*) turn methyl orange red? The dissociation constant for NH_4OH at 25 °C is $K_{base} = 1{\cdot}79 \times 10^{-5}$ mole/l. and the ionic product of water is $k_{H_2O} = 1{\cdot}1 \times 10^{-14}$ (mole/l.)². The transition points for phenolphthalein and methyl orange are pH = 9 and pH = 4, respectively. See note to Exercise 133, especially (v); also (iv) in Exercise 140.

Solution 147. The problem concerns the titration equation for a weak base with a strong acid so that, from eqn. (v) in Exercise 133:

$$\text{pH} = \log K_{base} - \log k_{H_2O} + \log \frac{[\text{alk}] - [\text{Ac}]}{[\text{Ac}]} \quad ([\text{salt}] = 0) \quad \ldots . \quad \text{(i)}$$

Substituting the numerical values gives for

$$(a) \qquad 9 = \log 1{\cdot}79 \times 10^{-5} - \log 1{\cdot}1 \times 10^{-14} + \log \frac{25 \times 2 - x}{x} \quad \ldots . \quad \text{(ii)}$$

where x = cm³ of N/10 HCl.
It follows from (ii) that

$$\log \frac{50 - x}{x} = 9 - 0{\cdot}253 + 5 + 0{\cdot}041 - 14 = 0{\cdot}788 - 1$$

$$\frac{50 - x}{x} = 0{\cdot}614$$

$$x = 31 \text{ cm}^3 \text{ N/10 HCl}$$

$$(b) \qquad \log \frac{50 - x}{x} = 4 - 0{\cdot}253 + 5 + 0{\cdot}041 - 14 = 0{\cdot}788 - 6$$

$$x = 50 \text{ cm}^3 \text{ N/10 HCl}$$

The correct indicator for the titration is, therefore, methyl orange; see also note to Exercise 140 (Ostwald's rule) and *Figure 20*.

13

ELECTROMOTIVE FORCE

GALVANIC CELLS. REDOX ELECTRODES. DECOMPOSITION VOLTAGE, POLARIZATION, POLAROGRAPHY. BATTERIES, OVERVOLTAGE. DIFFUSION POTENTIAL, MEMBRANE POTENTIAL

DEFINITIONS and fundamental laws are as follows:

(1) F = 1 faraday = 96495·1 coulomb/gramme equivalent = Faraday's constant, see eqn. (226)

R = gas constant = 8·31439 joule/(deg. mole)

$$\frac{R}{F} = \frac{8{\cdot}31439}{96\,495{\cdot}1} = 0{\cdot}86164 \times 10^{-4} \text{ volt/deg.}$$

$$\frac{R}{F}\ln x = 2{\cdot}3026 \times 0{\cdot}86164 \times 10^{-4} \log x = 1{\cdot}9840 \times 10^{-4} \log x \text{ (volt/deg.)} \quad \ldots\ldots (237)$$

$$\frac{RT}{F}\ln x = 0{\cdot}05776 \log x \text{ (volt) at 18 °C}, \quad \frac{RT}{F}\ln x = 0{\cdot}05816 \log x \text{ (volt) at 20 °C}$$

$$= 0{\cdot}05915 \log x \text{ (volt) at 25 °C}, \quad = 0{\cdot}06153 \log x \text{ (volt) at 37 °C}.$$

(2) If the reactions (cell reaction) (*a*) $Zn + Cu^{2+} \rightarrow Zn^{2+} + Cu$ and (*b*) $H_2 + Cl_2 \rightarrow 2H^+ + 2Cl^-$ take place in a galvanic cell (galvanic element) at different locations (electrodes), the process will be expressed in the following manner:

left (1)	I	II	III	IV	I′	*right* (r)
(*a*) Anode with oxidation; emission of electrons, i.e. reducing agent or electron donor; reduction stage	Zn/	Zn^{2+}//	Cu^{2+}/	Cu/	Zn	Cathode with reduction; take-up of electrons, i.e. oxidizing agent or electron acceptor; oxidation stage
(*b*) Anode with oxidation	Pt(H_2)/	HCl/			(Cl_2)Pt	Cathode with reduction

The solidus signs indicate phase boundaries.

In this symbolic representation, the sequence of the phases is so arranged that when the course of the reaction is spontaneous in the given direction (from left to right), the positive charge within the cell is transported from left to right.

(3) The (internal) potential difference $(I'_\varphi - I_\varphi)$ existing between the electrodes, when the flow of current is interrupted, is the driving force of the current and is called the electromotive force (e.m.f.), E, of the cell.

E is positive if the above sequence is observed. Negative values of E signify that positive charges are transported within the cell from right to left in the phase sequence taken and the reaction runs spontaneously from right to left. .... (238)

(Reversible) cell potential U is defined by $(I_\varphi - I'_\varphi) = -E$.

(4) The e.m.f., or cell potential, is the sum of the galvanic potentials at the phase boundaries, including the diffusion potential at the phase boundary between two liquids in contact with each other. Galvanic voltage is understood to be potential difference between two phases and cannot, in general, be measured. In this context, it is important that poles (end phases) should be of the same metal, since the galvanic potential between two metals [Cu/Zn at example (*a*) above] cannot be ignored. It is usual, however, to omit this last phase boundary from the symbolic representation: it is automatically included in the measured value of E.

The following relations are valid:

$$(-\Delta G) = n_e F E = n_e \times 96495{\cdot}1 \times E \text{ [joule, watt-seconds per mole]}$$
$$= n_e \times 23055 \times E \text{ (cal/mole) (1 J = 0·23892 cal)} \quad \text{.... (238a)}$$

$$(-\Delta G_0) = n_e F E_0$$

$+\Delta G$ = increase in free enthalpy, per mole of reactants, for a chemical reaction at constant pressure = maximum useful work or reaction work per mole converted

$(-\Delta G)$ = chemical affinity of the cell reaction, see eqn. (186)

n_e = number of faradays transported per mole of reactant converted; cell reaction charge number $n_e \equiv \nu_+ z_+ = \nu_- |z_-|$ for a single electrolyte = electrochemical valency of an electrolyte; see pp. 189 and 191.

E_h = e.m.f. relative to the standard hydrogen electrode (*N.B.* on the left) as reference electrode (25 °C, 1 atm. H_2 pressure, activity of $H^+ = a$ = unit of concentration)

E_{0h} = standard e.m.f. relative to the hydrogen electrode (*N.B.* on the left) as reference electrode under standard conditions (25 °C, 1 atm gas pressure, activity of the ions causing the potential $= a_1$ = unit of concentration) in the reference cell, e.g.

(*i*) $H_2 + Cu^{2+} \rightarrow 2H^+ + Cu$ or $Pt(H_2)/H^+//Cu^{2+}/Cu/Pt$

$$E_{0h}(Cu/Cu^{2+}) = +0{\cdot}34 \text{ V}$$

(*ii*) $H_2 + 2Cr^{3+} \rightarrow 2H^+ + 2Cr^{2+}$ or $Pt(H_2)/H^+//Cr^{2+}, Cr^{3+}/Pt$

$$E_{0h}\,(Pt/Cr^{2+}/Cr^{3+}) = -0{\cdot}41 \text{ V}$$

$$\left.\begin{array}{l} E = E_{hr} - E_{hl} = \text{e.m.f.} \\ E_0 = E_{0hr} - E_{0hl} = \text{standard e.m.f.} \end{array}\right\} \text{of a galvanic cell} \quad \text{....(238b)}$$

in which the electrode with the more positive value of E_h or E_{0h} is always the cathode, i.e. on the right, and that with the more negative value of E_h or E_{0h} is the anode, i.e. on the left.
Example: combining (i) and (ii) gives the galvanic cell

$$H_2 + Cu^{2+} \rightarrow 2H^+ + Cu \qquad E_{0hr} = +0{\cdot}34\ V$$

$$\text{minus}\ H_2 + 2Cr^{3+} \rightarrow 2H^+ + 2Cr^{2+} \qquad E_{0hl} = -0{\cdot}41\ V$$

$$Cu^{2+} - 2Cr^{3+} \rightarrow Cu - 2Cr^{2+}$$

i.e. $Cu^{2+} + 2Cr^{2+} \rightarrow Cu + 2Cr^{3+}$

or $Pt/Cr^{2+}, Cr^{3+}//Cu^{2+}/Cu/Pt$

$$E_{0hr} - E_{0hl} = 0{\cdot}34 - (-0{\cdot}41) = +0{\cdot}75\ V.$$

(5) Temperature dependence of the e.m.f.:

$$\frac{\partial(-\Delta G)}{\partial T} = n_e \times 23055 \frac{\partial E}{\partial T} = \Delta S \quad \Delta S = \text{reaction entropy (see pp. 168–169)} \quad \ldots. (239)$$

$$\Delta H = \Delta G + T\Delta S = T\Delta S - n_e \times 23055 E = n_e \times 23055 \left(T \frac{\partial E}{\partial T} - E\right) \quad \text{(cal/mole)} \quad \ldots. (240)$$

ΔH = reaction enthalpy, see eqn. (182)

(6) Dependence of e.m.f. on concentration and pressure:

c_r = concentration of the ions determining the potential in the right-hand side 'half-cell', with the solution (r) and the electrode (r)

c_l = concentration of the ions determining the potential in the left-hand side 'half-cell', with the solution (l) and the electrode (l)

$$E = \frac{RT}{zF} \ln \frac{c_r}{c_l} = \frac{RT}{zF} \ln \frac{x_r}{x_l} \quad \text{for dilute solutions,}$$

$$= \frac{RT}{zF} \ln \frac{a_r}{a_l} \quad \text{using activities for concentrated solutions} \quad \ldots. (241)$$

$-\frac{RT}{zF} \ln \frac{P_r}{P_l}$ for gas electrodes having the gas pressures or fugacities (see p. 121) P_r and P_l and the electrodes (r) and (l) in contact with the gas*.

(7) The charge sign should be inserted for the ion charge number, z, in eqn. (241). In gas reactions, z with its sign indicates the number of ions formed by the gas.

In accordance with the definitions at (238) and (238 b), one has that $c_r > c_l$ or $a_r > a_l$ [in eqn. (241)] when positive ions determine the potential. When negative ions determine the potential, then $c_r < c_l$ or $a_r < a_l$; likewise $P_r < P_l$ for gases which form positive ions and $P_r > P_l$ for those which form negative ions.

(8) General law for the dependence of the e.m.f. on concentration and pressure in the case of a current-producing chemical reaction

$$\nu_A A + \nu_B B + \cdots \rightleftarrows \nu_E E + \nu_F F + \cdots$$

* To avoid confusion with pH = $-\log[H^+]$, the gas pressure is here denoted by P.

taking place between the electrodes (r) and (1) [right and left, see (238)] and when the reaction proceeds in the direction of the arrow:

$$E = E_{hr} - E_{hl} = E_{0hr} - E_{0hl} - \frac{RT}{n_e F} \ln \frac{[E]^{\nu_E}[F]^{\nu_F}\ldots}{[A]^{\nu_A}[B]^{\nu_B}\ldots} \quad \ldots. (242)$$

$$E_0 = E_{0hr} - E_{0hl} = \frac{RT}{n_e F} \ln\{K\} \quad \text{[standard e.m.f. for the cell, see (238 b)]} \quad \ldots. (243)$$

If only one electrolyte takes part in the reaction and dissociates into $\nu_+ + \nu_- = \nu$ ions, one has the following relations when $P = 1$ atm (e.g. for the reaction $Zn + Cl_2 = Zn^{2+} + 2Cl^-$):

$$E = E_0 - \frac{RT}{n_e F} \ln \left[a_+^{\nu_+} a_-^{\nu_-}\right] = E_0 - \frac{\nu RT}{n_e F} \ln a_\pm \quad \text{[see eqn. (232)]} \quad \ldots (243a)$$

and, where $a_+ = f_+ c_+$, $a_- = f_- c_-$, $c_+ = \nu_+ c_{mol}$ $c_- = \nu_- c_{mol}$, $f_\pm^\nu = f_+^{\nu_+} f_-^{\nu_-}$

[see eqns. (230), (234a), (232)]

$$E = E_0 - \frac{\nu RT}{n_e F} \ln \left[\left(\nu_+^{\nu_+} \nu_-^{\nu_-}\right)^{1/\nu} c_{mol} f_\pm\right] \quad \ldots (243b)$$

Two cells of this type, connected in opposition but having different activities ($a_{\pm l}$ and $a_{\pm r}$) for solutions of the same electrolyte, comprise a concentration cell with two sets of potential-forming ions (e.g. $Zn/ZnCl_2$, $a_{\pm l}/(Cl_2)/Pt/ZnCl_2$, $a_\pm/Zn/Pt$). The following relation holds:

$$E = \frac{\nu RT}{n_e F} \ln \frac{a_{\pm r}}{a_{\pm l}} \quad \ldots (243c)$$

[A], [B], ···, [E], [F], ··· are the concentrations, activities, mole fractions or pressures of the initial and final products (molecules or ions) according to the definition ([A], [B], [E], [F] = 1 as standard) of the standard reference e.m.f.'s, E_{0hr} and E_{0hl}, or the standard e.m.f., $E_0 = E_{0hr} - E_{0hl}$, or of the equilibrium constants K (K_p, $K_{c(soln)}$, K_a, K_x): see eqns. (151), (154), (155), (190), (193), (194), (231). The right-hand side of the reaction equation features in the numerator.

Breakdown of the total e.m.f., $E = E_{hr} - E_{hl}$, according to eqn. (238b), into the relative e.m.f.'s of the 'half-cells', E_{hr} and E_{hl} [against the standard hydrogen electrode ($p_{H_2} = 1$ atm, activity $a_{H^+} = 1$)]; redox electrodes: oxidized stage + $H_2 \rightleftarrows$ reduced stage or $Pt/(H_2)/HCl$, oxidized stage, reduced stage/Pt. 'half-cell': E_h; reduced stage/oxidized stage + n_e electrons against standard H_2 reference electrode,

$$E_h = E_{0h} - \frac{RT}{n_e F} \ln \frac{\text{product of the concentrations in the reduced stage}}{\text{product of the concentrations in the oxidized stage}}$$

or

$$E_h = E_{0h} + \frac{RT}{n_e F} \ln \frac{\Pi\,(\text{oxidized stage})}{\Pi\,(\text{reduced stage})} \quad \ldots. (244)$$

Metal electrodes, H_2 and other gas electrodes, redox electrodes, the quinhydrone electrode and amalgam electrodes belong to this class.

For the hydrogen electrode (against the standard H_2 reference electrode):

$$2H^+ + 2\,\text{electrons} = H_2 \quad (H_2/2H^+ + 2\,\text{electrons})$$

and using the gas pressure or the fugacity P_{H_2} (atm) and the concentration or the activity $[H^+]$ (see p. 121), we find, using eqn. (244) or (241):

$$E_h = +\frac{RT}{2F}\ln\frac{[H^+]^2}{P_{H_2}} = +\frac{RT}{F}\ln\frac{[H^+]}{\sqrt{P_{H_2}}} \quad \ldots . (245)$$

For 18 °C and for 30 °C, one has:

$$E_h\,(18°) = -0{\cdot}0578\,\text{pH} - 0{\cdot}0289\log P_{H_2} = -0{\cdot}0578\,\text{pH} + 0{\cdot}0289\,\text{rH} \quad \ldots . (246)$$

$$E_h\,(30°) = -0{\cdot}0601\,\text{pH} - 0{\cdot}0301\log P_{H_2} = -0{\cdot}0601\,\text{pH} + 0{\cdot}0301\,\text{rH} \quad \ldots . (247)$$

if one puts $\text{rH} = -\log P_{H_2}$, in an analogous manner to $\text{pH} = -\log[H^+]$ [see eqn. (236)]. Accordingly,

$$\left.\begin{aligned} \text{rH} &= \frac{E_h + 0{\cdot}0578\,\text{pH}}{0{\cdot}0289} \quad \text{at } 18\,°\text{C} \\ \text{rH} &= \frac{E_h + 0{\cdot}0601\,\text{pH}}{0{\cdot}0301} \quad \text{at } 30\,°\text{C} \end{aligned}\right\} \quad \ldots (248)$$

For the oxygen electrode (against the standard H_2 reference electrode) it is found that:

(*a*) using the OH^- concentration, $4\,OH^-/O_2 + 2\,H_2O + 4$ electrons:

$$O_2 + 2\,H_2O + 4\,\text{electrons} = 4\,OH^-$$

$$E_{h(O_2,\,OH^-)} = E_{0h(O_2,\,OH^-)} + \frac{RT}{4F}\ln\frac{P_{O_2}}{[OH^-]^4} = E_{0h(O_2,\,OH^-)} - \frac{RT}{F}\ln\frac{[OH^-]}{\sqrt[4]{P_{O_2}}} \quad \ldots . (249)$$

$$E_{0h(O_2,\,OH^-)} = +0{\cdot}401\ \text{V at room temperature} \quad \ldots . (250)$$

(*b*) using the H^+ concentration, $2\,H_2O/O_2 + 4\,H^+ + 4$ electrons:

$$O_2 + 4\,H^+ + 4\,\text{electrons} = 2\,H_2O$$

$$E_{h(O_2,\,H^+)} = E_{oh(O_2,\,H^+)} + \frac{RT}{4F}\ln P_{O_2}[H^+]^4 \quad \ldots . (251)$$

$$E_{0h(O_2,\,H^+)} = +1{\cdot}229\ \text{V at room temperature} \quad \ldots . (252)$$

At 30 °C:

$$\begin{aligned} E_{h(O_2,\,H^+)} &= E_{0h(O_2,\,H^+)} + 0{\cdot}0150\log P_{O_2} - 0{\cdot}0601\,\text{pH} \\ &= +1{\cdot}229 - 0{\cdot}0150\,\text{rO} - 0{\cdot}0601\,\text{pH} \end{aligned} \quad \ldots . (253)$$

if one puts $\text{rO} = -\log P_{O_2}$ .... (254)

If a redox cell has an e.m.f. of $E_{h\,(\text{redox})}$, it is equivalent to a hydrogen electrode [eqns. (245)–(247)] and an oxygen electrode [eqns. (251), (253)] of the same e.m.f. Thus, at 30 °C [by equating eqns. (247) and (253)], we obtain

$$0{\cdot}0301\,\text{rH} = 1{\cdot}229 - 0{\cdot}0150\,\text{rO} \quad \ldots . (255)$$

for equal e.m.f. values, i.e. in the same solution.

By analogy with the neutral point for acid–base solutions, one may define the 'neutral point' of a redox cell as being that at which the oxygen pressure is equal to the hydrogen pressure, i.e. when rH = rO, or, from eqn. (255), 0·0301 rH = 1·229 − 0·0150 rO at 30 °C.

At 30 °C, therefore, the neutral point of the redox cell will be given by

$$\mathrm{rH}_{(\text{neut. pt.})} = \frac{1{\cdot}229}{0{\cdot}0150 + 0{\cdot}0301} = 27{\cdot}3 \qquad \ldots . (256)$$

The corresponding pH value at 30 °C will be, from eqns. (248) and (256)

$$\mathrm{pH}_{(\text{neut. pt.})} = 13{\cdot}65 - \frac{E_{\mathrm{h\,(redox)}}}{0{\cdot}0601} \qquad \ldots . (257)$$

Electrodes of the second type: the metal electrode is covered with a sparingly soluble salt of the metal. The e.m.f. is determined by the concentration of anions and, by using the solubility product, may be most simply referred back to the standard reference e.m.f., $E_{0\mathrm{h}}$:

$Ag + Cl^- = AgCl$ + 1 electron; this may be transcribed, since AgCl exists in equilibrium with $Ag_0^+ + Cl_0^-$ (suggested by the suffix 0):

$Ag + Cl^- = Ag_0^+ + Cl_0^-$ + 1 electron, as potential-forming electrode against the standard hydrogen electrode: reduced stage/oxidized stage + 1 electron.
So that, going back to eqn. (244):

$$\left.\begin{aligned} E_{\mathrm{h}} &= E_{0\mathrm{h}(\mathrm{Ag/Ag^+})} + \frac{RT}{1F}\ln\frac{[\mathrm{Ag_0^+}][\mathrm{Cl_0^-}]}{[\mathrm{Cl^-}]} \\ &= E_{0\mathrm{h}(\mathrm{Ag/Ag^+})} + \frac{RT}{1F}\ln K_s + \frac{RT}{1F}\ln\frac{1}{[\mathrm{Cl^-}]} \\ &\qquad \text{where } K_s = [\mathrm{Ag_0^+}][\mathrm{Cl_0^-}] = \text{solubility product; see eqn. (229)} \\ &= E'_{0\mathrm{h}(\mathrm{Ag})} - \frac{RT}{1F}\ln[\mathrm{Cl^-}] \\ &\qquad \text{where } E'_{0\mathrm{h}(\mathrm{Ag})} = E_{0\mathrm{h}(\mathrm{Ag/Ag^+})} + \frac{RT}{F}\ln K_s \end{aligned}\right\} \quad \ldots (258)$$

The calomel and antimony electrodes come into this class.

Luther's law for metals having different valency states:

Metal/Me^{n+} + n electrons: standard reference e.m.f. $E_{0\mathrm{h}(n)}$
Metal/Me^{m+} + m electrons: standard reference e.m.f. $E_{0\mathrm{h}(m)}$
Me^{n+}/Me^{m+} + $m - n$ electrons: standard reference e.m.f. $E_{0\mathrm{h}(m,\,n)}$

$$(m - n)\,E_{0\mathrm{h}(m,\,n)} = m\,E_{0\mathrm{h}(m)} - n\,E_{0\mathrm{h}(n)} \qquad \ldots . (259)$$

Diffusion potential (liquid junction potential):

(a) the same electrolyte at different concentrations (1,1-valent or 2,2-valent):

c_{r}, c_{l} are the concentrations (activities a_+) round the electrodes (r) and (l), n_{K} and n_{A} are the transport numbers of the cations and anions:

$$E = -\frac{n_{\mathrm{K}} - n_{\mathrm{A}}}{n_{\mathrm{K}} + n_{\mathrm{A}}}\,\frac{RT}{|z|F}\ln\frac{c_{\mathrm{r}}}{c_{\mathrm{l}}} \qquad \ldots . (260)$$

The more concentrated solution becomes negatively charged if the speed of the cation is greater than that of the anion. It is, of course, possible to use the ionic equivalent conductivities $\Lambda_{\mathrm{K(eq)}}$, $\Lambda_{\mathrm{A(eq)}}$ or the ionic mobilities u_{K}, u_{A} in place of the transport numbers; see eqns. (220), (222) and (223).

(*b*) different electrolytes at the same concentration (both 1,1-valent or 2,2-valent):

$$E = -\frac{RT}{|z|F}\ln\frac{n_{K1}+n_{A2}}{n_{K2}+n_{A1}} \quad \text{(approximation equation)} \qquad \ldots (260\text{a})$$

Membrane potential (Donnan potential):

In two cells (I, II) separated by a membrane, which is impermeable to one ion present only in cell I (e.g. a colloidal ion) but is permeable to the other ions, an equilibrium will be established (Donnan equilibrium) for any chosen pair of diffusing ions, e.g. for NaCl

$$[Na_I^+][Cl_I^-] = [Na_{II}^+][Cl_{II}^-] \quad \text{or} \quad \frac{[Na_{II}^+]}{[Na_I^+]} = \frac{[Cl_I^-]}{[Cl_{II}^-]} = r$$

for $CaCl_2$

$$[Ca_I^{2+}][Cl_I^-]^2 = [Ca_{II}^{2+}][Cl_{II}^-]^2 \quad \text{or} \quad \frac{[Ca_{II}^{2+}]^{1/2}}{[Ca_I^{2+}]^{1/2}} = \frac{[Cl_I^-]}{[Cl_{II}^-]} = r$$

$$\frac{\left[Cat_{i\,II}^{p_i+}\right]^{1/p_i}}{\left[Cat_{i\,I}^{p_i+}\right]^{1/p_i}} = \frac{\left[An_{i\,I}^{q_i-}\right]^{1/q_i}}{\left[An_{i\,II}^{q_i-}\right]^{1/q_i}} = r \qquad \ldots (261)$$

Membrane potential (Donnan potential):

$$E_{12} = \frac{RT}{F}\ln r \qquad \ldots (262)$$

p_i or q_i = charge number of the chosen cation, $Cat_i^{p_i+}$, or chosen anion, $An_i^{q_i-}$; r is a constant which may be calculated from eqn. (261), e.g. in a simple case:

(*a*) Cell I, initial concentration of RCl $= c_1$ (R^+ is a colloidal ion)
Cell II, initial concentration of NaCl $= c_2$

$$r = \frac{c_1 + c_2}{c_2} \qquad \ldots (263)$$

(*b*) Cell I, initial concentration of NaR $= c_1$ (R^- is a colloidal ion)
Cell II, initial concentration of NaCl $= c_2$

$$r = \frac{c_2}{c_1 + c_2} \qquad \ldots (264)$$

The phase boundary potential between the cells agrees in sign with that of the colloidal ion in cell I.

In the case of the glass electrode, the potential arises from the exchange of Na^+ ions from the glass against H^+ ions from the solution, taking place on both sides of the glass membrane. One has the relationship

$$E_{Ph\,I/II} = \frac{RT}{F}\ln\frac{[H_{II}^+]}{[H_I^+]} \qquad \ldots (265)$$

Diffusion Laws—Fick's first law:

$$dn = -Dq\frac{\partial c}{\partial x}dt \quad \text{[see also eqn. (54), p. 31]} \qquad \ldots (266)$$

to be used in the stationary state, i.e. when the concentration gradient is independent of time;

D = diffusion coefficient .... (266a)

$D_{\text{ion}} = \frac{u\,RT}{z\,F}\left[\frac{\text{cm}^2}{\text{sec}}\right]$ (valid when the diffusion of an ion can take place virtually unhindered by the oppositely charged accompanying ion; e.g. H^+ when a little HCl is present in excess KCl)

n = quantity of substance in moles or equivs.

q = cross-section, in cm^2

$\frac{\partial c}{\partial x}$ = concentration gradient (c in mole/cm^3 or equiv./cm^3)

t = time, in seconds

R = gas constant = 8·31439 J/(deg. mole)

u = ionic mobility in a field of 1 volt/cm $\left(\frac{\text{cm}}{\text{sec}}\bigg/\frac{\text{V}}{\text{cm}}\right) = \frac{\Lambda_{\text{eq}}}{F}$ [see eqn. (222)]

z = ionic charge number

F = 1 faraday = 96495·1 coulomb/gramme equiv.

Fick's second law:

$$\left(\frac{\partial c}{\partial t}\right)_x = D\left(\frac{\partial^2 c}{\partial x^2}\right)_t \quad \text{.... (267)}$$

(for the non-stationary state).

Current strength for concentration polarization:

$$I = zF\frac{\mathrm{d}n}{\mathrm{d}t} = zF\,D\,q\,\frac{c_0 - c_K}{\delta} = I_0\,\frac{c_0 - c_K}{c_0} \quad \text{.... (268)}$$

where the polarization voltage is

$$E_{\text{pol}} = \frac{RT}{zF}\ln\frac{c_0}{c_K} \quad \text{.... (269)}$$

δ = thickness of the boundary layer on the polarized electrode

c_K = concentration at the electrode (*N.B.* mole/cm^3)

c_0 = concentration in the solution (*N.B.* mole/cm^3)

I_0 = current strength at boundary when $c_K \to 0$

Eliminating c_K from eqns. (268)–(269) gives the polarization voltage curve, where the limiting current strength I_0 corresponds to $c_K \to 0$. .... (270)

*Exercise 148

Calculate the electromotive force E of the galvanic element $Ni/Ni(NO_3)_2$ (c_l = 0·005 mole/l.)//$AgNO_3$ (c_r = 0·1 mole/l.)/Ag/Ni at 25 °C. The activity coefficient $f_{Ni^{2+}}$ of the Ni ions is 0·57 in the given solution, the value for the Ag^+ ions being f_{Ag^+} = 0·717; the diffusion potential should be ignored. Standard reference e.m.f. of Ni/Ni^{2+} is $E_{0\,hl}$ = − 0·23 V; that for Ag/Ag^+ is $E_{0\,hr}$ = + 0·799 V.

Solution 148. The simplest procedure is to take the difference between the two reference e.m.f.'s, E_{hr} and E_{hl}, in accordance with eqns. (244) and (238b)

$$E = E_{0\,hr} + \frac{RT}{F} \ln c_r f_{Ag^+} - \left(E_{0\,hl} + \frac{RT}{2F} \ln c_l f_{Ni^{2+}}\right) \quad \ldots \quad (i)$$

Substituting the numerical values, taking eqn. (237) into account, gives

$$E = 0{\cdot}799 + 0{\cdot}0591 \log (0{\cdot}1 \times 0{\cdot}717) - (-0{\cdot}23) - \frac{0{\cdot}0591}{2} \log (0{\cdot}005 \times 0{\cdot}57)$$

$E = +1{\cdot}037$ V, i.e. in the cell the positive charge moves spontaneously from left to right; see (238).

Note. The cell may also be considered as a chemical reaction and the calculation made by using eqn. (242); e.g.

$$Ni + 2Ag^+ \rightleftarrows 2Ag + Ni^{2+} \quad \ldots \quad (ii)$$

If the equation is written in this form, $n_e = 2$ and Ag^+ is reduced to Ag; the Ag^+/Ag electrode is therefore the initial oxidized stage (oxidizing agent; electron acceptor) and becomes the cathode of the cell. It is also electrode (r). From eqn. (242) one has

$$E = E_{0\,(Ag/Ag^+)} - E_{0\,(Ni/Ni^{2+})} + \frac{RT}{2F} \ln \frac{(a_{Ag^+})^2}{a_{Ni^{2+}}} \quad \ldots \quad (iii)$$

$$= E_{0\,(Ag/Ag^+)} - E_{0\,(Ni/Ni^{2+})} + \frac{RT}{F} \ln (cf)_{Ag^+} - \frac{RT}{2F} \ln (cf)_{Ni^{2+}} \quad \ldots \quad (iv)$$

(iv) corresponds to E at (i) above. It may be pointed out (see relevant textbooks) that single ion activities are not definable by thermodynamics and cannot be calculated without additional non-thermodynamic assumptions. They are usually replaced, in the case of 1,1-valent electrolytes, by the mean ionic activity $a_\pm$ of the electrolyte in the solution in question; see eqn. (232). Individual ion activities and activity coefficients are generally calculated by means of eqn. (235).

It is desirable—as a supplementary procedure to e.m.f. calculations—to clarify the significance of the individual stages, and to examine the influences of concentration in the numerator and denominator, by visualizing the electrochemical process. For example, in the above case, Ag is more noble than Ni, i.e. the nickel electrode must be negative for the standard e.m.f., $E_0 = E_{0\,h\,(Ag)} - E_{0\,h\,(Ni)}$; Ni^{2+} ions have the tendency to pass into solution and to migrate to the Ag electrode. Ag^+ ions are deposited on the Ag electrode. An increase in the concentration of Ni^{2+} ions must lead to a greater tendency towards their deposition on the Ni, whereby the latter is positively charged, and to a counteraction of the initial e.m.f.; i.e. $c_{Ni^{2+}}$ at (i) must be in the denominator or $\ln c_{Ni^{2+}}$ must be in the negative term; for the same reason c_{Ag^+} must be in the numerator at (i) or $\ln c_{Ag^+}$ in the positive term.

*Exercise 149

The e.m.f. of the galvanic cell $Ag/AgNO_3$ ($c_l = 0{\cdot}001$ mole/l.)// saturated NH_4NO_3 solution//$AgNO_3$ ($c_r = 0{\cdot}01$ mole/l.)/Ag is $E = 0{\cdot}0572$ V at 25 °C. The activity coefficient of Ag^+ (0·001 mole/l.) is $f_{l\,(Ag^+)} = 0{\cdot}965$. The diffusion potential is largely excluded by interposing saturated NH_4NO_3 solution. Calculate the activity coefficient $f_{r\,(Ag^+)}$ of the Ag ions in the more concentrated solution.

Solution 149. Equation (241) is applicable to this case, which deals with a pure concentration cell. We find that

$$E = \frac{RT}{zF} \ln \frac{c_r f_{r\,(Ag)^+}}{c_l f_{l\,(Ag)^+}} \quad \ldots \quad (i)$$

Substituting the numerical values, taking eqn. (237) into account, and where $z = +1$ (Ag^+ monovalent):

$$0{\cdot}0572 = 0{\cdot}0591 \log \frac{0{\cdot}01 \times f_{r(Ag^+)}}{0{\cdot}001 \times 0{\cdot}965} \quad \ldots\ldots \quad \text{(ii)}$$

$$f_{r(Ag^+)} = 0{\cdot}896$$

Note. In this measurement also, one should bear in mind the uncertain nature of individual ion activity coefficients; see note to Exercise 148. The method for reducing the diffusion potential by interposing a 'salt bridge' of saturated KCl or NH_4NO_3 solution is dealt with in textbooks on the subject. It should be pointed out, however—as accurate calculation shows—that complete elimination of the diffusion potential is not possible by this method. The separate calculation of diffusion and electrode potentials presupposes a knowledge of single ion activity coefficients. As opposed to this, only the uniquely and thermodynamically defined mean activity coefficients of the electrolyte feature in the formulae for concentration cells with transport (sum of the electrode and diffusion potentials).

*Exercise 150

(*a*) Determine electrochemically the affinity $-\Delta G_0$ (in cal) of the reaction $2\,Ag + Cl_2\,(1\text{ atm}) \rightleftarrows 2\,AgCl_{\text{solid}}$ at 25 °C. The standard reference e.m.f. of $2\,Cl^-/Cl_2$ is $E_{0\,hr} = 1{\cdot}358$ V; that of Ag/Ag^+ is $E_{0\,hl} = 0{\cdot}799$ V. The solubility of AgCl in H_2O at 25 °C is $1{\cdot}31 \times 10^{-5}$ mole/l. (*b*) By way of comparison calculate the affinity thermodynamically, using eqn. (182).

Heat of formation, $\Delta H^F_{0(AgCl)} = -30{\cdot}15$ kcal/mole; standard entropy of AgCl is

$$S_{0(AgCl)} = 23{\cdot}0 \text{ cal/(deg. mole)} \qquad S_{0(Ag)} = 10{\cdot}20 \text{ cal/(deg. mole)}$$

$$S_{0(Cl_2)} = 53{\cdot}31 \text{ cal/(deg. mole)}.$$

Solution 150. The desired reaction may be carried out reversibly and electrochemically by using the system

$$Ag/AgCl(Ag_0^+,\, Cl_0^-;\ \text{saturated solution})/(Cl_2)Pt/Ag$$

From eqn. (242): $n_e = 2$; electrode (r) is the Cl_2 electrode. From the data given, it follows that the solubility product [see eqn. (229)] of AgCl is $K_{s(AgCl)} = (1{\cdot}31 \times 10^{-5})^2 = 1{\cdot}72 \times 10^{-10}$ (mole/l.)^2.

Therefore

$$(a) \qquad E = E_{0\,hr} - E_{0\,hl} - \frac{RT}{2F} \ln \frac{([Ag_0^+][Cl_0^-])^2}{p_{Cl_2}} \quad \ldots\ldots \quad \text{(i)}$$

where $p_{Cl_2} = 1$ atm and $[Ag_0^+][Cl_0^-] = K_{s(AgCl)}$

$$E = E_{0\,hr} - E_{0\,hl} - \frac{RT}{F} \ln K_{s(AgCl)} = 1{\cdot}358 - 0{\cdot}799 - 0{\cdot}0591 \log (1{\cdot}72 \times 10^{-10})$$

$$E = 1{\cdot}136 \text{ V} \quad \ldots\ldots \quad \text{(ii)}$$

From eqn. (238a):

$$-\Delta G_0 = 2 \times 23{,}055 \times 1{\cdot}136 = 52{\cdot}3 \text{ kcal/mole}$$

(*b*) Thermodynamically, from eqn. (182):

$$-\Delta G_0 = -\Delta H_0 + T\Delta S_0 = 2 \times 30{,}150 + 298\,(2 \times 23{\cdot}0 - 53{\cdot}31 - 2 \times 10{\cdot}20)$$

$$= +52{\cdot}05 \text{ kcal/mole}$$

*Exercise 151

Calculate the affinity of the reaction $4\,Ag + O_2 = 2\,Ag_2O$ (*a*) at 25 °C, $p_{O_2} = 1$ atm, (*b*) at 35 °C and $p_{O_2} = 12$ atm. For this small temperature difference, it is good enough to ascertain the temperature coefficient of the affinity at 25 °C by using the Gibbs–Helmholtz equation at (186a). The molar heat of formation is $\Delta H^F_{0\,(Ag_2O)} = -6{\cdot}95$ kcal/mole.

The e.m.f. of the detonating-gas cell $H_2/H_2O/O_2$ is known to be $E_{0h\,(O_2/H_2)} = +1{\cdot}229$ V, and that of the cell H_2/saturated solution of $Ag_2O(AgOH)/Ag$ is $E_{0h\,(Ag,\,AgOH)} = +1{\cdot}18$ V.

Solution 151. (*a*) the reaction $4\,Ag + O_2 = 2\,Ag_2O$ may be built up from the reactions

$$4\,Ag + 2\,H_2O = 2\,Ag_2O + 2\,H_2 \quad \ldots\ldots \quad \text{(i)}$$

and

$$2\,H_2 + O_2 = 2\,H_2O \quad \ldots\ldots \quad \text{(ii)}$$

Addition gives

$$4\,Ag + O_2 = 2\,Ag_2O \quad \ldots\ldots \quad \text{(iii)}$$

Reaction (ii) is that for the detonating-gas cell: $n_e = 4$, $E_{0h\,(O_2/H_2)} = +1{\cdot}229$ V. The affinity is, from eqn. (238a): $-\Delta G_{0\,(ii)} = +4 \times 23{,}055 \times (+1{\cdot}229)$ cal/mole.

Reaction (i) is that of the second cell given, but in reverse, because the sign of the e.m.f., $+1{\cdot}18$ V, shows that [eqn. (238)] Ag should become positively charged, and H_2 negatively charged, during reaction; i.e. the Ag^+ ions in the solution are discharged onto the Ag, and H_2 goes into solution as $2\,H^+$. For reaction (i) one must therefore put $-E_{0h\,(Ag,\,AgOH)} = -1{\cdot}18$ V and $n_e = 4$; the affinity, $-\Delta G_{0\,(i)}$, is $+4 \times 23{,}055 \times (-1{\cdot}18)$ cal/mole. It follows that the affinity for the overall reaction (iii) is

$$-\Delta G_{0\,(iii)} = -\Delta G_{0\,(i)} - \Delta G_{0\,(ii)} = +4 \times 23{,}055\,(1{\cdot}229 - 1{\cdot}18) = +4{\cdot}51 \text{ kcal/mole} \quad \ldots\ldots \quad \text{(iv)}$$

(*b*) Equations (242) or (190) and (191) are used in order to take variation of pressure into account. It is found that

$$-\Delta G_{(iii)} = -\Delta G_{0\,(iii)} + RT \ln p_{O_2}/\text{atm} \quad \ldots\ldots \quad \text{(v)}$$

The temperature dependence is obtained from the Gibbs–Helmholtz equation (186a):

$$\frac{\partial(-\Delta G)}{\partial T} = \frac{-\Delta G + \Delta H}{T} = \frac{-\Delta G_{0\,(iii)} + 2\,\Delta H^F_{0\,(Ag_2O)}}{T} + R \ln p_{O_2}/\text{atm}$$

$$[R = 1{\cdot}987 \text{ cal/(deg. mole)}] \quad \ldots\ldots \quad \text{(vi)}$$

Substituting:

$$\frac{\partial(-\Delta G)}{\partial T} = \frac{+4510 - 2 \times 6950}{298} + 1{\cdot}987 \times 2{\cdot}303 \quad \log 12 = -31{\cdot}15 + 4{\cdot}94$$

$$= -26{\cdot}6 \text{ cal/(deg. mole)} \quad \ldots\ldots \quad \text{(vii)}$$

It follows that a value of -266 cal/mole is obtained for a temperature rise of 10 °C (to 35 °C) .... (viii)

Hence, from (iv), (v) and (viii), for 35 °C and 12 atm [log 12 = 1·079], one has

$$-\Delta G_{(iii)} = +4510 + 1{\cdot}987 \times 2{\cdot}303 \times 1{\cdot}079 \times 298 - 266 = +5{\cdot}72 \text{ kcal/mole}$$

Note. The twofold effect in connection with the principle of least constraint, i.e. pressure and temperature effects, should be noted. The affinity increases with increasing O_2 pressure and decreases as the temperature rises (*N.B.* exothermic reaction).

*Exercise 152

Make a check calculation of the values given in the above exercise for the e.m.f. of the detonating-gas cell, $H_2/H_2O/O_2$, $E_{0h(O_2, H_2)} = +1{\cdot}229$ V, and for the cell, $H_2/AgOH, H_2O/Ag$, $E_{0h(Ag, AgOH)} = +1{\cdot}18$ V.

The standard reference e.m.f. for $4OH^-/O_2 + 2H_2O$ is $E_{0h(O_2/OH^-)} = +0{\cdot}401$ V;
the solubility product of water is $k_{H_2O} = 1{\cdot}1 \times 10^{-14}$ (mole/l.)^2;
the standard reference e.m.f. for Ag/Ag^+ is $E_{0h(Ag/Ag^+)} = +0{\cdot}799$ V;
the solubility product of AgOH is $K_{s(AgOH)} = 1{\cdot}5 \times 10^{-8}$ (mole/l.)^2.

The check is best obtained by using eqns. (242) and (244) or (258); all at 25 °C.

Solution 152. The detonating-gas reaction is:

$$O_2 + 2H_2 = 2H_2O = (2H^+ + 2OH^-) \quad [H^+][OH^-] = k_{H_2O} \qquad n_e = 2 \quad \ldots\ldots \quad \text{(i)}$$

$$E = E_{0\,hr} - E_{0\,hl} + \frac{RT}{2F} \ln \frac{P_{O_2} P_{H_2}^2}{k_{H_2O}^2} = E_{0h(O_2/OH^-)} - 0 - \frac{RT}{F} \ln k_{H_2O} \quad \ldots\ldots \quad \text{(ii)}$$

since $P_{O_2} = P_{H_2} = 1$ atm and $E_{0\,hl} = 0$ (standard reference hydrogen electrode). Substituting the numerical values gives

$$E = +0{\cdot}401 - 0{\cdot}0591 \log(1{\cdot}1 \times 10^{-14}) = +1{\cdot}226 \text{ V, instead of } 1{\cdot}229 \text{ V}$$

The reaction for the second cell is:

$$H_2 + 2AgOH = 2Ag + 2H_2O$$

or

$$H_2 + (2Ag^+ + 2OH^-) = 2Ag + (2H^+ + 2OH^-) \quad \ldots\ldots \quad \text{(iii)}$$

where $n_e = 2$, $[Ag^+][OH^-] = K_{s(AgOH)}$ and $[H^+][OH^-] = k_{H_2O}$. It follows that

$$E = E_{0h(Ag/Ag^+)} - E_{0h(H_2/H^+)} + \frac{RT}{2F} \ln \frac{P_{H_2} K_{s(AgOH)}^2}{k_{H_2O}^2} = E_{0h(Ag/Ag^+)} + \frac{RT}{F} \ln \frac{K_{s(AgOH)}}{k_{H_2O}} \quad \ldots\ldots \quad \text{(iv)}$$

since $P_{H_2} = 1$ atm and $E_{0h(H_2/H^+)} = 0$

Substituting the numerical values gives:

$$E = +0{\cdot}799 + 0{\cdot}0591 \log \frac{1{\cdot}5 \times 10^{-8}}{1{\cdot}1 \times 10^{-14}} = +1{\cdot}16 \text{ V instead of } 1{\cdot}18 \text{ V}$$

*Exercise 153

The e.m.f. of the standard hydrogen electrode is taken to be $E_{0h(H_2/H^+)} = 0$, when pH = 0 (activity = 1 mole/l.) and $P_{H_2} = 1$ atm. Calculate the reference e.m.f.'s of the hydrogen electrode when (*a*) the pH = 2·04 (Veibel's solution: 0·01 N HCl + 0·09 N KCl), (*b*) the pH = 4·62 (standard acetate: 0·1 N acetic acid + 0·1 N sodium acetate, i.e. 100 cm^3 N NaOH + 200 cm^3 N acetic acid made up with distilled water to 1000 cm^3) and (*c*) at the neutral point, pH $\approx$ 7; all at 20 °C.

Solution 153. Using eqns. (244)–(245) with (237), for the reference e.m.f. of $\frac{1}{2}H_2/H^+$ + 1 electron:

$$E_{h(H_2)} = \frac{RT}{F}\ln[H^+] = -1{\cdot}9840\times10^{-4}\,T\,\mathrm{pH} = -1{\cdot}9840\times10^{-4}[293+(\theta-20)]\,\mathrm{pH}$$
$$= -[0{\cdot}0582 + 0{\cdot}0002(\theta-20)]\,\mathrm{pH}$$
$$\theta = {}^\circ\mathrm{C}$$

Substituting the numerical values for 20 °C gives

$$\mathrm{pH} = 2{\cdot}04:\quad E_{h(H_2,\,2\cdot04)} = -118{\cdot}5\ \mathrm{mV}$$
$$\mathrm{pH} = 4{\cdot}62:\quad E_{h(H_2,\,4\cdot62)} = -268{\cdot}4\ \mathrm{mV}$$
$$\mathrm{pH} = 7:\quad E_{h(H_2,\,7)} = -406{\cdot}8\ \mathrm{mV}$$

*Exercise 154

The reference e.m.f. of the 0·1 N calomel electrode, Hg/0·1 N KCl saturated with Hg_2Cl_2, is $E_{h(0\cdot1-\mathrm{cal})} = +337{\cdot}9$ mV at 20 °C. What is the reference e.m.f. of the N calomel electrode if the activity coefficient for Cl^- in 0·1 N solution ($\approx f_\pm$ for 0·1 N KCl) is $f_{Cl^-} = 0{\cdot}771$ and the coefficient in N solution ($\approx f_\pm$ for N KCl) is $f_{Cl^-} = 0{\cdot}606$?

Solution 154. The chemical reaction $2Hg + 2Cl^- = Hg_2Cl_{2(\mathrm{solid})}$ + 2 electrons takes place in the calomel electrode. Hence, from eqn. (244)

$$E_{\mathrm{cal}} = E_{h(0\cdot1-\mathrm{cal})} + \frac{RT}{2F}\ln\frac{1}{[Cl^-]^2} = E_{h(0\cdot1-\mathrm{cal})} - \frac{RT}{F}\ln(f_{Cl^-}[Cl^-]) \quad \ldots\ldots \quad \text{(i)}$$

If the N calomel electrode [electrode (r)] is connected against the 0·1 N calomel electrode [electrode (1), N.B. reference electrode], one has, as concentration cell

$$E_{h(1-\mathrm{cal})} - E_{h(0\cdot1-\mathrm{cal})} = \frac{RT}{F}\ln\frac{0{\cdot}771\times0{\cdot}1}{0{\cdot}601\times1} \quad \ldots\ldots \quad \text{(ii)}$$

or

$$E_{h(1-\mathrm{cal})} = 0{\cdot}3379 - 0{\cdot}0582\log\frac{0{\cdot}606}{0{\cdot}0771} = 0{\cdot}3379 - 0{\cdot}0520 = 285{\cdot}9\ \mathrm{mV}$$

Note. Saturated KCl solution in the form of a KCl bridge is usually interposed between the 'half-cells'. The 3·5 N calomel electrode with E = 253·6 mV and the calomel electrode with saturated KCl solution, where E = 249·0 mV, are also used at 20 °C, mainly in order to reduce the diffusion potential as far as possible. See note to Exercise 149 and 163.

*Exercise 155

(*a*) Calculate the standard reference e.m.f. of Hg/Hg_2^{2+} from the reference e.m.f. of the 0·1 N calomel electrode, Hg/0·1 N KCl saturated with Hg_2Cl_2, where $E_{h(0\cdot1-\mathrm{cal})}$ = +337·6 mV at 25 °C. The solubility product of calomel Hg_2Cl_2 at 25 °C is $K_{s(Hg_2Cl_2)} = [Hg_2^{2+}][Cl^-]^2 = 1{\cdot}43\times10^{-18}$ (mole/l.)^3; the activity coefficient for Cl^-, f_{Cl^-} ($\approx f_\pm$ in 0·1 N KCl) = 0·771.

(b) Using the value obtained for $E_{0\,h(Hg/Hg_2^{2+})}$ and the standard reference e.m.f. for Hg/Hg^{2+}, $E_{0\,h(Hg/Hg^{2+})} = 0{\cdot}854$ V, calculate the standard reference e.m.f. of the redox electrode $Hg_2^{2+}/2\,Hg^{2+} + 2\,e^-$ (2 electrons).

Solution 155. (a) According to eqn. (244), one has for $2\,Hg = Hg_2^{2+} + 2\,e^-$

$$E_h = E_{0\,h(Hg/Hg_2^{2+})} + \frac{RT}{2F}[\ln Hg_2^{2+}] \qquad \ldots. \quad (i)$$

and, where

$$K_{s\,(Hg_2Cl_2)} = [Hg_2^{2+}][Cl^-]^2$$

$$E_h = E_{0\,h(Hg/Hg_2^{2+})} + \frac{RT}{F}\ln\frac{\sqrt{K_{s\,(Hg_2Cl_2)}}}{f_{Cl^-}[Cl^-]} \qquad \ldots. \quad (ii)$$

When $[Cl^-] = 0{\cdot}1$ mole/l., E_h is the reference e.m.f. for the 0·1 N calomel electrode, so that

$$E_{h(0\cdot1-cal)} = E_{0\,h(Hg/Hg_2^{2+})} + 0{\cdot}0591 \log\frac{\sqrt{1{\cdot}43 \times 10^{-18}}}{0{\cdot}1 \times 0{\cdot}771} = +0{\cdot}3376 \text{ V}$$

or

$$E_{0\,h(Hg/Hg_2^{2+})} = 0{\cdot}3376 - 0{\cdot}0591(-7{\cdot}810) = +0{\cdot}799 \text{ V}$$

(b) Taking $E_{0\,h(m)}$ for $Hg/Hg^{2+} + 2\,e^-$ and $E_{0\,h(n)}$ for $Hg/{}^1/_2Hg_2^{2+} + 1\,e^-$, one has from eqn. (259):

$$(2-1)\,E_{0\,h(Hg_2^{2+})/Hg^{2+}} = 2\,E_{0\,h(m)} - E_{0\,h(n)} \qquad \ldots. \quad (iii)$$

or

$$E_{0\,h(Hg_2^{2+}/Hg^{2+})} = 2 \times 0{\cdot}854 - 0{\cdot}799 = 0{\cdot}909 \text{ V}$$

*Exercise 156

Calculate the solubility product of AgBr, $K_{s(AgBr)}$, from the e.m.f. $E = +0{\cdot}593$ V at 25 °C of the cell:

Ag/AgBr (saturated) in 0·1 N KBr//saturated NH_4NO_3 solution//0·1 N $AgNO_3$/Ag. The activity coefficient of Br^- in 0·1 N KBr is f_{Br^-} ($\approx f_\pm$ in KBr) $= 0{\cdot}777$; the figure for Ag^+ in 0·1 N $AgNO_3$ is f_{Ag^+} ($\approx f^\pm_{AgNO_3}$) $= 0{\cdot}717$. Interposing the saturated NH_4NO_3 solution reduces the diffusion potential as much as possible (see note to Exercise 149 and 163).

Solution 156. The relationship for the concentration cell is, from eqns. (241) and (258):

$$E = \frac{RT}{F}\ln\frac{a_{r(Ag^+)}}{a_{l(Ag^+)}} = \frac{RT}{F}\ln\frac{a_{r(Ag^+)}\,a_{l(Br^-)}}{K_{s(AgBr)}} \qquad \ldots. \quad (i)$$

where

$$K_{s(AgBr)} = a_{l(Ag^+)}\,a_{l(Br^-)}$$

Substituting the numerical values gives

$$0{\cdot}593 = 0{\cdot}0591[\log(0{\cdot}1 \times 0{\cdot}777 \times 0{\cdot}1 \times 0{\cdot}717) - \log\{K_{s(AgBr)}\}]$$

$$\log\{K_{s(AgBr)}\} = -10{\cdot}022 + 0{\cdot}746 - 3 = 0{\cdot}724 - 13$$

$$K_{s(AgBr)} = 5{\cdot}3 \times 10^{-13}\,(\text{mole/l.})^2$$

*Exercise 157

Calculate the e.m.f. of the chlorine detonating gas cell at 25 °C, (*a*) for N HCl and partial pressures of H_2 and Cl_2 gas each of 1 atm, (*b*) for 0·1 N HCl and partial pressures of the gases of 0·1 atm. The mean activity coefficient for N HCl is $f^{\pm}_{HCl} = 0{\cdot}8090$ and the figure for 0·1 N HCl is $f^{\pm}_{HCl} = 0{\cdot}7964$. The standard reference e.m.f. of the Cl^-/Cl_2 electrode is $E_{0\,h(Cl^-/Cl_2)} = +1{\cdot}358$ V.

Solution 157. $n_e = 2$ for the reaction $Cl_2 + H_2 = 2H^+ + 2Cl^-$. The cell in question is $Pt(H_2)/HCl/(Cl_2)Pt$. Equation (242) gives

$$E = E_{h\,0(Cl^-/Cl_2)} - 0 + \frac{RT}{2F} \ln \frac{p_{Cl_2} p_{H_2}}{[Cl^-]^2 [H^+]^2 (f^{\pm}_{HCl})^4}$$

(*a*) $E = +1{\cdot}358 + 0{\cdot}0591 \log \dfrac{1}{0{\cdot}8090^2} = +1{\cdot}358 + 0{\cdot}0109 = +1{\cdot}369$ V

(*b*) $E = +1{\cdot}358 + 0{\cdot}0591 \log \dfrac{0{\cdot}1}{0{\cdot}01 \times 0{\cdot}7964^2} = +1{\cdot}358 + 0{\cdot}0708 = +1{\cdot}429$ V

*Exercise 158

Using thermal data, calculate the standard reference e.m.f. at 25 °C, E_{0h}, for (*a*) aluminium, $Al/Al^{3+} + 3e^-$ (3 electrons), (*b*) fluorine, $F^-/\frac{1}{2}F_2 + e^-$ (1 electron). The standard entropy for Al is $S_{0(Al)} = 6{\cdot}75$ cal/(deg. mole); for Al^{3+}_{aq}, $S_{0(Al^{3+}_{aq})} = -76$ cal/(deg. mole)*; the heat of formation $\Delta H^F_{(Al^{3+}_{aq})} = -126{\cdot}3$ kcal/mole. The standard entropy for F_2 is $S_{0(F_2)} = 47{\cdot}99$ cal/(deg. mole); for F^-_{aq}, $S_{0(F^-_{aq})} = -2{\cdot}3$ cal/(deg. mole); the heat of formation, $\Delta H^F_{(F^-_{aq})} = -78{\cdot}2$ kcal/mole. The standard entropy for H_2 is $S_{0(H_2)} = 31{\cdot}23$ cal/(deg. mole).

Solution 158. From eqns. (238a), (186a) and (196)

$$E = \frac{-\Delta G}{n_e \times 23\,055} = \frac{T\Delta S - \Delta H}{n_e \times 23\,055} \quad \text{(volt)} \qquad \ldots \quad \text{(i)}$$

hence

$$E_0 = \frac{298\,\Delta S_0 - \Delta H_0}{n_e \times 23\,055} \quad \text{(volt)} \qquad \ldots \quad \text{(ii)}$$

where [see eqn. (196)] $\Delta S_0 = \Delta \sum \nu_i S_{0\,298}$.

In the case of Al, the reaction in question is

$$Al^{3+}_{aq} + \frac{3}{2} H_2 = Al + 3H^+_{aq} \qquad n_e = 3$$

In the case of fluorine, the reaction is

$$\frac{1}{2} F_2 + \frac{1}{2} H_2 = F^-_{aq} + H^+_{aq} \qquad n_e = 1$$

(*a*) $$\Delta S_0 = 6{\cdot}75 - (-76) - \frac{3}{2} \times 31{\cdot}23 = 35{\cdot}90 \text{ cal/(deg. mole)}$$

$$\Delta H_0 = -(-126{,}300) \text{ cal/mole} = +126{,}300 \text{ cal/mole}$$

i.e.

$$E_{0\,h(Al/Al^{3+})} = \frac{298 \times 35{\cdot}90 - 126\,300}{3 \times 23\,055} = -1{\cdot}67 \text{ V}$$

* See note on p. 206.

(b) $$\Delta S_0 = -2{\cdot}3 - \frac{1}{2} \times 47{\cdot}99 - \frac{1}{2} \times 31{\cdot}23 = -41{\cdot}91 \text{ cal/(deg. mole)}$$

$$\Delta H_0 = -78{,}200 \text{ cal/mole}$$

i.e.

$$E_{0\,h(F^-/F_2)} = \frac{298(-41{\cdot}91) - (-78\,200)}{1 \times 23\,055} = +2{\cdot}85 \text{ V}$$

Note. In the case of Al the reaction therefore proceeds spontaneously from right to left. In the case of F_2 it proceeds from left to right; see (238).

*Exercise 159

A solution of $FeCl_3$ in water ($c_0 = 0{\cdot}001$ mole/l.) is shaken at 25 °C with mercury and solid calomel, Hg_2Cl_2. This causes Fe^{3+} to be reduced to Fe^{2+} and shaking is continued until equilibrium is established. What is the ratio $[Fe^{3+}]/[Fe^{2+}] = x$ after equilibrium has been established if the standard reference e.m.f. of the redox electrode at 25 °C Fe^{2+}/Fe^{3+} is $E_{0\,hr} = +0{\cdot}772$ V and that for the N calomel electrode is $E_{0\,hl} = +0{\cdot}2847$ V? The activity coefficients may be ignored for the purpose of this Exercise.

Solution 159. The reduction takes place according to the equation

$$Hg + Fe^{3+} + Cl^- = \tfrac{1}{2}Hg_2Cl_2 + Fe^{2+} \quad n_e = 1 \qquad \ldots\ldots \quad \text{(i)}$$

The cell in question is: $Pt/Hg/[Hg_2Cl_2]Cl^-//Fe^{3+}, Fe^{2+}/Pt$. Hence, from eqn. (242), for equilibrium:

$$\left.\begin{aligned} E = 0 &= E_{0\,hr} - E_{0\,hl} + \frac{RT}{F}\ln\frac{[Fe^{3+}][Cl^-]}{[Fe^{2+}]}\Big/(\text{mol./l.}) \\ &= 0{\cdot}772 - 0{\cdot}2847 + 0{\cdot}0591\log\frac{[Fe^{3+}][Cl^-]}{[Fe^{2+}]}\Big/(\text{mol./l.}) \end{aligned}\right\} \quad \ldots \quad \text{(ii)}$$

Rearrangement gives

$$\frac{[Fe^{3+}][Cl^-]}{[Fe^{2+}]} = e^{[F(E_{0\,hr} - E_{0\,hl})]/RT} = 10^{-\frac{0{\cdot}487}{0{\cdot}0591}} = 5{\cdot}752 \times 10^{-9} \text{ mol./l.} \quad \ldots \quad \text{(iii)}$$

From eqn. (i), one has the following relations for the concentrations:

$[Fe^{2+}] = c_0 - [Fe^{3+}]$ (1 Fe^{3+} and 1 Cl^- is expended for each Fe^{2+} formed)

$$[Cl^-] = 3c_0 - [Fe^{2+}] = 3c_0 - (c_0 - [Fe^{3+}]) = 2c_0 + [Fe^{3+}]$$

$$x = \frac{[Fe^{3+}]}{[Fe^{2+}]} = \frac{[Fe^{3+}]}{c_0 - [Fe^{3+}]} \qquad [Fe^{3+}] = c_0\frac{x}{x+1} \qquad \ldots\ldots \quad \text{(iv)}$$

$$[Cl^-] = 2c_0 + c_0\frac{x}{x+1} = c_0\frac{(3x+2)}{x+1} \qquad \ldots\ldots \quad \text{(v)}$$

Substitution the expressions at (iv) and (v) in (iii), the latter becomes

$$\left.\begin{aligned} \frac{x(3x+2)c_0}{x+1} &= 5{\cdot}752 \times 10^{-9} \quad \text{or} \quad \frac{x(3x+2)}{x+1} = \frac{5{\cdot}752 \times 10^{-9}}{c_0} \\ &= \frac{5{\cdot}752 \times 10^{-9}}{0{\cdot}001} = 5{\cdot}752 \times 10^{-6} = C \end{aligned}\right\} \quad \ldots \quad \text{(vi)}$$

Rearrangement of (vi) gives the quadratic equation

$$\left.\begin{aligned} &3x^2 + (2 - C)x - C = 0 \\ &x = \frac{-(2 - C) + \sqrt{(2 - C)^2 + 12C}}{6} \end{aligned}\right\} \quad \ldots \text{(vii)}$$

Since, in this special case ($C \ll 1$), x is obviously very small, the x^2 term in (vii) may be ignored; C may also be neglected in comparison with 2, thus giving

$$x \approx \frac{C}{2} = 2{\cdot}876 \times 10^{-6} = \frac{[Fe^{+3}]}{[Fe^{2+}]} \quad \ldots\ldots \text{(viii)}$$

i.e. under the given conditions, practically all the Fe^{3+} is reduced to Fe^{2+}.

Note. If activity coefficients are to be taken into account in exercises of this kind, the following procedure is advisable. A first approximate value is calculated using the concentrations as above. According to the result, appropriate activity coefficients are then introduced and the calculation repeated using the new numerical values (second approximation). If the result differs too much from the first approximation, the calculation must be repeated yet again, using appropriately revised activity coefficients (third approximation).

*Exercise 160

The standard reference e.m.f. for Cu/Cu^{2+} is $E_{0h(Cu/Cu^{2+})} = +0{\cdot}345$ V. The equilibrium constant for the reaction $Cu + Cu^{2+} = 2Cu^+$ is $K = 1{\cdot}2 \times 10^{-6}$ mole/l. Calculate from these values the standard reference e.m.f. for Cu/Cu^+ and that for the redox electrode Cu^+/Cu^{2+}. Also calculate the reference e.m.f. of a Cu electrode in 0·1 N HCl solution saturated with CuCl. Finally, determine the reference e.m.f. of a Cu electrode in 0·1 N HBr solution saturated with CuBr. The activity coefficient of Cl^- in 0·1 N HCl is $f_{Cl^-} = 0{\cdot}7964$ ($\approx f^{\pm}_{HCl}$); $f_{Br^-} = 0{\cdot}1$ N HBr $= 0{\cdot}81$ ($\approx f^{\pm}_{HBr}$). The solubility product of CuCl is $K_{s\,(CuCl)} = 1{\cdot}02 \times 10^{-6}$ (mole/l.)^2; $K_{s\,(CuBr)} = 4{\cdot}15 \times 10^{-8}$ (mole/l.)^2. All data relate to 25 °C.

Solution 160. In the case of the reaction $Cu + Cu^{2+} = 2Cu^+$, $n_e = 2$ and the cell is: $Cu/Cu^+//Cu^{2+}/Cu$; see (238). Hence, from eqn. (243)

$$E_{0h(Cu/Cu^{2+})} - E_{0h(Cu/Cu^+)} = \frac{RT}{2F}\ln\{K\} \quad K = \frac{[Cu^+]^2}{[Cu^{2+}]} \quad \ldots\ldots \text{(i)}$$

Substituting the numerical values gives

$$E_{0h(Cu/Cu^+)} = +0{\cdot}345 - \frac{0{\cdot}0591}{2}\log(1{\cdot}2 \times 10^{-6}) = +0{\cdot}345 + 0{\cdot}175 = +0{\cdot}52\text{ V}$$

The standard reference e.m.f. for the redox electrode Cu^+/Cu^{2+} is, from eqn. (259)

$$(2 - 1)E_{0h(Cu^+/Cu^{2+})} = 2E_{0h(Cu/Cu^{2+})} - 1E_{0h(Cu/Cu^+)} \quad \ldots\ldots \text{(ii)}$$

i.e. $$E_{0h(Cu^+/Cu^{2+})} = 2 \times 0{\cdot}345 - 0{\cdot}52 = +0{\cdot}17\text{ V}$$

Equation (244) gives the general expression for the reference e.m.f. of a Cu/Cu^+ electrode:

$$E_h = E_{0h(Cu/Cu^+)} + 0{\cdot}0591\log a_{Cu^+} \quad \ldots\ldots \text{(iii)}$$

Combining (iii) with the solubility products

$$K_{s\,(CuCl)} = a_{Cu^+}\, a_{Cl^-} \quad \text{and} \quad K_{s\,(CuBr)} = a_{Cu^+}\, a_{Br^-}$$

one has

$$E_h = E_{0\,h\,(Cu/Cu^+)} + 0{\cdot}0591 \log \frac{K_{s\,(CuCl)}}{a_{Cl^-}} \qquad \dots \quad \text{(iv)}$$

or

$$E_h = E_{0\,h\,(Cu/Cu^+)} + 0{\cdot}0591 \log \frac{K_{s\,(CuBr)}}{a_{Br^-}} \qquad \dots \quad \text{(v)}$$

Substituting the numerical values gives

for the HCl solution:

$$E_h = +0{\cdot}52 + 0{\cdot}0591 \log \frac{1{\cdot}02 \times 10^{-6}}{0{\cdot}7964 \times 0{\cdot}1} = +0{\cdot}231 \text{ V}$$

for the HBr solution:

$$E_h = +0{\cdot}52 + 0{\cdot}0591 \log \frac{4{\cdot}15 \times 10^{-8}}{0{\cdot}81 \times 0{\cdot}1} = +0{\cdot}148 \text{ V}$$

*Exercise 161

Calculate the e.m.f. at 18 °C of the cell cadmium amalgam (c_l)/0·1 N $CdSO_4$ solution/ cadmium amalgam (c_r), where $c_l = 0{\cdot}03$ g Cd in 150 g Hg; $c_r = 0{\cdot}11$ g Cd in 150 g Hg. What is the composition of the two amalgams and the e.m.f. after current equivalent co 40 coulombs has been taken off? What is the total number of coulombs that the tell can deliver?

Solution 161. The reference e.m.f. of an amalgam electrode Cd(c)/Cd^{2+} (c') + $2e^-$ is, from eqn. (244)

$$E_h = E_{0\,h\,(am)} + \frac{RT}{n_e F} \ln \frac{c'}{c} \qquad n_e = 2 \qquad \dots \quad \text{(i)}$$

Therefore we have for the amalgam cell:

$$E = E_{0\,hr\,(am)} - E_{0\,hl\,(am)} + \frac{RT}{n_e F}\left(\ln \frac{c'_r}{c_r} - \ln \frac{c'_l}{c_l}\right) \qquad \dots \quad \text{(ii)}$$

and, where $E_{0\,hr\,(am)} = E_{0\,hl\,(am)}$ and $c'_r = c'_l$,

$$E = \frac{RT}{n_e F} \ln \frac{c_l}{c_r} \qquad \dots \quad \text{(iii)}$$

From eqn. (226), $It = Q = n\, n_e F$, where Q = quantity of electricity in coulombs;

$$n = \frac{Q}{n_e F} = \frac{G}{M} \quad \frac{G}{M} = n = \text{molar quantity transported or converted by the quantity of electricity } Q \qquad \dots \quad \text{(iv)}$$

One has, from (iii) and (iv), for the given experimental conditions (atomic weight $M_{(Cd)} = 112{\cdot}41$), $n_e = 2$:

$$E = \frac{0{\cdot}0578}{2} \log \frac{0{\cdot}03}{0{\cdot}11} = -\frac{0{\cdot}0578 \times 0{\cdot}564}{2} = -16{\cdot}3 \text{ mV}$$

From (iv):

$$G = \frac{MQ}{n_e F} = \frac{112{\cdot}41 \times 40}{2 \times 96\,493} = 0{\cdot}0233 \text{ g}$$

this being the amount of Cd transported for a current consumption of 40 coulombs. Thus the final amount of Cd in the amalgam electrode (r) is $0{\cdot}11 - 0{\cdot}0233 = 0{\cdot}0867$ g Cd, the figure for electrode (1) being $0{\cdot}03 + 0{\cdot}0233 = 0{\cdot}0533$ g Cd. It follows that the resultant e.m.f. is

$$E = -\frac{0{\cdot}0578}{2} \log \frac{0{\cdot}0867}{0{\cdot}0533} = -6{\cdot}1 \text{ mV}$$

Equilibrium is reached if the cadmium concentrations become equal on both sides, i.e. when $c_e = \dfrac{0{\cdot}11 + 0{\cdot}03}{2} = 0{\cdot}07$ g Cd. In order to reach this state it is necessary to transport $0{\cdot}11 - 0{\cdot}07 = 0{\cdot}04$ g Cd. It follows from (iv) that the total possible delivery of current from the cell will be

$$Q = \frac{G n_e F}{M} = \frac{0{\cdot}04 \times 2 \times 96\,495}{112{\cdot}41} = 68{\cdot}6 \text{ coulombs}$$

Note. The negative sign of the e.m.f. indicates that the positive charges, i.e. the Cd^{2+} ions, are transported from right to left inside the cell; see (238). Visualizing the mechanism of the electrochemical process (in the manner described in Exercise 148) shows that the amalgam on the right-hand side is richer in Cd and tends to become diluted. This is only possible by loss of Cd^{2+} ions, i.e. by transport from right to left.

*Exercise 162

The reference e.m.f. of a Pt,Tl^+/Tl^{3+} redox electrode at 25 °C was found to be $E_h = 1{\cdot}140$ V. The diffusion potential was eliminated. The actual experiment was made by immersing a platinum sheet in a solution containing 0·0337 moles $Tl(NO_3)_3$, 0·0216 moles $TlNO_3$ and 0·42 moles HNO_3 [to suppress hydrolysis of $Tl(NO_3)_3$]. Calculate the standard reference e.m.f., $E_{0h(Tl^+/Tl^{3+})}$. The activity coefficients for Tl^{3+} and Tl^+ should be calculated from the Debye and Hückel eqn. (235). The ionic radius of Tl^{3+} is $r_{Tl^{3+}} = 1{\cdot}05 \times 10^{-8}$ cm. The value for Tl^+ is $r_{Tl^+} = 1{\cdot}49 \times 10^{-8}$ cm.

Solution 162. The reference e.m.f. for the redox electrode $Tl^+/Tl^{3+} + 2e^-$ is, from eqn. (244)

$$E_h = E_{0h(Tl^+/Tl^{3+})} + \frac{RT}{2F} \ln \frac{c_{Tl^{3+}} f_{Tl^{3+}}}{c_{Tl^+} f_{Tl^+}} \quad \ldots . \quad \text{(i)}$$

Substituting the numerical values gives

$$E_{0h(Tl^+/Tl^{3+})} = 1{\cdot}140 - \frac{0{\cdot}0591}{2} \log \frac{0{\cdot}0337}{0{\cdot}0216} + \frac{0{\cdot}0591}{2} [(-\log f_{Tl^{3+}}) - (-\log f_{Tl^+})] \quad \ldots . \quad \text{(ii)}$$

From eqn. (235)

$$\left.\begin{aligned} &(-\log f_{Tl^{3+}}) - (-\log f_{Tl^+}) \\ &= 0{\cdot}5092 \times 0{\cdot}802 \left(\frac{3^2}{1 + 0{\cdot}329 \times 1{\cdot}05 \times 0{\cdot}802} - \frac{1}{1 + 0{\cdot}329 \times 1{\cdot}49 \times 0{\cdot}802} \right) \end{aligned}\right\} \quad \ldots \quad \text{(iii)}$$

where the ionic strength J is calculated by means of eqn. (234) from the following concentrations:

$$[Tl^{3+}] = 0{\cdot}0337 \text{ mole/l.}$$
$$[Tl^{+}] = 0{\cdot}0216 \text{ mole/l.}$$
$$[H^{+}] = 0{\cdot}42 \text{ mole/l.}$$
$$[NO_3^-] = 3 \times 0{\cdot}0337 + 0{\cdot}0216 + 0{\cdot}42 = 0{\cdot}5427 \text{ mole/l.}$$

Hence
$$J = \tfrac{1}{2}(3^2 \times 0{\cdot}0337 + 0{\cdot}0216 + 0{\cdot}42 + 0{\cdot}5427) = 0{\cdot}6438$$
$$\sqrt{J} = 0{\cdot}802 \qquad \ldots\ldots \quad \text{(iv)}$$

Working out (iii) gives a figure of $+2{\cdot}59$ which, substituted in (ii), gives

$$E_{0\text{h}(Tl^+/Tl^{3+})} = 1{\cdot}140 - 0{\cdot}0057 + 0{\cdot}0765 = +1{\cdot}211 \text{ V}$$

*Exercise 163

Determine the pH of a solution at 20 °C which, as an experimental electrode (on the right-hand side), contains a hydrogen electrode at atmospheric pressure and is connected against a saturated calomel electrode as reference ($E_{\text{hl}} = 249{\cdot}0$ mV at 20 °C). $E = -626$ mV was the measured value of the e.m.f. of the solution.

Solution 163. According to eqn. (245), the reference e.m.f. of a hydrogen electrode, $H_2/2H^+ + 2e^-$, is given by

$E_{\text{hr}} = \dfrac{RT}{F} \ln \dfrac{H^+}{\sqrt{P_{H_2}}}$; hence against the calomel electrode and when $P_{H_2} = 1$ atm:

$$E = E_{\text{hr}} - E_{\text{hl}} = 1{\cdot}9840 \times 10^{-4}\, T \log[H^+] - E_{\text{hl(cal},\theta)} \qquad \ldots\ldots \quad \text{(i)}$$

with $\text{pH} = -\log[H^+]$, we have

$$\text{pH} = \frac{-E - E_{\text{hl(cal},\theta)}}{1{\cdot}9840 \times 10^{-4}\, T} = \frac{-E - E_{\text{hl(cal},\theta)}}{1{\cdot}9840 \times 10^{-4}[293{\cdot}16 + (\theta - 20)]} = \frac{-E - E_{\text{hl(cal},\theta)}}{0{\cdot}0582 + 0{\cdot}0002(\theta - 20)} \qquad \ldots\ldots \quad \text{(ii)}$$

where θ = test temperature in °C and E_{hl} is the reference e.m.f. of the reference electrode against the standard H_2 electrode at test temperature (to be taken from tables).

In this specific case:

$$\text{pH} = \frac{-(-0{\cdot}626) - 0{\cdot}249}{0{\cdot}0582} = \frac{0{\cdot}377}{0{\cdot}0582} = 6{\cdot}48$$

Note. In accordance with definition [eqn. (236)], a knowledge of the single ion activity of the H_3O^+ ion, in the solution in question, is essential for the accurate determination of the pH. It will have been seen from the notes to Exercises 148 and 149 that single ion activities can only be determined from concentration cell measurements with transport (mean ionic activities) and then only in the range where Debye and Hückel's limiting law is applicable. In practice, however, pH measurements must often be made on mixed solutions where the composition is unknown. One attempts to eliminate diffusion potentials as far as possible and their dependence on concentration is usually ignored. The resulting 'conventional pH scale' is therefore only approximate and cannot be used where great accuracy is required. Estimated corrections for diffusion potentials are included in the tables for the e.m.f.'s, E_{hl}, of the reference electrodes (calomel electrodes; silver—silver chloride electrodes). More details may be found in textbooks on this subject.

*Exercise 164

Using a quinhydrone test electrode for the measurement of the pH of a sample of urine, the e.m.f. against a saturated calomel reference electrode ($E_{\text{hl}} = 249{\cdot}0$ mV at 20 °C) was found to be $E = +0{\cdot}1087$ mV. What is the pH of the urine?

In the case of the quinhydrone electrode, the reaction (quinone) $C_6H_4O_2 + H_2 =$ (hydroquinone) $C_6H_4(OH)_2$ is broken down* into the electrode reaction: (quinone) $C_6H_4O_2 + 2H^+ + 2e^- = C_6H_4(OH)_2$ for the quinhydrone electrode (hydroquinone/quinone $+ 2H^+ + 2e^-$) and into the electrode reaction for the standard hydrogen electrode ($H_2/2H^+ + 2e^-$). Quinhydrone (quinone:hydroquinone = 1:1) is present as solid phase. The reference e.m.f. of the quinhydrone electrode against a hydrogen electrode of the same pH is $E_{0\text{h(quin)}} = +702{\cdot}7$ mV at 20 °C.

Solution 164. According to eqn. (244) the equation for the reference e.m.f. of a redox electrode, applicable in this case, is

$$E_{\text{hr}} = E_{0\text{h(quin)}} + \frac{RT}{2F} \ln \frac{[\text{quinone}][H^+]^2}{[\text{hydroquinone}]} \quad \dots \quad \text{(i)}$$

so that, under the conditions given

$$E_{\text{hr}} = +0{\cdot}7027 - 0{\cdot}0582 \text{ pH} \quad \dots \quad \text{(ii)*}$$

$$E = +0{\cdot}7027 - E_{\text{hl(cal)}} - 0{\cdot}0582 \text{ pH} \quad \dots \quad \text{(iii)}$$

$$\text{pH} = \frac{-E + 0{\cdot}7027 - E_{\text{hl(cal)}}}{0{\cdot}0582} = \frac{-E + 0{\cdot}4537}{0{\cdot}0582} \quad \dots \quad \text{(iv)}$$

where $E_{\text{hl(cal)}} = 0{\cdot}2490$ V at 20 °C.
Substitution gives

$$\text{pH} = \frac{-0{\cdot}1087 + 0{\cdot}4537}{0{\cdot}0582} = 5{\cdot}93$$

Exercise 165

For the determination of the pH in a muscle, the e.m.f. was measured using a glass electrode at 20 °C. The glass electrode was, as is usual, fitted with a silver rod and filled with AgCl + 0·1 N HCl. It was connected against a saturated calomel reference electrode ($E_{\text{hl}} = +249{\cdot}0$ mV). The reference e.m.f. of a glass electrode of this sort, relative to a hydrogen electrode of the same pH, is $E_{0\text{h(gl)}} = +349$ mV. In the present experiment an e.m.f. of $E = -322{\cdot}5$ mV was recorded. What was the pH in the muscle tissue?

Solution 165. The total e.m.f. (E) is equal to the reference e.m.f. of the glass electrode, $[E_{\text{hr(gl)}}]$, less the reference e.m.f. of the calomel electrode, $E_{\text{hl(cal)}}$.

* In this connection, see note to Exercise 167.

The e.m.f. of the cell is the sum of the phase boundary potential at the glass, $E_{ph\,\mathrm{I\,(inner)/II\,(outer)}}$, and the electrode potential E'_{Ag} of the silver rod inside the glass sphere, including the galvanic potential Hg/Ag (see p. 229), i.e. eqn. (265):

$$E = E'_{\mathrm{Ag}} + \frac{RT}{F} \ln \frac{[\mathrm{H^+\,(II, outer)}]}{[\mathrm{H^+\,(I, inner)}]} - E_{\mathrm{hl\,(cal)}} \quad \ldots\ldots \quad \text{(i)}$$

The saturated calomel electrode, E_{hl}, is measured against the standard hydrogen electrode, $[H^+] = 1$.

If, therefore, in the experimental arrangement, $[\mathrm{H^+\,(II,\ outer)}]$ were equal to 1, one would have the standard reference e.m.f. of a glass electrode in comparison with a hydrogen electrode of the same pH, viz. $E_{0\,\mathrm{h(gl)}} = +349$ mV. Therefore, from (i)

$$E_{0\,\mathrm{h(gl)}} = E'_{\mathrm{Ag}} + \frac{RT}{F} \ln \frac{1\,\mathrm{(II, outer)}}{[\mathrm{H^+\,(I, inner)}]} = +349\,\mathrm{mV} \quad \ldots\ldots \quad \text{(ii)}$$

Substituting (ii) in (i) we get for E

$$E = E_{0\,\mathrm{h(gl)}} - E_{\mathrm{hl\,(cal)}} + \frac{RT}{F} \ln [\mathrm{H^+\,(outer)}] \quad \ldots\ldots \quad \text{(iii)}$$

and

$$E = 0{\cdot}349 - 0{\cdot}249 - 0{\cdot}0582\,\mathrm{pH} = 0{\cdot}100 - 0{\cdot}0582\,\mathrm{pH} \quad \ldots\ldots \quad \text{(iv)}$$

$$\mathrm{pH} = \frac{0{\cdot}100 - E}{0{\cdot}0582} \quad \ldots\ldots \quad \text{(v)}$$

Substituting:

$$\mathrm{pH} = \frac{0{\cdot}100 - (-\,0{\cdot}3225)}{0{\cdot}0582} = 7{\cdot}26$$

See also Exercise 140 (*a*), (electrometric titration).

Exercise 166

The standard reference e.m.f. of the glass electrode (Ag/AgCl in 0·1 N HCl) against a hydrogen electrode of the same pH (see Exercise 165) is, at 20 °C, $E_{0\,\mathrm{h(gl)}} = +349$ mV This value was obtained by careful standardization measurements. Derive it by calculation. The activity coefficient of 0·1 N HCl is $f^{\pm}_{\mathrm{HCl}} = 0{\cdot}7964$; the standard reference e.m.f. for Ag/Ag^+ is $E_{0\,\mathrm{h(Ag)}} = +0{\cdot}799$ V and the solubility product of AgCl is $K_{s\,\mathrm{(AgCl)}} = 1{\cdot}61 \times 10^{-10}$ (mole/l.)^2; see Exercise 165 (ii).

Solution 166. According to Exercise 165 (ii), the standard reference e.m.f. of the glass electrode is

$$E_{0\,\mathrm{h(gl)}} = E'_{\mathrm{Ag}} + \frac{RT}{F} \ln \frac{1}{[\mathrm{H^+\,(inner)}]} \quad \ldots\ldots \quad \text{(i)}$$

The reference e.m.f. of the silver electrode is, from eqn. (244)

$$E'_{\mathrm{Ag}} = E_{0\,\mathrm{h(Ag)}} + \frac{RT}{F} \ln [\mathrm{Ag^+}] \quad \ldots\ldots \quad \text{(ii)}$$

or, using the solubility product $K_{s\,\mathrm{(AgCl)}} = [\mathrm{Ag^+}][\mathrm{Cl^-}]$

$$E'_{\mathrm{Ag}} = E_{0\,\mathrm{h(Ag)}} + \frac{RT}{F} \ln \frac{K_{s\,\mathrm{(AgCl)}}}{[\mathrm{Cl^-}]} \quad \ldots\ldots \quad \text{(iii)}$$

Taking $[H^+][Cl^-] = c_{H^+} c_{Cl^-} (f^{\pm}_{HCl})^2$, see eqns. (229) to (232), (i) and (iii) give

$$E_{0\,h\,(gl)} = E_{0\,h\,(Ag)} + \frac{R\,T}{F} \ln \frac{K_{s\,(AgCl)}}{c_{Cl^-} \times c_{H^+}\,(\text{inner})\,(f^{\pm}_{HCl})^2} \quad \ldots\ldots \quad \text{(iv)}$$

Substitution gives:

$$E_{0\,h\,(gl)} = 0{\cdot}799 + 0{\cdot}0582 \log \frac{1{\cdot}61 \times 10^{-10}}{0{\cdot}1 \times 0{\cdot}1 \times 0{\cdot}7964^2} = 0{\cdot}799 + 0{\cdot}0582\,(0{\cdot}4046 - 8)$$

$$= 0{\cdot}799 - 0{\cdot}442 = +0{\cdot}357 \text{ V}$$

This calculated value of 357 mV is in good agreement with the experimental value of 349 mV.

*Exercise 167

Over what range of pH at 20 °C is it possible, by means of dichromate, to oxidize ethyl alcohol to acetaldehyde, but not hydroquinone to quinone, if, in the reaction mixture, the ratio of oxidation stage to reduction stage is 1:1 for all substances? The standard reference e.m.f.'s are:

$$Cr^{3+} + 4\,H_2O/HCrO_4^- + 7\,H^+ + 3\,e^-: \quad E_{0\,h\,(chr)} = +1{\cdot}3 \text{ V}$$

$$\text{hydroquinone/quinone} + 2\,H^+ + 2\,e^-: \quad E_{0\,h\,(quin)} = +0{\cdot}703 \text{ V}$$

$$\text{ethyl alcohol/acetaldehyde} + 2\,H + 2\,e^-: \quad E_{0\,h\,(alc)} = +0{\cdot}23 \text{ V}$$

What are the values of rH at the range limits?

Solution 167. One finds the dependence of the given redox reference e.m.f.'s on the pH by using eqn. (244):

$$E_{h\,(chr)} = E_{0\,h\,(chr)} + \frac{RT}{3F} \ln \frac{[HCrO_4^-]\,[H^+]^7}{[Cr^{3+}]}$$

which, under the given conditions, becomes

$$E_{h\,(chr)} = 1{\cdot}3 - 0{\cdot}0582 \times \frac{7}{3}\,\text{pH} = 1{\cdot}3 - 0{\cdot}1356\,\text{pH} \quad \ldots\ldots \quad \text{(i)}$$

$$E_{h\,(quin)} = E_{0\,h\,(quin)} + \frac{R\,T}{2\,F} \ln \frac{[\text{quinone}]\,[H^+]^2}{[\text{hydroquinone}]} \qquad E_{h\,(quin)} = 0{\cdot}703 - 0{\cdot}0582\,\text{pH} \quad \ldots\ldots \quad \text{(ii)}$$

$$E_{h\,(alc)} = E_{0\,(alc)} + \frac{R\,T}{2\,F} \ln \frac{[\text{acetald.}]\,[H^+]^2}{[\text{EtOH}]} \qquad E_{h\,(alc)} = 0{\cdot}23 - 0{\cdot}0528\,\text{pH} \quad \ldots\ldots \quad \text{(iii)}$$

The limits are given by the point of intersection of the straight line (i) on the one hand with (ii), or with (iii) on the other hand (equality of potential). Oxidation occurs if $E_{h\,(chr)}$ is greater than $E_{h\,(quin)}$ or $E_{h\,(alc)}$. This follows from the fact that, if the chromate electrode is the positive one, it will take up electrons and will be reduced, whilst the other electrode will be negative, will liberate electrons and be oxidized. The points of intersection may be determined graphically or, in this simple case, they can be calculated.

There will be no oxidation of hydroquinone if, from (i) and (ii), $E_{h(chr)} \leqq E_{h(quin)}$, i. e.

$$1{\cdot}3 - 0{\cdot}1356 \text{ pH} \leqq 0{\cdot}703 - 0{\cdot}0582 \text{ pH} \qquad \ldots\ldots \quad \text{(iv)}$$

$$\text{pH} \geqq 7{\cdot}7$$

Oxidation of ethyl alcohol will occur if, from (i) and (iii), $E_{h(chr)} \geqq E_{h(alc)}$

$$1{\cdot}3 - 0{\cdot}1356 \text{ pH} \geqq 0{\cdot}23 - 0{\cdot}0582 \text{ pH} \qquad \ldots\ldots \quad \text{(v)}$$

$$\text{pH} \leqq 13{\cdot}8$$

It follows that, under the given conditions of concentration, the range of pH over which the alcohol, but not the hydroquinone, is oxidized by dichromate, will be

$$\text{pH} = 7{\cdot}7 \text{ to } 13{\cdot}8$$

The value of rH corresponding to these limits will be, from eqns. (248) and (237)

$$\text{rH} = \frac{E_h + 0{\cdot}0582 \text{ pH}}{0{\cdot}0291} \quad \text{for } 20^\circ \text{C} \qquad \ldots\ldots \quad \text{(vi)}$$

Substituting (ii) gives for the upper limit, rH = 0·703/0·0291 = 24·2 and substituting (iii) gives the lower limit, rH = 0·23/0·0291 = 7·92.

Note. (1) The result of the calculation does not mean that below a pH of 13·8 the extent of the oxidation of the alcohol suddenly changes from 0 to 100 per cent; on the contrary, it increases gradually as the limiting pH is passed. This is because, at the commencement of oxidation, the redox e.m.f. for the alcohol–aldehyde system increases in accordance with (iii) when the aldehyde/alcohol ratio is > 1. On the other hand, and at the same time, the redox e.m.f. for the dichromate/Cr^{3+} system falls in accordance with (i) when the $HCrO_4^-/Cr^{3+}$ ratio is < 1. It follows that a new equilibrium will be established unless steps are taken to maintain the initial conditions of concentration.

(2) The reaction quinone ($C_6H_4O_2$) + $2H^+$ + $2e^-$ = hydroquinone, [$C_6H_4(OH)_2$], was taken as the basic reaction for the redox quinhydrone electrode. It is better however, having due regard to the contemporary theory of electrolytes, if the hydroquinone ion, $C_6H_4O_2^{2-}$, is regarded as the actual reduction stage in this (and similar) organic redox systems. The equation is then written

$$\text{quinone} + 2e^- = \text{hydroquinone ion } (C_6H_4O_2 + 2e^- = C_6H_4O_2^{2-}) \qquad \ldots\ldots \quad \text{(vii)}$$

where the hydroquinone acts as a very weak dibasic acid with the two dissociation constants $k_1 = 4{\cdot}5 \times 10^{-11}$ [$C_6H_4(OH)_2 = C_6H_4OHO^- + H^+$] and $k_2 = 3 \times 10^{-12}$ ($C_6H_4OHO^- = C_6H_4O_2^{2-} + H^+$).

If this is done, it means that the previously used expression [formula (ii)] will still be applicable in the acid range and for pH values up to about 8, i.e. when the hydroquinone is practically undissociated. At higher pH values, however, in the alkaline region, the first dissociation stage

$$C_6H_4O_2 + H^+ + 2e^- = C_6H_4OHO^- \qquad \ldots\ldots \quad \text{(viii)}$$

will play a part and the slope of the E versus pH curve will fall from $-0{\cdot}0581$ to about half this value (approx. $-0{\cdot}03$); according to (viii), (H^+) in (i) will feature as the first power. At still higher pH values, and where dissociation is almost complete, the second stage will be operative and the slope will become independent of pH; according to (vii), (H^+) will no longer feature in (ii). By plotting this kind of redox curve, it is possible to determine the dissociation constants. Quantitative treatment of this subject may be found in MICHAELIS, L., *Oxydations-Reduktions-Potentiale*. Springer.

Exercise 168

Calculate the e.m.f. of a lead battery at 25 °C. In the case of the lead battery, reaction takes place between the PbO_2 and the Pb electrode in the presence of 2 M sulphuric acid:

$$PbO_{2\,(solid)} + Pb_{(solid)} + 4\,H^+ + 2\,SO_4^{2-} = 2\,PbSO_{4\,(solid)} + 2\,H_2O$$

The standard reference e.m.f.'s are known to be:

Pb/Pb^{2+}:

$$E_{0\,h(Pb/Pb^{2+})} = -\;0{\cdot}126\ \mathrm{V}$$

$Pb^{2+} + 2\,H_2O/PbO_2 + 4\,H^+ + 2\,e^-$:

$$E_{0\,h(PbO_2)} = +\,1{\cdot}456\ \mathrm{V}$$

The solubility product of $PbSO_4$ at 25 °C is

$$K_{s(PbSO_4)} = [Pb^{2+}][SO_4^{2-}] = 1{\cdot}58 \times 10^{-8}\ (\mathrm{mole/l.})^2$$

The mean activity coefficient for 2 M H_2SO_4 is $f^{\pm}_{H_2SO_4} = 0{\cdot}143$.

Solution 168. The e.m.f. of the lead battery at 25 °C is, from eqn. (242) and where $n_e = 2$:

$$E = E_{hr} - E_{hl} = E_{0\,hr} - E_{0\,hl} + \frac{0{\cdot}0591}{2}\log\left([H^+]^4\,[SO_4^{2-}]^2\right) \quad \ldots. \quad (i)$$

$$= E_{0\,hr} - E_{0\,hl} + 0{\cdot}0591\log\left([H^+]^2\,[SO_4^{2-}]\right) \quad \ldots. \quad (ii)$$

Division into 'half cells' gives

E_{hr}:

$$PbSO_4 + 2\,H_2O/PbO_2 + 4\,H^+ + SO_4^{2-} + 2\,e^-$$

$$E_{hr} = E_{0\,hr} + \frac{0{\cdot}0591}{2}\log\left([H^+]^4\,[SO_4^{2-}]\right) \quad \ldots. \quad (iii)$$

E_{hl}:

$$Pb + SO_4^{2-}/PbSO_4 + 2\,e^-$$

$$E_{hl} = E_{0\,hl} + \frac{0{\cdot}0591}{2}\log\frac{1}{[SO_4^{2-}]} \quad \ldots. \quad (iv)$$

It is now a matter of relating the unknowns, $E_{0\,hr}$ and $E_{0\,hl}$, to the given standard reference e.m.f.'s, $E_{0\,h(Pb/Pb^{2+})}$ and $E_{0\,h(PbO_2)}$.

From eqn. (244) we find

$$E_{h(Pb/Pb^{2+})} = E_{0\,h(Pb/Pb^{2+})} + \frac{0{\cdot}0591}{2}\log[Pb^{2+}] \quad \ldots. \quad (v)$$

which, by using the solubility product

$$K_{s(PbSO_4)} = [Pb^{2+}]\,[SO_4^{2-}]$$

may be rewritten as

$$E_{h(Pb/Pb^{2+})} = E_{0\,h(Pb/Pb^{2+})} + \frac{0{\cdot}0591}{2}\log K_{s(PbSO_4)} + \frac{0{\cdot}0591}{2}\log\frac{1}{[SO_4^{2-}]} \quad \ldots. \quad (vi)$$

Hence, by comparing (iv) and (vi):

$$E_{0\,hl} = E_{0\,h(Pb/Pb^{2+})} + \frac{0{\cdot}0591}{2}\log K_{s(PbSO_4)} \quad \text{[see also eqn. (285)]} \quad \ldots. \quad (vii)$$

Similarly, from eqn. (244)

$$E_{h(PbO_2)} = E_{0h(PbO_2)} + \frac{0 \cdot 0591}{2} \log \frac{[H^+]^4}{[Pb^{2+}]} \quad \ldots \text{(viii)}$$

which, by introducing $K_{s(PbSO_4)}$, is rewritten as

$$E_{h(PbO_2)} = E_{0h(PbO_2)} - \frac{0 \cdot 0591}{2} \log K_{s(PbSO_4)} + \frac{0 \cdot 0591}{2} \log ([H^+]^4 [SO_4^{2-}]) \quad \ldots \text{(ix)}$$

Hence, by comparing (iii) and (ix)

$$E_{0hr} = E_{0h(PbO_2)} - \frac{0 \cdot 0591}{2} \log K_{s(PbSO_4)} \quad \ldots \text{(x)}$$

One then has the following relation from (x) and (vii):

$$E_{0hr} - E_{0hl} = E_{0h(PbO_2)} - E_{0h(Pb/Pb^{2+})} - 0 \cdot 0591 \log K_{s(PbSO_4)} \quad \ldots \text{(xi)}$$

This expression may also, of course, be obtained directly from (i) and the solubility product; taking $[H^+] = 1$, $[Pb^{2+}] = 1$, $[SO_4^{2-}] = K_{s(PbSO_4)}/[Pb^{2+}] = K_{s(PbSO_4)}$, (i) then becomes: $E_{0h(PbO_2)} - E_{0h(Pb/Pb^{2+})} = E_{0hr} - E_{0hl} + 0 \cdot 0591 \log K_{s(PbSO_4)}$. Substituting the numerical values gives

$$\left.\begin{aligned} E_{0hr} - E_{0hl} &= +1 \cdot 456 - (-0 \cdot 126) - 0 \cdot 0591 \log (1 \cdot 58 \times 10^{-8}) \\ &= 1 \cdot 582 + 0 \cdot 0591 \times 7 \cdot 801 = 2 \cdot 043 \text{ V} \end{aligned}\right\} \quad \ldots \text{(xii)}$$

Thus (ii) becomes

$$E = 2 \cdot 043 + 0 \cdot 0591 \log ([H^+]^2 [SO_4^{2-}]) \quad \ldots \text{(xiii)}$$

where $[H^+]$ and $]SO_4^{2-}]$ represent the ionic activities in 2 M H_2SO_4.

One has, by definition [see eqns. (230) to (232)] where c = concentration of H_2SO_4 = 2 mole/l.):

$$[H^+]^2 [SO_4^{2-}] = (f_+ 2c)^2 (f_- c) = (f_+)^2 f_- 4c^3 = (f_\pm)^3 4c^3 \quad \ldots \text{(xiv)}$$

where

$$f^{\pm}_{H_2SO_4} = \sqrt[3]{(f_+)^2 f_-}$$

Substituting:

$$\begin{aligned} E = 2 \cdot 043 + 0 \cdot 0591 \log [4(0 \cdot 143 \times 2)^3] &= 2 \cdot 043 + 0 \cdot 0591 (0 \cdot 971 - 2) \\ &= 2 \cdot 043 - 0 \cdot 0608 = 1 \cdot 982 \text{ V} \end{aligned}$$

Experience shows that the e.m.f. of the lead battery lies between 1·8 and 2·1 V, depending on the sulphuric acid concentration. (The density of the acid lies between 1·15 and 1·20 g/cm³, according to the state of charge.)

Exercise 169

Aluminium is manufactured by the electrolysis of alumina (Al_2O_3) dissolved in fused cryolite (Na_3AlF_6). The alumina is obtained from bauxite, AlO(OH). Cryolite is a complex salt which is easily decomposed ($3NaF + AlF_3$) and is used because Al_2O_3 is a poor conductor of electricity and also has a very high melting point. The melt temperature is 950 °C and the liberated molten aluminium (m.pt. 659 °C) sinks to the bottom. Fluorspar is also added to lower the melting point of the cryolite (m.pt. 1000 °C). The Al_2O_3 content of the bath is 10 per cent; 30 per cent would represent saturation. Retort graphite (electrode carbon) is used as anode.

Calculate the decomposition voltage E_0 of Al_2O_3 under the given conditions, both for the case when an unattackable anode is used and when a graphite anode is used and CO is formed. Also check whether the decomposition voltage of the fluoride is sufficiently high (in the case of both types of anode) to ensure that no significant quantities of fluorine (F_2) or carbon tetrafluoride (CF_4) are formed during electrolysis. The calculation should be only a 'first approximation', i.e. specific heats should not be taken into account. One finds the following data from tables (see p. 103):

	ΔH^F_{298} (kcal/mole)	$S_{0\,298}$ [cal/(deg. mole)]	*Heat of fusion*, l_f (kcal/mole)
Al	0	6·75	2·49 at 932 °K
Al_2O_3	− 394·5	12·5	
O_2	0	49·02	
C (electrode carbon)	+ 1·92	1·36	
CO	− 26·84	47·32	
F_2	0	47·99	
CF_4	− 163	62·0	
Ca	0	9·95	3·15 at 1123 °K
CaF_2	− 290·2	16·4	
Na	0	12·2	0·63 at 371 °K
NaF	− 135·95	12	
AlF_3	− 329	8·4	

Solution 169. Using eqns. (199) and (238a), calculation of the reaction work at constant pressure, $\Delta G = \Delta H - T\Delta S$, and the electromotive force for the reactions in question gives

$$E_0 = \frac{-\Delta G_0}{n_e \times 23\,055}\ (\text{volt}) = \frac{T\Delta S - \Delta H}{n_e \times 23\,055} \quad \ldots\ldots \quad \text{(i)}$$

where $T = 950 + 273 = 1223$ °K

As a first approximation [see eqn. (197)], we now introduce ΔH^F_{298} and $\Delta S_{0\,298}$ into this expression—increased, if necessary, by the heats of fusion (l_f) and entropies of fusion ($\Delta S_{Tf} = l_f/T_f$).

(1) $Al_2O_3 = 2\,Al + \frac{3}{2}O_2$ ($n_e = 6$, unattackable electrodes)

$$\Delta S = 2 \times 6{\cdot}75 + \frac{2 \times 2490}{932} + \frac{3 \times 49{\cdot}02}{2} - 12{\cdot}5 = +79{\cdot}8\ \text{cal/(deg. mole)}$$

$$\Delta H = +2 \times 2{\cdot}49 - (-394{\cdot}5) = +399{\cdot}5\ \text{kcal/mole} \quad [\text{eqn. (146)}]$$

$$E_0 = \frac{1223 \times 79{\cdot}8 - 399{\cdot}5 \times 10^3}{6 \times 23\,055} = -2{\cdot}18\ \text{V decomposition voltage} \quad \ldots\ldots \quad \text{(ii)}$$

The negative sign signifies that the process does not take place spontaneously in the given direction, but must be induced (by application of the decomposition voltage).

The validity of the calculation depends on the assumptions that $p_{O_2} = 1$ atm and that solid Al_2O_3, or a saturated solution of it in equilibrium with solid Al_2O_3, is present, i.e. causing no difference in free enthalpy. The heat of solution of Al_2O_3 in cryolite has been ignored. If the oxygen pressure and Al_2O_3 concentration are taken into account, one obtains from eqn. (242):

$$E = E_0 + \frac{RT}{6F} \ln \frac{c_{Al_2O_3}}{c_{Al_2O_3\,(\text{saturated})}\, p_{O_2}^{3/2}} \quad \ldots\ldots \quad \text{(iii)}$$

The term $c_{Al_2O_3\,(\text{saturated})}$ must be included as a reference, so that the ratio of the Al_2O_3 concentrations under the logarithm becomes equal to 1 at saturation. If only 10 per cent Al_2O_3, instead of 30 per cent (saturation), is dissolved in the cryolite and if $p_{O_2} = 1$ atm, one has

$$E = -2{\cdot}18 + \frac{1{\cdot}984 \times 10^{-4}}{6} 1223 \log \frac{10}{30} = -2{\cdot}18 - 0{\cdot}0193 = -2{\cdot}20\ \text{V}$$

For practical purposes, therefore, the supplementary calculation (iii) may be ignored.

(2) $Al_2O_3 + 3C = 2Al + 3CO$ ($n_e = 6$, retort carbon as anode)

$$\Delta S = 2 \times 6{\cdot}75 + \frac{2 \times 2490}{932} + 3 \times 47{\cdot}32 - 12{\cdot}5 - 3 \times 1{\cdot}36 = 144{\cdot}2\ \text{cal/(deg. mole)}$$

$$\Delta H = 2 \times 2{\cdot}49 + (-3 \times 26{\cdot}84) - (-394{\cdot}5 + 3 \times 1{\cdot}92) = 313{\cdot}2\ \text{kcal/mole}$$

$$E_0 = \frac{1223 \times 144{\cdot}2 - 313{\cdot}2 \times 10^3}{6 \times 23\,055} = -0{\cdot}99\ \text{V in the saturated state}$$

$$E = -1{\cdot}01\ \text{V at 10 per cent } Al_2O_3$$

It is thus possible to obtain a considerable reduction in decomposition voltage if carbon anodes are used.

(3) $2NaF = 2Na + F_2$ ($n_e = 2$, unattackable electrodes)

$$\Delta S = 2 \times 12{\cdot}2 + \frac{2 \times 630}{371} + 47{\cdot}99 - 2 \times 12 = 51{\cdot}8\ \text{cal/(deg. mole)}$$

$$\Delta H = 2 \times 0{\cdot}63 - (-2 \times 135{\cdot}95) = +273{\cdot}2\ \text{kcal/mole}$$

$$E_0 = \frac{1223 \times 51{\cdot}8 - 273{\cdot}2 \times 10^3}{2 \times 23\,055} = -4{\cdot}54\ \text{V}$$

(4) $4NaF + C = 4Na + CF_4$ ($n_e = 4$, retort carbon as anode)

$$\Delta S = 4 \times 12{\cdot}2 + \frac{4 \times 630}{371} + 62{\cdot}0 - 4 \times 12 - 1{\cdot}36 = 68{\cdot}2\ \text{cal/(deg. mole)}$$

$$\Delta H = 4 \times 0{\cdot}63 + (-163) - (-4 \times 135{\cdot}95 + 1{\cdot}92) = 381{\cdot}4\ \text{kcal/mole}$$

$$E_0 = \frac{1223 \times 68{\cdot}2 - 381{\cdot}4 \times 10^3}{4 \times 23\,055} = -3{\cdot}23\ \text{V}$$

The decomposition potentials for NaF, either with or without retort carbon, are therefore much greater than the value for Al_2O_3. It follows that only traces of CF_4 or F_2 can be formed during the electrolysis.

(5) $CaF_2 = Ca + F_2$ ($n_e = 2$, unattackable electrodes)

$$\Delta S = 9{\cdot}95 + \frac{3150}{1123} + 47{\cdot}99 - 16{\cdot}4 = 44{\cdot}35 \text{ cal/(deg. mole)}$$

$$\Delta H = 3{\cdot}15 - (-290{\cdot}2) = 293{\cdot}35 \text{ kcal/mole}$$

$$E_0 = \frac{1223 \times 44{\cdot}35 - 293{\cdot}35 \times 10^3}{2 \times 23\,055} = -5{\cdot}18 \text{ V}$$

(6) $2CaF_2 + C = 2Ca + CF_4$ ($n_e = 4$, retort carbon as anode)

$$\Delta S = 2 \times 9{\cdot}95 + \frac{2 \times 3150}{1123} = 62{\cdot}0 - 2 \times 16{\cdot}4 - 1{\cdot}36 = 53{\cdot}3 \text{ cal/(deg. mole)}$$

$$\Delta H = 2 \times 3{\cdot}15 + (-163) - (-2 \times 290{\cdot}2 + 1{\cdot}92) = 421{\cdot}8 \text{ kcal/mole}$$

$$E_0 = \frac{1223 \times 53{\cdot}3 - 421{\cdot}8 \times 10^3}{4 \times 23\,055} = -3{\cdot}87 \text{ V}$$

(7) $2AlF_3 = 2Al + 3F_3$ ($n_e = 6$, unattackable electrodes)

$$\Delta S = 2 \times 6{\cdot}75 + \frac{2 \times 2490}{932} + 3 \times 47{\cdot}99 - 2 \times 8{\cdot}4 = 146{\cdot}0 \text{ cal/(deg. mole)}$$

$$\Delta H = 2 \times 2{\cdot}49 - (-2 \times 329) = 663 \text{ kcal/mole}$$

$$E_0 = \frac{1223 \times 146{\cdot}0 - 663 \times 10^3}{6 \times 23\,055} = -3{\cdot}50 \text{ V}$$

(8) $4AlF_3 + 3C = 4Al + 3CF_4$ ($n_e = 12$, retort carbon as anode)

$$\Delta S = 4 \times 6{\cdot}75 + \frac{4 \times 2490}{932} + 3 \times 62{\cdot}0 - 4 \times 8{\cdot}4 - 3 \times 1{\cdot}36 = 186{\cdot}0 \text{ cal/(deg. mole)}$$

$$\Delta H = 4 \times 2{\cdot}49 + (-3 \times 163) - (-4 \times 329 + 3 \times 1{\cdot}92) = 831{\cdot}2 \text{ kcal/mole}$$

$$E_0 = \frac{1223 \times 186{\cdot}0 - 831{\cdot}2 \times 10^3}{12 \times 23\,055} = -2{\cdot}18 \text{ V}$$

in comparison with $-1{\cdot}01$ V for Al_2O_3 with retort carbon. All decomposition voltages for possible side reactions therefore have appreciably higher values than the corresponding values for Al_2O_3.

Note. The actual bath voltage is, of course, higher, in order to overcome the internal ohmic resistance of the melt. The energy required to do this helps to maintain the bath temperature. Although fluorine can only be formed in trace quantities, these do constitute a difficulty in aluminium works because of their harmful effect (as HF) on agriculture even when present in small concentrations, depending on weather conditions, e.g. fog.

Exercise 170

An electrolytic trough contains a small rotating platinum tip, of surface area $0{\cdot}3$ cm², as cathode, and a large unpolarizable platinum anode. The solution consists of $0{\cdot}1$ N KI, in which $0{\cdot}002$ g of iodine are dissolved; the temperature is 18 °C. Calculate the limiting current and the overall course of the current/voltage (polarographic) curve, on the assumption that the boundary layer adhering to the rotating platinum electrode has a thickness of 5×10^{-4} cm. The diffusion coefficient of I_2 is $0{\cdot}6$ cm²/day.

The standard reference e.m.f. of (solid) iodine, $2\,I^-/I_2 + 2\,e^-$, is $E_{0h(I_2)} = +0{\cdot}535$ V; see eqns. (266) to (270).

Solution 170. It is explained in textbooks that a flow of current takes place even before the decomposition voltage of the HI is reached. This is because the cathode, charged with hydrogen, becomes depolarized by reduction of I_2 to HI, insofar as I_2 diffuses through the boundary layer onto the cathode. The current is determined by the rate of diffusion of I_2, i.e. until the voltage becomes so high that hydrogen can escape in gaseous form (decomposition voltage).

The limiting current, I_0, is defined by eqn. (268) where $c_k = 0$. The concentration is in mole/cm³ and the diffusion coefficient in cm²/sec. Since there are 86,400 sec in 1 day, the diffusion coefficient must be divided by 86,400 in order to convert from cm²/day to cm²/sec. Taking the atomic weight of iodine as 126·9, we have from eqn. (268):

$$I_0 = \frac{2 \times 96495 \times 0{\cdot}6 \times 0{\cdot}3 \times 0{\cdot}002}{86400 \times 126{\cdot}9 \times 2 \times 5 \times 10^{-4}} = 6{\cdot}34 \times 10^{-3} \text{ amp, for the limiting current} \quad \ldots \quad \text{(i)}$$

Equations (269) and (270) determine the current/voltage curve up to the point when the limiting current is reached. Hence, under the given conditions

$$E_{pol} = \frac{0{\cdot}0578}{2} \log \frac{0{\cdot}002}{c'_k} \quad \ldots \quad \text{(ii)}$$

$I = I_0 \dfrac{c'_0 - c'_k}{c'_0}$ where c' indicates the concentration in g/cm²

$$I = 6{\cdot}34 \times 10^{-3} \frac{0{\cdot}002 - c'_k}{0{\cdot}002} \quad \ldots \quad \text{(iii)}$$

The current/voltage curve is obtained by calculating E_{pol} and I for a number of values of the parameter c'_k. It should be noted that a new rise in the curve (above the limiting current) takes place when the voltage is increased into the range of the standard reference e.m.f. for I_2 (0·535 V), i.e. in the region of the decomposition voltage for HI.

The following values are obtained from (ii) and (iii):

c'_k (g/cm³)	E_{pol} (volt)	I (amp)
1·6 × 10^{-3}	0·0028	0·2 I_0
1·2 × 10^{-3}	0·0064	0·4 I_0
0·8 × 10^{-3}	0·0115	0·6 I_0
0·4 × 10^{-3}	0·0202	0·8 I_0
0·2 × 10^{-3}	0·0289	0·9 I_0
0·1 × 10^{-3}	0·0375	0·95 I_0
0·04 × 10^{-3}	0·049	0·98 I_0
0·02 × 10^{-3}	0·0578	0·99 I_0
0·002 × 10^{-3}	0·0866	0·999 I_0

It will be seen from the figures, especially when I is plotted as ordinate against E_{pol} as abscissa, that the current/voltage (polarographic) curve increases asymptotically from $E_{pol} = 0$ and virtually reaches the value for the limiting current at a figure of 0·1 V. This limiting value will be maintained until the voltage enters the region of the decomposition voltage for HI, i.e. about 0·5 V. A new rise will then occur.

Exercise 171

An electrolytic trough contains a solution of 0·01 N $AgNO_3$ + 0·1 N KNO_3. The cathode is a rotating silver tip of 0·08 cm² surface area; the anode is a large, virtually unpolarizable silver electrode; the test temperature is 18 °C. In determining the polarographic curve, the limiting current was found to be $I_0 = 1{\cdot}5 \times 10^{-3}$ amp. Determine the thickness of the boundary layer round the rotating silver tip. The diffusion coefficient should be calculated from eqn. (266a). The equivalent conductivity of Ag^+ is $\Lambda_{K\,(eq)} = 44$ mho cm²/mole in the given solution (0·11 N).

Solution 171. The diffusion coefficient may be calculated from eqn. (266a):

$$D = \frac{44 \times 8{\cdot}3144 \times 291}{1 \times 96\,495 \times 96\,495} = 1{\cdot}14 \times 10^{-5} \text{ cm}^2/\text{sec} \quad \ldots\ldots \quad \text{(i)}$$

where $z = 1$, $u_k = \Lambda_{k\,(eq)}/F$ and R is in joule/(deg. mole). Substituting this in eqn. (268) (concentration in mole/cm³)

$$1{\cdot}5 \times 10^{-3} = \frac{1 \times 96\,495 \times 1{\cdot}14 \times 10^{-5} \times 0{\cdot}08 \times 0{\cdot}01 \times 10^{-3}}{\delta} \quad \ldots\ldots \quad \text{(ii)}$$

$\delta = 5{\cdot}86 \times 10^{-4}$ cm as the thickness of the boundary layer.

Note. In contrast to Exercise 170, concentration polarization takes place in this case. This is because, at the cathode and as a result of deposition of silver, the solution in the boundary layer becomes weak in silver ions; i.e. the diffusion current of the Ag^+ ions through the boundary layer, to the cathode, will be the current-determining factor and the concentration difference will determine the potential.

Exercise 172

Appraise, by calculation, the reduction of CO_2-saturated water (or better still, a solution of K_2SO_4 saturated with CO_2) to formic acid at 25 °C: $H_2O + CO_2 = HCOOH + \frac{1}{2}O_2$. It is to be shown that this reduction is not possible if an unpolarizable platinum cathode is used since, in this case, decomposition of water takes place with the generation of hydrogen. However, formation of formic acid does occur without the generation of hydrogen, if lead or zinc cathodes are used on which a hydrogen overpotential of about 0·6 V exists. The following thermal data have been taken from tables (see p. 103):

	ΔH^F_{298} (kcal/mol.)	$S_{0\,298}$ [cal/(deg. mole)]
$H_{2\,(gas)}$	—	31·23
$O_{2\,(gas)}$	—	49·02
$H_2O_{\,(liq)}$	− 68·32	16·75
$CO_{2\,(gas)}$	− 94·03	51·09
$HCOOH_{(liq)}$	− 99·53	33·0

Solution *172*. The reaction work at constant pressure, from eqns. (199) and (238), is $\Delta G = \Delta H - T\Delta S$ and

$$E_0 = \frac{-\Delta G_0}{n_e \times 23\,055}\,(\text{volt}) = \frac{T\Delta S - \Delta H}{n_e \times 23\,055} \qquad T = 25 + 273 = 298^\circ\,\text{K}$$

For the decomposition of water, $H_2O_{(liq)} = H_2 + \frac{1}{2} O_2$ ($n_e = 2$), we obtain:

$$\Delta H = 0 - (-68{\cdot}32) = +68{\cdot}32 \text{ kcal/mole} \quad \text{[see (146)]}$$

$$\Delta S = 31{\cdot}23 + \tfrac{1}{2} \times 49{\cdot}02 - 16{\cdot}75 = 38{\cdot}99 \text{ cal/(deg. mole)}$$

$$E_{0\,(H_2O)} = \frac{298 \times 38{\cdot}99 - 68{\cdot}32 \times 10^3}{2 \times 23055} = -1{\cdot}229 \text{ V} \qquad \ldots . \quad \text{(i)}$$

as the decomposition voltage for water. The negative sign indicates that the reaction does not take place spontaneously with the liberation of current, but that electrical energy must be supplied in order to decompose the water.

For the reduction of CO_2, $CO_{2\,(gas)} + H_2O_{(liq)} = HCOOH_{(liq)} + \frac{1}{2} O_{2\,(gas)}$, ($n_e = 2$), one has

$$\Delta H = -99{\cdot}53 - (-68{\cdot}32 - 94{\cdot}03) = +62{\cdot}82 \text{ kcal/mole}$$

$$\Delta S = 33 + 24{\cdot}51 - 16{\cdot}75 - 51{\cdot}09 = -10{\cdot}33 \text{ cal/(deg. mole)}$$

$$E_{0\,(\text{formic acid})} = \frac{-298 \times 10{\cdot}33 - 62{\cdot}82 \times 10^3}{2 \times 23055} = -1{\cdot}429 \text{ V} \qquad \ldots . \quad \text{(ii)}$$

This reduction voltage is valid for CO_2 at 1 atm, or for CO_2-saturated water existing in equilibrium with gaseous CO_2 at 1 atm pressure, and for pure liquid formic acid. If the formic acid is strongly diluted with water (since formic acid is miscible with water in all proportions), an expression of the form in eqn. (242) is to be added:

$$\Delta E = +\frac{0{\cdot}0591}{2} \log \frac{[\text{formic acid (pure)/l.}]}{[\text{formic acid (diluted)/l.}]} = +0{\cdot}02955 \log (\text{degree of dilution})$$

i.e. at a dilution of 1000:1 [ca. $0{\cdot}03 \times 3 = +0{\cdot}09$ V (approx.)] there would be a decrease by this amount in the reduction voltage, i.e. to a value of $-1{\cdot}34$ V, not taking activity coefficients into account.

Comparison of (i) and (ii) shows that, in fact, reduction of CO_2 in water is not possible when normal, unpolarizable cathodes (platinum and palladium) are used. This is because a voltage of 1·429 would be required whereas water decomposes, with generation of hydrogen at the cathode, at a voltage of only 1·229. If, however, one uses lead or zinc cathodes, at which a hydrogen overvoltage of about 0·6 V exists (and where, therefore, decomposition of water occurs not at 1·229 V but only at $1{\cdot}229 + 0{\cdot}6 = 1{\cdot}829$ V) CO_2 can be reduced to formic acid without prior liberation of hydrogen. No consideration is given here to the possible existence of an overvoltage at the anode, since it works out at the same level in both cases, i.e. is of no use for the purpose of comparison. It is not possible to reduce CO_2 using silver, iron or copper cathodes. With these, a hydrogen overvoltage is present but amounts to only about 0·2 to 0·3 V and is therefore insufficient to allow reduction to be effected.

14

REACTION KINETICS AND CATALYSIS CHAIN REACTIONS. PHOTOCHEMISTRY. RADIOACTIVITY. ADSORPTION

First-order Reactions

$$\left.\begin{aligned}&\frac{\mathrm{d}x}{\mathrm{d}t} = k^{\mathrm{I}}(a-x), \quad -\frac{\mathrm{d}N}{\mathrm{d}t} = k^{\mathrm{I}}N, \quad -\frac{\mathrm{d}c}{\mathrm{d}t} = k^{\mathrm{I}}c \quad \text{i.e. } N = N_0\,\mathrm{e}^{-k^{\mathrm{I}}t}\\ &\ln\frac{N_0}{N} = \ln\frac{a}{a-x} = \ln\frac{c_0}{c} = k^{\mathrm{I}}t = \frac{t}{T^{\mathrm{I}}}\ln 2 \quad \text{or} \quad \ln\frac{a-x_1}{a-x_2} = k^{\mathrm{I}}(t_2-t_1)\end{aligned}\right\} \quad \ldots (271)$$

$$\tau^{\mathrm{I}} = \frac{1}{k^{\mathrm{I}}};\ T^{\mathrm{I}} = \tau^{\mathrm{I}}\ln 2 = \frac{\ln 2}{k^{\mathrm{I}}} = \frac{\log 2}{0{\cdot}4343\,k^{\mathrm{I}}} = \frac{0{\cdot}6931}{k^{\mathrm{I}}} \quad \begin{pmatrix}\log = 0{\cdot}4343\ln\\ \ln = 2{\cdot}303\log\end{pmatrix} \quad \ldots\ldots (272)$$

N = number of particles, N_0 = initial number of reactant particles

a, b, c_0 = initial concentrations of reactants, usually in mole/l.

x_i = concentrations of reactants (usually in mole/l.) which are converted up to time t_i (usually in min)

k^{I} = velocity constant of the first order, [time^{-1}], independent of concentration; decay constant

τ = mean life

T = half-life period

Radioactive decay is a reaction of the first order and eqns. (271)–(272) are therefore applicable. The radioactive decay constant will usually be denoted by λ [time^{-1}] instead of k^{I}.

Second-order Reactions

$$\frac{\mathrm{d}x}{\mathrm{d}t} = k^{\mathrm{II}}(a-x)^2, \quad k^{\mathrm{II}}t = \frac{x}{a(a-x)} = -\frac{1}{a} + \frac{1}{a-x}, \quad T^{\mathrm{II}} = \frac{1}{k^{\mathrm{II}}a} \quad \ldots\ldots (273)$$

$$\frac{\mathrm{d}x}{\mathrm{d}t} = k^{\mathrm{II}}(a-x)(b-x), \quad k^{\mathrm{II}}t = \frac{1}{a-b}\ln\frac{(a-x)\,b}{(b-x)\,a} \quad \ldots\ldots (274)$$

k^{II} = velocity (rate) constant of the second order [concentration^{-1} × time^{-1}].

Third-order Reactions

$$\frac{\mathrm{d}x}{\mathrm{d}t} = k^{\mathrm{III}}(a-x)^3, \quad k^{\mathrm{III}}t = \frac{(2a-x)\,x}{2a^2(a-x)^2}, \quad T^{\mathrm{III}} = \frac{3}{2\,k^{\mathrm{III}}a^2} \quad \ldots\ldots (275)$$

General formula for reactions of the nth order:

$$\left.\begin{aligned} \frac{dx}{dt} = k^{(n)}(a - x)^n, \quad k^{(n)}(t_2 - t_1) = \frac{1}{n-1}\left[\frac{1}{(a - x_2)^{n-1}} - \frac{1}{(a - x_1)^{n-1}}\right] \\ T^{(n)} = \frac{1}{n-1} \times \frac{2^{n-1} - 1}{k^{(n)} a^{n-1}} \end{aligned}\right\} \quad .. (276)$$

In the case of a large number of heterogeneous chemical reactions, especially in those where extensive boundary surfaces or a large homogeneous or interface reaction velocity exist, the rate of reaction is determined by the rate of transport or diffusion, e.g. from inside the solution, through the boundary layer to the interface. In this case, we have, using Fick's first law (266):

$$\frac{dx}{dt} = \frac{DA}{V} \times \frac{a - x}{\delta}$$

which appears to be a reaction of the first order, with $k^{\mathrm{I}} = DA/V\delta$, where D is the diffusion coefficient, A the surface area, δ the thickness of the boundary layer and V the volume of solution. Note the dimensions; see eqn. (266).

Zero-order Reactions

$$\frac{dx}{dt} = k^{(0)} \quad .... (278)$$

for heterogeneous reactions with strong adsorption.

Compound Reactions

(1) $\mathrm{A} \xrightarrow{k_1} \mathrm{B} \qquad \mathrm{B} \xrightarrow{k_2} \mathrm{C}$

First-order monomolecular decomposition of A and B, reverse reaction to be ignored.

Application: radioactive decay series.

From eqn. (271):

$$\left.\begin{array}{lll} (a) & -\dfrac{d[\mathrm{A}]}{dt} = k_1[\mathrm{A}] & \text{rate of decomposition of initial substance A} \\ (b) & -\dfrac{d[\mathrm{B}]}{dt} = -k_1[\mathrm{A}] + k_2[\mathrm{B}] & \text{rate of decrease of unstable intermediate product B} \\ (c) & +\dfrac{d[\mathrm{C}]}{dt} = +k_2[\mathrm{B}] & \text{rate of formation of stable end product C} \end{array}\right\} \quad .. (279)$$

The general solutions for eqn. (279) are (see Exercise 184):

$$\left.\begin{array}{ll} (a) & [\mathrm{A}] = [\mathrm{A}_0]\, e^{-k_1 t} \\ (b) & [\mathrm{B}] = \dfrac{[\mathrm{A}_0]\, k_1}{k_2 - k_1}(e^{-k_1 t} - e^{-k_2 t}) \\ (c) & [\mathrm{C}] = [\mathrm{A}_0]\left\{1 - \dfrac{k_1 k_2}{k_2 - k_1}\left(\dfrac{e^{-k_1 t}}{k_1} - \dfrac{e^{-k_2 t}}{k_2}\right)\right\} \end{array}\right\} \quad .. (280)$$

If the reaction series is in stationary equilibrium, i.e. the concentration of the intermediate product is temporarily constant, then one has from eqn. (279b):

rate of decomposition = rate of formation

$$\left.\begin{array}{ll}\text{or} & \dfrac{-\,\mathrm{d}[\mathrm{B}]}{\mathrm{d}t} = -\,k_1[\mathrm{A}] + k_2[\mathrm{B}] = 0 \quad \text{i.e. } k_1[\mathrm{A}] = k_2[\mathrm{B}] \\ \text{or} & \dfrac{[\mathrm{A}]}{[\mathrm{B}]} = \dfrac{k_2}{k_1} = \dfrac{T_1}{T_2} \quad \text{condition for [B] being a maximum}\end{array}\right\} \quad ..(281)$$

If k_2 is large in comparison with k_1, i.e. B has a short life period, it follows from eqn. (281) that the concentration of B will always be low and that a maximum will be reached at an early stage within a short induction period. One then has the approximation

$$\frac{\mathrm{d}[\mathrm{B}]}{\mathrm{d}t} \approx 0 \quad ....(282)$$

This is referred to as a quasi-stationary state and its assumption greatly simplifies the handling of eqn. (280) and of corresponding equations for other series of reactions. From eqn. (279) and taking eqn. (281) into account, one obtains the following expressions for the quasi-stationary state:

$$-\frac{\mathrm{d}[\mathrm{A}]}{\mathrm{d}t} = k_1[\mathrm{A}] \qquad +\frac{\mathrm{d}[\mathrm{C}]}{\mathrm{d}t} = k_2[\mathrm{B}] = k_1[\mathrm{A}] = -\frac{\mathrm{d}[\mathrm{A}]}{\mathrm{d}t} \quad ....(283)$$

In this case, the slowest reaction, i.e. the decomposition of A, will be the rate-determining factor for total decomposition and formation of the end product C:

$$\left.\begin{array}{l}[\mathrm{A}] = [\mathrm{A}_0]\,\mathrm{e}^{-k_1 t}, \quad [\mathrm{C}] = [\mathrm{A}_0] - [\mathrm{A}] = [\mathrm{A}_0]\,(1 - \mathrm{e}^{-k_1 t}) \\ \dfrac{[\mathrm{C}]}{[\mathrm{A}]} = \dfrac{1 - \mathrm{e}^{-k_1 t}}{\mathrm{e}^{-k_1 t}} = \mathrm{e}^{k_1 t} - 1 = \mathrm{e}^{\frac{\ln 2}{T_1} t} - 1 = 2^{\frac{t}{T_1}} - 1\end{array}\right\} \quad ..(284)$$

See Exercise 184 regarding the establishment of a kinetic equilibrium.

(2) $$\mathrm{A} \underset{k_2}{\overset{k_1}{\rightleftharpoons}} \mathrm{B} \qquad \mathrm{B} \xrightarrow{k_2} \mathrm{C}$$

First-order monomolecular decomposition of A and B, reverse reaction $\mathrm{B} \rightarrow \mathrm{A}$ plays a part.

$$\left.\begin{array}{lr}(a) & -\dfrac{\mathrm{d}[\mathrm{A}]}{\mathrm{d}t} = k_1[\mathrm{A}] - k_1'[\mathrm{B}] \\ (b) & -\dfrac{\mathrm{d}[\mathrm{B}]}{\mathrm{d}t} = -k_1[\mathrm{A}] + (k_1' + k_2)[\mathrm{B}] \\ (c) & +\dfrac{\mathrm{d}[\mathrm{C}]}{\mathrm{d}t} = k_2[\mathrm{B}]\end{array}\right\} \quad ..(285)$$

In the quasi-stationary state $\{\mathrm{d}[\mathrm{B}]/\mathrm{d}t \approx 0$; see eqn. (282)$\}$ one has in place of eqns. (281) and (283):

$$[\mathrm{B}] \approx \frac{k_1[\mathrm{A}]}{k_1' + k_2} \qquad -\frac{\mathrm{d}[\mathrm{A}]}{\mathrm{d}t} \approx \frac{\mathrm{d}[\mathrm{C}]}{\mathrm{d}t} \approx \frac{k_1 k_2[\mathrm{A}]}{k_1' + k_2} \quad ....(286)$$

This case is the same as that for eqns. (279)–(284) if $k_2 \gg k_1'$ but, if $k_2 \ll k_1'$, then

$$[B] = \frac{k_1}{k_1'}[A] = K[A] \qquad -\frac{d[A]}{dt} \approx \frac{d[C]}{dt} \approx \frac{k_1 k_2}{k_1'}[A] = K k_2 [A] \quad \ldots . (287)$$

where $K = k_1/k_1' = [B]/[A]$ is the equilibrium constant of the reaction $A \rightleftharpoons B$.

This is the case of initial activation equilibrium; decomposition of the intermediate body is the rate-determining factor (Arrhenius intermediate body).

Temperature dependence of reaction rate:

$$\log k = -\frac{A'}{T} + B = -\frac{A}{2{\cdot}303\,RT} + B = -\frac{A}{4{\cdot}574\,T} + \log H \quad \ldots . (288)$$

or

$$k = H e^{-\frac{A}{RT}} \text{ (Arrhenius equation)} \quad \ldots . (289)$$

A = energy of activation (in cal/mole)

H = frequency factor, collision number

R = gas constant = 1·9865 cal/(deg. mole)

For bimolecular gas reactions,

$$\frac{dx}{dt} = k^{II} c^2 \quad \text{or} \quad \frac{dx}{dt} = k^{II} c_1 c_2 \quad \ldots . (290)$$

[see eqns. (273) and (274)]; the factor H is related to the gas kinetic collision number Z per unit time and unit concentration; see eqns. (37) and (42). We then have for a single gas, e.g. $2AB = A_2 + B_2$:

$$H = 2\alpha Z = 2 \times 2\alpha\sigma^2 \left(\frac{\pi RT}{M}\right)^{1/2} \quad \ldots . (291)$$

α = steric factor (probability factor)

σ = molecular diameter

unit of concentration: molecules/cm³

The factor 2 is due to the fact that 2 molecules of AB disappear per collision. If σ is measured in Å (10^{-8} cm) and $R = 8{\cdot}134 \times 10^7$ erg/(deg. mole), eqn. (291) becomes

$$\left.\begin{array}{ll} H = 6{\cdot}46 \times 10^{-12}\,\alpha\sigma^2 (T/M)^{1/2} & \text{and, where } T = 298\ ^\circ K \\ H = 11{\cdot}16 \times 10^{-11}\,\alpha\sigma^2 M^{-1/2} & \end{array}\right\} \quad \ldots (292)$$

If, in eqn. (290), the concentration is in mole/cm³, it will be necessary to multiply eqn. (292) by $N_A = 6{\cdot}023 \times 10^{23}$ molecules/mol. [k^{II} has the dimensions (concentration^{-1} time^{-1})]. In this case, therefore

$$\left.\begin{array}{ll} H = 3{\cdot}90 \times 10^{12}\,\alpha\sigma^2 (T/M)^{1/2} & \text{and, where } T = 298\ ^\circ K \\ H = 6{\cdot}72 \times 10^{13}\,\alpha\sigma^2 M^{-1/2} & \text{(cm}^3\text{/mole sec)} \end{array}\right\} \quad \ldots (293)$$

When, as is usual in chemistry, the concentration unit is mole/l. [molecular diameter in Å (10^{-8} cm)], eqn. (293) must be multiplied by 10^{-3}, i.e.

$$\left.\begin{array}{ll} H = 3{\cdot}90 \times 10^{9}\,\alpha\sigma^2 (T/M)^{1/2} & \text{and, where } T = 298\ ^\circ K \\ H = 6{\cdot}72 \times 10^{10}\,\alpha\sigma^2 M^{-1/2} & \text{(l./mole sec)} \end{array}\right\} \quad \ldots (294)$$

For gas mixtures, e.g. $A_2 + B_2 = 2\,AB$, one has, from eqn. (42):

$$H = \alpha Z = 2\,\alpha\sigma_{12}^2\left(\frac{2\,\pi RT}{M_r}\right)^{1/2} \quad M_r = \frac{M_1 M_2}{M_1 + M_2}, \text{ the so-called reduced mass} \quad \ldots . (295)$$

$\sigma_{12} = r_1 + r_2$, the mean molecular diameter
units of concentration: molecules/cm³

If σ_{12} is in Å (10^{-8} cm), the concentration in molecules/cm³ and $R = 8{\cdot}314 \times 10^7$ erg/(deg. mole):

$$\left.\begin{aligned} H &= 4{\cdot}57 \times 10^{-12}\alpha\,\sigma_{12}^2 (T/M_r)^{1/2} \quad \text{and, where} \quad T = 298\,°\text{K} \\ H &= 7{\cdot}89 \times 10^{-11}\alpha\,\sigma_{12}^2 M_r^{-1/2} \end{aligned}\right\} \quad . . (296)$$

When the concentration is in mol./cm³:

$$\left.\begin{aligned} H &= 2{\cdot}76 \times 10^{12}\alpha\,\sigma_{12}^2 (T/M_r)^{1/2} \quad \text{and, where} \quad T = 298\,°\text{K} \\ H &= 4{\cdot}75 \times 10^{13}\alpha\,\sigma_{12}^2 M_r^{-1/2} \end{aligned}\right\} \quad . . (297)$$

When the concentration is measured in the usual unit of mole/l. [molecular diameter in Å (10^{-8} cm)]:

$$\left.\begin{aligned} H &= 2{\cdot}76 \times 10^{9}\alpha\,\sigma_{12}^2 (T/M_r)^{1/2} \quad \text{and, where} \quad T = 298\,°\text{K} \\ H &= 4{\cdot}75 \times 10^{10}\alpha\,\sigma_{12}^2 M_r^{-1/2} \end{aligned}\right\} \quad . . (298)$$

Should d[AB]/dt be given, it is necessary to multiply eqns. (296)–(298) by 2; this is because 2 molecules of AB are formed per collision. If, in the equation for rate of reaction [eqn. (290)], the concentrations c_i and x are expressed in terms of the partial pressures p_i and p_x, and where $c_i = p_i/RT$ [eqn. (8)], one then has from eqn. (290):

$$\frac{\mathrm{d}\left(\frac{p_x}{RT}\right)}{\mathrm{d}t} = k^{\text{II}}\frac{p_1}{RT} \times \frac{p_2}{RT} \quad \text{or} \quad \frac{\mathrm{d}p_x}{\mathrm{d}t} = \left[\frac{k^{\text{II}}}{RT}\right] p_1 p_2$$

It follows that, if p is measured in atm or in torr [$R = 0{\cdot}082$ l. atm/(deg. mole) or 62·4 l. torr/(deg. mole)], eqns. (294) and (298) must be divided by $0{\cdot}082\,T$ or $62{\cdot}4\,T$ . . . . (299)

Equation (288) shows that, if $\log k$ is plotted against $1/T$, a straight line should be obtained. According to eqns. (291)–(298), however, H is also dependent on temperature:

$$\log H = 0{\cdot}5 \log T + \log H' \quad \ldots . (300)$$

but much less so than k (not an exponential relationship). Taking eqn. (300) into account and combining eqns. (288) and (294) or (298), one has for bimolecular reactions:

$$\log k^{\text{II}} - 0{\cdot}5 \log T = -\frac{A}{4{\cdot}574\,T} + \log H' \quad \ldots . (301)$$

where $H' = 3{\cdot}90 \times 10^9 \alpha\,\sigma^2 M^{-1/2}$ for a single gas, or $H' = 2{\cdot}76 \times 10^9 \alpha_{12}^2 \sigma M_r^{-1/2}$ for gas mixtures; molecular diameter is in Å (10^{-8} cm), concentration in mole/l.

In order to obtain a straight line, it is therefore better to plot $\log k^{\mathrm{II}} - 0{\cdot}5 \log T$ against $1/T$. .... (302)

The Freundlich adsorption isotherm:

$$\frac{x}{m} = B c^{1/n} \qquad \text{.... (303)}$$

x is the total quantity of substance adsorbed by m grammes of adsorbent in equilibrium with a solution of the adsorbate of concentration c. It is customary to use the following units: $x/m = a$: millimoles adsorbate per 1 g of adsorbent; B is a constant; n is a constant (>1); c is mole/l. of dissolved substance undergoing adsorption.

The Langmuir–Reichinstein adsorption isotherm:

$$a = \frac{x}{m} = \frac{z_s c}{b + c} \quad \text{or} \quad a = \frac{x}{m} = \frac{z_s p}{b + p} \qquad \text{.... (304)}$$

a, x/m and c have the same meaning as above; p indicates the pressure of the material adsorbed when gas adsorption is being considered; z_s is the adsorption saturation value, i.e. the number of adsorption centres (in millimoles of substance adsorbed per gramme of adsorbent) when the surface is saturated with a monomolecular layer of adsorbate; b is a constant [see eqn. (319) below].

The Michaelis and Menten reaction equation has often been found to hold true for enzyme reactions; it is analogous to eqn. (304):

$$\text{rate of reaction} \quad v = \frac{\mathrm{d}x}{\mathrm{d}t} = C\Phi \frac{[\mathrm{S}]}{[\mathrm{S}] + K_s} = C\varphi \qquad \varphi = \Phi \frac{[\mathrm{S}]}{[\mathrm{S}] + K_s} \qquad \text{.... (305)}$$

C = rate-constant factor (monomolecular)
[S] = free substrate concentration (molar, large excess, i.e. virtually the total substrate concentration)
Φ = molar concentration of the total enzyme
The remaining symbols can be described as follows:

(*a*) *Heterogeneous*

φ = concentration of the substrate adsorbed in an enzyme–colloidal carrier system
K_s = the constant b in the Langmuir adsorption isotherm

(*b*) *Homogeneous*

φ = concentration of enzyme-substrate compound (intermediate body; bound enzyme)
K_s = equilibrium dissociation constant (affinity constant):

$$\text{Enzyme substrate } \varphi \rightleftharpoons \text{Enzyme}(\Phi - \varphi) + \text{Substrate [S]}$$

$$\frac{(\Phi - \varphi)[\mathrm{S}]}{\varphi} = K_s \qquad \varphi = \Phi \frac{[\mathrm{S}]}{[\mathrm{S}] + K_s} \qquad \text{.... (307)}$$

Both approaches have proved to be formally and materially identical from the microheterogeneous point of view.

If, especially in ion-exchange reactions, e.g. $A^- + BC^- = AB^- + C^-$, an intermediate body ABC^{2-} features whose formation is the rate-determining factor, then the rate of reaction is expressed by the Brønsted equation for the primary salt effect

$$v = k[A^-][BC^-]\frac{f_{A^-} f_{BC^-}}{f_{ABC^{2-}}} \qquad \ldots . (308)$$

[see also note to Exercise 200 (p. 310)]; f_i are the activity coefficients of the reactants; see eqn. (230).

Using eqn. (233) we find that: $\log f_- = -0.5092\, z_-^2 \sqrt{J}$ and since $z_{ABC^{2-}} = z_{A^-} + z_{BC^-}$, it follows that

$$\log \frac{f_{A^-} f_{BC^-}}{f_{ABC^{2-}}} = +2 \times 0.5092\, z_{A^-} z_{BC^-} \sqrt{J} \qquad \ldots . (310)$$

for very dilute solutions; thus

$$\log v = \log v_0 + 1.0184 + z_{A^-} z_{BC^-} \sqrt{J} \qquad \ldots . (311)$$

A relationship between the rate constants of such bimolecular exchange reactions as $Y + CA = YA + C$ and the affinity of the reactant Y for the exchanged substance A, i.e. the dissociation constant $K_{YA} = [A][Y]/[YA]$ of the substance YA, is in many cases given by Brønsted's expression

$$\overrightarrow{k} = g\, K_{YA}^{-\alpha} \; (1 > \alpha > 0) \qquad \ldots . (312)$$

$$\overleftarrow{k'} = g'\, K_{YA}^{1-\alpha} \qquad \ldots . (313)$$

This relationship has, above all, been shown to be true for base and acid catalysis where A is a proton, H^+ (i.e. $Y + CH^+ = YH^+ + C$).

In this context, and in the Brønsted sense, a base is generally understood to be a proton acceptor (neutral or ion) and an acid to be a proton donor (neutral or ion). In this sence, K_{YA} is the dissociation constant of an acid.

Case 1: neutral base $\underset{\text{base}}{B} + H^+ \rightleftharpoons \underset{\text{acid}}{BH^+}$ ($A = H^+$ $Y = B$)

Here, B is a neutral (non-ionized) base, such as NH_3 or H_2O, and BH^+ is a charged (ionized) acid, such as NH_4^+ or H_3O^+.

The exchange reaction may be written as $B + XH \rightleftharpoons BH^+ + X^-$ with XH or X^- as substrate and where

$$K_{YA} = \frac{[B][H^+]}{[BH^+]} \quad \text{e.g.} \quad \frac{[NH_3][H^+]}{[NH_4^+]} \qquad \ldots . (314)$$

N.B. From left to right represents base catalysis [eqn. (312)] and from right to left, acid catalysis [eqn. (313)].

Case 2: charged base $\underset{\text{base}}{B^-} + H^+ \rightleftharpoons \underset{\text{acid}}{BH}$ ($A = H^+$ $Y = B^-$)

Here, B^- is a charged (ionized) base, such as the acetate ion, and BH is a neutral (undissociated) acid, such as acetic acid.

The exchange reaction may be written as $B^- + XH \rightleftharpoons BH + X^-$ with XH or X^- as substrate and where

$$K_{YA} = \frac{[B^-][H^+]}{[BH]} = K_s \qquad \text{.... (315)}$$

i.e. the dissociation constant of an ordinary acid. *N.B.* from left to right is base catalysis [eqn. (312)], from right to left, acid catalysis [eqn. (313)].

In Case II, for a negatively charged base, the Brønsted expressions at (312) and (313) must be extended to include a statistical factor q/p, in which p indicates the number of (dissociable) protons which the acid BH is able to give up, and q the number of positions at which the base B^- can take up protons; thus

$$\frac{\overrightarrow{k}}{q} = g\left(\frac{q}{p} K_{YA}\right)^{-\alpha} \qquad \text{(base catalysis)} \qquad \text{.... (316)}$$

$$\frac{\overleftarrow{k'}}{p} = g'\left(\frac{q}{p} K_{YA}\right)^{1-\alpha} \qquad \text{(acid catalysis)} \qquad \text{.... (317)}$$

The dissociation constant K_{YA} in Case 1 (neutral base) [eqn. (314)] – more precisely, using H_3O^+ instead of H^+ – is related to the dissociation constant for an ordinary base

$$K_B = \frac{[BH^+][OH^-]}{[B]} \qquad \text{e.g.} \quad \frac{[NH_4^+][OH^-]}{[NH_3 \cdot H_2O]}$$

by means of the expression

$$K_{YA} K_B = [H^+][OH^-] = k_{H_2O}$$

$$K_{YA} = \frac{k_{H_2O}}{K_B} \qquad \text{.... (318)}$$

where $k_{H_2O} \approx 0{\cdot}8 \times 10^{-14}$ (mole/l.)^2 is the ionic product of water (see Exercise 130 for actual values).

Determination of surface by adsorption isotherm measurements:

$A_a = z_s q_M N_A$ .... (319)

A_a = specific surface of adsorbent (per gramme of adsorbent)

z_s = number of adsorption centres (millimoles adsorbate per gramme adsorbent) in connection with the Langmuir adsorption isotherm (304): $a = z_s \frac{p}{b + p}$, where a is the amount adsorbed (millimoles per gramme adsorbent) and p is the total gas pressure of the adsorbate; b is a constant, equal to the pressure at which exactly half the centres z_s are saturated; $1/b$ is therefore a (temperature-dependent) measure of the strength of the adsorptive power of the centres

q_M = surface area occupied by one adsorbed molecule

N_A = Avogadro constant = $6{\cdot}023 \times 10^{20}$ molecules/millimole

$A_a = \alpha A_s$ .... (320)

A_s = accessible specific surface (per gramme adsorbent)

$\alpha = A_a/A_s$ = the adsorbing fraction of the surface (i.e. of the total surface accessible)

$$q_M = \pi r_M^2 = 1{\cdot}21 \left(\frac{V_{mol}}{N_A}\right)^{2/3} \quad (cm^2) \qquad \ldots . (321)$$

= surface area occupied by a single spherically-shaped molecule, where

$$V_{mol} = \frac{M}{\varrho}$$

ϱ = density of the adsorbate (usually in the liquid state);

$$q_M = 3{\cdot}46\, r_M^2 = 1{\cdot}33 \left(\frac{V_{mol}}{N_A}\right)^{2/3} \qquad \ldots . (322)$$

= surface area occupied by a single molecule, for the case of the closest packing of spheres (= area of a regular hexagon circumscribing a circle of molecular radius r_M)

In order to determine z_s from the Langmuir adsorption isotherm, the latter is rearranged as follows:

(*a*) $$1/a = 1/z_s + b/p z_s \qquad \ldots . (323)$$

which gives a straight-line plot of $1/a$ against $1/p$; $1/z_s$ is given as the point of intersection of the straight line with the ordinate axis ($1/p = 0$).

(*b*) $$p/a = p/z_s + b/z_s \qquad \ldots . (324)$$

which gives a straight-line plot of p/a against p, the slope being equal to $1/z_s$.

The Langmuir adsorption isotherm can only be used if the isotherm tends towards a saturation value. Usually, however, the adsorption isotherm is $\sim$-shaped. This is due to multilayer adsorption and to a transition towards capillary condensation. In this case, the adsorption isotherm due to Brunauer, Emmett and Teller (BET method) is used:

$$a = \frac{z_s\, c\, x}{1 - x} \times \frac{1 - (n + 1)\, x^n + n\, x^{n+1}}{1 + (c - 1)\, x - c\, x^{n+1}} \qquad \ldots . (325)$$

where $x = p/p_0$ and p_0 is the vapour pressure (saturation pressure) of the pure adsorbate; c is a constant*; n is the number of molecules adsorbed for each adsorption centre ($n = 1$ for monomolecular coverage of the adsorbing surface); a and z_s are as in eqn. (319).

When $p \ll p_0$ and $n = 1$, and since c is usually $\gg 1$, eqn. (325) can be multiplied out by ignoring square and higher powers of x. This gives:

$$a = z_s \frac{c\, p/p_0}{1 + c\, p/p_0} \qquad \ldots . (326)$$

i.e. the Langmuir type of adsorption isotherm [eqn. (304)] if the numerator and denominator are multiplied by $p_0/c = b$.

---

* x is therefore in the nature of a mol. fraction; x and c are not identical with the similarly indicated quantities in the Freundlich and Langmuir adsorption isotherms, eqn. (303) and (304).

When $n \to \infty$ and $p \ll p_0$, it follows from eqn. (325) that

$$a = \frac{z_s c\, p/p_0}{(1 - p/p_0)[1 + (c-1)\, p/p_0]} \qquad \ldots . (327)$$

When using this formula, it is important that the limiting curve ($n \to \infty$) for $p \ll p_0$ should be reached when n is about 4 or 5.

Evaluation of eqn. (327) enables one to determine z_s from $\sim$-shaped adsorption isotherms for small values of p (i.e. $p \ll p_0$); this is especially so if eqn. (327) is rearranged to give

$$\frac{p}{a\,(p_0 - p)} = \frac{c-1}{z_s c}\, p/p_0 + \frac{1}{z_s c} \qquad \ldots . (328)$$

i.e. a straight-line plot of $p/a(p_0 - p)$ against p/p_0.

z_s is obtained either by addition of the slope $(c-1)/z_s c = \nu$ to the intercept $1/z_s c = \beta$ on the ordinate axis ($p/p_0 = 0$):

$$z_s = \frac{1}{\nu + \beta} \qquad \ldots . (329)$$

or by extrapolation of the rectilinear plot [eqn. (328)] to $p/p_0 = 1$; the ordinate intercept is then $1/z_s$.

In this way, it is possible to determine c. If n is also required, the values found for z_s and c are substituted in eqn. (325) and as close a fit as possible made with the experimental adsorption isotherm, with n as the only parameter.

Photochemical Reactions

$$E_q = N_A h\nu = N_A hc/\lambda = N_A hc\bar{\nu} \qquad \ldots . (331)$$

Planck and Einstein's frequency law for the magnitude of the energy quantum E_q per mole (photochemical equivalent) for light of frequency ν or wavelength λ or wave number $\bar{\nu} = 1/\lambda$

$N_A = 6{\cdot}02368 \times 10^{23}$ molecules per mole (Avogadro constant)

$h = 6{\cdot}6252 \times 10^{-27}$ erg $\times$ sec — Planck's quantum of action

$c = 2{\cdot}99792 \times 10^{10}$ cm/sec — velocity of light

$$\left.\begin{aligned} N_A hc &= 1{\cdot}19641 \times 10^{8} \text{ erg cm/mole} \\ &= 2{\cdot}85846 \text{ cal cm/mole} \\ &= 1{\cdot}23987 \times 10^{-4} \text{ electron volts cm/equiv.} \end{aligned}\right\} = Z$$

$$\left.\begin{aligned} E_q = N_A h\nu = N_A hc/\lambda &= \frac{1{\cdot}196 \times 10^{16}}{\lambda(\text{Å})} \text{ erg/mole} = 1 \text{ einstein} \\ &\qquad\qquad = 1 \text{ mole quantum} \\ &= \frac{2{\cdot}858 \times 10^{8}}{\lambda(\text{Å})} \text{ cal/mole} \end{aligned}\right\} \quad ..(332)$$

where λ is measured in ångstrøm units.

If $\{n_r\}$ is the number of moles of a reactant which is transformed by the absorption of $\{n_q\}$ mol. quanta of light, and $E_{abs} = \{n_q\} E_q$ is the light energy absorbed, then

$$\varphi = \frac{\{n_r\}}{\{n_q\}} \text{ quantum yield of the reaction} \qquad \ldots . (333)$$

where
$$\{n_q\} = \frac{E_{abs}}{N_A h \nu} = \frac{E_{abs}\lambda}{N_A h c} \quad \ldots . (334)$$

Thus

$$\varphi = \frac{\{n_r\} N_L h c}{E_{abs}\lambda} = \frac{1{\cdot}196 \times 10^{16}\{n_r\}}{E_{abs}\lambda} \quad \text{where } E_{abs} \text{ is in erg/mole and } \lambda \text{ in Å} \quad \ldots . (335)$$

$$= \frac{2{\cdot}858 \times 10^{8}\{n_r\}}{E_{abs}\lambda} \quad \text{where } E_{abs} \text{ is in cal/mole and } \lambda \text{ in Å} \quad \ldots . (336)$$

Einstein's law of the photochemical equivalent (fundamental law of photochemistry) requires that each molecule taking part in a chemical reaction induced by exposure to light absorbs one quantum of the radiation causing the reaction, i.e. $\varphi = 1$ .... (337)

It is a fact, however, that φ can be considerably greater than 1, especially in chain reactions, since subsequent reactions can be induced by the primary reaction, φ can also be smaller then 1, e.g. when only a part of the absorbed light leads to primary chemical reaction, the other part being converted to heat by a second type of collision. .... (338)

$E = mc^2$ (Einstein mass–energy relation) .... (339)

m = mass in grammes

$c^2 = 8{\cdot}987524 \times 10^{20}$ erg/g = Y (Einstein's constant)

E = energy in ergs

Heterogeneous Gas Reactions on Catalysts

On the assumption that the gaseous reactants are adsorbed on the catalyst in accordance with Langmuir's adsorption isotherm [eqn. (304)], the following equations may be derived for the relation between rate of reaction, $\mathrm{d}x/\mathrm{d}t = v$, and pressure, p:

(1) Reactions for a single initial substance (no adsorption of the reaction products):

$$\frac{\mathrm{d}x}{\mathrm{d}t} = \frac{kp}{1+bp} \quad (k \text{ and } b = \text{constants}) \quad \ldots . (340)$$

i.e. $\mathrm{d}x/\mathrm{d}t$ is proportional to the fraction of the surface covered by the adsorbed initial reactant.

At low pressures (weak adsorption), $bp \ll 1$, hence

$$\frac{\mathrm{d}x}{\mathrm{d}t} = kp \quad \text{first-order reaction} \quad \ldots . (341)$$

At higher pressures (strong adsorption), $bp \gg 1$, hence

$$\frac{\mathrm{d}x}{\mathrm{d}t} = \frac{k}{b} = \text{constant} \quad \text{zero-order reaction; see eqn. (278)} \quad \ldots . (342)$$

In the case of moderate adsorption, the general equation may be written as

$$\frac{\mathrm{d}x}{\mathrm{d}t} = kp^{1/n} \quad \ldots . (343)$$

with n between 1 and ∞, corresponding to the Freundlich adsorption isotherm [eqn. (303)].

(2) Bimolecular reactions with two initial reactants: the rate of reaction is proportional to the product of the fractions of the surface covered by the adsorbed initial reactants.

At low pressures and weak adsorption of both reactants:

$$\frac{\mathrm{d}x}{\mathrm{d}t} = k\,p_{\mathrm{A}}\,p_{\mathrm{B}} \qquad \ldots\ldots (344)$$

If the reactant A is moderately or strongly adsorbed but reactant B only weakly so, eqn. (304) for the Langmuir adsorption isotherm shows that A will cover a fraction of the surface

$$A_{\mathrm{A}} = \frac{b_{\mathrm{A}}\,p_{\mathrm{A}}}{1 + b_{\mathrm{A}}\,p_{\mathrm{A}}}$$

and B will occupy the remainder

$$1 - A_{\mathrm{A}} = \frac{1}{1 + b_{\mathrm{A}}\,p_{\mathrm{A}}}$$

which will be covered by B according to eqn. (341) to an extent depending on the partial pressure p_{B}, i.e.

$$A_{\mathrm{B}} = \frac{p_{\mathrm{B}}}{1 + b_{\mathrm{A}}\,p_{\mathrm{A}}}$$

It follows that

$$\frac{\mathrm{d}x}{\mathrm{d}t} = k'\,A_{\mathrm{A}}\,A_{\mathrm{B}} = \frac{k\,p_{\mathrm{A}}\,p_{\mathrm{B}}}{(1 + k_{\mathrm{A}}\,p_{\mathrm{A}})^2} \qquad \ldots\ldots (345)$$

i.e. when A is very strongly adsorbed ($b_{\mathrm{A}}\,p_{\mathrm{A}} \gg 1$)

$$\frac{\mathrm{d}x}{\mathrm{d}t} = \frac{k_2\,p_{\mathrm{B}}}{p_{\mathrm{A}}} \quad \text{(reaction inhibition by A)} \qquad \ldots\ldots (346)$$

At higher pressures the factor $k p_B$ in eqn. (341) for the weakly adsorbed component B must also be replaced by the factor $k p_B/(1 + b_{\mathrm{B}}\,p_{\mathrm{B}})$ [eqn. (340)]. Equation (346) then becomes

$$\frac{\mathrm{d}x}{\mathrm{d}t} = k_2\,\frac{p_{\mathrm{B}}}{p_{\mathrm{A}}} \times \frac{1}{1 + b_{\mathrm{B}}\,p_{\mathrm{B}}} \qquad \ldots\ldots (347)$$

Other cases may easily be derived from the above. See also: Hinshelwood, C. N., *Reaction Kinetics*, Oxford Press; Schwab, G.-M., *Katalyse vom Standpunkt der chemischen Kinetik*, Springer, Berlin.

*Exercise 173

The decomposition of an oxalomanganic (III) acid is the reaction-determining factor in the case of the reduction of $KMnO_4$ with excess oxalic acid, $H_2C_2O_4$, in the presence of manganous (II) salts. Skrabal obtained the following series of measurements at 14 °C:

Expt. No.	*Time, t* min	*Concentration of undecomposed substance in arbitrary units*		
		$(a-x)$	$\log(a-x)$	$1/(a-x)$
1	0	54·0	1·7324	$18{\cdot}52 \times 10^{-3}$
2	10	40·14	1·6036	$24{\cdot}91 \times 10^{-3}$
3	19	30·60	1·4857	$32{\cdot}68 \times 10^{-3}$
4	28	23·40	1·3692	$42{\cdot}74 \times 10^{-3}$
5	35	19·02	1·2792	$52{\cdot}58 \times 10^{-3}$
6	42	15·48	1·1898	$64{\cdot}60 \times 10^{-3}$
7	54	10·68	1·0286	$93{\cdot}63 \times 10^{-3}$
8	60	9·94	0·9513	$111{\cdot}86 \times 10^{-3}$
9	66	7·48	0·8739	$133{\cdot}69 \times 10^{-3}$
10	75	5·81	0·7642	$172{\cdot}12 \times 10^{-3}$
	∞	0	—	—

(*a*) Show, by plotting the logarithms and reciprocals of the concentrations against time, that the reaction is of the first and not the second order. (*b*) Determine the value of the reaction constant and the half-life period, by means of graphical averaging. (*c*) Calculate the best possible mean value of the reaction constant, e.g. by combining the first and sixth, the second and seventh, etc., measured values and averaging the six values so obtained. Do the values show a trend?

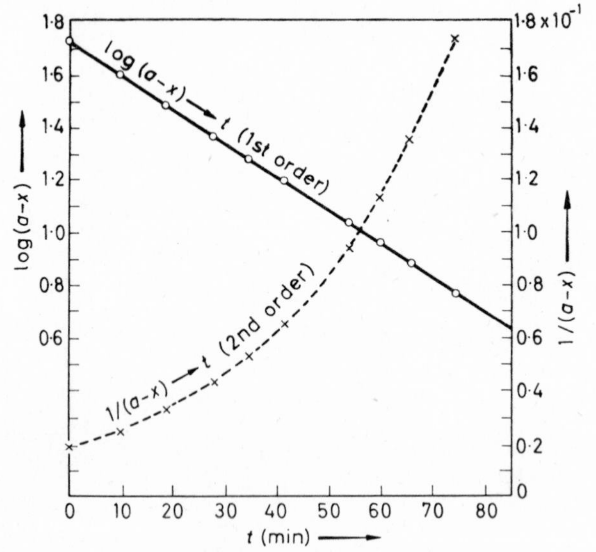

Figure 24. Determination of the order of reaction and the reaction constant for the reduction of $KMnO_4$ *by oxalic acid*

Solution 173. For a first-order reaction, one has from eqn. (271):

$$\ln(a-x) = \ln a - k^{\mathrm{I}}t \quad \text{or} \quad \log(a-x) = \log a - 0{\cdot}4343\,k^{\mathrm{I}}t \quad \ldots\ldots \quad \text{(i)}$$

It follows that a plot of the logarithms of the concentrations of undecomposed substance against time should give a straight line, the slope of which has the value $0{\cdot}4343\,k^{I}$.

For a second-order reaction, one has from eqn. (273):

$$\frac{1}{a-x} = \frac{1}{a} + k^{II} t \qquad \ldots\ldots \quad \text{(ii)}$$

It follows that a plot of the reciprocals of the concentrations of undecomposed substance against time should give a straight line, the slope of which has the value k^{II}.

Both these curves are plotted in *Figure 24.* It will be clearly seen that the reaction is of the first order, since only the plot of $\log(a - x)$ against time gives a straight line – and a truly straight line. The slope of the line is obtained from two readings, e.g. for $\log(a - x) = 1{\cdot}700$, $t = 2{\cdot}50$ min and for $\log(a - x) = 0{\cdot}870$, $t = 66{\cdot}50$ min. Hence

$$\frac{1{\cdot}700 - 0{\cdot}870}{66{\cdot}50 - 2{\cdot}50} = 0{\cdot}01297 = 0{\cdot}4343\,k^{I}$$

$$k^{I} = 0{\cdot}02986\ \text{min}^{-1} \qquad \ldots\ldots \quad \text{(iii)}$$

and from eqn. (272):

$$T^{I} = \frac{\log 2}{0{\cdot}01297} = 23{\cdot}21\ \text{min}$$

Calculation according to eqn. (271) gives for experiments No.

(1,6) $$\frac{\log(a-x_1) - \log(a-x_2)}{t_2 - t_1} = \frac{1{\cdot}7324 - 1{\cdot}1898}{42 - 0} = 0{\cdot}01292$$

(2,7) $$\frac{1{\cdot}6063 - 1{\cdot}0286}{54 - 10} = 0{\cdot}01307$$

(3,8) $$\frac{1{\cdot}4857 - 0{\cdot}9513}{60 - 19} = 0{\cdot}01303$$

(4,9) $$\frac{1{\cdot}3692 - 0{\cdot}8739}{66 - 28} = 0{\cdot}01303$$

(5,10) $$\frac{1{\cdot}2792 - 0{\cdot}7642}{75 - 35} = 0{\cdot}01287$$

Mean value: $$0{\cdot}01298 = 0{\cdot}4343\,k^{1}$$

$$k^{I} = 0{\cdot}02988\ \text{min}^{-1}$$

A trend in the values is not apparent.

*Exercise 174

For the saponification of the diacetate of acetaldehyde hydrate (ethylidene diacetate) under the action of H^{+} ions,

$$(CH_3COO)_2CHCH_3 + H_2O = 2\,CH_3COOH + CH_3CHO$$

Skrabal obtained the following series of measurements relating to a 0·1 M aqueous solution of the ester with an HCl concentration of 0·05 mole/l. at a temperature of

25 °C; t is the time in minutes and x is the concentration of acetic acid formed during reaction (in mole/l.):

t	x	t	x
0	0·02160	1640	0·10180
40	0·03475	2093	0·11520
120	0·03940	2818	0·13270
240	0·04570	3403	0·14475
420	0·05435	4543	0·16135
660	0·06495	6369	0·17915
1400	0·09395	8769	0·19050

Determine the order of reaction graphically, by plotting the logarithms and reciprocals of the concentration of undecomposed substance against time (see Exercise 173). Also determine, by graphical averaging, the values of the reaction constant and the half-life period.

Solution 174. During saponification, one mole of the ester produces two moles of acetic acid. If the initial concentration (of undecomposed acetic acid in the ester) is a, it follows that $a = 2 \times 0{\cdot}1 = 0{\cdot}2$ mole/l. when the concentration x of acetic acid is taken as the reaction variable. Hence in eqns. (271) and (273), $(a - x) = 0{\cdot}2 - x$, and the table may now be written

t	$a - x$	$\log (a - x)$	$1/(a - x)$
0	0·17840	0·2514 − 1	5·605
40	0·16525	0·2181 − 1	6·051
120	0·16060	0·2057 − 1	6·226
240	0·15430	0·1884 − 1	6·481
420	0·14565	0·1633 − 1	6·865
660	0·13505	0·1305 − 1	7·404
1400	0·10605	0·0255 − 1	9·429
1640	0·09820	0·9921 − 2	10·18
2093	0·08480	0·9284 − 2	11·79
2818	0·06730	0·8280 − 2	14·86
3403	0·05525	0·7423 − 2	18·10
4543	0·03865	0·5871 − 2	25·87
6369	0·02085	0·3191 − 2	47·96
8769	0·00950	0·9777 − 3	105·26

If $\log (a - x)$ on the one hand, $1/(a - x)$ on the other, are plotted against time, it becomes immediately apparent (see *Figure 25*) that the reaction is of the first order. Taking two readings from the curve obtained, e.g. $\log (a - x) = 0{\cdot}160 - 1$ at $t = 450$ min and $\log (a - x) = 0{\cdot}330 - 2$ at $t = 6325$ min, one obtains, by using eqn. (271):

$$\frac{0{\cdot}160 - 1 - (0{\cdot}330 - 2)}{6325 - 450} = 1{\cdot}412 \times 10^{-4} = 0{\cdot}4343\, k^{\mathrm{I}}$$

$$k^{\mathrm{I}} = 3{\cdot}255 \times 10^{-4}\ \mathrm{min}^{-1}$$

from eqn. (272)

$$T^{\mathrm{I}} = \frac{\log 2}{1{\cdot}412 \times 10^{-4}}$$

$$= 2155\ \mathrm{min}$$

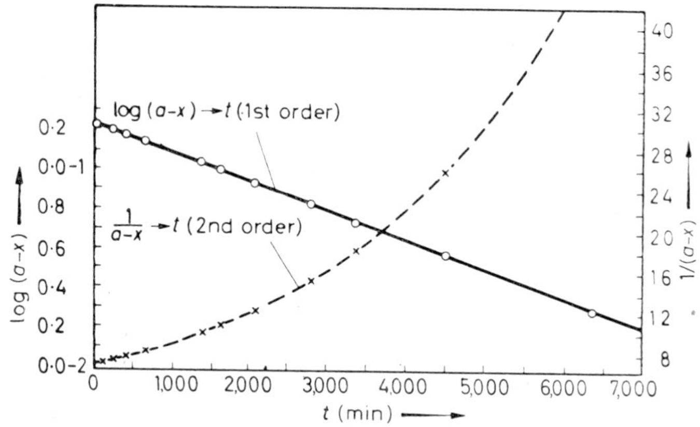

Figure 25. Determination of order of reaction and the reaction constant for a saponification process (first order)

Note. The first point in the series of measurements — and to some extent the second point also — turns out to be high. This feature is often noted in taking a series of measurements of this kind. The effect is due to the fact that certain impurities react at a different rate. When these impurities have disappeared, the course of the curve becomes regular.

The present reaction is, as the reaction equation shows, a bimolecular one. The course of the reaction is, however, of the first order, because it takes place in an aqueous medium. The reaction component H_2O is then present in such great excess that its concentration hardly decreases at all during the saponification. This factor determines the order of the reaction in relation to an individual reactant, viz. the ester. Evaluation of the order of reaction with reference to individual reactants is more important than evaluation of the overall order in the case of complex reactions where many reactants take part, e.g. in redox reactions.

*Exercise 175

The series of measurements shown below were obtained (concentration in mole/l.) during the saponification of ethyl propionate in alkaline aqueous solution at 20 °C:

$$\text{Ester} + OH^- = \text{propionate ion} + \text{ethyl alcohol}$$

$$C_2H_5COOC_2H_5 + OH^- = C_2H_5COO^- + C_2H_5OH$$

The initial concentrations of ester and caustic soda were identical, i.e. $a = 0{\cdot}025$ mole/l.

t (min)	*Ester concentration* $a - x$	t (min)	*Ester concentration* $a - x$
0	$25{\cdot}00 \times 10^{-3}$	80	$2{\cdot}32 \times 10^{-3}$
5	$15{\cdot}53 \times 10^{-3}$	100	$1{\cdot}89 \times 10^{-3}$
10	$11{\cdot}26 \times 10^{-3}$	120	$1{\cdot}60 \times 10^{-3}$
20	$7{\cdot}27 \times 10^{-3}$	150	$1{\cdot}29 \times 10^{-3}$
40	$4{\cdot}25 \times 10^{-3}$	180	$1{\cdot}09 \times 10^{-3}$
60	$3{\cdot}01 \times 10^{-3}$		

Determine the order of reaction by plotting $\log(a - x)$ and $1/(a - x)$ against t; also determine the rate constant and half-life period of the reaction. After what period of time is the concentration of the ester only 1 per cent of the initial concentration?

Solution 175. The following tabulated values of $\log(a - x)$ and $1/(a - x)$ are obtained from the experimental data:

t (min)	$\log(a - x)$	$1/(a - x)$	t (min)	$\log(a - x)$	$1/(a - x)$
0	0·3972 − 2	40·0	80	0·3655 − 3	431
5	0·1912 − 2	64·4	100	0·2765 − 3	529
10	0·0515 − 2	88·8	120	0·2041 − 3	625
20	0·8615 − 3	138	150	0·1106 − 3	775
40	0·6284 − 3	235	180	0·0374 − 3	917
60	0·4786 − 3	332			

A plot of the data shows, without doubt, that the reaction is of the second order (see *Figure 26*). Taking two readings from the curve obtained, e.g. $1/(a - x_1) = 185$ at $t_1 = 30$ min and $1/(a - x_2) = 780$ at $t_2 = 152$ min, one obtains by using eqn. (273):

$$k^{\mathrm{II}} = \frac{1/(a - x_2) - 1/(a - x_1)}{t_2 - t_1}$$

$$\frac{780 - 185}{185 - 30} = 4{\cdot}88 \text{ l./mole min} = k^{\mathrm{II}} \qquad \dots \quad \text{(i)}$$

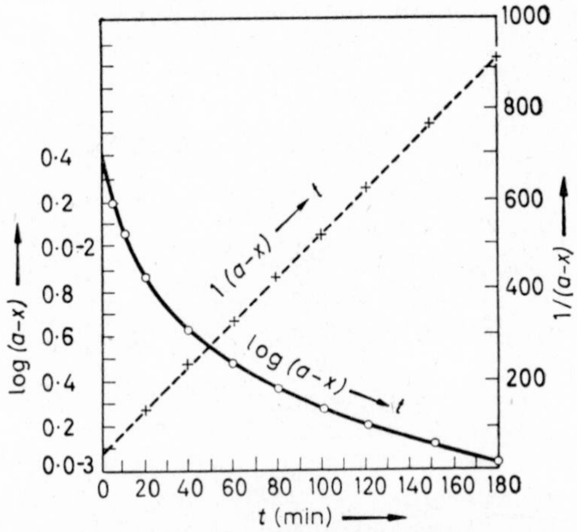

Figure 26. Determination of order of reaction and the reaction constant for a saponification process (second order)

Using eqn. (273), the half-life period is:

$$T^{\mathrm{II}} = \frac{1}{k^{\mathrm{II}} a} = \frac{1}{4{\cdot}88 \times 0{\cdot}025} = 8{\cdot}20 \text{ min} \qquad \dots \quad \text{(ii)}$$

Using eqn. (273), $1/(a - x) = 1/a + k^{\mathrm{II}} t$, and taking $(a - x) = a/100$, one obtains

$$t = \frac{99}{k^{\mathrm{II}} a} = \frac{99}{4{\cdot}88 \times 0{\cdot}025} = 811 \text{ min} \qquad \dots \quad \text{(iii)}$$

Note. It is well known that edible fats and oils (esters of fatty acids with glycerol) are similarly decomposed (saponified) by alkalis. This should be taken into account when cleaning containers, intended for use with fats, with soda solution. Such containers should be thoroughly rinsed after treatment with soda. If this is not done, the subsequent addition of fat will cause the latter to be saponified where it is in contact with the container.

*Exercise 176

Under the influence of H^+ ions (or more accurately H_3O^+ ions) as catalyst, the inversion of cane sugar in aqueous solution $C_{12}H_{22}O_{11} + H_2O = 2\,C_6H_{12}O_6$ (glucose + fructose or invert sugar), proceeds as a first-order reaction. The rate constant k^{I} is approximately proportional to the H^+ ion concentration; in 0·5 N HCl at 25 °C, $k = 2{\cdot}17 \times 10^{-3}$ [min^{-1}]. The specific rotation of cane sugar is $[\varphi_1]_\theta^\lambda = 100\varphi/Lc = +\,66{\cdot}45$ deg./(dm × g/cm³) at 25 °C for the $\mathrm{Na}_\alpha^{\mathrm{D}}$ line (5893 Å); the specific rotation of invert sugar under the same conditions is $[\varphi_2]_\theta^\lambda = -21{\cdot}5$ deg./(dm × g/cm³). The inversion is measured using a solution of $a = 20$ g cane sugar in 100 cm³ of solution (*a*) in 0·5 N HCl and (*b*) in 0·25 N HCl. The rotation is measured in a polarimeter with a cell length of $L = 1{\cdot}5$ dm. The angle of rotation, $\varphi = [\varphi]_\theta^\lambda L c/100$, is equal to the sum of the angles of rotation for the mixture components.

φ = angle of rotation in degrees; L = cell length in decimetres; c = grammes of optically active substance in 100 cm³ of solution.

What is the concentration of cane and invert sugar and the angle of rotation of both sugar solutions 12 h after the experiment is started?

Solution 176. From eqn. (271) we have:

$$\log(a - x) = \log a - 0{\cdot}4343\,k^{\mathrm{I}}t \qquad \text{(i)}$$

where $a = 20$ g/100 cm³ solution and $k^{\mathrm{I}} = 2{\cdot}17 \times 10^{-3}$ min^{-1} in Case (*a*)

$= 1{\cdot}085 \times 10^{-3}$ min^{-1} in Case (*b*)

and $t = 12 \times 60 = 720$ min.

It follows that the concentration of cane sugar $(a - x)$ is:

(i)
$$\log(a - x) = 1{\cdot}30103 - 0{\cdot}4343 \times 2{\cdot}17 \times 10^{-3} \times 720 = 0{\cdot}6225$$
$$a - x = 4{\cdot}19 \text{ g/100 cm}^3 \text{ solution}$$

where $x = 20 - 4{\cdot}19 = 15{\cdot}81$ g/100 cm³ solution indicates the concentration of converted cane sugar. The cane sugar is hydrolysed by water to invert sugar according to the equation given at the start of the exercise. It follows that the concentration y of invert sugar formed will be given by

$$y = x\,\frac{M_{\text{cane sugar}} - M_{H_2O}}{M_{\text{cane sugar}}} = x\,\frac{342{\cdot}3 + 18{\cdot}0}{342{\cdot}3} = 1{\cdot}0526\,x \qquad \text{(ii)}$$

Hence
$$y = 1{\cdot}0526 \times 15{\cdot}81 = 16{\cdot}64 \text{ g/100 g solution}$$

The optical rotation of the mixture is equal to the sum of the rotations of its components and since the rotations given above, $\varphi_i = [\varphi_i]_\theta^\lambda L c_i/100$, are proportional to the concentrations c_i of the relevant components, it follows that

$$\varphi = \frac{L}{100}([\varphi_1]c_1 + [\varphi_2]c_2) = \frac{L}{100}\{[\varphi_1](a-x) + [\varphi_2]y\} \ (L = 1{\cdot}5\,\text{dm}) \quad \ldots\ldots \text{(iii)}$$

$$= \frac{1{\cdot}5}{100}[+66{\cdot}45 \times 4{\cdot}19 + (-21{\cdot}5)\,1{\cdot}0526 \times 15{\cdot}81] = -1{\cdot}191 \text{ degrees}$$

$$= -71{\cdot}5 \text{ minutes of arc}$$

(ii) $\log(a-x) = 1{\cdot}30103 - 0{\cdot}4343 \times 1{\cdot}085 \times 10^{-3} \times 720 = 0{\cdot}9618$

$$a - x = 9{\cdot}16 \text{ g/100 cm}^3 \text{ solution}$$

$$x = 20 - 9{\cdot}16 = 10{\cdot}84 \text{ g/100 cm}^3 \text{ solution}$$

$$y = 1{\cdot}0526\,x = 1{\cdot}0526 \times 10{\cdot}84 = 11{\cdot}41 \text{ g/100 cm}^3 \text{ solution}$$

$$\varphi = \frac{1{\cdot}5}{100}[+66{\cdot}45 \times 9{\cdot}16 + (-21{\cdot}5)\,11{\cdot}41] = +5{\cdot}45 \text{ degrees} = 5°27'$$

The angle of rotation can, of course, also be calculated directly, without using the concentrations, by replacing the concentrations in (iii) and (i) by the corresponding angles of rotation

For $x = 0$, $a - x = a$, $y = 0$, (iii) gives

$$\varphi_{\text{initial}} = [\varphi_1]\frac{aL}{100} \quad \ldots\ldots \text{(iv)}$$

For $x = a$, $x - a = 0$, $y = 1{\cdot}0526a$ [see (ii)], (iii) gives

$$\varphi_{\text{final}} = 1{\cdot}0526\,[\varphi_2]\frac{aL}{100} \quad \ldots\ldots \text{(v)}$$

If eqn. (v) is subtracted from (iii), one obtains with (ii), (iv) and (v):

$$\varphi - \varphi_F = \frac{L}{100}[\varphi_1](a-x) - \frac{L}{100}1{\cdot}0526\,[\varphi_2]\,a + \frac{L}{100}1{\cdot}0526\,[\varphi_2]\,x$$

$$= \frac{a-x}{a}(\varphi_I - \varphi_F) \quad \ldots\ldots \text{(vi)}$$

Substituting (vi) in (i): $\log(\varphi - \varphi_F) = \log(\varphi_I - \varphi_F) - 0{\cdot}4343\,k^I t$ .... (vii)

Equation (vii) is especially useful for determining k^I from measured values of φ, φ_I, φ_F and t.

Exercise 177

In Exercise 174 the first-order reaction constant k^I was calculated for the saponification of ethylidene diacetate under the catalytic effect of H^+ ions (0·05 M HCl) at 25 °C. The value obtained was $k^I = 3{\cdot}255 \times 10^{-4}\ \text{min}^{-1}$. Now determine the time after which 10 per cent of the ethylidene diacetate (0·1 M or 0·2 M with respect to the unsaponified acetic acid in the ester) is decomposed if the initial concentration of H^+ ions (HCl) is $[H_0^+] = 2 \times 10^{-4}$ mole/l. and the catalytic effect of the H^+ ions is proportional to their concentration. At this small concentration of H^+ ions, the progressive increase in their concentration, due to the formation of acetic acid, should be taken into account, i.e. the autocatalytic nature of the reaction. The dissociation constant of acetic acid is $K = 1{\cdot}76 \times 10^{-5}$ mole/l. (25 °C).

Solution 177. From eqn. (271): $$\frac{\mathrm{d}x}{\mathrm{d}t} = k(a - x) \quad \ldots\ldots \quad \text{(i)}$$

where it is convenient to take x = concentration of acetic acid formed as the reaction variable; hence $a - x$ = concentration of unsaponified acetic acid, a = concentration of unsaponified acetic acid at time $t = 0$, i.e. twice the concentration of the ethylidine diacetate ester ($a = 0{\cdot}2$ mole/l.).

Since k is proportional to the total H^+ ion concentration, i.e.

$$k = k_0[H^+_{\text{total}}] \quad \ldots\ldots \quad \text{(ii)}$$

k varies during the reaction. Using the data given above, one obtains by substituting in (ii):

$$k = 3{\cdot}255 \times 10^{-4}\ \text{min}^{-1} = k_0 \times 0{\cdot}05$$

It follows that the proportionality factor k_0 (reaction constant for 1 M H^+) is

$$k_0 = \frac{3{\cdot}255 \times 10^{-4}}{0{\cdot}05} = 6{\cdot}51 \times 10^{-3}\ \text{min}^{-1} \quad \ldots\ldots \quad \text{(iii)}$$

In order to calculate the H^+ ion concentration, the law of mass action gives

$$\frac{[H^+_{\text{total}}][\text{acetate ion}]}{[\text{acetic acid}]} = K \quad \ldots\ldots \quad \text{(iv)}$$

or

$$K = \frac{([H^+_0] + [H^+])([H^+])}{x - [H^+]} \quad \ldots\ldots \quad \text{(v)}$$

where $[H^+_{\text{total}}] = [H^+_0] + [H^+]$ (H^+ ions from the initially present HCl and H^+ ions which result from dissociation of the acetic acid formed during saponification).

Concentration of acetate ions $= [\bar{A}^-] = [H^+]$

concentration of acetic acid $= x - [H^+]$ (acetic acid formed by saponification x, less dissociated acetic acid).

Solution of (v) gives $[H^+]^2 + ([H^+]_0 + K)[H^+] - Kx = 0$

$$H^+ = \frac{-([H^+_0] + K)}{2} + \frac{([H^+_0] + K)}{2}\sqrt{1 + \frac{4Kx}{([H^+_0] + K)^2}} \quad \ldots\ldots \quad \text{(vi)}$$

or

$$[H^+_{\text{total}}] = [H^+_0] + [H^+] = \frac{([H^+_0] - K)}{2} + \frac{([H^+_0] + K)}{2}\sqrt{1 + \frac{4Kx}{([H^+_0] + K)^2}} \quad \ldots\ldots \quad \text{(vii)}$$

Substituting the numerical values in (vii), one obtains with (i), (ii) and (iii) $\mathrm{d}x/\mathrm{d}t = 6{\cdot}51 \times 10^{-3}(0{\cdot}2 - x)$ multiplied by

$$\left[\frac{20 \times 10^{-5} - 1{\cdot}76 \times 10^{-5}}{2} + \frac{20 \times 10^{-5} + 1{\cdot}76 \times 10^{-5}}{2}\sqrt{1 + \frac{4 \times 1{\cdot}76 \times 10^{-5}x}{(20 \times 10^{-5} + 1{\cdot}76 \times 10^{-5})^2}}\right]$$

If this expression is suitably reduced and factorized, one has

$$\frac{\mathrm{d}x}{\mathrm{d}t} = 7{\cdot}083 \times 10^{-7}(0{\cdot}2 - x)\left(0{\cdot}8382 + \sqrt{1 + 1487x}\right) \quad \ldots\ldots \quad \text{(viii)}$$

or, in general

$$\frac{dx}{dt} = -P(x-a)\left(b+\sqrt{1+cx}\right) \qquad \ldots\ldots \text{(ix)}$$

where $P = 7{\cdot}083 \times 10^{-7}$ [min^{-1}]

$a = 0{\cdot}2$ mole/l. acetic acid (esterified) $\qquad d^2 = ac + 1 = 298{\cdot}4$

$b = 0{\cdot}8382 \qquad d = 17{\cdot}274$

$c = 1487$ [mole/l.]$^{-1}$

When $t = 0$ min, $x = 0$ mole/l. acetic acid.

The integration may be carried out by separating the variables, rationalizing by substituting $\sqrt{1+cx} = z$, and resolving into partial fractions. Since this type of treatment arises quite often in the study of reaction kinetics, the mathematical procedure will be given in detail.

(1) Rearrangement of (ix), for separation of the variables, gives

$$-P\,dt = \frac{dx}{(x-a)\left(b+\sqrt{1+cx}\right)} \qquad \ldots\ldots \text{(x)}$$

(2) Substituting $\sqrt{1+cx} = z$:

$$x = \frac{z^2-1}{c} \qquad dx = \frac{2z\,dz}{c} \qquad (x-a) = \frac{z^2-(ac+1)}{c} = \frac{z^2-d^2}{c} \qquad \ldots\ldots \text{(xi)}$$

when $t = 0$, $x = 0$ and $z = 1$.

(3) Substituting the expressions at (xi) in (x) gives:

$$-P\,dt = \frac{2z\,dz}{(z+d)(z-d)(z+b)} = \frac{f(z)}{F(z)}\,dz \qquad \ldots\ldots \text{(xii)}$$

where $f(z) = 2z$ and $F(z) = (z+d)(z-d)(z+b)$ are polynomial functions. The three roots of $F(z)$ are all different in value, so that the term on the right-hand side at (xii) may be split into partial fractions:

$$\frac{2z}{(z+d)(z-d)(z+b)} = \frac{A}{z+d} + \frac{B}{z-d} + \frac{C}{z+b} \qquad \ldots\ldots \text{(xiii)}$$

A, B and C may be determined by putting the right-hand side of (xiii) over a common denominator and then equating the coefficients for the different powers of z in the two sides of the expression. This leads to three soluble linear equations for A, B and C. This treatment gives:

$$2z = A(z-d)(z+b) + B(z+d)(z+b) + C(z+d)(z-d)$$

$$2z = (A+B+C)z^2 + [A(b-d) + B(b+d)]\,z - d\,[(A-B)\,b + Cd]$$

Comparing coefficients on the left-hand side and right-hand side of the equation gives:

(1) $A + B + C = 0$, (2) $(A+B)b - (A-B)d = 2$, (3) $(A-B)b + Cd = 0$.

Adding (2) and (3) and subtracting $d \times$ (1) gives

$$2Ab - 2Ad = 2, \text{ or } A = 1/(b-d)$$

Similarly, (2)–(3) + $d \times$ (1) gives

$$2Bb + 2Bd = 2 \quad \text{or} \quad B = 1/(b+d)$$

Finally, it follows from (xi) that

$$C = -A - B = -2b/(b^2 - d^2)$$

The result may generally be more quickly obtained by using the following method, which is taken from the theory for resolving into partial fractions:

$$A = \frac{f(-d)}{F'(-d)} \qquad B = \frac{f(d)}{F'(d)} \qquad C = \frac{f(-b)}{F'(-b)} \qquad \ldots . \text{(xiv)}$$

Here, F′ is the differential quotient of F and $(-d)$, $(+d)$ and $(-b)$ are the respective zero values of F* featuring in the partial fractions:

$$f(z) = 2z \quad F'(z) = (z-d)(z+b) + (z+d)(z+b) + (z+d)(z-d) \qquad \ldots . \text{(xv)}$$

One therefore has from (xiv) and (xv):

$$\left.\begin{aligned} A &= \frac{f(-d)}{F'(-d)} = \frac{-2d}{-2d(b-d)} = \frac{+1}{(b-d)} = \frac{-1}{16{\cdot}44} \\ B &= \frac{f(+d)}{F'(+d)} = \frac{+2d}{2d(b+d)} = \frac{1}{(b+d)} = \frac{1}{18{\cdot}11} \\ C &= \frac{f(-b)}{F'(-b)} = \frac{-2b}{b^2-d^2} = \frac{-1{\cdot}6764}{0{\cdot}7026 - 298{\cdot}4} = \frac{1}{177{\cdot}6} \end{aligned}\right\} \quad \ldots \text{(xvi)}$$

(4) Taking (xiii) and (xvi) into account, it is now possible to integrate (xii). The left-hand side is integrated from 0 to t and the right-hand side over the corresponding range from $z = 1$ to $z = z$ [see under (1)].

One has:

$$\int_0^t -P\,dt = \int_1^z \frac{A\,dz}{z+d} + \int_1^z \frac{B\,dz}{z-d} + \int_1^z \frac{C\,dz}{z+b}$$

$$-Pt = A \ln \frac{z+d}{1+d} + B \ln \frac{z-d}{1-d} + C \ln \frac{z+b}{1+b} \qquad \ldots . \text{(xvii)}$$

$$t = +\frac{2{\cdot}303}{P}\left(A \log \frac{1+d}{z+d} + B \log \frac{d-1}{d-z} + C \log \frac{1+b}{z+b}\right) \qquad \ldots . \text{(xviii)}$$

where $z = \sqrt{1 + cx}$, in accordance with (xi).

Using (xviii), the question in the exercise may now be answered. If 10 per cent is decomposed, then $x = 0{\cdot}1 \times a = 0{\cdot}02$ mole/l. acetic acid; hence

$$z = \sqrt{1 + 1487 \times 0{\cdot}02} = \sqrt{1 + 29{\cdot}74} = \sqrt{30{\cdot}74} = 5{\cdot}544 \qquad \ldots . \text{(xix)}$$

and substituted in (xviii) gives:

$$t = \frac{2{\cdot}303}{7{\cdot}083 \times 10^{-7}}\left(\frac{-1}{16{\cdot}44} \log \frac{18{\cdot}274}{22{\cdot}818} + \frac{1}{18{\cdot}11} \log \frac{16{\cdot}274}{11{\cdot}730} + \frac{1}{177{\cdot}6} \log \frac{1{\cdot}838}{6{\cdot}382}\right)$$

$$= \frac{2{\cdot}303 \times 10^7}{7{\cdot}083}\left(\frac{0{\cdot}0964}{16{\cdot}44} + \frac{0{\cdot}1422}{18{\cdot}11} - \frac{0{\cdot}5406}{177{\cdot}6}\right) = 34{,}700 \text{ min} = 24{\cdot}1 \text{ days}$$

* $f(z)$ and $F(z)$ mean 'function of z'.

*Exercise 178

In naturally occurring minerals containing uranium, where a stationary radioactive equilibrium has been established, one regularly finds radium in the mole ratio [Ra]:[U] = $3{\cdot}47 \times 10^{-7}$. What is the half-life period of uranium, if that of radium is found to be 1580 years?

Solution 178. In the case of stationary equilibrium, one has from eqn. (281):

$$\frac{T_{Ra}}{T_U} = \frac{[Ra]}{[U]} \quad \text{so that } T_U = \frac{1580}{3{\cdot}47 \times 10^{-7}} = 4{\cdot}56 \times 10^{9} \text{ years}$$

*Exercise 179

How many grammes of solid radium bromide, $RaBr_2$, which has been stored for years and in which a radioactive equilibrium has been established, are required in order that 1 mg of polonium (one of the decay products) may be isolated from it? How many tons of pitchblende would be required for this purpose? Atomic weight of Ra = 226, of Br = 79·9, of Po = 210. Half-life period, T_{Ra} = 1580 years, T_{Po} = 136·5 days. One ton of pitchblende contains, on average, 0·14 grammes of radium.

Solution 179. In the case of stationary equilibrium, we find from eqn. (281):

$$\frac{[Po]}{[Ra]} = \frac{T_{Po}}{T_{Ra}} \qquad \ldots. \quad \text{(i)}$$

or

$$\frac{G_{Po}/M_{Po}}{G_{RaBr_2}/M_{RaBr_2}} = \frac{1{\cdot}10^{-3}/210}{G_{RaBr_2}/385{\cdot}8} = \frac{136{\cdot}5}{1580 \times 365} \qquad \ldots. \quad \text{(ii)}$$

i.e. G_{RaBr_2} = 7·76 grammes; this contains 7·76/385·8 × 226 = 4·55 g Ra, for which 4·55/0·14 = 32·5 tons of pitchblende will be required.

Exercise 180

How long does it take to reach the maximum polonium content in a radium preparation if the formation of RaD is the time-determining factor and if this element has the greatest stability, with a half-life period of T_{RaD} = 16·0 years, of the elements in the radioactive decay series between Ra and Po? T_{Ra} = 1580 years. See eqn. (280b).

Solution 180. The concentration of the temporary intermediate product RaD from Ra is defined by eqn. (280b). In order to obtain the maximum value, the equation is differentiated with respect to t and the result equated to zero. This gives:

$$\frac{d[B]}{dt} = \frac{[A_0]\lambda_1}{\lambda_2 - \lambda_1}(-\lambda_1 e^{-\lambda_1 t} + \lambda_2 e^{-\lambda_2 t}) = 0 \qquad \ldots. \quad \text{(i)}$$

or

$$-\lambda_1 e^{-\lambda_1 t} + \lambda_2 e^{-\lambda_2 t} = 0$$

i.e.

$$\frac{\lambda_2}{\lambda_1} = e^{(\lambda_2 - \lambda_1)t} \quad \ln\frac{\lambda_2}{\lambda_1} = \ln\frac{T_1}{T_2} = (\lambda_2 - \lambda_1)t$$

and, with eqn. (272):

$$\log \frac{T_1}{T_2} = 0{\cdot}4343\,(\lambda_2 - \lambda_1)\,t = 0{\cdot}4343\,(\ln 2)\,(1/T_2 - 1/T_1)\,t$$
$$= (\log 2)\,(1/T_2 - 1/T_1)\,t$$

hence

$$t = \frac{\log (T_1/T_2)}{(\log 2)\,(1/T_2 - 1/T_1)} \qquad \ldots . \quad \text{(ii)}$$

Substituting:

$$t = \frac{\log (1580/16)}{0{\cdot}301\,(1/16 - 1/1580)} = 107 \text{ years}$$

*Exercise 181

In a middle pre-Cambrian mineral containing uranium, the ratio of the content by weight of lead, as RaG (at. wt. = 206), to that of uranium (at. wt. = 238·1) was found to be 0·155. How old is this geological formation? The half-life period of uranium is $T = 4{\cdot}56 \times 10^9$ years. The intermediate stages down to the stable RaG are short-lived in comparison with uranium. See eqn. (284).

Solution 181. Equation (284) gives

$$\frac{[\mathrm{RaG}]}{[\mathrm{U}]} = \frac{G_{\mathrm{RaG}}}{G_{\mathrm{U}}}\,\frac{M_{\mathrm{U}}}{M_{\mathrm{RaG}}} = 2^{t/T} - 1 \qquad \ldots . \quad \text{(i)}$$

or

$$0{\cdot}155\,\frac{238{\cdot}1}{206} = 2^{t/T} - 1$$

hence

$$t = \frac{T \times \log 1{\cdot}1792}{\log 2} = \frac{4{\cdot}56 \times 10^9 \times 0{\cdot}07158}{0{\cdot}30103} = 1084 \text{ million years} \qquad \ldots . \quad \text{(ii)}$$

*Exercise 182

A meteor was tested for uranium and helium content. It was free from thorium and protactinium, parent substances of the thorium and actinium decay series, which terminate, as in the case of uranium, with a lead isotope and helium as the end products. A content of 350 mm³ of helium to 1 mg of uranium was found at an external pressure of 720 mm Hg and at a temperature of 21 °C. Determine the age of the meteor. The half-life period of uranium is $T = 4{\cdot}56 \times 10^9$ years; the atomic weight of uranium is 238·1, of radium lead RaG = 206 and of helium = 4. See eqn. (284).

Solution 182. Since the atomic weight of uranium is 238 and that of RaG is 206, the difference, i.e. 238 – 206 = 32, must be represented by helium. From one decayed U atom we therefore obtain 1 RaG atom and 32/4 = 8 helium atoms. This gives the volume of He at s.t.p. (0 °C, 760 mm Hg) as

$$\frac{pV}{T} = \frac{p_0 V_0}{T_0} \quad \text{i.e.} \quad V_0 = \frac{350 \times 273 \times 720}{294 \times 760} = 308 \text{ mm}^3 \qquad \ldots . \quad \text{(i)}$$

It follows that the mole quantity of He is

$$n_{\mathrm{He}} = \frac{\text{volume at s.t.p.}}{\text{molar volume}} = \frac{308 \times 10^{-6}\text{ l.}}{22{\cdot}4\text{ l./mole}} = 13{\cdot}75 \times 10^{-6} \text{ moles of helium}$$

This corresponds to

$$n_{\mathrm{RaG}} = 13{\cdot}75 \times 10^{-6}/8 = 1{\cdot}72 \times 10^{-6} \text{ moles of radium lead} \qquad \text{(ii)}$$

The molar quantity of uranium is

$$n_{\mathrm{U}} = \frac{1 \times 10^{-3}}{238{\cdot}1} = 4{\cdot}20 \times 10^{-6} \text{ moles} \qquad \text{(iii)}$$

so that, from eqn. (284)

$$\frac{n_{\mathrm{RaG}}}{n_{\mathrm{U}}} = \frac{1{\cdot}72 \times 10^{-6}}{4{\cdot}20 \times 10^{-6}} = 0{\cdot}4095 = 2^{t/T} - 1$$

$$t = 4{\cdot}56 \times 10^{9}\,\frac{\log 1{\cdot}4095}{\log 2} = 2260 \text{ million years}$$

*Exercise 183

Carbon is known to consist of three isotopes; 98·9 per cent $^{12}_{6}C$ and 1·1 per cent $^{13}_{6}C$ are stable, but the trace content of $^{14}_{6}C$ is radioactive. This radioactive carbon arises from the neutrons induced in cosmic radiation and is a result of the nuclear reaction $^{14}_{7}N + ^{1}_{0}n = ^{14}_{6}C + ^{1}_{1}H$ (about 2·12 to 2·4 ^{14}C atoms/sec × cm² of the earth's surface); this isotope is a β-emitter, $^{14}_{6}C = ^{14}_{7}N + _{-1}^{0}e$, with a half-life period of $T = 5568 \pm 30$ years. After formation of CO_2 by assimilation in plants, the radioactive carbon enters the carbon cycle of organic life and becomes intermixed with the other forms of carbon. A stationary biological equilibrium is therefore established, in which an always constant fraction of radioactive carbon is present in living matter [specific radioactivity of living matter: 2·12/8·3 of ^{14}C atoms decaying per second per gramme of carbon at approximately 8·3 grammes C (total)/cm² of the earth's surface]. If the life process stops, the decaying radioactive carbon is no longer replaced and the radioactivity of the material in question fades away.

It was established that the radioactivity in a mummy, due to carbon (and referred to equal quantities of C), was only 56·2 per cent of the radioactivity in living matter. How old is the mummy? See eqns. (271) and (272).

Solution 172. One has from eqn. (283):

$$\ln \frac{[^{14}C_{(\mathrm{stationary})}]}{[^{14}C_{(\mathrm{mummy})}]} = \frac{t}{T}\ln 2$$

$$t = T\,\frac{\log \dfrac{[^{14}C_{(\mathrm{stationary})}]}{[^{14}C_{(\mathrm{mummy})}]}}{\log 2} = 5568\,\frac{\log \dfrac{100}{56{\cdot}2}}{0{\cdot}3010} = 4630 \text{ years}$$

Note. Regarding radioactivity, see also Exercises 207 to 210.

**Exercise 184

Derive a general expression for the time dependence of the compound series of first-order monomolecular reactions A → B, B → C, with reaction constants k_1 and k_2 and without any reverse reaction. In other words, integrate the linear differential equations (279), (*a*) by the method of variation of constants and (*b*) by the eigenvalue method. Initial conditions: when $t = 0$, $[A] = [A_0]$; $[B] = [C] = 0$.

Solution 184. From eqn. (279) we find

$$(a)\ -\frac{\mathrm{d}[\mathrm{A}]}{\mathrm{d}t} = k_1[\mathrm{A}] \quad (b)\ -\frac{\mathrm{d}[\mathrm{B}]}{\mathrm{d}t} = k_2[\mathrm{B}] - k_1[\mathrm{A}] \quad (c)\ +\frac{\mathrm{d}[\mathrm{C}]}{\mathrm{d}t} = +k_2[\mathrm{B}]$$

Method of Variation of Constants

Direct integration of (*a*) gives, like eqn. (272):

$$[\mathrm{A}] = [\mathrm{A}_0]\,\mathrm{e}^{-k_1 t} \qquad \ldots\ldots \quad \text{(i)}$$

Taking (i) into account, (ii) gives

$$\frac{\mathrm{d}[\mathrm{B}]}{\mathrm{d}t} = k_1[\mathrm{A}_0]\,\mathrm{e}^{-k_1 t} - k_2[\mathrm{B}] \qquad \ldots\ldots \quad \text{(ii)}$$

According to the method of variation of constants, one looks for a solution for (ii) analogous to that for (i). In (i), however, the first term (independent of [B]) of eqn. (i) does not exist. This is sought by taking into account the fact that in solution (i) the factor $[\mathrm{A}_0]$, which is a constant, will be regarded as a function $C(t)$ of t.

One then has the following for [B]:

$$[\mathrm{B}] = C(t)\,\mathrm{e}^{-k_2 t} \qquad \ldots\ldots \quad \text{(iii)}$$

so that

$$\frac{\mathrm{d}[\mathrm{B}]}{\mathrm{d}t} = C'(t)\,\mathrm{e}^{-k_2 t} + C(t)(-k_2)\,\mathrm{e}^{-k_2 t} \qquad \ldots\ldots \quad \text{(vi)}$$

Substituting the expression (iv) in (ii) and taking (iii) into account gives for $C'(t)$

$$C'(t)\,\mathrm{e}^{-k_2 t} = k_1[\mathrm{A}_0]\,\mathrm{e}^{-k_1 t} \quad \text{or} \quad C'(t) = [\mathrm{A}_0]\,k_1\,\mathrm{e}^{(k_2-k_1)t} \qquad \ldots\ldots \quad \text{(v)}$$

Integrating:

$$C(t) = \frac{[\mathrm{A}_0]\,k_1}{k_2 - k_1}\,\mathrm{e}^{(k_2-k_1)t} + C_0 \qquad \ldots\ldots \quad \text{(vi)}$$

Substituting in (iii):

$$[\mathrm{B}] = \left(\frac{[\mathrm{A}_0]\,k_1}{k_2 - k_1}\,\mathrm{e}^{(k_2-k_1)t} + C_0\right)\mathrm{e}^{-k_2 t} \qquad \ldots\ldots \quad \text{(vii)}$$

where the constant C_0 is determined from the initial conditions ($[\mathrm{B}] = 0$, when $t = 0$) and is found from (vii) to be

$$C_0 = \frac{-[\mathrm{A}_0]\,k_1}{k_2 - k_1} \qquad \ldots\ldots \quad \text{(viii)}$$

Hence, from (vii) and (viii):

$$[\mathrm{B}] = \frac{[\mathrm{A}_0]\,k_1}{k_2 - k_1}\left(\mathrm{e}^{-k_1 t} - \mathrm{e}^{-k_2 t}\right) \qquad \ldots\ldots \quad \text{(ix)}$$

Equation (279c) therefore gives for $\mathrm{d}[\mathrm{C}]/\mathrm{d}t$

$$\frac{\mathrm{d}[\mathrm{C}]}{\mathrm{d}t} = \frac{[\mathrm{A}_0]\,k_1 k_2}{k_2 - k_1}\left(\mathrm{e}^{-k_1 t} - \mathrm{e}^{-k_2 t}\right) \qquad \ldots\ldots \quad \text{(x)}$$

which, on integration, becomes

$$[\mathrm{C}] = -\frac{[\mathrm{A}_0]\,k_1 k_2}{k_2 - k_1}\left(\frac{\mathrm{e}^{-k_1 t}}{k_1} - \frac{\mathrm{e}^{-k_2 t}}{k_2}\right) + D_0 \qquad \ldots\ldots \quad \text{(xi)}$$

The integration constant D_0 is determined by the initial conditions ([C] = 0, when $t = 0$) and is obtained from (xi) as

$$D_0 = [A_0] \qquad \text{.... (xii)}$$

Thus, finally

$$[C] = [A_0]\left\{1 - \frac{k_1 k_2}{k_2 - k_1}\left(\frac{e^{-k_1 t}}{k_1} - \frac{e^{-k_2 t}}{k_2}\right)\right\} \qquad \text{.... (xiii)}$$

Note. If there are several successive intermediate products, the problem is solved by an appropriate number of applications of the same method.

Eigenvalue Method

For the sake of clarity the concentrations [A], [B] and [C] will be denoted by x_1, x_2 and x_3, respectively. Thus the originally formulated first-order differential equations (where $\mathrm{d}x/\mathrm{d}t = \dot{x}$) will read:

i) $\dot{x}_1 = -k_1 x_1$

(ii) $\dot{x}_2 = +k_1 x_1 - k_2 x_2$

(iii) $\dot{x}_3 = +k_2 x_2$

This linear transformation may be abbreviated to $\dot{\boldsymbol{x}} = K\boldsymbol{x}$,

$$\text{where } K = \begin{pmatrix} -k_1 & 0 & 0 \\ k_1 & -k_2 & 0 \\ 0 & k_2 & 0 \end{pmatrix} \qquad \text{.... (i)}$$

K is a transformation matrix converting the vector

$$\boldsymbol{x} = \begin{pmatrix} x_1 \\ x_2 \\ x_3 \end{pmatrix} \text{ into the vector } \dot{\boldsymbol{x}} = \begin{pmatrix} \dot{x}_1 \\ \dot{x}_2 \\ \dot{x}_3 \end{pmatrix}^{*}$$

One attempts to solve differential equations of this kind by means of an exponential law

$$x_1 = r_1 e^{\lambda t} \quad x_2 = r_2 e^{\lambda t} \quad x_3 = r_3 e^{\lambda t} \quad \text{or} \quad \boldsymbol{x} = \boldsymbol{r} e^{\lambda t} \qquad \text{.... (ii)}$$

where r_1, r_2, r_3 (i. e. an amplitude vector $\boldsymbol{r}$) and the parameter λ represent constants still to be determined.

Differentiating (ii) with respect to time, t, we find that

$$\dot{x}_1 = \lambda r_1 e^{\lambda t} \quad \dot{x}_2 = \lambda r_2 e^{\lambda t} \quad \dot{x}_3 = \lambda r_3 e^{\lambda t} \quad \text{or} \quad \dot{\boldsymbol{x}} = \lambda \boldsymbol{r} e^{\lambda t} \qquad \text{.... (iii)}$$

Substituting the expressions at (ii) in (iii) gives

$$\dot{x}_1 = \lambda x_1 \quad \dot{x}_2 = \lambda x_2 \quad \dot{x}_3 = \lambda x_3 \quad \text{or} \quad \dot{\boldsymbol{x}} = \lambda \boldsymbol{x} \qquad \text{.... (iv)}$$

$\dot{x}_1$, $\dot{x}_2$, $\dot{x}_3$ can now be eliminated from the above differential equations by using (iv). If, moreover, all terms are taken over to the left-hand side, the following system of homogeneous linear equations is obtained:

$$\begin{aligned} (-k_1 - \lambda)x_1 + 0 \times x_2 + 0 \times x_3 &= 0 \\ k_1 x_1 + (-k_2 - \lambda)x_2 + 0 \times x_3 &= 0 \quad \text{or} \quad (K - \lambda I)\boldsymbol{x} = 0 \qquad \text{.... (v)} \\ 0 \times x_1 + k_2 x_2 - \lambda x_3 &= 0 \end{aligned}$$

* A knowledge of vector and matrix calculation is not necessary in order to understand and solve this problem.

where

$$(K - \lambda I) = \begin{pmatrix} -k_1 - \lambda & 0 & 0 \\ k_1 & -k_2 - \lambda & 0 \\ 0 & k_2 & -\lambda \end{pmatrix} \text{ and } I \text{ represents the unit matrix } \begin{pmatrix} 1 & 0 & 0 \\ 0 & 1 & 0 \\ 0 & 0 & 1 \end{pmatrix}$$

It is well known that such a system of linear homogeneous equations only has solutions (apart from the trivial solution $x_1 = x_2 = x_3 = 0$) if the determinant

$$\begin{vmatrix} -k_1 - \lambda & 0 & 0 \\ k_1 & -k_2 - \lambda & 0 \\ 0 & k_2 & -\lambda \end{vmatrix} = 0 \quad \text{or} \quad |K - \lambda I| = 0 \qquad \ldots . \text{(vi)}$$

This equation determines the eigenvalues.

Multiplying out the determinant, one straight away obtains:

$$\left.\begin{array}{l} (-k_1 - \lambda)(-k_2 - \lambda)(-\lambda) = 0, \quad \text{i.e. for } \lambda, \text{ the values} \\ \qquad\qquad\qquad\qquad\qquad\qquad \text{(eigenvalues of the matrix } K) \\ \lambda_1 = -k_1 \qquad \lambda_2 = -k_2 \qquad \lambda_3 = 0 \end{array}\right\} \quad \ldots \text{(vii)}$$

By solving the equations at (v), one obtains, for each eigenvalue λ, a set x_1, x_2, x_3, it being well known that only the ratio $x_1 : x_2 : x_3$ can be determined by a set of homogeneous linear equàtions of this type. The absolute values can be taken (normalized) optionally; $\lambda_1 = -k_1$. Substitution in (v) gives

$$\begin{aligned} 0 \times x_1 + 0 \times x_2 + 0 \times x_3 &= 0 \\ k_1 x_1 + (-k_2 + k_1) x_2 + 0 \times x_3 &= 0 \\ 0 \times x_1 + k_2 x_2 + k_1 x_3 &= 0 \end{aligned}$$

It follows from the normal rules of calculation [ratio of the sub-determinants pertinent to the elements a_{ik} multiplied by $(-1)^{i+k}$, called also algebraic complement A_{ik}] that, for $x_1 : x_2 : x_3$

$$x_1 : x_2 : x_3 = + \begin{vmatrix} (-k_2 + k_1) & 0 \\ k_2 & k_1 \end{vmatrix} : - \begin{vmatrix} k_1 & 0 \\ 0 & k_1 \end{vmatrix} : + \begin{vmatrix} k & (-k_2 + k_1) \\ 0 & k_2 \end{vmatrix}$$

$$= (-k_2 + k_1) k_1 : -k^2 : k_1 k_2 = 1 : \frac{k_1}{k_2 - k_1} : \frac{-k_2}{k_2 - k_1}$$

This set (x_1, x_2, x_3) represents – with any desired normalization factor – the components of the eigenvector $\boldsymbol{x}_1$ corresponding to the eigenvalue $\lambda_1 = -k_1$. In order to take the equations at (ii) into account, the values of the ratio are further multiplied by the common normalization factor $e^{\lambda_1 t} = e^{-k_1 t}$; this finally gives:

$$x_1 = e^{-k_1 t} \quad x_2 = \frac{k_1}{k_2 - k_1} e^{-k_1 t} \quad x_3 = \frac{-k_2}{k_2 - k_1} e^{-k_1 t}$$

or

$$\boldsymbol{x}_1 = \begin{pmatrix} 1 \\ \dfrac{k_1}{k_2 - k_1} \\ \dfrac{-k_2}{k_2 - k_1} \end{pmatrix} e^{-k_1 t} \qquad \ldots . \text{(xiii)}$$

as the eigenvector for the eigenvalue $\lambda_1 = -k_1$.

$\lambda_2 = -k_2$. A calculation similar to that above gives

$$\begin{aligned}(-k_1 + k_2)\,x_1 + 0 \times x_2 + 0 \times x_3 &= 0\\ k_1 x_1 + 0 \times x_2 + 0 \times x_3 &= 0\\ 0 \times x_1 + k_2 x_2 + k_2 x_3 &= 0\end{aligned}$$

$$x_1 : x_2 : x_3 = + \begin{vmatrix} 0 & 0 \\ k_2 & k_2 \end{vmatrix} : - \begin{vmatrix} k_1 & 0 \\ 0 & k_2 \end{vmatrix} : + \begin{vmatrix} k_1 & 0 \\ 0 & k_2 \end{vmatrix} = 0 : -k_1 k_2 : k_1 k_2$$
$$= 0 : -1 : +1$$

Now multiplying by $e^{\lambda_2 t} = e^{-k_2}$, taking (ii) into account, finally gives:

$$x_1 = 0 \quad x_2 = -e^{-k_2 t} \quad x_3 = +e^{-k_2 t} \quad \text{or} \quad \boldsymbol{x}_2 = \begin{pmatrix} 0 \\ -1 \\ +1 \end{pmatrix} e^{-k_2 t} \qquad \ldots\ldots \text{(ix)}$$

as eigenvector for the eigenvalue $\lambda_2 = -k_2$.

$\lambda_3 = 0$. Substitution in (v) gives

$$\begin{aligned}-k_1 x_1 + 0 \times x_2 + 0 \times x_3 &= 0\\ k_1 x_1 - k_2 x_2 + 0 \times x_3 &= 0\\ 0 \times x_1 + k_2 x_2 + 0 \times x_3 &= 0\end{aligned}$$

$$x_1 : x_2 : x_3 = + \begin{vmatrix} -k_2 & 0 \\ k_2 & 0 \end{vmatrix} : - \begin{vmatrix} k_1 & 0 \\ 0 & 0 \end{vmatrix} : + \begin{vmatrix} k_1 & -k_2 \\ 0 & +k_2 \end{vmatrix} = 0 : 0 : k_1 k_2 = 0 : 0 : 1$$

Taking (ii) into account:

$$x_1 = 0 \quad x_2 = 0 \quad x_3 = e^{0 \times t} = 1 \quad \text{or} \quad \boldsymbol{x}_3 = \begin{pmatrix} 0 \\ 0 \\ 1 \end{pmatrix} \times 1 \qquad \ldots\ldots \text{(x)}$$

as eigenvector for the eigenvalue $\lambda_3 = 0$.

It is known that the general solution of the system of linear differential equations formulated at the outset is a linear superposition of all individual solutions. Hence:

$$\left.\begin{aligned} x_1 &= \alpha \times 1 \times e^{-k_1 t} + \beta \times 0 \times e^{-k_2 t} + \gamma \times 0\\ x_2 &= \alpha \frac{+k_1}{k_2 - k_1} e^{-k_1 t} + \beta(-1)\, e^{-k_2 t} + \gamma \times 0\\ x_3 &= \alpha \frac{-k_2}{k_2 - k_1} e^{-k_1 t} + \beta \times 1 \times e^{-k_2 t} + \gamma \times 1\\ \text{or} \quad \boldsymbol{x} &= \alpha \boldsymbol{x}_1 + \beta \boldsymbol{x}_2 + \gamma \boldsymbol{x}_3\\ \boldsymbol{x} &= \alpha \begin{pmatrix} 1 \\ \dfrac{k_1}{k_2 - k_1} \\ \dfrac{-k_2}{k_2 - k_1} \end{pmatrix} e^{-k_1 t} + \beta \begin{pmatrix} 0 \\ -1 \\ +1 \end{pmatrix} e^{-k_2 t} + \gamma \begin{pmatrix} 0 \\ 0 \\ 1 \end{pmatrix} \end{aligned}\right\} \quad \ldots \text{(xi)}$$

The constants α, β, γ are determined by the initial conditions for $t = 0$, $x_1 = [A_0]$, $x_2 = x_3 = 0$. By substituting in (xi) for $t = 0$, one obtains

$$[A_0] = \alpha \qquad\qquad \alpha = [A_0]$$

$$0 = \alpha \frac{+k_1}{k_2 - k_1} - \beta \qquad \text{i.e} \qquad \beta = [A_0] \frac{k_1}{k_2 - k_1} \qquad \ldots\ldots \text{(xii)}$$

$$0 = \alpha \frac{-k_2}{k_2 - k_1} + \beta + \gamma \qquad\qquad \gamma = [A_0]$$

If the values for α, β, γ obtained at (xii) are substituted in (xi), the solutions to the problem are found to be

$$\left.\begin{aligned}
x_1 &= [A] = [A_0]\,e^{-k_1 t} \\
x_2 &= [B] = [A_0] \frac{k_1}{k_2 - k_1} (e^{-k_1 t} - e^{-k_2 t}) \\
x_3 &= [C] = [A_0] \left\{1 - \frac{k_1 k_2}{k_2 - k_1} \left(\frac{e^{-k_1 t}}{k_1} - \frac{e^{-k_2 t}}{k_2}\right)\right\} \\
\text{or} \quad \boldsymbol{x} &= [A_0] \begin{pmatrix} 1 \\ \dfrac{k_1}{k_2 - k_1} \\ \dfrac{-k_2}{k_2 - k_1} \end{pmatrix} e^{-k_1 t} + [A_0] \frac{k_1}{k_2 - k_1} \begin{pmatrix} 0 \\ -1 \\ +1 \end{pmatrix} e^{-k_2 t} + [A_0] \begin{pmatrix} 0 \\ 0 \\ 1 \end{pmatrix}
\end{aligned}\right\} \quad \ldots \text{(xiii)}$$

as in section A, eqns. (i), (ix) and (xiii).

Note. (1) The eigenvalue method has the advantage of clarity, even for complicated systems; the solution of complicated numerical systems of linear equations and characteristic equations presents no difficulty with modern calculating machines.

(2) If the rate of decay of the first substance, A, is very small relative to that for B (and to that for any further possible intermediate product), i.e. $k_1 \ll k_2$, and the concentration [A] remains virtually constant, one may then, for the concentration [B] in eqn. (xiii), (i) ignore k_1 in comparison with k_2 in the denominator and (ii) ignore $e^{-k_2 t}$ in comparison with $e^{-k_1 t}$ in the bracket.

$$\left.\begin{aligned}
&\text{Hence when } k_1 \ll k_2 \qquad [B] \to [A_0] \frac{k_1}{k_2} e^{-k_1 t} \\
&\text{and, with } [A] = [A_0]\,e^{-k_1 t} \text{ (see eqn. (xiii))} \quad \frac{[A]}{[B]} \to \frac{k_2}{k_1} \quad \text{or} \quad [A]k_1 = [B]k_2
\end{aligned}\right\} \quad \ldots \text{(xiv)}$$

where [A] and [B] are virtually constant, this being a condition for stationary equilibrium, as has already been explained under eqn. (281).

If the rate of decay of the first substance, A, is small, but not very small relative to that for B (and to that for any further possible intermediate product), i.e. $k_1 < k_2$, it is then no longer possible, for the concentration [B] in eqn. (xiii), to ignore k_1 in comparison with k_2 in the denominator. On the other hand, it will still be possible to disregard $e^{-k_2 t}$ in comparison with $e^{-k_1 t}$ in the bracket, since small differences between k_2 and k_1 will undoubtedly result in a much faster dying away of $e^{-k_2 t}$. Hence, when $k_1 < k_2$, but not $k_1 \ll k_2$,

$$[B] \to [A_0] \frac{k_1}{k_2 - k_1} e^{-k_1 t} \quad \text{and} \quad \frac{[A]}{[B]} = \frac{k_2 - k_1}{k_1} \qquad \ldots\ldots \text{(xv)}$$

or $[A]k_1 = [B](k_2 - k_1)$, as a condition for a so-called running equilibrium. In this case, the concentration of the unstable intermediate products does not remain constant but varies according to the fall in concentration of the parent substance; thus [A] and [B] are no longer constant but the ratio [A]/[B] still remains constant. A comparison may be made with the flow of a river or waterfall where, in the ideal case of stationary equilibrium, high-speed photographs taken at given intervals will show an identical picture. If, however, the water supply gradually decreases, the series of photographs will certainly give different pictures, but the pictures will still be similar insofar as the volume of water decreases in the same ratio at all points. The basic pattern of the picture therefore remains the same and one then has a 'running equilibrium'.

**Exercise 185

The overall reaction A + B + C + D = ABCD is made up from the separate second-order reactions:

(I) $$\mathrm{A + B \rightleftharpoons AB} \qquad k_1/k_1'$$

(II) $$\mathrm{AB + C \rightleftharpoons ABC} \qquad k_2/k_2'$$

(III) $$\mathrm{ABC + D \rightleftharpoons ABCD} \qquad k_3/k_3'$$

where AB and ABC represent intermediate products and k_i and k_i' indicate the reaction constants of the forward or reverse reaction in question. One has, for example, at equilibrium, $k_1[\mathrm{A}][\mathrm{B}] = k_1'[\mathrm{AB}]$, which gives $[\mathrm{AB}]/[\mathrm{A}][\mathrm{B}] = k_1/k_1' = K_1$ = equilibrium constant; or, in general, $k_i/k_i' = K_i$.

Derive the equation for the rate of formation of ABCD in the stationary state [see eqn. (281)].

Solution 185. The rate of formation of the intermediate products AB and ABC must be equal to zero in the stationary state. This gives two equations:

for AB: $$\frac{\mathrm{d}[\mathrm{AB}]}{\mathrm{d}t} = k_1[\mathrm{A}][\mathrm{B}] - k_1'[\mathrm{AB}] - k_2[\mathrm{AB}][\mathrm{C}] + k_2'[\mathrm{ABC}] = 0$$

or $$-(k_1' + k_2[\mathrm{C}])[\mathrm{AB}] + k_1[\mathrm{A}][\mathrm{B}] + k_2'[\mathrm{ABC}] = 0 \qquad \ldots\ldots \quad \text{(i)}$$

for ABC: $$\frac{\mathrm{d}[\mathrm{ABC}]}{\mathrm{d}t} = k_2[\mathrm{AB}][\mathrm{C}] - k_2'[\mathrm{ABC}] - k_3[\mathrm{ABC}][\mathrm{D}] + k_3'[\mathrm{ABCD}] = 0$$

or $$k_2[\mathrm{C}][\mathrm{AB}] - (k_2' + k_3[\mathrm{D}])[\mathrm{ABC}] + k_3'[\mathrm{ABCD}] = 0 \qquad \ldots\ldots \quad \text{(ii)}$$

The equation for the rate of formation of ABCD is

$$\frac{\mathrm{d}[\mathrm{ABCD}]}{\mathrm{d}t} = k_3[\mathrm{ABC}][\mathrm{D}] - k_3'[\mathrm{ABCD}] \qquad \ldots\ldots \quad \text{(iii)}$$

In order to solve this set of equations, [AB] is eliminated from (i) and (ii) and the resulting expression (iv), for [ABC], is then substituted in (iii). In order to eliminate [AB], (i) is multiplied by $k_2[\mathrm{C}]$ and (ii) by $(k_1' + k_2[\mathrm{C}])$. Addition then gives

$$k_1k_2[\mathrm{A}][\mathrm{B}][\mathrm{C}] + k_2k_2'[\mathrm{C}][\mathrm{ABC}] + (k_1' + k_2[\mathrm{C}])k_3'[\mathrm{ABCD}]$$
$$-(k_1' + k_2[\mathrm{C}])(k_2' + k_3[\mathrm{D}])[\mathrm{ABC}] = 0$$

or

$$[\mathrm{ABC}] = \frac{k_1k_2[\mathrm{A}][\mathrm{B}][\mathrm{C}] + (k_1'k_3' + k_2k_3'[\mathrm{C}])[\mathrm{ABCD}]}{k_1'k_2' + k_1'k_3[\mathrm{D}] + k_2k_3[\mathrm{C}][\mathrm{D}]} \qquad \ldots\ldots \quad \text{(iv)}$$

Substituting (iv) in (iii) and reducing to a common denominator gives

$$\frac{d[ABCD]}{dt} = \frac{k_1 k_2 k_3 [A][B][C][D] - k'_1 k'_2 k'_3 [ABCD]}{k'_1 k'_2 + k'_1 k_3 [D] + k_2 k_3 [C][D]}$$

$$= \frac{K_1 K_2 K_3 [A][B][C][D] - [ABCD]}{1/k'_3 + K_3 [D]/k'_2 + K_2 K_3 [C][D]/k'_1} \quad \ldots\ldots \text{(v)}$$

Exercise 186

The following reaction scheme, representing a chain mechanism, has been found to apply for the thermal formation of hydrogen bromide from the elements, $H_2 + Br_2 = HBr$:

(1)	Initiating reaction	$Br_2 = 2\,Br$	with k_1
(2)	Chain reaction	$Br + H_2 = HBr + H$	with k_2
(3)	Chain reaction	$H + Br_2 = HBr + Br$	with k_3
(4)	Chain reaction	$H + HBr = H_2 + Br$	with k'_2
(5)	Terminating reaction	$2\,Br = Br_2$	with k'_1

$$\frac{k_1}{k'_1} = K_1 = \frac{[Br]^2}{[Br_2]} \quad \text{(dissociation constant for } Br_2\text{)}$$

Formulate the equation for the rate of formation of HBr, on the assumption that the reaction takes a quasi-stationary course.

Solution 186. The rate of formation of the intermediate products, H and Br, must approximate to zero in the stationary state. Hence

$$\frac{d[H]}{dt} = k_2 [Br][H_2] - k_3 [H][Br_2] - k'_2 [H][HBr] = 0 \quad \ldots\ldots \text{(i)}$$

$$\frac{d[Br]}{dt} = 2k_1[Br_2] - 2k'_1[Br]^2 - \underbrace{k_2[Br][H_2] + k_3[H][Br_2] + k'_2[H][HBr]}_{= 0 \text{ on account of (i)}} = 0 \quad \ldots\ldots \text{(ii)}$$

or

$$\frac{[Br]^2}{[Br_2]} = \frac{k_1}{k'_1} = K_1 \qquad [Br] = \sqrt{K_1 [Br_2]} \quad \ldots\ldots \text{(iii)}$$

This result could, of course, also have been obtained directly from the given equations at (1) and (5) above.

The rate of formation of HBr is obtained as follows:

$$\frac{d[HBr]}{dt} = k_2 [Br][H_2] + k_3 [H][Br_2] - k'_2 [H][HBr] \quad \ldots\ldots \text{(iv)}$$

or, after adding (i)

$$\frac{d[HBr]}{dt} = 2(k_2 [Br][H_2] - k'_2 [H][HBr]) \quad \ldots\ldots \text{(v)}$$

The H concentration is given by (i):

$$[H] = \frac{k_2 [Br][H_2]}{k_3 [Br_2] + k'_2 [HBr]} \quad \ldots\ldots \text{(vi)}$$

Substituting (vi) in (v) gives

$$\frac{d[HBr]}{dt} = 2k_2[Br][H_2]\left(1 - \frac{k_2'[HBr]}{k_3[Br_2] + k_2'[HBr]}\right)$$

or, with (iii):

$$\frac{d[HBr]}{dt} = \frac{2k_2\sqrt{(k_1/k_1')[Br_2]}\,[H_2]}{1 + \dfrac{k_2'[HBr]}{k_3[Br_2]}} \quad \ldots . \text{(vii)}$$

Exercise 187

Referring to Exercise 186, what will be the form of the equation for the rate of formation of HBr if the Br atoms originate as a result of the photochemical reaction $Br_2 + h\nu = 2Br$, instead of as a result of thermal equilibrium? The unit for the intensity of the absorbed light may be taken as 1 mole quantum per second per litre $= 6{\cdot}0236 \times 10^{23}$ quanta/sec × l. = 1 einstein/(sec l.). Let the number of mole quanta per second per litre be $\dot{n}_q$; see eqns. (332) to (334).

Solution 187. One now simply has $2\dot{n}_q$ instead of $2k_1[Br_2]$ in (ii) and (vii) of Exercise 186. Hence:

$$\frac{d[HBr]}{dt} = \frac{2k_2\sqrt{\dot{n}_q/k_1'}\,[H_2]}{1 + \dfrac{k_2'[HBr]}{k_3[Br_2]}}$$

Exercise 188

The following reaction scheme has been found to describe the overall equation $CO + Cl_2 = COCl_2$ for the thermal formation and dissociation of phosgene, $COCl_2$:

(1) Initiating reaction
$Cl_2 + M = 2Cl + M$ (k_1) (M = three-body collision partner, the wall)

(2) $Cl + CO + M = COCl + M$ (k_2)
(3) $COCl + M = Cl + CO + M$ (k_3)
} in equilibrium; very rapidly established

(4) $COCl + Cl_2 = COCl_2 + Cl$ (k_4) [eqns. (2) to (4) = a reaction chain]

(5) $COCl_2 + Cl = COCl + Cl_2$ (k_5)

(6) $2Cl + M = Cl_2 + M$ (k_6) terminating reaction; proceeds rapidly in comparison with eqn. (2), so that the dissociation equilibrium for chlorine is virtually set

What is the equation describing the rates of formation and dissociation of $COCl_2$?

Solution 188. Cl and the radical COCl feature as chain carriers and intermediate products. The dissociation equilibrium of COCl, obtained from (2) and (3), is

$$\frac{[CO][Cl]}{[COCl]} = K_{COCl} = \frac{k_3}{k_2} \quad (M \text{ cancels out}) \quad \ldots . \text{(i)}$$

Similarly, the dissociation equilibrium for chlorine is, from (1) and (6):

$$\frac{[Cl]^2}{[Cl_2]} = K_{Cl_2} = \frac{k_1}{k_6} \quad (M \text{ cancels out}) \qquad \ldots . \quad \text{(ii)}$$

The following is the expression for the rate of formation and dissociation of $COCl_2$:

$$\frac{d\,[COCl_2]}{d\,t} = k_4\,[COCl]\,[Cl_2] - k_5\,[COCl_2]\,[Cl] \qquad \ldots . \quad \text{(iii)}$$

Substituting (i) and (ii) for [COCl] and [Cl] gives

$$\frac{d\,[COCl_2]}{d\,t} = \left(\frac{k_4}{K_{COCl}}\,[CO]\,[Cl_2] - k_5\,[COCl_2]\right)\sqrt{K_{Cl_2}\,[Cl_2]} \qquad \ldots . \quad \text{(iv)}$$

$$= k_F\,[CO]\,\sqrt{[Cl_2]^3} - k_d\,[COCl_2]\,\sqrt{[Cl_2]} \qquad \ldots . \quad \text{(v)}$$

where $k_F = \frac{k_4\sqrt{K_{Cl_2}}}{K_{COCl}}$ and $k_d = k_5\sqrt{K_{Cl_2}}$

Exercise 189

The photochemical formation of phosgene (see Exercise 188) differs from that under the effect of heat in that the initiating reaction (1) now becomes $Cl_2 + h\nu = 2\,Cl$, and the terminating reaction (6) is $COCl + Cl = CO + Cl_2$ ($k_6^\star$). The number of mol. quanta per second per litre is $\dot{n}_q$ (see Exercise 187).

One therefore has the following reaction scheme for the formation of $COCl_2$:

(1)	$Cl_2 + h\nu = 2\,Cl$		(initiating reaction)
(2)	$Cl + CO + M = COCl + M$	(k_2)	virtually in equilibrium:
(3)	$COCl + M = Cl + CO + M$	(k_3)	$\frac{k_3}{k_2} \approx K_{COCl} = \frac{[CO]\,[Cl]}{[COCl]}$
(4)	$COCl + Cl_2 = COCl_2 + Cl$	(k_4)	
(5)	$COCl_2 + Cl = COCl + Cl_2$	(k_5)	(only formation is considered)
(6)	$COCl + Cl = CO + Cl_2$	($k_6^\star$)	

What is the equation for the rate of formation of $COCl_2$?

Solution 189. Equation (ii) in Exercise 188 can, of course, no longer be valid. The equations for the formation of stationary concentrations of Cl and COCl are:

$$\frac{d\,[Cl]}{d\,t} = 2\,\dot{n}_q - k_6^\star\,[Cl]\,[COCl] + k_3\,[COCl]\,[M] - k_2\,[Cl]\,[CO]\,[M] + k_4\,[COCl]\,[Cl_2] = 0 \qquad \ldots . \quad \text{(i)}$$

$$\frac{d\,[COCl]}{d\,t} = +\,k_2\,[Cl]\,[CO]\,[M] - k_3\,[COCl]\,[M] - k_4\,[COCl]\,[Cl_2] - k_6^\star\,[COCl]\,[Cl] = 0 \qquad \ldots . \quad \text{(ii)}$$

Addition of (i) and (ii) gives

$$\frac{d\,[Cl]}{d\,t} = 2\,\dot{n}_q - 2\,k_6^\star\,[COCl]\,[Cl] = 0 \qquad \ldots . \quad \text{(iii)}$$

or
$$[Cl] = \frac{\dot{n}_q}{k_6^\star [COCl]} \quad \dots . \quad (iv)$$

and, where $[COCl] = [CO][Cl]/K_{COCl}$ (see above)

$$[Cl] = \sqrt{\frac{\dot{n}_q K_{COCl}}{k_6^\star [CO]}} \quad \dots . \quad [v]$$

Hence, using (iv) and (v), the rate of formation of $COCl_2$ is

$$\left.\begin{aligned}\frac{d[COCl_2]}{dt} &= k_4[Cl_2][COCl] = k_4[Cl_2]\frac{[CO][Cl]}{K_{COCl}} = \frac{k_4[Cl_2][CO]}{K_{COCl}} = \sqrt{\frac{\dot{n}_q K_{COCl}}{k_6^\star [CO]}} \\ &= k_4\sqrt{\frac{\dot{n}_q}{k_6^\star K_{COCl}}}\sqrt{[CO]}[Cl_2]\end{aligned}\right\} \quad \dots \quad (vi)$$

EXERCISE 190

The photochemical (chlorine detonating gas) reaction $H_2 + Cl_2 = 2HCl$ may be described by the following reaction scheme when oxygen is present in limited quantities:

(1) $Cl_2 + h\nu = 2Cl$ initiating reaction, ($\dot{n}_q$ = number of mole quanta per sec per litre; see Exercise 187)

(2) $Cl + H_2 = HCl + H$ (k_2) } reaction chain
(3) $H + Cl_2 = HCl + Cl$ (k_3) }

(4) $H + O_2 + M = HO_2 + M$ (k_4) } terminating reactions (inhibition by oxygen)
(5) $Cl + O_2 + M = ClO_2 + M$ (k_5) }

Formulate the equation for the rate of formation of HCl. Terms involving the square of $[O_2]$ may be ignored because of the small oxygen concentration.

Solution 190. The concentrations of the intermediate products Cl and H are, for the stationary state, given by:

$$\frac{d[Cl]}{dt} = 2\dot{n}_q - k_2[H_2][Cl] + k_3[Cl_2][H] - k_5[O_2][M][Cl] = 0 \quad \dots . \quad (i)$$

$$\frac{d[H]}{dt} = k_2[H_2][Cl] - k_3[Cl_2][H] - k_4[O_2][M][H] = 0 \quad \dots . \quad (ii)$$

Eliminating [Cl] from (i) and (ii):

$$[H] = \frac{2\dot{n}_q k_2[H_2]}{(k_2[H_2] + k_5[O_2][M])(k_3[Cl_2] + k_4[O_2][M]) - k_2 k_3[H_2][Cl_2]} \quad \dots . \quad (iii)$$

The expression for the rate of formation of HCl is

$$\frac{d[HCl]}{dt} = k_2[H_2][Cl] + k_3[Cl_2][H] \quad \dots . \quad (iv)$$

Subtracting (ii) from (iv):

$$\frac{d[HCl]}{dt} = (2k_3[Cl_2] + k_4[O_2][M])[H] \quad \dots . \quad (v)$$

Multiplying (iii) out, and neglecting the term involving $[O_2]^2$, one has

$$[H] = \frac{2\dot{n}_g k_2 [H_2]}{(k_2 k_4 [H_2] + k_3 k_5 [Cl_2])[O_2][M]} \quad \ldots\ldots \text{(vi)}$$

Substituting (vi) in (v) and ignoring the small term $k_4[O_2][M]$ (because of the vanishingly small O_2 concentration), one finally obtains

$$\frac{d[HCl]}{dt} = \frac{4 k_2 k_3 \dot{n}_g [H_2][Cl_2]}{(k_2 k_4 [H_2] + k_3 k_5 [Cl_2])[O_2][M]} \quad \ldots\ldots \text{(vii)}$$

or

$$\frac{d[HCl]}{dt} = \frac{k_A \dot{n}_g [H_2][Cl_2]}{([H_2] + k_B [Cl_2])[O_2][M]} \quad \ldots\ldots \text{(viii)}$$

where $k_A = \frac{4k_3}{k_4}$ $\quad k_B = \frac{k_3 k_5}{k_2 k_4}$

Note to Exercises 186 to 190. The converse problem of determining the detailed course of a reaction from an empirical reaction equation is much more difficult than formulating the reaction equation from a given reaction scheme. There is no simple general way of solving the former. Extensive research is usually required. Having obtained the reaction equation — as in Exercise 186 to 190 — a check must be made that the collision mechanism is consistent with empirical data. In particular, a check must be made that the values for the reaction constants k_i and their temperature dependence, as well as the stationary concentrations of the intermediate products, are plausible from the thermochemical and kinetic points of view. Such tests are beyond the scope of normal routine calculations; they require special research and will therefore not be dealt with here. See also note to Exercise 194.

*Exercise 191

The dissociation of nitrogen dioxide, $2NO_2 = 2NO + O_2$, is a homogeneous, second-order reaction between 320° and 390 °C. The following rate constants k^{II} have been established:

T (°K)	$k \times 10^{-3}$ (cm³/mole sec)
592	0·522
603·5	0·755
627	1·700
651·5	4·020
656	5·030

Determine the energy of activation A, the frequency factor H, and the steric factor α, if the diameter of NO_2 is taken as 2·4 Å. Use eqns. (301), (302) and (293).

Solution 191. One first plots $\log k - 0{\cdot}5 \log T$ against $1/T$. The following are obtained by calculation:

T (°K)	$1/T \times 10^3$	$0{\cdot}5 \log T$	$\log k$	$\log k - 0{\cdot}5 \log T$
592	1·689	1·3862	2·7177	1·3315
603·5	1·657	1·3903	2·8779	1·4876
627	1·595	1·3986	3·2304	1·8318
651·5	1·535	1·4070	3·6042	2·1972
656	1·524	1·4085	3·7016	2·2931

The values are plotted in *Figure 27* and a straight line drawn through the points. In order to determine the activation energy, two points on this line may be taken, e.g. at

$$1/T = 1{\cdot}520 \times 10^{-3} \qquad \log k - 0{\cdot}5 \log T = 2{\cdot}29$$

$$1/T = 1{\cdot}692 \times 10^{-3} \qquad \log k - 0{\cdot}5 \log T = 1{\cdot}29$$

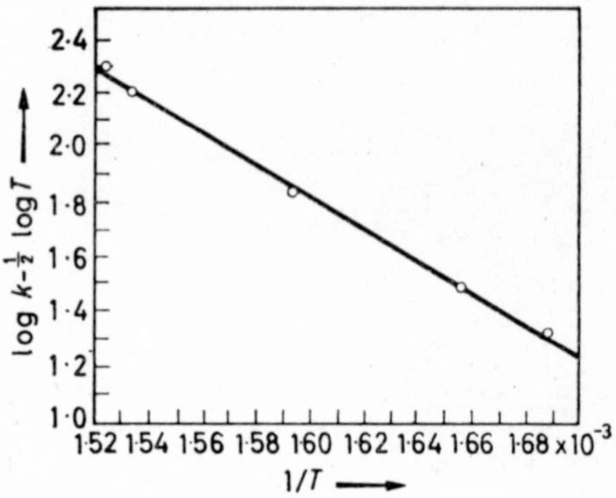

Figure 27. Determination of activation energy and the frequency factor for the dissociation of NO_2

One then has from eqn. (301)

$$\frac{2{\cdot}29 - 1{\cdot}29}{(1{\cdot}520 - 1{\cdot}692)\,10^{-3}} = -\frac{A}{4{\cdot}574}$$

or

$$A = \frac{1{\cdot}00 \times 4{\cdot}574}{0{\cdot}172 \times 10^{-3}} = 26{\cdot}6 \text{ kcal/mole} \qquad \dots \quad \text{(i)}$$

The frequency factor, $H = H' T^{1/2}$ [see eqn. (300)], is obtained from eqn. (301) by substituting the numerical values:

$$\log H' = 2{\cdot}29 + \frac{26\,600 \times 1{\cdot}520 \times 10^{-3}}{4{\cdot}574} = 2{\cdot}29 + 8{\cdot}83 = 11{\cdot}12$$

$$H' = 1{\cdot}32 \times 10^{11} \qquad H = 1{\cdot}32 \times 10^{11}\, T^{1/2} \text{ (cm}^3\text{/mole sec)} \qquad \dots \quad \text{(ii)}$$

Taking $\sigma = 2{\cdot}4$ Å and M = 46, substituting in eqn. (293) gives

$$H = 3{\cdot}90 \times 10^{12}\, \alpha\, \frac{(2{\cdot}4)^2}{\sqrt{46}}\, T^{1/2} = 1{\cdot}32 \times 10^{11}\, T^{1/2}$$

$$\alpha = \frac{1{\cdot}32 \times 10^{11} \sqrt{46}}{3{\cdot}90 \times 10^{12} (2{\cdot}4)^2} = 0{\cdot}04 = \tfrac{1}{25} \qquad \dots \quad \text{(iii)}$$

*Exercise 192

The dissociation of nitrosyl chloride, $2\,NOCl = 2\,NO + Cl_2$, is a homogeneous, second-order reaction between 150° and 250 °C. The dissociation constants k^{II} are

θ (°C)	k (cm³/mole sec)	θ (°C)	k (cm³/mole sec)
150·1	3·65	209·8	123
170·0	12·9	219·6	223
179·8	23·7	229·9	370
189·9	43·0	240·4	565
200·0	76·3	250·7	1048

Calculate the activation energy A, the frequency factor H and the steric factor α, taking the diameter of NOCl as 3 Å. See eqns. (301), (302) and (293).

Solution 192. One must first plot $\log k - 0{\cdot}5 \log T$ against $1/T$. Calculation gives

T (°K)	1/T × 10³	0·5 log T	log k	log k − 0·5 log T
423·1	2·363	1·3132	0·5623	0·2491 − 1
443·0	2·257	1·3232	1·1106	0·7874 − 1
452·8	2·208	1·3280	1·3747	0·0467
462·9	2·160	1·3328	1·6335	0·3007
473·0	2·114	1·3375	1·8825	0·5450
482·8	2·071	1·3419	2·0899	0·7480
492·6	2·030	1·3463	2·3483	1·0020
502·9	1·988	1·3508	2·5682	1·2174
513·4	1·948	1·3553	2·7520	1·3967
523·7	1·909	1·3596	3·0204	1·6608

The values are plotted in *Figure 28*, with a straight line drawn through the points. The activation energy is found by taking two points on this straight line, e.g. at

$$1/T = 1{\cdot}908 \times 10^{-3} \qquad \log k - 0{\cdot}5 \log T = 1{\cdot}640$$
$$1/T = 2{\cdot}404 \times 10^{-3} \qquad \log k - 0{\cdot}5 \log T = 0{\cdot}010 - 1$$

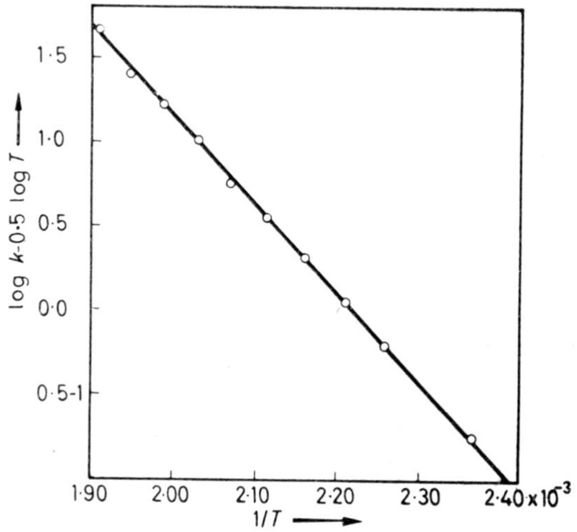

Figure 28. Determination of activation energy and the frequency factor for dissociation of NOCl

Hence, from eqn. (301):

$$\frac{1{\cdot}640 - (0{\cdot}010 - 1)}{(1{\cdot}908 - 2{\cdot}404)10^{-3}} = \frac{-A}{4{\cdot}574}$$

or

$$A = \frac{2{\cdot}630 \times 4{\cdot}574}{0{\cdot}496 \times 10^{-3}} = 24{\cdot}2 \text{ kcal/mole} \qquad \ldots\ldots \quad \text{(i)}$$

H' is obtained by substituting the numerical values in eqn. (301):

$$\log H' = 1{\cdot}640 + \frac{24\,200 \times 1{\cdot}908 \times 10^{-3}}{4{\cdot}574} = 1{\cdot}640 + 10{\cdot}09 = 11{\cdot}73$$

$$H' = 5{\cdot}37 \times 10^{11} \qquad H = 5{\cdot}37 \times 10^{11}\, T^{1/2} \text{ (cm}^3\text{/mole sec)} \qquad \ldots\ldots \quad \text{(ii)}$$

Taking $\sigma = 3$ Å and $M = 65{\cdot}5$, substitution of H in eqn. (293) gives

$$H = 3{\cdot}90 \times 10^{12}\, \alpha\, 3^2 \frac{T^{1/2}}{\sqrt{65{\cdot}5}} = 5{\cdot}37 \times 10^{11}\, T^{1/2}$$

$$\alpha = \frac{5{\cdot}37 \times 10^{11} \sqrt{65{\cdot}5}}{3{\cdot}90 \times 10^{12} \times 3^2} = 0{\cdot}124 \approx \tfrac{1}{8} \qquad \ldots\ldots \quad \text{(iii)}$$

*Exercise 193

The formation and dissociation of hydrogen iodide $H_2 + I_2 \rightleftharpoons 2HI\,(\overrightarrow{k}/\overleftarrow{k'})$ is an homogeneous second-order reaction. The following values have been found for the rate constants k^{II} (cm³/mole sec) expressed as functions of temperature:

formation: $$\log k = \frac{-8500}{T} + 0{\cdot}5 \log T + 12{\cdot}518 \qquad \ldots\ldots \quad \text{(I)}$$

dissociation: $$\log k' = \frac{-9550}{T} + 0{\cdot}5 \log T + 12{\cdot}312 \qquad \ldots\ldots \quad \text{(II)}$$

The measurements were made at a temperature of about 400 °C. Calculate the activation energies, the frequency factors and molecular diameter of HI, and the mean (reaction) diameters of H_2 and I_2, when the steric factor is taken as 1.

Solution 193. (*a*) Formation of HI. Equations (288) and (301) give the activation energy as

$$A = 8500 \times 4{\cdot}574 = 38{\cdot}9 \text{ kcal/mole} \qquad \ldots\ldots \quad \text{(i)}$$

The frequency factor is obtained from eqn. (300):

$$\log H = 0{\cdot}5 \log (400 + 273) + 12{\cdot}518 = 1{\cdot}414 + 12{\cdot}518 = 13{\cdot}932 \qquad \ldots\ldots \quad \text{(ii)}$$

$$H = 8{\cdot}55 \times 10^{13} \text{ cm}^3\text{/mole sec}$$

The mean (reaction) diameters of H_2 and I_2 are obtained from eqn. (297). The right-hand side of eqn. (297) must be multiplied by 2 because two molecules of HI are formed per collision:

$$H = 2 \times 2{\cdot}76 \times 10^{12}\, \sigma_{12}^2\, (1/M_r)^{1/2}\, T^{1/2} = 10^{12{\cdot}518}\, T^{1/2} = 3{\cdot}3 \times 10^{12}\, T^{1/2}$$

This follows since comparison of eqn. (288) with (I) shows that $\log H = 0{\cdot}5 \log T + 12{\cdot}518$ and $H = 3{\cdot}3 \times 10^{12}\, T^{1/2}$.

$$1/M_r = 1/M_{H_2} + 1/M_{I_2} = 1/2{\cdot}016 + 1/253{\cdot}8 = 0{\cdot}496 + 0{\cdot}004 = 0{\cdot}50$$

Hence

$$\sigma_{12}^2 = \frac{3{\cdot}3 \times 10^{12}}{2 \times 2{\cdot}76 \sqrt{0{\cdot}50} \times 10^{12}} = 0{\cdot}85\,[\text{Å}]^2 \qquad \sigma_{12} = 0{\cdot}92\ \text{Å} \qquad \ldots\ldots \text{(iii)}$$

This diameter is somewhat too small. A steric factor must therefore be present.

(*b*) Dissociation of HI. Equations (288) and (301) give the activation energy as

$$A = 9550 \times 4{\cdot}574 = 43{\cdot}7\ \text{kcal/mole} \qquad \ldots\ldots \text{(iv)}$$

The frequency factor is obtained from eqn. (300):

$$\log H = 0{\cdot}5 \log(400 + 273) + 12{\cdot}312 = 1{\cdot}414 + 12{\cdot}312 = 13{\cdot}726$$

$$H = 5{\cdot}32 \times 10^{13}\ \text{cm}^3/\text{mole sec} \qquad \ldots\ldots \text{(v)}$$

The diameter of HI is, from eqn. (293):

$$H = 3{\cdot}90 \times 10^{12} \sigma^2 (1/M)^{1/2}\, T^{1/2} = 10^{12 \cdot 312}\, T^{1/2} = 2{\cdot}05 \times 10^{12}\, T^{1/2}$$

as comparison of eqn. (288) with (II) gives: $\log H = 0{\cdot}5 \log T + 12{\cdot}312$ and $H = 2{\cdot}05 \times 10^{12}\, T^{1/2}$.

With $M = 127{\cdot}9$, it follows that

$$\sigma^2 = \frac{2{\cdot}05 \times 10^{12} \sqrt{127{\cdot}9}}{3{\cdot}90 \times 10^{12}} = 5{\cdot}94\,[\text{Å}]^2 \qquad \sigma = 2{\cdot}44\ \text{Å} \qquad \ldots\ldots \text{(vi)}$$

*Exercise 194

Show that the frequency factor for bimolecular reactions must always be of the order of magnitude of 10^{11} (or somewhat smaller if the steric factor α is less than 1), i.e. when the concentrations are measured in mole/l. and the reaction constant k^{II} has the unit l./mole sec. The molecular diameter has a value between 1 and 10 Å, i.e. $\sigma^2 \approx 10\,[\text{Å}]^2$; see eqn. (294).

Solution 194. Taking 350 °C, i.e. 625 °K, as a typical reaction temperature, and assuming the molecular weight to be of the order of 100, eqn. (294) then gives

$$H = 390 \times 10^9 \times 10 \sqrt{625/100} = 9{\cdot}75 \times 10^{10} \approx 10^{11}\ \text{l./mole sec}$$

Note. The correct order of magnitude of the frequency factor for a bimolecular reaction (10^{11} l./mole sec) and that for a termolecular reaction (ca. 1/1000 to 1/100 times smaller than the collision number for a bimolecular reaction), at atmospheric pressure and room temperature, is one of the criteria for checking that the assumed collision mechanism is reasonable. This was explained in the note to Exercises 186 to 190. In the case of monomolecular reactions, the frequency factors may spread over a wide range (10^9 to 10^{15} sec^{-1}). A further criterion results from consideration of the activation energy, i.e. whether the value of the latter is reasonable, having regard to the heats of reaction of the (exothermic or endothermic) reactions in question. A strongly endothermic reaction cannot have a reaction constant with a high value. Finally, it is important to make a breakdown of experimentally determined constants when the latter represent a combination of a number of reaction constants. This may be done, for example, by evaluating individual reaction constants from known equilibrium constants or by comparing thermal and photochemical reactions. These segregated values may then be examined separately; see, for example, the splitting-up of k_1/k_1' in (vii) of Exercise 186 (formation of hydrogen bromide under the effect of heat) by considering the photochemical formation of HBr in Exercise 187. The term $\dot{n}_q/k_1'$ takes the place of $k_1/k_1'[Br_2]$ in the relevant formulae.

The following is a discussion of the collision mechanism for the case of the formation of hydrogen bromide, based on the work by Bodenstein and by Jost.

In the reaction equation for the thermal formation of HBr [(vii) at Exercise 186], the constant $2k_2\sqrt{k_1/k_1'}$ is in the numerator and its value and temperature dependence were determined experimentally. The dissociation constant for Br_2, $K_1 = k_1/k_1'$, whose magnitude and temperature dependence are also known, features as the square root. It follows that k_2 may be individually determined. Jost found a value of $k_2 = 7{\cdot}95 \times 10^9\, T^{1/2}\, e^{-19410/RT}$ (l./mole sec). Reaction 2, i.e. $Br + H_2 = HBr + H$, is an atomic reaction; it is endothermic and has a heat of reaction $\Delta H = +16{,}800$ cal/mole. The activation energy, $A = +19{,}410$ cal/mole, therefore has a reasonable value; i.e. on the one hand being greater than the heat of reaction, $\Delta H = +16{,}800$ cal/mole; on the other, not exceeding this value by more than 10,000 cal/mole. This latter feature is a requirement because the heat of activation of exothermic atomic reactions is always small, viz. between 0 and 10,000 cal/mole. Correspondingly, the activation energies of endothermic atomic reactions are, at most, just about the same amount above the heat of reaction (in this case, $19{,}410 - 16{,}800 = 2610$ cal/mole). The reverse reaction 4, i.e. $HBr + H = Br + H_2$, $\Delta H = -16{,}800$ cal/mole, with the reaction constant k_2' and with an activation energy of only about 2600 cal/mole, must be practically independent of temperature. This means that the experimentally determined constant, $k_2'/k_3 = 1/8{\cdot}4$, in the denominator of eqn. (vii) in Exercise 186 is virtually independent of temperature. Reaction 3, with the reaction constant k_3, is also a strongly exothermic atomic reaction: $H + Br_2 = HBr + Br$, $\Delta H = -40{,}800$ cal/mole; a practically zero activation energy is, therefore, to be expected. Eqn. (301) gives the collision factor H' for reaction 2 as

$$H' = 2{\cdot}76 \times 10^9\, \alpha\, \sigma_{12}^2\, M_r^{-1/2} \quad \text{where} \quad \sigma_{12} = r_{H_2} + r_{Br} \approx 5\ \text{Å}$$

and where

$$M_r = \frac{2 \times 80}{2 + 80} = 1{\cdot}95$$

Hence

$$H' = 49 \times 10^9\, \alpha$$

and if a steric factor α of, say, 1/6 is taken, this value is in reasonable agreement with that found experimentally by Jost and given above, viz. $7{\cdot}95 \times 10^9$.

Finally, as was explained above, an examination of the photochemical formation of hydrogen bromide (Exercise 187) permits a further breakdown of k_1/k_1'. The constant $2k_2/\sqrt{k_1'}$ features in the numerator of the equation for the photochemical rate of formation of HBr (see Exercise 187); k_1' can therefore be obtained by elimination of k_2. The reaction that applies, $Br + Br = Br_2$, with k_1', must, as is well known, be regarded as a three-body collision on mechanical grounds (to dissipate the heat of reaction). All such atomic reactions follow this mechanism. Its collision frequency is, as was explained above, only 1/1000 to 1/100 times that of corresponding two-body collision reactions. In the case of k_1', H was found to be $2{\cdot}5 \times 10^8$ l./mole sec, whilst for a two-body collision reaction (Br + Br) at 200 °C, and where $\sigma \approx 2{\cdot}3$ Å, H would be $3{\cdot}90 \times 10^9 \times 2{\cdot}3^2 (473/80)^{1/2} = 5{\cdot}0 \times 10^{10}$ l./mole sec, according to eqn. (294).

The ratio of the number of three-body collisions found, to the number of two-body collisions under the same conditions, is therefore $2{\cdot}5 \times 10^8/(5{\cdot}0 \times 10^{10}) = 1/200$. This ratio is of the correct order of magnitude.

These discussions are generally beyond the scope of ordinary routine calculations. The reader is therefore referred to textbooks and literature dealing specifically with this subject.

*Exercise 195

Benzoic acid is adsorbed from solutions in benzene by shaking with blood charcoal until equilibrium is established. The following table shows the observed relation between the concentration of the initial solutions and the amount of acid adsorbed at 18 °C.

Concentration, c, of benzoic acid in benzene (mol./l.)	*Amount, x/m, of benzoic acid adsorbed on blood charcoal* (millimole/g *of charcoal*)
$2{\cdot}82 \times 10^{-3}$	0·269
$6{\cdot}17 \times 10^{-3}$	0·355
$2{\cdot}57 \times 10^{-2}$	0·631
$5{\cdot}01 \times 10^{-2}$	0·776
$1{\cdot}21 \times 10^{-1}$	1·21
$2{\cdot}82 \times 10^{-1}$	1·55
$7{\cdot}42 \times 10^{-1}$	2·19

Determine the constants B and $1/n$ in Freundlich's adsorption isotherm, by plotting $\log x/m$ against $\log c$ and evaluating the constants of the straight line obtained.

Solution 195. Figure 29 shows a straight-line plot of the logarithms of the given data.

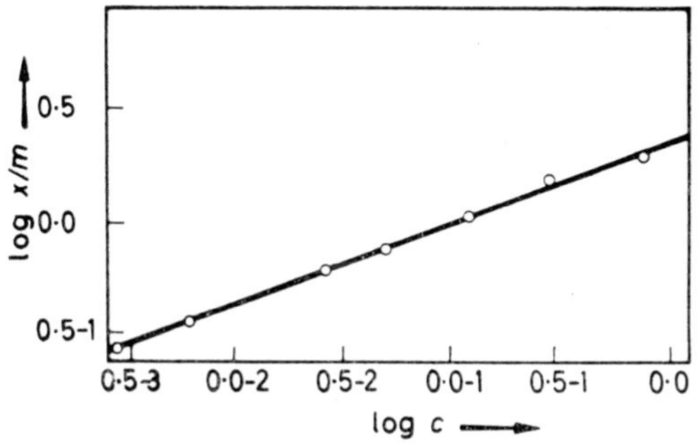

log c	log x/m
0·45 − 3	0·43 − 1
0·79 − 3	0·55 − 1
0·41 − 2	0·80 − 1
0·70 − 2	0·89 − 1
0·08 − 1	0·08
0·45 − 1	0·19
0·87 − 1	0·34

Figure 29. Freundlich adsorption isotherm for the adsorption of benzoic acid by blood charcoal

The Freundlich adsorption isotherm is, according to eqn. (303):

$$x/m = B\,c^{1/n}$$

or, in logarithmic form

$$\log x/m = \log B + \frac{1}{n}\log c \qquad \text{(i)}$$

A linear plot is therefore obtained for $\log(x/m)$ against $\log c$. $1/n$ is obtained by taking two points on the straight line shown in *Figure 29*, e.g.

$\log c = 0{\cdot}00 \qquad \log(x/m) = 0{\cdot}40$

$\log c = 0{\cdot}64 - 3 \qquad \log(x/m) = 0{\cdot}50 - 1$

Hence

$$\frac{1}{n} = \frac{0{\cdot}40 - (0{\cdot}50 - 1)}{0{\cdot}00 - (0{\cdot}64 - 3)} = \frac{0{\cdot}9}{2{\cdot}36} = 0{\cdot}382 = \frac{1}{2{\cdot}62} \quad \ldots\ldots \quad \text{(ii)}$$

Log B is obtained by substituting the numerical values in (i), e.g.

$$\log B = 0{\cdot}40 - \frac{1}{2{\cdot}62} \times 0{\cdot}00 = 0{\cdot}40 \qquad B = 2{\cdot}51 \quad \ldots\ldots \quad \text{(iii)}$$

It follows that the values for the adsorption isotherm are

$$x/m = 2{\cdot}51\, c^{0{\cdot}382} = 2{\cdot}51\, c^{1/2{\cdot}62} \quad \ldots\ldots \quad \text{(iv)}$$

Note. The Freundlich adsorption isotherm is, in general, found to be useful over the medium range of adsorption, i.e. when the concentrations are neither too low (linear range, Henry's law) nor too high (close to saturation).

*Exercise 196

A colloidal sol owing its stability to electric charges can be flocculated by adding a given quantity of oppositely-charged ions. These ions are adsorbed on the surface of the colloidal particles. If, under given conditions, a quantity A of adsorbed singly-charged ions is necessary to neutralize and flocculate a colloid, then $A/2$, $A/3$ and $A/4$

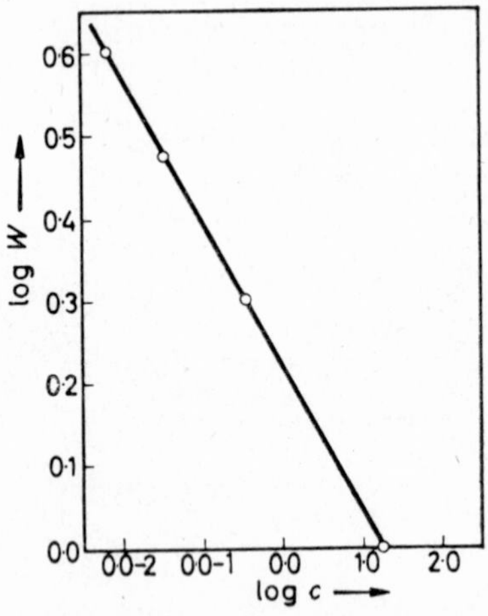

Figure 30. Freundlich adsorption isotherm for the flocculation of an As_2S_3 *solution*

will represent the corresponding amounts of ions with double, triple and quadruple charges required for the same effect. The ratios of the concentrations of solutions of these various ions are not the same as the ratios given above, but are generally related by an adsorption isotherm; thus

$$\frac{A}{W} = B\, c^{1/n} \qquad 1/W = \frac{B}{A}\, c^{1/n} = B'\, c^{1/n} \quad (W = \text{valency})$$

Determine the constants B' and $1/n$ in the Freundlich adsorption isotherm (see Exercise 195) for a negatively-charged arsenic sulphide sol (obtained by passing H_2S through an aqueous As_2O_3 solution) if the following ionic concentrations are found to be necessary to promote flocculation:

	c (millimole/l.)	$\log c$	$\log W$
NaCl	17·8	1·250	0·000
$BaCl_2$	0·34	0·531 − 1	0·301
$AlCl_3$	0·032	0·502 − 2	0·477
$Th(NO_3)_4$	0·0062	0·792 − 3	0·602

Solution 196. The logarithmic form of the Freundlich adsorption isotherm is

$$-\log W = \log B' + \frac{1}{n}\log c \quad \text{or} \quad \log W = -\log B' - \frac{1}{n}\log c \quad \ldots\ldots \quad \text{(i)}$$

Figure 30 shows a logarithmic plot of valency against the measured concentrations required to cause flocculation, a straight line being drawn through the four points. The slope of the line may be obtained by taking the first and third points:

$$-\frac{1}{n} = \frac{\log 1 - \log 3}{\log 17{\cdot}8 - \log 0{\cdot}032} = -0{\cdot}174$$

$$\frac{1}{n} = 0{\cdot}174 = 1/5{\cdot}75 \quad \ldots\ldots \quad \text{(ii)}$$

The intercept on the ordinate axis ($\log c = 0{\cdot}0$) gives the value of $-\log B'$:

$$-\log B' = 0{\cdot}218$$

$$B' = 0{\cdot}605 \quad \ldots\ldots \quad \text{(iii)}$$

The required adsorption isotherm is therefore

$$1/W = 0{\cdot}605\, c^{0{\cdot}174}$$

$$= 0{\cdot}605\, c^{1/5{\cdot}75} \quad \ldots\ldots \quad \text{(iv)}$$

Exercise 197

Acetic acid is adsorbed from an aqueous solution by shaking with a given quantity of animal charcoal. The adsorption equilibrium was studied at 18 °C by taking acid solutions varying over a large range of concentrations. The data shown in the table were obtained. Determine the coefficients of the Langmuir adsorption isotherm, in particular the saturation value z_s for the adsorption [see eqn. (304)], i.e. by plotting $1/(x/m)$ against $1/c$ and determining the coefficients of the equation of the straight line obtained.

Concentration of acetic acid, c (mole/l.)	*Amount adsorbed* (x/m) (millimole/g *charcoal*)
0·00202	0·202
0·00246	0·244
0·00305	0·299
0·00410	0·394
0·00581	0·541
0·0128	1·05
0·100	3·38
0·200	4·03
0·500	4·57

Solution 197. $x/m = \frac{z_s c}{b + c}$ [see eqn. (304)]. Taking the reciprocal, one has

$$\frac{1}{(x/m)} = \frac{1}{z_s} + \frac{b}{z_s} \times \frac{1}{c} \quad \ldots\ldots \text{(i)}$$

i.e. a straight line if $1/(x/m)$ is plotted against $1/c$, and where $1/z_s$ is a constant and b/z_s is the slope.

Calculation of $1/c$ and $1/(x/m)$ gives:

$1/c$	$1\,(x/m)$	$1/c$	$1/(x/m)$
494	4·94	78·0	0·949
406	4·10	10·0	0·296
328	3·34	5·00	0·248
244	2·54	2·00	0·219
172	1·85		

These values are plotted to give the straight line in *Figure 31*. Extrapolating to $1/c = 0$, one obtains

$$\frac{1}{(x/m)} = 1/z_s = 0{\cdot}200$$

i.e. $z_s = 5{\cdot}00$ millimoles of acetic acid/gramme of animal charcoal .... (ii)

as the saturation value for the adsorption.

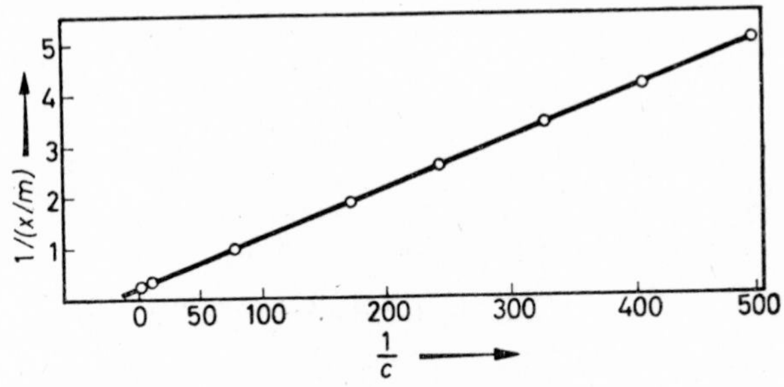

Figure 31. Langmuir adsorption isotherm for the adsorption of acetic acid on animal charcoal

The slope of the line may be obtained by taking two of the plotted points, e.g. the first and seventh:

$$\frac{b}{z_s} = \frac{4{\cdot}94 - 0{\cdot}296}{494 - 10{\cdot}0} = 9{\cdot}60 \times 10^{-3} \quad \ldots\ldots \text{(iii)}$$

i.e.

$$b = 9{\cdot}60 \times 10^{-3} \times 5{\cdot}00 = 4{\cdot}80 \times 10^{-2} \quad \ldots\ldots \text{(iv)}$$

The Langmuir adsorption isotherm therefore reads

$$\frac{x}{m} = \frac{5\,c}{4{\cdot}80 \times 10^{-2} + c}$$

*Exercise 198

Hydrogen is atomically adsorbed on pure copper powder.

Since

$$[H]^2/[H_2] = K \quad \text{or} \quad [H] = \sqrt{K[H_2]}$$

the amount of hydrogen atomically adsorbed, for small amounts of adsorbate and as given by the Langmuir isotherm, will depend, not on the total hydrogen pressure p_{H_2} [analogous to eqn. (219)], but on $\sqrt{p_{H_2}}$; hence

$$x/m = (z_s\sqrt{p})/(\sqrt{b} + \sqrt{p})$$

In view of this behaviour, determine the constants of the adsorption isotherm, in particular, the saturation value z_s for the adsorption (see Exercise 196). The following data were obtained at equilibrium:

Hydrogen pressure, p torr	$1/\sqrt{p}$ $\times 10^2$	*Hydrogen adsorbed per gramme of copper, x/m* mm³	$1/(x/m)$ $\times 10^2$
862	3·41	19·0	5·26
595	4·10	17·2	5·81
308	5·70	14·1	7·09
188	7·30	11·9	8·40
113	9·40	9·90	10·1
75·6	11·5	8·47	11·8
54·1	13·6	7·41	13·5
45·4	14·8	6·90	14·5

Solution 198. $1/(x/m)$ is plotted against $1/\sqrt{p}$ and a straight line obtained; see *Figure 32*. Extrapolation gives, for $1/\sqrt{p} = 0$, a value of

$$1/(x/m) = 2{\cdot}50 \times 10^{-2} = 1/z_s \quad \text{or} \quad z_s = 40 \text{ mm}^3\ H_2/\text{gramme of copper} \quad \ldots . \quad \text{(i)}$$

This is the saturation value for the adsorption.

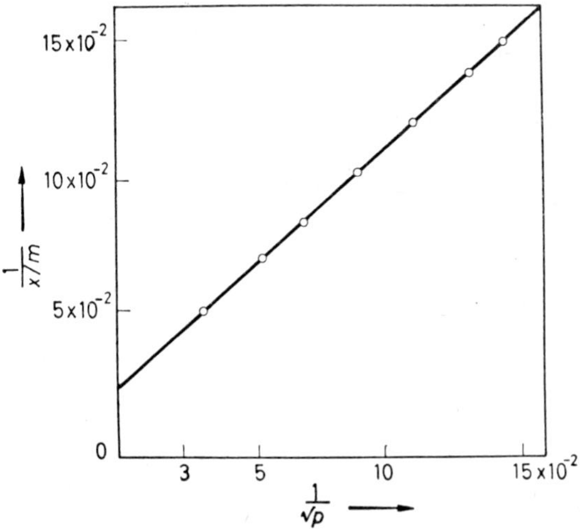

Figure 32. Langmuir adsorption isotherm for the adsorption of hydrogen on copper powder

The reciprocal isotherm, similar to that in Exercise 197, is

$$\frac{1}{(x/m)} = \frac{\sqrt{b}}{z_s} \times \frac{1}{\sqrt{p}} + \frac{1}{z_s} \qquad \ldots\ldots \text{(ii)}$$

The slope, $\sqrt{b}/z_s$, is again found by taking two points on the straight line, e.g. the first and last:

$$\frac{\sqrt{b}}{z_s} = \frac{(14{\cdot}5 - 5{\cdot}26)\,10^{-2}}{(14{\cdot}8 - 3{\cdot}41)\,10^{-2}} = 0{\cdot}81 \qquad \text{i.e. } \sqrt{b} = 0{\cdot}81 \times 40 = 32{\cdot}4 \qquad \ldots\ldots \text{(iii)}$$

The adsorption isotherm is therefore

$$\frac{x}{m} = \frac{40\sqrt{p}}{32{\cdot}4 + \sqrt{p}} \qquad \ldots\ldots \text{(iv)}$$

where the hydrogen pressure p is measured in torr, and x/m in mm³ H_2/g Cu.

Note. In the case of gas mixtures, the shape of adsorption isotherms is generally complex because displacement of adsorbate often takes place. Further information on this aspect may be obtained from the literature or appropriate textbooks.

*Exercise 199

Cane sugar, as is well known, is hydrolysed (inverted) to fructose and glucose under the effect of yeast, which contains the enzyme saccharase (β-h-fructosidase, invertin, invertase). The reaction may be followed by the change in optical rotation. The following data were obtained from a series of experiments to determine the relation between rate of inversion and cane sugar concentration, the temperature and total ferment concentration being maintained constant:

Cane sugar concentration, [S] (mole/l.)	1/[S]	*Rate of inversion, v, measured as decrease in rotation* (deg./min) × 10²	$1/v$
0·0052	192·3	0·919	108·8
0·0104	96·2	1·485	67·3
0·0208	48·1	2·15	46·5
0·0416	24·0	2·76	36·2
0·0833	12·0	3·22	31·1
0·167	5·99	3·52	28·4
0·333	3·00	3·685	27·1

Set up the Michaelis–Menten equation (305) and, in a manner similar to that used for the Langmuir adsorption isotherm (see Exercises 197 and 198), determine the constants; in particular, the affinity constant K_s, i.e. by plotting $1/v$ against 1/[S] and evaluating the constants for the straight line obtained.

Solution 199. The Michaelis–Menten equation

$$v = C\Phi \frac{[S]}{[S] + K_s} \qquad \ldots\ldots \text{(i)}$$

when rearranged to the reciprocal form, reads

$$1/v = \frac{1}{C\Phi} + \frac{K_s}{C\Phi} \times \frac{1}{[S]} \qquad \ldots . \quad \text{(ii)}$$

If $1/v$ is plotted against $1/[S]$, a straight line should be obtained. *Figure 33* shows a plot of the reciprocal of the rate of inversion against the reciprocal of the substrate (cane sugar) concentration, and a straight line is drawn through the points.The intercept on the ordinate axis is obtained by extrapolating to $1/[S] = 0$:

$$25{\cdot}85 = \frac{1}{C\Phi} \quad \text{or} \quad C\Phi = 0{\cdot}0387 \qquad \ldots . \quad \text{(iii)}$$

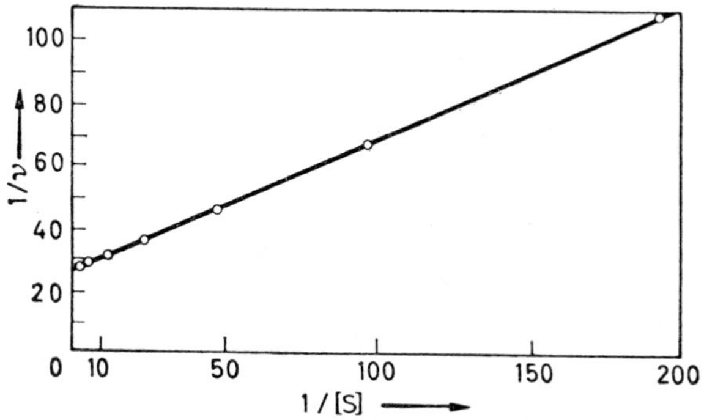

Figure 33. Michaelis–Menten curve for the inversion of cane sugar by invertase

The slope of the line is obtained by taking two suitable points, e.g. the first and the last. Thus

$$\frac{K_s}{C\Phi} = \frac{108{\cdot}8 - 27{\cdot}1}{192{\cdot}3 - 3{\cdot}00} = 0{\cdot}4315 \qquad \ldots . \quad \text{(iv)}$$

The affinity constant (dissociation constant) therefore is

$$K_s = 0{\cdot}4315 \times 0{\cdot}0387 = 0{\cdot}0167 \text{ mole/l.} \qquad \ldots . \quad \text{(v)}$$

and the Michaelis–Menten equation reads

$$v = \frac{0{\cdot}0387\,[S]}{[S] + 0{\cdot}0167} \qquad \ldots . \quad \text{(vi)}$$

Note. K_s may also be obtained by plotting v as ordinate against log [S] as abscissa and finding the abscissa value of the point of inflection of the resulting ∼-shaped curve. The value in question is

$$\left.\begin{aligned} \log [S]_{\text{point of inflection}} &= \log K_s \\ \text{or} \quad [S]_{\text{point of inflection}} &= K_s \end{aligned}\right\} \quad \ldots \quad \text{(vii)}$$

The ordinate value of the point of inflection is, according to eqn. (i), given by

$$v_{\text{point of inflection}} = \frac{C\Phi}{2} \qquad \ldots . \quad \text{(viii)}$$

This procedure is not, however, as accurate as the method described above, where reciprocals were used.

The point of inflection for v as a function of log [S], or for log [S] as a function of v, may be derived directly from (i), if the latter is rearranged to read

$$[S] = \frac{K_s v}{C\Phi - v} \quad \text{or} \quad \log[S] = \log K_s + \log v - \log(C\Phi - v) \qquad \text{(ix)}$$

The point of inflection of a function (or of a function inverse to it) is obtained, as is well known, by equating its second differential to zero. Hence, the condition for a point of inflection in the present case is

$$\frac{d^2 \log[S]}{d v^2} = 0 \qquad \text{(x)}$$

Differentiating eqn. (ix) twice gives

$$\frac{d \log[S]}{d v} = \frac{0{\cdot}4343}{v} + \frac{0{\cdot}4343}{C\Phi - v} \qquad \frac{d^2 \log[S]}{d v^2} = -\frac{0{\cdot}4343}{v^2} + \frac{0{\cdot}4343}{(C\Phi - v)^2} = 0 \qquad \text{(xi)}$$

It follows from eqn. (xi) that the condition for a point of inflection is given by

$$v^2 = (C\Phi - v)^2 \quad \text{or} \quad v_{\text{point of inflection}} = \frac{C\Phi}{2} \qquad \text{(xii)}$$

and, substituting (xii) in (ix):

$$\log[S]_{\text{point of inflection}} = \log K_s \qquad \text{(xiii)}$$

It will also be seen from eqn. (ix) that all curves for log [S] as a function of v will have the same shape for equal values of $C\Phi$; they will merely be displaced parallel to the ordinate axis according to the value of $\log K_s$. The same naturally applies for the inverse curves, i.e. for v as a function of log [S], of interest in the present context; in this case, for equal values of $C\Phi$, all curves will have the same shape but will be displaced parallel to the abscissa axis according to the value of $\log K_s$.

The same graphical method may also be used for evaluating dissociation constants, e.g. of an acid, from conductivity and pH measurements. One has

$$\left.\begin{aligned} &HA \rightleftharpoons H^+ + A^- \\ &\frac{[H^+][A^-]}{[HA]} = K_s \end{aligned}\right\} \qquad \text{(xiv)}$$

where [HA] indicates the concentration of undissociated acid. If c is the total concentration of acid in the solution, the concentration of the dissociated fraction will be given by

$$[A^-] = c - [HA] \qquad \text{(xv)}$$

Substituting (xv) in (xiv)

$$\frac{[H^+](c - [HA])}{[HA]} = K_s \qquad \text{(xvi)}$$

and solving for [HA]

$$[HA] = c\,\frac{[H^+]}{[H^+] + K_s} \quad \text{(curve for undissociated acid)} \qquad \text{(xvii)}$$

Solving for $[H^+]$:

$$[H^+] = \frac{K_s[HA]}{c - [HA]} \quad \text{or} \quad \log[H^+] = -\text{pH} = \log K_s + \log[HA] - \log(c - [HA]) \qquad \text{(xviii)}$$

Equation (xvii) corresponds to eqn. (i), and eqn. (xviii) to eqn. (ix), i.e. if $C\Phi$ is replaced by c, v by [HA] and [S] by $[H^+]$ in (i) and (ix).

If one now plots the concentration of undissociated acid [HA] as ordinate against $\log[H^+] = -\text{pH}$ as abscissa, the abscissa value of the point of inflection will be given by

$$\left.\begin{aligned} &\log[H^+]_{\text{point of inflection}} = -\text{pH}_{\text{point of inflection}} = \log K_s \\ &\text{for an ordinate value of } [HA]_{\text{point of inflection}} = c/2 \end{aligned}\right\} \qquad \text{(xix)}$$

All curves for [HA] plotted in this manner have the same shape for the same value of c; they are merely displaced parallel to the abscissa axis, depending on the value of K_s. See also notes regarding titration curves: Exercise 133, pp. 198–200 and Exercise 140, p. 215.

Both the Michaelis–Menten equation and the Langmuir adsorption isotherm may be extended to cover the case when the substrate is a mixture, or when breakdown products compete with the substrate during adsorption and affect the course of the reaction. See note to Exercise 198.

**Exercise 200

A + BC = AB + C is a commonly occurring type of gross reaction. This may be broken down into a sequence of reactions:

(1) $A = BC \underset{k_1'}{\overset{k_1}{\rightleftharpoons}} ABC^\star$ (intermediate body)

(2) $ABC^\star \underset{k_2'}{\overset{k_2}{\rightleftharpoons}} ABC^{\star\star}$ rearrangement of intermediate body, practically in equilibrium (e.g. tautomerism):

$$\frac{[ABC^{\star\star}]}{[ABC^\star]} = \frac{k_2}{k_2'} \approx K_2$$

(3) $ABC^{\star\star} \underset{k_3'}{\overset{k_3}{\rightleftharpoons}} AB + C$ descomposition of intermediate body

(in general: equilibrium constant $K_i = k_i/k_i'$).

Determine the rate of formation of C: $d[C]/dt = -d[A]/dt$, for stationary equilibrium of the intermediate body [using the type of solution given in Exercise 185; see eqn. (281)].

Solution 200. In the case of stationary equilibrium, the rate of formation of the intermediate products $ABC^\star$ and $ABC^{\star\star}$ must be equal to zero. This leads to two equations:

for $ABC^\star$:

$$\frac{d[ABC^\star]}{dt} = k_1[A][BC] - k_1'[ABC^\star] + k_2'[ABC^{\star\star}] - k_2[ABC^\star] = 0 \quad \ldots . \quad \text{(i)}$$

for $ABC^{\star\star}$:

$$\frac{d[ABC^{\star\star}]}{dt} = k_2[ABC^\star] - k_2'[ABC^{\star\star}] + k_3'[AB][C] - k_3[ABC^{\star\star}] = 0 \quad \ldots . \quad \text{(ii)}$$

Adding (i) and (ii) gives

$$k_1[A][BC] - k_1'[ABC^\star] - k_3[ABC^{\star\star}] + k_3'[AB][C] = 0 \quad \ldots . \quad \text{(iii)}$$

Assuming that

$$\frac{[ABC^{\star\star}]}{[ABC^\star]} \approx K_2 \quad \ldots . \quad \text{(iv)}$$

one has, from (iii) and (iv)

$$k_1[A][BC] - (k_1' + k_3K_2)[ABC^\star] + k_3'[AB][C] = 0 \quad \ldots . \quad \text{(v)}$$

or

$$[ABC^\star] = \frac{k_1[A][BC] + k_3'[AB][C]}{k_1' + k_3K_2} \quad \ldots . \quad \text{(vi)}$$

If

$$-\frac{[dA]}{dt} = \frac{d[C]}{dt}$$

then

$$-\frac{d[A]}{dt} = k_1[A][BC] - k_1'[ABC^\star] \qquad \ldots. \quad \text{(vii)}$$

Substituting (vi) in (vii):

$$-\frac{d[A]}{dt} = +\frac{d[C]}{dt} = \frac{k_1 k_3 K_2 [A][BC] - k_1' k_3' [AB][C]}{k_1' + k_3 K_2} \qquad \ldots. \quad \text{(viii)}$$

$$= \frac{k_1' k_3'}{k_1' + k_3 K_2} (K_1 K_2 K_3 [A][BC] - [AB][C]) \qquad \ldots. \quad \text{(ix)}$$

In this expression, it will be readily seen from the law of mass action that

$$K = K_1 K_2 K_3 = \frac{[AB][C]}{[A][BC]} \quad \text{(at equilibrium)} \qquad \ldots. \quad \text{(x)}$$

Note. This result is noteworthy; it shows that, in the case of an exchange reaction such as A + BC = AB + C where the reaction proceeds via intermediate bodies, the equilibrium constants of the latter feature in the reaction equation. In the case of a unidirectional reaction, with a reaction velocity $\vec{v}$, eqn. (ix) shows that

$$\vec{v} = k^\star K_1[A][BC] \quad (k^\star \text{ being an abbreviation})$$

When ionic reactions are involved, the equilibrium constants K_i will be strongly dependent on concentration. As a first approximation they may be taken as being dependent on the total ionic strength [see eqn. (234)]. Hence, from eqns. (230) and (231):

$$K_1^\star = \frac{a_{ABC^\star}}{a_A\, a_{BC}} = \frac{[ABC^\star] f_{ABC^\star}}{[A] f_A [BC] f_{BC}} = K_1 \frac{f_{ABC^\star}}{f_A f_{AB}}$$

or

$$K_1 = K_1^\star \frac{f_A f_{BC}}{f_{ABC^\star}}$$

where a_i are the activities, f_i are the activity coefficients, varying with the concentration, and $K_1^\star$ is the true equilibrium constant. Thus

$$\vec{v} = k^\star K_1^\star \times \frac{f_A f_{BC}}{f_{ABC^\star}} [A][BC]$$

which is the Brønsted equation; see eqn. (308).

Here, the reaction velocity, $\vec{v}$, is dependent on a combination of activity coefficients, i.e. in the first place on the activity coefficients in K_1, when the first reaction for the formation of the intermediate body is the rate-determining factor.

*Exercise 201

Deduce and plot the dependence of rate of reaction, v, on ionic strength, $J = \frac{1}{2}\sum z_i^2 c_i$, in very dilute solutions (up to $J \approx 0{\cdot}1$) for the ion exchange reactions A + BC = AB + C where the components may be either ions of arbitrary positive or negative charge, or neutral substances (charges ± 2, ± 1, 0). This is best done by plotting $\log v/v_0$ against $\sqrt{J}$; [see Brønsted equation (311)] (so-called primary salt effect of the catalytic salt action).

Solution 201. Taking the form of the Brønstedt equation suitable for the present case [see eqn. (311)], one has

$$\log \frac{v}{v_0} = 1{\cdot}0184\, z_A\, z_{BC} \sqrt{J} \qquad \ldots. \quad \text{(i)}$$

Straight lines, with different slopes, will be obtained by plotting $\log v/v_0$ against $\sqrt{J}$; i.e. with a positive slope if the charges on the ions A and BC are the same; negative if they have different signs. All the lines pass through the origin. When $\sqrt{J} = 0{\cdot}1$, the ordinate values will be:

Case 1: $A^{2+} + B^{2+}$ $A^{2-} + BC^{2-}$ $\log \frac{v}{v_0} = +1{\cdot}0184 \times 2 \times 2 \times 0{\cdot}1 = +0{\cdot}407$

Case 2: $A^{2+} + BC^{+}$ $A^{+} + BC^{2+}$ $\log \frac{v}{v_0} = +1{\cdot}0184 \times 2 \times 1 \times 0{\cdot}1 = +0{\cdot}204$
$A^{2-} + BC^{-}$ $A^{+} + BC^{2+}$

Case 3: $A^{+} + BC^{+}$ $A^{-} + BC^{-}$ $\log \frac{v}{v_0} = +1{\cdot}0184 \times 1 \times 1 \times 0{\cdot}1 = +0{\cdot}102$

Case 4: One component neutral (charge $z = 0$) $\log \frac{v}{v_0} = 0$

Case 5: $A^{+} + BC^{-}$ $A^{-} + BC^{+}$ $\log \frac{v}{v_0} = -1{\cdot}0184 \times 1 \times 1 \times 0{\cdot}1 = -0{\cdot}102$

Case 6: $A^{2+} + BC^{-}$ $A^{-} + BC^{2+}$ $\log \frac{v}{v_0} = -1{\cdot}0184 \times 2 \times 1 \times 0{\cdot}1 = -0{\cdot}204$
$A^{2-} + BC^{+}$ $A^{-} + BC^{2+}$

Case 7: $A^{2+} + BC^{2-}$ $A^{2-} + BC^{2+}$ $\log \frac{v}{v_0} = -1{\cdot}0184 \times 2 \times 0{\cdot}1 = -0{\cdot}407$

The straight lines are shown in *Figure 34.*

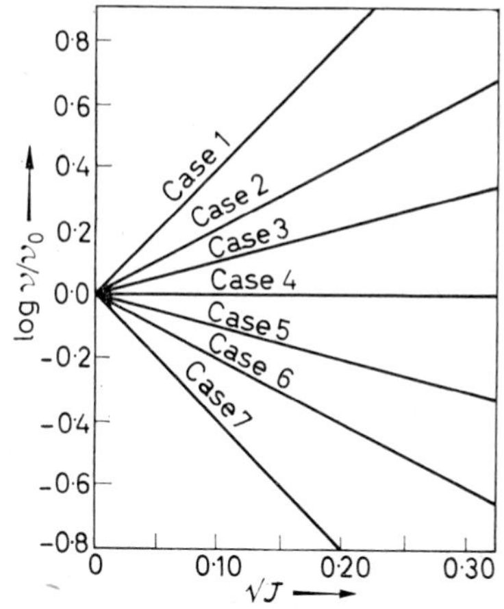

Figure 34. Brønsted equation and primary salt effect for ion exchange reactions A + BC = AB + C *with differently charged ions; from* La Mer

Note. La Mer has compiled a number of experimental examples, e.g. for

Case 1: $2[Co(NH_3)_5Br]^{2+} + Hg^{2+} + 2H_2O = 2[Co(NH_3)_5H_2O]^{3+} + HgBr_2$

Case 2: $S_2O_8^{2-} + 2I^- = 2SO_4^{2-} + I_2$

Case 3: Saponification of the nitrourethane ion by the hydroxyl ion $[NO_2-N-COOC_2H_5]^- + OH^- = N_2O + CO_3^{2-} + C_2H_5OH$

Case 4: Cane sugar inversion by the hydroxyl ion $C_{12}H_{22}O_{11} + OH^- =$ invert sugar

Case 5: $H_2O_2 + 2H^+ + 2Br^- = 2H_2O + Br_2$

Case 6: $[Co(NH_3)_5Br]^{2+} + OH^- = [Co(NH_3)_5\,OH]^{2+} + Br^-$

See relevant textbooks for further information.

Exercise 202

The decomposition of nitroamide, which may be represented formally by the reaction $NH_2NO_2 = N_2O + H_2O$, is catalysed by bases. The reaction presumably proceeds via the following stages:

(1) $H_2N{-}NO_2 \rightleftharpoons NH{=}NO{-}OH$ (equilibrium; tautomerism)

(2) $B + H{-}N{=}N(O){-}O{-}H \rightarrow BH^+ + [N{=}N(O){-}O{-}H]^-$ (rate-determining)

(3) $[N{=}N(O){-}O{-}H]^- + BH^+ \rightleftharpoons \overset{(-)}{N}{=}\overset{(+)}{N}{=}O + H_2O + B$ (equilibrium)

(4) $\overset{(-)}{N}{=}\overset{(+)}{N}{=}O \leftrightarrow |N{\equiv}\overset{(+)}{N}{-}\overset{(-)}{O}|$ (mesomerism)

The reaction therefore corresponds to the type of base-catalysed exchange reaction for which the Brønsted equation [312), (313) and (316), (317)] is applicable.

By plotting $\log \vec{k}$ against $\log K_{YA}$, or $\log \vec{k}/q$ against $\log K_{YA}\, q/p$, and determining the constants for the resulting straight lines, formulate the appropriate expressions (constants g and α, as well as the equations) for the following two cases.

Case 1: Catalysis by neutral bases; see eqns. (312), (314), (318). The ionic product of water, $k_{H_2O} = 0{\cdot}8 \times 10^{-14}$ (mole/l.)^2.

No.	*Catalytic base*	*Dissociation constant,* K_B	$\vec{k}$ *(measured)*
1	*p*-Toluidine	$1{\cdot}18 \times 10^{-9}$	1·16
2	*m*-Toluidine	$4{\cdot}92 \times 10^{-10}$	0·64
3	Aniline	$3{\cdot}82 \times 10^{-10}$	0·54
4	*o*-Toluidine	$2{\cdot}47 \times 10^{-10}$	0·38
5	*p*-Chloraniline	$8{\cdot}80 \times 10^{-11}$	0·21
6	*m*-Chloraniline	$2{\cdot}67 \times 10^{-11}$	0·081
7	*o*-Chloraniline	$3{\cdot}81 \times 10^{-12}$	0·018

Case 2: Catalysis by ionized bases (acid ions); see eqns. (315), (316).

No.	*Catalytic base*	*Dissociation constant* $K_s = K_{YA}$ *of the relevant acid*	$\vec{k}$ *(measured)*
8	Trimethylacetate ion	9.4×10^{-6}	0·822
9	Propionate ion	1.32×10^{-5}	0·649
10	Acetate ion	1.76×10^{-5}	0·504
11	Acid succinate ion	6.4×10^{-5}	0·320
12	Phenylacetate ion	5.4×10^{-5}	0·232
13	Benzoate ion	6.46×10^{-5}	0·189
14	Formate ion	1.765×10^{-4}	0·0822
15	Acid malic acid anion	3.8×10^{-4}	0·0765
16	Acid tartrate ion	1.04×10^{-3}	0·0363
17	Acid orthophthalate ion	1.25×10^{-3}	0·0290
18	Salicylate ion	1.07×10^{-3}	0·0206
19	Monochloracetate ion	1.4×10^{-3}	0·0158
20	Primary phosphate ion	7.52×10^{-3}	0·0096
21	*o*-Nitrobenzoate ion	6.95×10^{-3}	0·0042
22	Dichloracetate ion	5.5×10^{-2}	0·0007

Solution 202. Case 1: One has, from eqn. (312)

$$\vec{k} = g K_{YA}^{-\alpha}, \quad \text{and from eqn. (318),} \quad K_{YA} = k_{H_2O}/K_B \qquad \ldots. \quad \text{(i)}$$

i.e.

$$\log \vec{k} = \log g - \alpha \log k_{H_2O} + \alpha \log K_B \qquad \ldots. \quad \text{(ii)}$$

One also has:

Substance No.	$\log K_B$	$\log \vec{k}$
1	0·0719 − 9	0·0645
2	0·6920 − 10	0·8062 − 1
3	0·5821 − 10	0·7324 − 1
4	0·3927 − 10	0·5798 − 1
5	0·9445 − 11	0·3222 − 1
6	0·4265 − 11	0·9085 − 2
7	0·5809 − 12	0·2553 − 2

Figure 35 shows a plot of $\log \vec{k}$ against $\log K_B$ with a straight line drawn through the points. The slope of the line is found by taking two points on it, e.g.

$$\frac{0.20 - (0.80 - 3)}{(0.20 - 9) - (0.0 - 12)} = \frac{2.40}{3.20} = 0.75 = \alpha \qquad \ldots. \quad \text{(iii)}$$

Substituting the numerical values in (ii) gives, for example,

$$0.80 - 3 = \log g - 0.75 \log (0.8 \times 10^{-14}) + 0.75 (0.00 - 12)$$

or

$$\log g = 0.80 - 3 + 0.75(-0.00 + 12 + 0.903 - 15) = 0.23 - 4 \qquad \ldots. \quad \text{(iv)}$$

i.e.

$$g = 1.70 \times 10^{-4} \qquad \ldots. \quad \text{(v)}$$

so that

$$\vec{k} = 1.70 \times 10^{-4} K_{YA}^{-0.75} \qquad \ldots. \quad \text{(vi)}$$

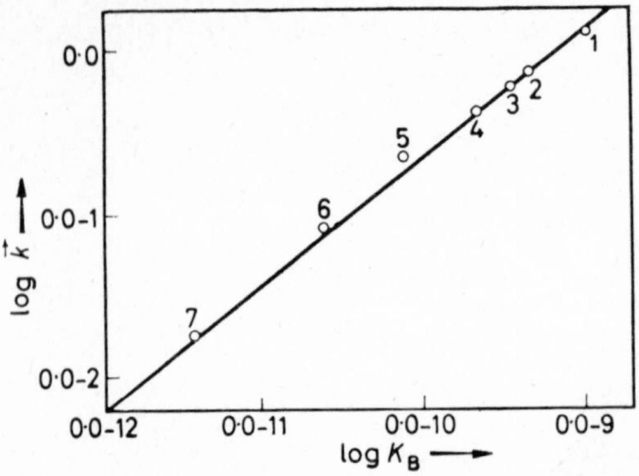

Figure 35. Brønsted equation for the catalysis of the decomposition of nitroamide by neutral bases

Case 2: This case relates to catalysis by bases, all of which have a single negative charge; one therefore uses eqn. (316)

$$\frac{\vec{k}}{q} = g\left(\frac{q}{p}K_{\text{YA}}\right)^{-\alpha} \qquad \text{.... (vii)}$$

where, according to eqn. (315), $K_{\text{YA}} = K_s$, the dissociation constant of the acid; q, the number of positions at which a proton may be added, is always 2 for organic acid anions, since a proton can be added to either of the two oxygen atoms in the carbonyl group $-CO_2\}^-$ and likewise to the primary phosphate ion, $(HO_2)PO_2\}^-$ .... (viii)

On the other hand, p, the number of dissociable protons available from the acid, changes from case to case, viz.

$p = 1$ for the monobasic acids 8-10, 12-14, 18, 19, 21, 22
$p = 2$ for the dibasic acids 11, 15-17 .... (ix)
$p = 3$ for the tribasic phosphoric acid 20

Thus, taking (vii) and (viii):

$$\log \vec{k} = \log(2g) - \alpha \log\left(\frac{2}{p}K_s\right) \qquad \text{.... (x)}$$

One has for

Substance No.	$\log\left(\frac{q}{p}K_s\right)$	$\log \vec{k}$
8	0·2742 − 5	0·9149 − 1
9	0·4216 − 5	0·8122 − 1
10	0·5465 − 5	0·7024 − 1
11	0·8062 − 5	0·5051 − 1
12	0·0342 − 4	0·3655 − 1
13	0·1113 − 4	0·2765 − 1
14	0·5478 − 4	0·9149 − 2
15	0·5798 − 4	0·8837 − 2
16	0·0170 − 3	0·5599 − 2
17	0·0969 − 3	0·4624 − 2
18	0·3304 − 3	0·3139 − 2
19	0·4472 − 3	0·1987 − 2
20	0·7001 − 3	0·9823 − 3
21	0·1430 − 2	0·6232 − 3
22	0·0414 − 1	0·8451 − 4

Figure 36 shows a plot of $\log \overrightarrow{k}$ against $\log (q/p)K_s$ with a straight line drawn through the points. The slope of the line is obtained by taking two points on it, e.g.

$$\frac{0{\cdot}600 - 3 - 0{\cdot}00}{0{\cdot}200 - 2 - (0{\cdot}200 - 5)} = -\frac{2{\cdot}400}{3{\cdot}000} = -0{\cdot}80 = -\alpha$$

$$\alpha = +0{\cdot}80 \qquad \ldots . \text{(xi)}$$

g is obtained by substituting the numerical values in (x), e.g.

$$0{\cdot}600 - 3 = \log (2g) - 0{\cdot}80\,(0{\cdot}200 - 2)$$

$$\log (2g) = 0{\cdot}160 - 4 \qquad 2g = 1{\cdot}44 \times 10^{-4}$$

i.e.

$$g = 7{\cdot}2 \times 10^{-5} \qquad \ldots . \text{(xii)}$$

Hence

$$\frac{\overrightarrow{k}}{q} = 7{\cdot}2 \times 10^{-5} \left(\frac{q}{p} K_{\mathrm{YA}}\right)^{-0{\cdot}80} \qquad \ldots . \text{(xiii)}$$

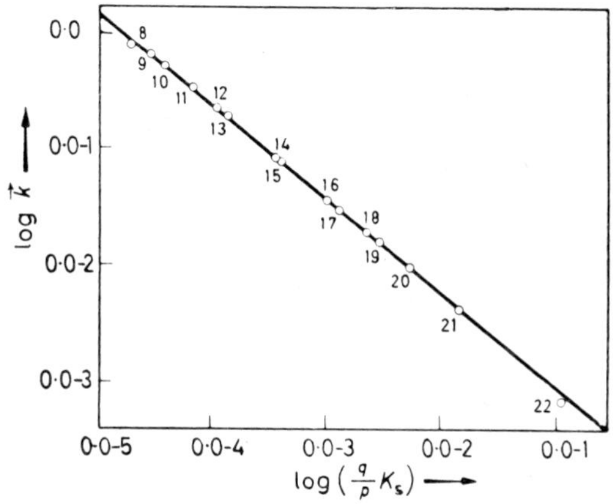

Figure 36. Brønsted equation for the catalysis of the decomposition of nitroamide by negatively charged bases

Exercise 203

Enolization of acetone

$$CH_3{-}CO{-}CH_3 \rightarrow CH_2{=}\underset{\displaystyle CH_3}{\underset{|}{C}}{-}O{-}H$$

is catalysed by acids, and proceeds via the following stages:

(1) $$CH_3{-}\underset{\displaystyle CH_3}{\underset{|}{C}}{=}\overline{\underline{O}} + HB \rightarrow \left[CH_3{-}\underset{\displaystyle CH_3}{\underset{|}{C}}{=}\underline{O}{-}H\right]^+ + B^- \quad \text{(rate-determining)}$$

(2) $B + \left[H{-}CH_2{-}\underset{\underset{CH_3}{|}}{C}{=}\overset{-}{O}{-}H\right]^+ \rightleftharpoons BH + |\overset{(-)}{C}H_2{-}\underset{\underset{CH_3}{|}}{C}{=}\overset{(+)}{\overset{-}{O}}{-}H$ (equilibrium)

(3) $|\overset{(-)}{C}H_2{-}\underset{\underset{CH_3}{|}}{C}{=}\overset{(+)}{\overset{-}{O}}{-}H \leftrightarrow CH_2{=}\underset{\underset{CH_3}{|}}{C}{-}\overset{-}{O}{-}H$ (mesomerism)

The enolic form can be determined by reaction with Br_2 or I_2.

It will be apparent that the enolization of acetone corresponds to the acid-catalysed type of exchange reaction [eqn. (315)], for which the Brønsted relation [eqn. (317)] is applicable.

The following rate constants were found for various catalysing acids:

No.	Acid catalyst	Dissociation constant, K_s	$\overleftarrow{k} \times 10^6$ (measured)
1	Oxalic acid	$5 \cdot 9 \times 10^{-2}$	330
2	Dichloracetic acid	$5 \cdot 5 \times 10^{-2}$	220
3	α, β-Dibromopropionic acid	$6 \cdot 7 \times 10^{-3}$	63
4	Monochloracetic acid	$1 \cdot 41 \times 10^{-3}$	35
5	Glycollic acid	$1 \cdot 48 \times 10^{-4}$	9·1
6	β-Chlorpropionic acid	$1 \cdot 04 \times 10^{-4}$	5·9
7	Succinic acid	$6 \cdot 4 \times 10^{-5}$	6·8
8	Acetic acid	$1 \cdot 76 \times 10^{-5}$	2·1
9	Propionic acid	$1 \cdot 32 \times 10^{-5}$	1·7
10	Acid oxalate ion	$6 \cdot 4 \times 10^{-5}$	21

Derive the Brønsted relationship [eqn. (317)] by plotting $\log(\overleftarrow{k'}/p)$ against $\log(q/p \times K_s)$ and determining the constants of the resulting straight line.

Solution 203. Equation (317) is applicable, i.e.

$$\frac{\overleftarrow{k'}}{p} = g'\left(\frac{q}{p}K_s\right)^{1-\alpha} \qquad \dots \text{ (i)}$$

p, the number of dissociable protons available from the acid, has a value of 2 for acids 1 and 7; in the case of the other acids, $p = 1$; q, the number of positions in the acid anion at which a proton may be added, has a value of 2 in the case of monobasic organic acids, since either of the two oxygen atoms in the carboxyl group can take up a proton.

It follows that $q = 2$ for acids Nos. 2, 3, 4, 5, 6, 8 and 9; q is also equal to 2 in the case of dibasic acids where only the first dissociation stage is considered, i.e. in Nos. 1 and 7. On the other hand, $q = 4$ for the acid oxalate ion (acid no. 10), since the $C_2O_4^{2-}$ anion has four oxygen positions at which protons may be taken up.

Taking logs at (i) gives

$$\log\left(\frac{\overrightarrow{k'}}{p}\right) = \log g' + (1-\alpha)\log\left(\frac{q}{p}K_s\right) \qquad \dots \text{ (ii)}$$

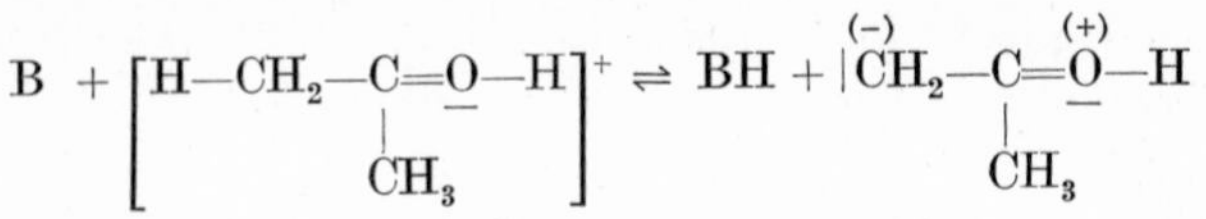

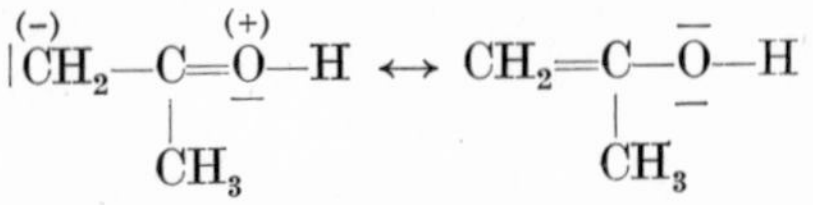

One has for:

Substance No.	p	q	$\log\left(\frac{q}{p}K_s\right)$	$\log\left(\frac{\overleftarrow{k'}}{p}\right)$
1	2	2	0·7708 − 2	0·2175 − 4
2	1	2	0·0414 − 1	0·3424 − 4
3	1	2	0·1271 − 2	0·7993 − 5
4	1	2	0·4502 − 3	0·5441 − 5
5	1	2	0·4713 − 4	0·9590 − 6
6	1	2	0·3181 − 4	0·7708 − 6
7	2	2	0·8062 − 5	0·5315 − 6
8	1	2	0·5464 − 5	0·3222 − 6
9	1	2	0·4216 − 5	0·2304 − 6
10	1	4	0·4082 − 4	0·3222 − 5

Figure 37 shows a plot of these values with a straight line drawn through the points. The slope of the line $(1 - \alpha)$ is obtained by taking two points on it, e.g.

$$\frac{0{\cdot}84 - 5 - (0{\cdot}34 - 6)}{0{\cdot}00 - 2 - (0{\cdot}58 - 5)} = \frac{1{\cdot}50}{2{\cdot}42} = 0{\cdot}62 = 1 - \alpha \qquad \ldots . \quad \text{(iii)}$$

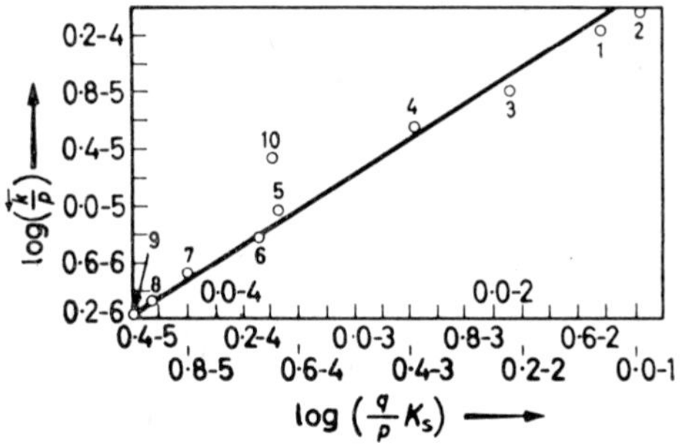

Figure 37. Brønsted equation for the enolization of acetone catalysed by acids

g' is obtained by substituting the numerical values in (ii), e.g.

$$0{\cdot}84 - 5 = \log g' + 0{\cdot}62\,(0{\cdot}00 - 2) \qquad \ldots . \quad \text{(iv)}$$

$$\log g' = 0{\cdot}08 - 3 \qquad \ldots . \quad \text{(v)}$$

$$g' = 1{\cdot}2 \times 10^{-3} \qquad \ldots . \quad \text{(v)}$$

Hence

$$\frac{\overleftarrow{k'}}{p} = 1{\cdot}2 \times 10^{-3}\left(\frac{q}{p}K_s\right)^{0{\cdot}62} \qquad \ldots . \quad \text{(vi)}$$

****Exercise 204**

Determine the accessible surface area of (*a*) a mixture of ZnO and Fe_2O_3, and (*b*) a sample of kaolin, by measuring the adsorption isotherm for methanol vapour at 20 °C. At this temperature the vapour pressure (saturation pressure) of methanol is $p_0 = 96$ torr and the density $\varrho = 0{\cdot}7923\,\text{g/cm}^3$; the molecular weight $M = 32{\cdot}04$; $\alpha = A_a/A_s = 1$; see eqn. (320). Adsorption measurements gave the following data:

Case (*i*). $ZnO–Fe_2O_3$. a = millimoles of methanol adsorbed per gramme of $ZnO–Fe_2O_3$ mixture; p = pressure of methanol vapour, in torr

No.	*a*	*p*	*No.*	*a*	*p*
1	0·27	3	8	0·64	30
2	0·32	4	9	0·645	40
3	0·35	5	10	0·655	50
4	0·48	10	11	0·66	60
5	0·55	15	12	0·71	70
6	0·585	20	13	0·96	80
7	0·62	25			

Case (*ii*). Kaolin. a = millimoles of methanol adsorbed per gramme of kaolin; p = pressure of methanol vapour, in torr [see eqns. (319) to (330)].

No.	*a*	*p*	*No.*	*a*	*p*
1	0·072	1	8	0·405	20
2	0·120	2	9	0·467	25
3	0·158	3	10	0·524	30
4	0·189	4	11	0·678	40
5	0·212	5	12	0·867	50
6	0·289	10	13	1·054	60
7	0·343	15	14	1·288	70

Solution 204. Figure 38 shows a plot of the experimental results. It will be seen that in Case (*i*) the central part of the adsorption isotherm is almost horizontal, i.e. a saturation value features. It follows that the Langmuir adsorption isotherm [eqn. (304)] may therefore be used to determine the number of adsorption centres, z_s. In contrast to the above, the adsorption curve for kaolin, Case (*ii*), is ~-shaped and has no horizontal portion. In this case, therefore, one must make use of the more general adsorption isotherm (with capillary condensation) due to Brunauer, Emmett and Teller [eqns. (325) and (327)].

z_s for Case (*i*) is obtained by calculating and plotting the rearranged Langmuir adsorption isotherm [eqn. (324)] on a p/a versus p diagram. For the purpose of comparison, the results have also been worked out using the rearranged form of the equation for the general adsorption isotherm [eqn. (328)] and making a plot of $p/a(p_0 - p)$ against p/p_0.

The same procedure has been adopted for Case (*ii*) and, although evaluation of the more general isotherm is standard practice for this case, evaluation of the Langmuir adsorption isotherm again affords a means for comparison.

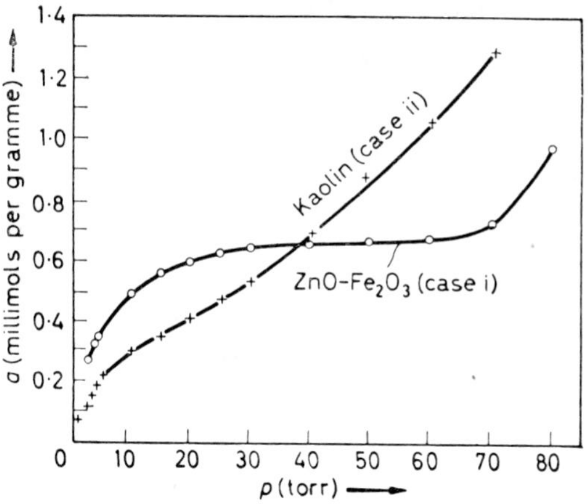

Figure 38. Adsorption curves for methanol vapour; $a \to p$ diagram

The numerical factors required have been worked out and included in the following tables; the vapour pressure of methanol is given by $p_0 = 96$ torr.

Case (*i*):

No.	p	p/a	$(p/p_0) \times 10^2$	$\frac{p}{a(p_0-p)} \times 10^2$
1	3	11·1	3·125	11·95
2	4	12·5	4·165	13·6
3	5	14·3	5·21	15·7
4	10	20·8	10·42	24·2
5	15	27·3	15·63	33·7
6	20	34·2	20·83	45·0
7	25	40·3	26·05	56·8
8	30	46·9	31·25	71·0
9	40	62·0	41·65	111
10	50	76·4	52·1	166
11	60	90·9	62·5	
12	70	98·6	72·9	
13	80	83·3	83·3	

Case (*ii*):

No.	p	p/a	$(p/p_0) \times 10^2$	$\frac{p}{a(p_0-p)} \times 10^2$
1	1	13·90	1·042	14·6
2	2	16·67	2·084	17·7
3	3	19·0	3·125	20·4
4	4	21·2	4·165	23·0
5	5	23·6	5·21	26·0
6	10	34·6	10·42	40·2
7	15	43·7	15·63	54·0
8	20	49·4	20·83	65·0
9	25	53·5	26·05	75·4
10	30	57·3	31·25	86·8
11	40	59·0	41·65	105·4
12	50	57·7	52·1	125·4
13	60	56·9	62·5	158·0
14	70	54·3	72·9	209·0

The p/a versus p diagram, for both cases, is shown in *Figure 39*. It follows from eqn. (324) that the slope of the straight line gives the value of $1/z_s$. A reading of the slope for Case (*i*) gives

$$1/z_s = \frac{90{\cdot}9 - 11{\cdot}1}{60 - 3} = 1/0{\cdot}714 \qquad \ldots. \quad \text{(i)}$$

i.e. $$z_s = 0{\cdot}714 \text{ millimole/gramme}$$

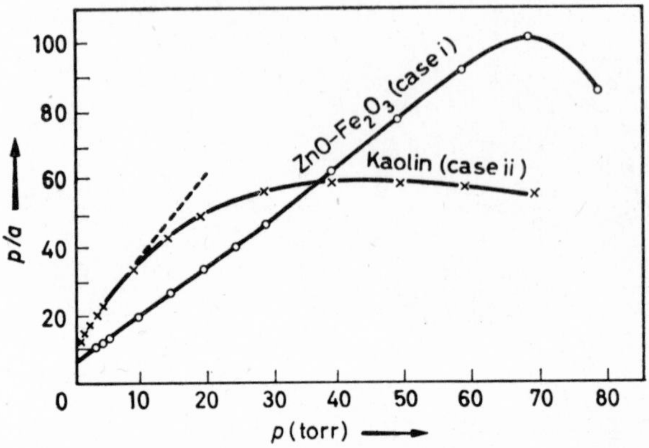

Figure 39. Adsorption curves for methanol vapour:
$p/a \rightarrow p$ diagram

or $0{\cdot}714 \times 6{\cdot}024 \times 10^{20} = 4{\cdot}3 \times 10^{20}$ molecules of methanol per gramme of $ZnO-Fe_2O_3$ mixture .... (ii)

For Case (*ii*) one would have

$$1/z_s = \frac{38{\cdot}5}{17} = 1/0{\cdot}442 \qquad \ldots. \quad \text{(iii)}$$

i.e. $$z_s = 0{\cdot}442 \text{ millimole/gramme}$$

or $0{\cdot}442 \times 6{\cdot}024 \times 10^{20} = 2{\cdot}66 \times 10^{20}$ molecules of methanol per gramme of kaolin .... (iv)

Figure 40 shows a plot of $p/a(p_0 - p)$ against p/p_0 for both cases. According to eqn. (330), $1/z_s$ is obtained as the value of the ordinate by extrapolating the straight line to $p/p_0 = 1$.

For Case (*i*), one finds

$$1/z_s = 187 \times 10^{-2} \qquad z_s = 0{\cdot}535 \text{ millimole/gramme}$$

or $0{\cdot}535 \times 6{\cdot}024 \times 10^{20} = 3{\cdot}22 \times 10^{20}$ molecules of methanol per gramme of $ZnO-Fe_2O_3$ mixture .... (v)

For Case (*ii*):

$$1/z_s = 289 \times 10^{-2} \qquad z_s = 0{\cdot}346 \text{ millimole/gramme}$$

or $0{\cdot}346 \times 6{\cdot}024 \times 10^{20} = 2{\cdot}08 \times 10^{20}$ molecules of methanol per gramme of kaolin .... (vi)

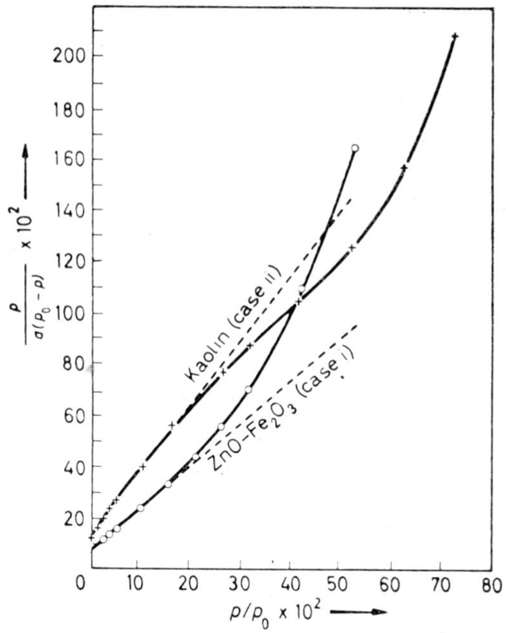

Figure 40. Adsorption curves for methanol vapour: $p/a(p_0 - p) \rightarrow p/p_0$ diagram

z_s may also be determined from eqn. (329):

$$z_s = \frac{1}{\nu + \beta}$$

i.e. for Case (*i*), with the slope of the line $\nu = \frac{33{\cdot}7 - 11{\cdot}95}{15{\cdot}63 - 3{\cdot}125} = 1{\cdot}74$ .... (vii)

and the intercept on the ordinate axis $(p/p_0 = 0)$, $\beta = 6{\cdot}5 \times 10^{-2}$,

$$z_s = \frac{1}{1{\cdot}74 + 0{\cdot}065} = 0{\cdot}555 \text{ millimole/gramme} \quad \text{.... (viii)}$$

or

$3{\cdot}35 \times 10^{20}$ molecules of methanol per gramme of $ZnO{-}Fe_2O_3$ mixture .... (ix)

For Case (*ii*):

$$\nu = \frac{40{\cdot}2 - 14{\cdot}6}{10{\cdot}42 - 1{\cdot}042} = 2{\cdot}37 \quad \text{and} \quad \beta = 12 \times 10^{-2} \quad \text{.... (x)}$$

$$z_s = \frac{1}{2{\cdot}73 + 0{\cdot}12} = 0{\cdot}351 \text{ millimole/gramme}$$

or

$2{\cdot}12 \times 10^{20}$ molecules of methanol per gramme of kaolin .... (xi)

Equation (322) shows that the surface area required per molecule of methanol is

$$q_M = 1{\cdot}33 \left(\frac{32{\cdot}04}{0{\cdot}7923 \times 6{\cdot}024 \times 10^{23}}\right)^{2/3} \text{cm}^2 = 22 \times 10^{-16} \text{ cm}^2 \quad \text{.... (xii)}$$

so that the accessible surface area, A_s, of the adsorbent will be, from eqns. (319) and (320), taking $\alpha = 1$

for Case (*i*), using (ii):

$$A_s = 4.3 \times 10^{20} \times 22 \times 10^{-16} = 94.6 \times 10^4\ \text{cm}^2 = 94.6\ \text{m}^2/\text{g} \qquad \ldots . \text{(xiii)}$$

and for Case (*ii*), using (xi):

$$A_s = 2.12 \times 10^{20} \times 22 \times 10^{-16} = 46.7\ \text{m}^2/\text{g} \qquad \ldots . \text{(xiv)}$$

Note. Comparison of the values obtained for the number of adsorption centres shows that those computed from the general adsorption isotherm, viz.

$$z_s[\text{Case } (i)] = 3.35 \times 10^{20} \quad \text{[see (ix)]}$$
$$z_s[\text{Case } (ii)] = 2.12 \times 10^{20} \quad \text{[see (xi)]}$$

are about 20 per cent lower than the corresponding values estimated from the Langmuir adsorption isotherm where capillary condensation is not taken into account; these latter values were

$$z_s[\text{Case } (i)] = 4.3 \times 10^{20} \quad \text{[see (ii)]}$$
$$z_s[\text{Case } (ii)] = 2.66 \times 10^{20} \quad \text{[see (iv)]}$$

This is quite plausible. Ignoring capillary condensation leads to saturation values which are too high in the case of the Langmuir adsorption isotherm. This is because further layers of molecules start to build up before monomolecular surface coverage is complete. These further layers are included in the value for z_s as determined by the Langmuir isotherm.

In contrast to this, Zimens (in Schwab, G.-M., *Handbuch der Katalyse*, Vol. IV, pp. 197—199), comparing adsorption isotherms for methanol on a number of different adsorbents, comes to the surprising conclusion that the number of adsorption centres calculated from the general isotherm of Brunauer, Emmett and Teller comes only to between $\frac{1}{2}$ and $\frac{1}{7}$ of the z_s value given by the Langmuir adsorption isotherm. In the examples dealt with here, for example, he finds (Table 10), $z_s[\text{Case } (i)] = 0.7 \times 10^{20}$, $z_s[\text{Case } (ii)] = 0.42 \times 10^{20}$. An examination of his calculations, however, shows that this marked discrepancy is due to the presence of a systematic error: the author has inadvertently omitted the factor 10^{-2} in all values of β when calculating $z_s = 1/(\nu + \beta)$; the denominator is therefore too large and his conclusions are not valid.

The adsorption of nitrogen at its boiling point is generally used today as the standard way of determining surface area. Argon or butane may also be used as secondary standards.

*Exercise 205

Calculate the quantum yield for the photochemical decomposition of hydrogen iodide in hexane solution, $2HI = H_2 + I_2$. Light with a wavelength of 2820 Å was passed through an absorption cell of volume $V = 10.00$ cm³ which was filled with an 0.8045 M solution of HI in hexane. By taking measurements with a calibrated thermopile, it was found that 1.315×10^9 ergs of light energy were absorbed during the course of the experiment. The final concentration of the HI solution was found to be $c_2 = 0.7493$ mole/l. See eqn. (335).

Solution 205. $n_r = (c_1 - c_2)V$ moles will be converted during the reaction. Since c is given in mole/l., V must be taken as 0.010 l. Substituting the numerical values in eqn. (335) gives:

$$\varphi = \frac{1.196 \times 10^{16}(0.8045 - 0.7493)\,0.01}{1.315 \times 10^9 \times 2820} = 1.78 \text{ quantum yield}$$

**Exercise 206

During the synthesis of hydrocarbons by the Fischer–Tropsch process, $CO + 2H_2 = CH_2< + H_2O$, a mixture of hydrogen and carbon monoxide in the ratio 2:1 (synthesis gas) is used, together with about 20 per cent of inert gas (e.g. nitrogen). The temperature range is 185–200 °C, either at atmospheric pressure or at pressures between 5 and 20 atm. A cobalt contact bed (cobalt–thorium–magnesium–kieselguhr mixed catalyst) is used with a gas flow of about 100 m³ (at s.t.p.) of synthesis gas per hour per cubic metre of contact material. (It may be noted that iron contacts have recently proved to be very effective). In order to obtain an insight into the reaction kinetics of this heterogeneous gas reaction on a cobalt contact, the following measurements for the rate of conversion, $-d[CO]/dt$, were made by suitably varying the technical conditions:

$[R\ \%]$ *as vol.-% of reactants*	$-\frac{d[CO]}{dt} \times 10^7$ (moles CO/sec × cm³ *of contact*)
20·5	2·64
33·5	4·22
46·2	5·75
51·5	6·37
63·6	7·76
74·0	8·91
85·1	10·11
97·8	11·46

(1) $\theta = 185$ °C, total pressure $p_{tot} = 18$ atm, volume ratio $y = [H_2]/[CO] = 2{\cdot}0$; variation of total partial pressure or total volume per cent of the reactants (CO, H_2), $[R\ \%]$.

(2) $\theta = 185$ °C, total pressure $p_{tot} = 18$ atm, $p_{CO} = 2$ atm; variation of the volume ratio, $y = [H_2]/[CO]$.

p_{H_2} (atm)	y	$-\frac{d[CO]}{dt} \times 10^7$ (moles CO/sec × cm³ *of contact*)
2·94	1·47	2·30
3·22	1·61	2·76
3·58	1·79	3·39
4·00	2·00	4·22
4·46	2·23	5·24
4·76	2·38	5·93
4·98	2·49	6·47

Deduce from these values the equation for the rate of reaction and explain the mechanism of the reaction; see eqns. (340) to (347).

Solution 206. The data at (1) are plotted in *Figure 41.* A practically linear relationship is obtained between rate of conversion of CO and the concentration of the reactants. There is, however, a deviation from the rectilinear at higher concentrations, of the sort found with an adsorption isotherm using eqns. (304) and (340).

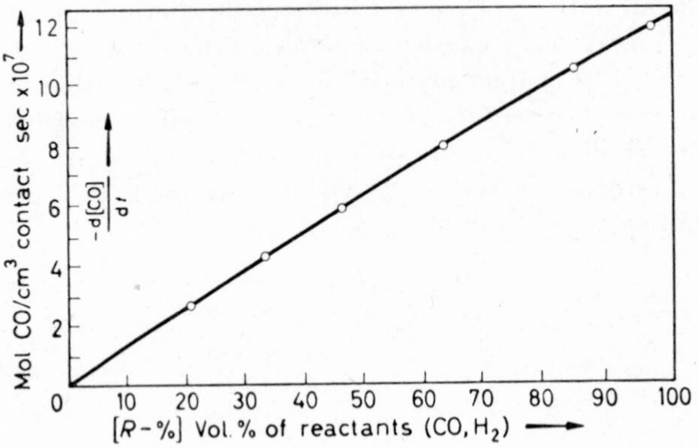

Figure 41. Fischer–Tropsch synthesis $CO + 2H_2 = > CH_2 + H_2O$*: dependence of rate of reaction on concentration of reactants*

$1/[R\,\%]$ $\times 10^2$	$-1\Big/\dfrac{d[CO]}{dt}$ $\times 10^{-7}$
4·88	0·379
3·00	0·237
2·16	0·174
1·94	0·157
1·57	0·129
1·35	0·112
1·175	0·099
1·023	0·087

In order to investigate and eliminate this possible adsorption effect, a plot is made of $-1/d[CO]/dt$ against $1[R\ \%]$ (see *Figure 42*), similar to the manner used for Langmuir adsorption isotherms [see eqn. (323) and Exercise 197)].

The linear relationship between $1/d[CO]/dt$ and $1/[R\ \%]$ is at once apparent. The relation between the functions $d[CO]/dt$ and $[R\ \%]$, as in the case of adsorption isotherms represented by eqn. (340), may therefore be expressed as

$$-\frac{d[CO]}{dt} = \frac{k[R\,\%]}{1 + b[R\,\%]} \quad \text{or} \quad -1\Big/\frac{d[CO]}{dt} = \frac{1}{k} \times \frac{1}{[R\,\%]} + \frac{b}{k} \quad \ldots \quad \text{(i)}$$

$1/k$ and b/k, the parameters of the straight line, may be obtained either from *Figure 42* or by calculation from the experimental data.

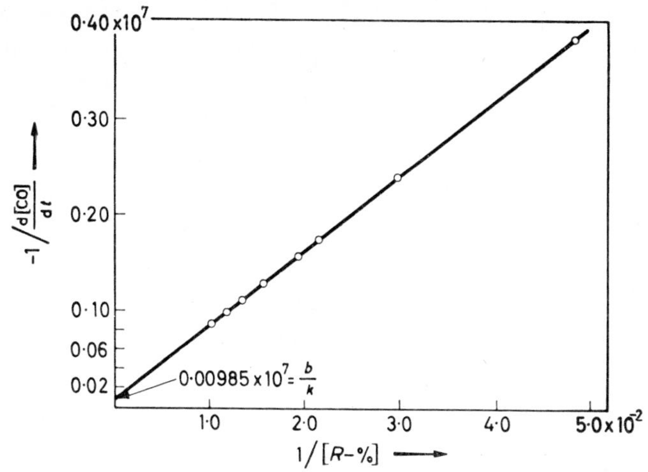

Figure 42. Fischer–Tropsch synthesis: determination of Langmuir adsorption isotherm constants and overall order of reaction

The slope, $1/k$, of the straight line at (i), for example, is from the data given

$$1/k = \frac{(0{\cdot}379 - 0{\cdot}087)\,10^7}{(4{\cdot}88 - 1{\cdot}023)\,10^{-2}} = 7{\cdot}575 \times 10^7 \quad k = 0{\cdot}132 \times 10^{-7} \qquad \ldots\ldots \text{(ii)}$$

Likewise, where according to (i)

$$b = k\Big/\left(\frac{-\,\mathrm{d}[\mathrm{CO}]}{\mathrm{d}t}\right) - 1/[R\,\%]$$

one has, for example

$$b = 0{\cdot}132 \times 10^{-7}/(11{\cdot}46 \times 10^{-7}) - 1{\cdot}023 \times 10^{-2} = 0{\cdot}13 \times 10^{-2} \qquad \ldots\ldots \text{(iii)}$$

Extrapolation to $1/[R\ \%] = 0$ of the straight line at (i) shown in *Figure 42* gives $b/k = 0{\cdot}00985 \times 10^7$, which is in agreement with (iii) and (ii). Substituting in (i) the values for k and b from (ii) and (iii) gives

$$-\frac{\mathrm{d}[\mathrm{CO}]}{\mathrm{d}t} = \frac{0{\cdot}132 \times 10^{-7}[R\,\%]}{1 + 0{\cdot}13 \times 10^{-2}[R\,\%]} \qquad \ldots\ldots \text{(iv)}$$

as the formula describing the first series of experiments (*Figure 41*).

It follows that the rate of reaction is of the first order in relation to the total concentration of H_2 and CO, provided their partial pressure in the synthesis gas is not too high. The rate of reaction must therefore be obtained from the linear portion of the range:

$$-\frac{\mathrm{d}[\mathrm{CO}]}{\mathrm{d}t} = k'\,p_{\mathrm{H_2}}^{u}\,p_{\mathrm{CO}}^{v} = k'\,y^u\,p_{\mathrm{CO}}^{u+v} \quad \text{where} \quad y = p_{\mathrm{H_2}}/p_{\mathrm{CO}} \qquad \ldots\ldots \text{(v)}$$

and where, according to the above result, $u + v = 1$; hence

$$-\frac{\mathrm{d}[\mathrm{CO}]}{\mathrm{d}t} = k'\,p_{\mathrm{CO}}\,y^u \qquad \ldots\ldots \text{(vi)}$$

The index u is obtained by working out the second series of experimental results in which p_{CO} is kept constant whilst y is varied.

Taking logs at (vi) gives

$$\log\left(-\frac{d[CO]}{dt}\right) = u \log y + \log (k' p_{CO}) \quad \ldots . \text{(vii)}$$

i.e. a straight line of slope u when $\log(-d[CO]/dt)$ is plotted against $\log y$ (*Figure 43*).

$\log y$	$\log\left(-\frac{d[CO]}{dt}\right)$
0·168	0·362 − 7
0·207	0·441 − 7
0·253	0·530 − 7
0·301	0·625 − 7
0·348	0·719 − 7
0·377	0·773 − 7
0·396	0·811 − 7

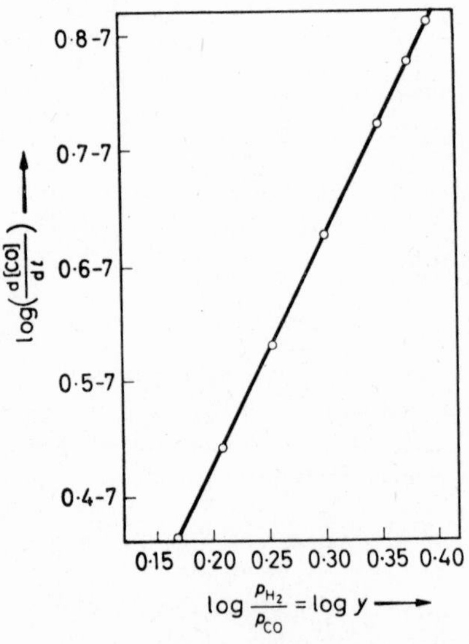

Figure 43. Fischer–Tropsch synthesis: determination of order of reaction for individual reactants

It will be seen from *Figure 43*, or by working out the second series of experimental results, that the slope u is practically equal to 2; for example

$$u = \frac{0{\cdot}719 - 0{\cdot}362}{0{\cdot}348 - 0{\cdot}168} = \frac{0{\cdot}357}{0{\cdot}180} = 1{\cdot}985 \approx 2 \quad \ldots . \text{(viii)}$$

so that

$$v = 1 - u = -1$$

The adsorption term at eqn. (iv) now has only a minor percentage-wise influence, since the partial pressures in the second series of experiments were chosen so as to be relatively small. The reaction equation at (v) therefore becomes

$$-\frac{d[CO]}{dt} = k' p_{H_2}^2 / p_{CO} \qquad \ldots \quad \text{(ix)}$$

This signifies, in accordance with eqn. (346), that the CO is so strongly adsorbed on the contact material that almost the whole of the active surface is saturated with carbon monoxide. In regions free of CO, weakly adsorbed hydrogen reacts according to the equation $2H_2 + CO = CH_2< + H_2O$ (which is of second order in relation to the H_2 pressure). It follows that the conversion of CO is hindered by virtue of its own strong affinity for the active surface. The adsorption term at eqn. (iv), found in the first series of experiments dealing with higher partial pressures of the reactant mixture, must therefore result from the fact that adsorption of hydrogen at the CO-free active surface becomes appreciable at high pressures; see eqn. (347). The adsorption term at eqn. (iv) is therefore a function of the H_2 partial pressure. This means that for a greater range of pressures the generalization at (ix) becomes

$$-\frac{d[CO]}{dt} = k' \frac{p_{H_2}^2}{p_{CO}} \times \frac{1}{1 + b' p_{H_2}} \qquad \ldots \quad \text{(x)}$$

The constants may be determined by comparing (iv) with (x), after appropriate rearrangement of the latter.

One has

$$\left.\begin{aligned} &[R\,\%] = \text{vol. \% CO} + \text{vol. \% } H_2 = \text{vol. \% CO}(1 + y) \\ \text{where} \quad &y = [H_2]/[CO], \text{ from (v).} \end{aligned}\right\} \quad \ldots \quad \text{(xi)}$$

$$\frac{[R\,\%]}{100} = \frac{p_{CO}}{p_{tot}}(1 + y) \quad \text{or} \quad p_{CO} = p_{tot}\frac{[R\,\%]}{100}\Big/(1 + y) \qquad \ldots \quad \text{(xii)}$$

and

$$p_{H_2} = p_{CO}\, y \quad \text{or} \quad p_{H_2} = p_{tot}\frac{[R\,\%]}{100}\, y/(1 + y) \qquad \ldots \quad \text{(xiii)}$$

Substituting (xii) and (xiii) in (x) gives

$$-\frac{d[CO]}{dt} = k' p_{tot}\frac{y^2}{1 + y}\,\frac{[R\,\%]}{100}\,\frac{1}{1 + b' p_{tot}\frac{[R\,\%]}{100}\, y/(1 + y)} \qquad \ldots \quad \text{(xiv)}$$

In accordance with the conditions for the first series of experiments and valid for eqn. (iv), $p_{tot} = 18$ atm and $y = 2$; hence, in this case, (xiv) becomes

$$-\frac{d[CO]}{dt} = \frac{k' \times 18}{100} \times \frac{4}{3}[R\,\%]\,\frac{1}{1 + \frac{b' \times 18 \times 2}{100 \times 3}[R\,\%]} \qquad \ldots \quad \text{(xv)}$$

Comparing (xv) and (iv) gives

$$\frac{k' \times 18 \times 4}{3 \times 100} = 0{\cdot}132 \times 10^{-7} \qquad \frac{b' \times 18 \times 2}{3 \times 100} = 0{\cdot}13 \times 10^{-2}$$

$$k' = 0{\cdot}550 \times 10^{-7} \qquad b' = 1{\cdot}083 \times 10^{-2} \qquad \ldots \quad \text{(xvi)}$$

Finally, by substituting (xvi) in (x), one obtains the required reaction equation which gives a quantitative description of the results of both series of experiments:

$$-\frac{d[CO]}{dt} = 0{\cdot}550\,\frac{p_{H_2}^2}{p_{CO}} \times \frac{1}{1 + 1{\cdot}083 \times 10^{-2}\,p_{H_2}} \quad \ldots . \text{(xvii)}$$

Note. It is usually not possible to make a direct calculation for the rates of conversion under technical conditions; it cannot be assumed, for example, that furnace performance will be uniform over the entire length of the catalyst bed. The rate of conversion in the last layer of contact material may, however, be calculated by using an expression derived by Damköhler (in EUCKEN and JAKOB, *Der Chemieingenieur*, Vol. III, 1, p. 382, formula b 26). A further difficulty arises from the fact that, especially in the case of strongly exothermic reactions, the wall temperature differs from that in the interior of the furnace. The temperature, at a maximum along the axis of the furnace, falls towards the walls in accordance with a parabolic law and then drops abruptly to the temperature of the cooling medium. Knowing the activation energy of the contact reaction, the thermal conductivity in the contact space and the heat transfer coefficient, it is possible to calculate the rate of conversion for the wall temperature. This is done by using the equation for the heat loss in a cylinder and where the rate of conversion is averaged over the cross-section of the tube. See BRÖTZ, W., *Z. Elektrochem.* 53 (1949) 301; BRÖTZ, W. and ROTTIG, W., *ibid.* 56 (1952) 896.

*EXERCISE 207

Nickel (atomic weight 58·69) may be determined gravimetrically as nickel dimethylglyoxime (mol. wt. $M = 288{\cdot}92$), the latter being insoluble in water. The equation is

$$Ni^{2+} + 2\,CH_3C(NOH)C(NOH)CH_3 + 2\,NH_3 = Ni[CH_3(NO)C(NOH)CH_3]_2 + 2\,NH_4^+$$

This may also be carried out in the presence of considerable quantities of cobalt (Co^{2+}); cobalt is precipitated but, at the same time, nickel remains in solution.

Investigate the behaviour in a solution which contains 1 mole of Ni^{2+} and 1 mole of Co^{2+} ions, i.e. (*a*) the reliability of the gravimetric method for determining nickel, (*b*) the purity of the nickel dimethylglyoxime in the precipitate (ratio of Ni-dimethylglyoxime to the total precipitate); as a result of this, (*c*) calculate the ratio between the nickel precipitated and the total nickel originally present in the solution.

For the purpose of the investigation, the solution is labelled by adding 0·50 mc (millicuries) of $(^{63}Ni)^{2+}$, and addition of dimethylglyoxime gives a precipitate weighing 285·0 g. Measurement of its radioactivity shows the specific activity S of the precipitate to be 1·61 μc/g (microcuries/gramme).

Solution 207. (*a*) The theoretical yield of precipitate from 1 mole of Ni^{2+} is 288·9 g, as opposed to an actual value of 285·0 g. It follows that the amount of precipitate is too low by $285{\cdot}0 - 288{\cdot}9/288{\cdot}9 \times 100 = 1{\cdot}35$ per cent, and the method is therefore still just about usable under these particular conditions.

(*b*) The specific activity of the nickel (0·50 mc/mole of Ni) in the test solution must remain the same in the case of the precipitate. It will appear to be reduced according to the extent to which the precipitated nickel dimethylglyoxime is contaminated with cobalt. Thus:

specific activity of the precipitate $\qquad 1{\cdot}61\ \mu c/g$

specific activity of pure nickel dimethylglyoxime $= \dfrac{0{\cdot}50}{288{\cdot}9} = 1{\cdot}73\ \mu c/g$

purity of the precipitate $= \frac{1{\cdot}61}{1{\cdot}75} \times 100 = 93{\cdot}0$ per cent

(*c*) yield of nickel $= \frac{285{\cdot}0}{288{\cdot}9} \times 93{\cdot}0 = 91{\cdot}7$ per cent Ni

In spite of the fact that more than 8 per cent of the nickel remains in solution, the gravimetric method is still serviceable since, under the conditions described, cobalt is precipitated and very largely compensates for the deficiency of nickel.

Note. This exercise is a simple example of the use of radioactive isotopes as indicators. The indicator method has now become valuable in the field of research. The addition of a radioactive isotope is equivalent to labelling the atoms of an element, whose transfer in diffusion processes, chemical and biological reactions can then be followed. Radioactive methods permit the detection of substances in amounts (10^{-24} g) which are much too small to be weighed, the limit of chemical microanalysis being 10^{-6} g.

A whole series of artificially prepared radioactive isotopes is available for medical purposes; ^{14}C and ^{11}C for studies in metabolism; ^{32}P for studies of phosphorus metabolism and research into bone diseases, the formation and destruction of white and red blood corpuscles; ^{35}S for protein research and treatment of leukemia; ^{22}Na, ^{24}Na, ^{42}K and ^{45}Ca for research into mineral metabolism, blood flow (blood volume), diagnosis of circulation, research into the permeability of the capillary walls of the stomach, intestine, eye and ear; ^{131}I for studying thyroid functions, thyroid diseases, and especially for the diagnosis of tumours; ^{32}P is also used for this purpose. The localization and demarcation of brain tumours depends on the use of ^{32}P and ^{74}As, where concentration and activity of these isotopes increase by as much as a factor of 100.

Wherever possible, radioactive isotopes with not too short half-life periods should be used as indicators. The next exercise affords an example of the difficulties which may otherwise be encountered.

Exercise 208

Determine the distribution equilibrium of iodine between two solvents I and II. For this purpose, a 0·1 N solution of iodine in solvent I (stock solution) is labelled with radioactive but short-lived ^{132}I. A measured quantity of the stock solution is then shaken with a measured quantity of solvent II until equilibrium is established. A 10 cm³ sample of one of the solutions in equilibrium is then taken and its activity determined. Next, a determination is made of the activity of a 10 cm³ sample drawn from the unused stock solution (standard), and so on.

The first test measurement takes 30·0 minutes and shows a count of 300 min/10 cm³ of solution. A comparable measurement on the stock solution is started 10·0 min later; this takes 15·0 min and shows a count of 750 min/10 cm³ of solution. What is the iodine concentration in the first sample? The half-life period of ^{132}I is $T = 135{\cdot}6$ min.

Solution 208. The time taken in making a measurement cannot be ignored in comparison with the half-life period of the isotope. Change in activity during measurement must therefore be taken into account. This is done by converting the activities measured at different times so that they apply to a common time and thus afford a true comparison.

Equation (271) shows that the activity S decays exponentially:

$$S = S_0 e^{-\lambda t} \quad \ldots\ldots \quad \text{(i)}$$

Measured, however, is a mean value of the activity $\bar{S}$

$$\bar{S} = \frac{1}{t_2 - t_1} \int_{t_1}^{t_2} S_0 e^{-\lambda t} dt = \frac{S_0}{\lambda (t_2 - t_1)} (e^{-\lambda t_1} - e^{-\lambda t_2}) \quad \ldots \quad \text{(ii)}$$

Equation (272) shows that $\lambda = 0{\cdot}6931/T = 0{\cdot}6931/135{\cdot}6 = 5{\cdot}11 \times 10^{-3}\ \text{min}^{-1}$

$$\ldots \quad \text{(iii)}$$

If the time at which measurement of the first sample was started ($t_1 = 0{\cdot}0$ min) is taken as the reference point, then, with $t_2 = 30{\cdot}0$ min for this sample, eqn. (ii) gives

$$\bar{S}_{0\,\text{test}} = \frac{S_{0\,\text{test}}}{\lambda t_2} (1 - e^{-\lambda t_2}) \quad \text{or} \quad S_{0\,\text{test}} = \frac{\bar{S}_{\text{test}}\, \lambda t_2}{1 - e^{-\lambda t_2}} \quad \ldots \quad \text{(iv)}$$

Substitution gives

$$S_{0\,\text{test}} = \frac{300 \times 5{\cdot}11 \times 10^{-3} \times 30{\cdot}0}{1 - e^{-5{\cdot}11 \times 10^{-3} \times 30{\cdot}0}} = \frac{300 \times 0{\cdot}1533}{1 - e^{-0{\cdot}1533}} = 324\ \text{counts/min} \quad \ldots \quad \text{(v)}$$

Taking $t_3 = 40{\cdot}0$ min and $t_4 = 55{\cdot}0$ min, the expression for this later measurement on the standard stock solution is

$$\bar{S}_{\text{st}} = \frac{S_{0\,\text{st}}}{\lambda (t_4 - t_3)} (e^{-\lambda t_3} - e^{-\lambda t_4}) \quad \text{or} \quad S_{0\,\text{st}} = \frac{S_{\text{st}}\, \lambda (t_4 - t_3)}{e^{-\lambda t_3} - e^{-\lambda t_4}} \quad \ldots \quad \text{(vi)}$$

Substituting:

$$S_{0\,\text{st}} = \frac{750 \times 5{\cdot}11 \times 10^{-3} (55{\cdot}0 - 40{\cdot}0)}{e^{-5{\cdot}11 \times 10^{-3} \times 40{\cdot}0} - e^{-5{\cdot}11 \times 10^{-3} \times 55{\cdot}0}} = \frac{750 \times 0{\cdot}07665}{e^{-0{\cdot}2044} - e^{-0{\cdot}2810}} = 956\ \text{counts/min} \quad \ldots \quad \text{(vii)}$$

The specific activities (per gramme of iodine) are the same for both the test sample and the stock solution, since they arise from the same labelling operation. It follows that the concentrations of the iodine in the solutions must be proportional to their activities (per 10 cm^3), i.e.

$$c_{\text{test}}/c_{\text{st}} = S_{0\,\text{test}}/S_{0\,\text{st}} \quad \ldots \quad \text{(viii)}$$

Substituting:

$$c_{\text{test}} = 0{\cdot}1 \times \frac{324}{956} = 0{\cdot}0339\ \text{N}$$

If the uncorrected values of the activites, $\bar{S}_{\text{test}}$ and $\bar{S}_{\text{st}}$ were substituted in eqn. (viii), one would obtain

$$c^{\star}_{\text{test}} = 0{\cdot}1 \times \frac{300}{750} = 0{\cdot}040\ \text{N}$$

i.e. a value too high by 18 per cent.

Note. This experiment would be better carried out using ^{131}I as the tracer, its half-life period of $T = 8{\cdot}08$ days being more suitable for the purpose. This simple example, however, was chosen intentionally to describe the procedure in experiments using radioactive materials with short lives.

For comparative studies of metabolism on the same object, one would, for example, prefer the use of ^{132}I to ^{131}I as labelling substance and, likewise, ^{11}C (half-life period $T = 20{\cdot}4$ min) in preference to ^{14}C (half-life period $T = 5568$ years), see Exercise 183; i.e. because, thanks to the short half-life periods of ^{132}I and ^{11}C, the same experiment, or a comparative one, could then be repeated after a few days, without the danger of interference from the previous experiment or of damaging the object.

The most important instruments for the quantitative measurement of radioactivity are

(a) The ionization chamber with an electrometer, if necessary with a multiplication counter; this method is not very sensitive, but is reliable and indispensable for gauging.

(b) The Geiger-Müller counter with a resolving power 4×10^{-4} sec.

(c) The scintillation counter with an electron multiplier and counting or integrating device, with a resolving power of 10^{-7} sec.

*Exercise 209

A sample of uranium, enriched in ^{235}U and ^{234}U and examined for radioactivity, showed a specific activity of $S = 1{\cdot}635 \times 10^6$ counts/min $\times$ g. Neutron activation showed the ^{235}U content to be 7·4 per cent by weight. The measuring equipment was calibrated with natural uranium, and pure natural uranium, measured under the same conditions, showed a specific activity of $S_0 = 261{,}000$ counts/min $\times$ g. What is the concentration of ^{234}U (weight per cent of ^{234}U) in the sample?

Natural uranium consists of

0·0058 per cent ^{234}U: half-life period, $T_1 = 2{\cdot}5 \times 10^5$ years
decay constant, $\lambda_1 = 8{\cdot}8 \times 10^{-14}$ sec^{-1}

0·715 per cent ^{235}U: half-life period, $T_2 = 7{\cdot}1 \times 10^8$ years
decay constant, $\lambda_2 = 3{\cdot}1 \times 10^{-17}$ sec^{-1}

99·28 per cent ^{238}U: half-life period, $T_3 = 4{\cdot}49 \times 10^9$ years
decay constant, $\lambda_3 = 4{\cdot}89 \times 10^{-18}$ sec^{-1}

Since the specific activities of ^{234}U, ^{235}U and ^{238}U are all different, the specific activity of the above isotope mixture may be conveniently used to determine its isotope ratios; this may be done by using the mixture rule as applied in eqn. (65).

Explanation. The activity of a radioactive preparation is proportional to the number of particles disintegrating in unit time $(-\mathrm{d}N/\mathrm{d}t)$; the specific activity is proportional to the number of particles disintegrating in unit time per unit quantity of substance $[(-\mathrm{d}N/\mathrm{d}t)/N]$. One has from eqn. (271)

$$\frac{-\mathrm{d}N}{\mathrm{d}t} = \lambda N \quad \text{or} \quad \frac{-\mathrm{d}N}{\mathrm{d}t} \Big/ N = \lambda \qquad \ldots\ldots \quad \text{(i)}$$

hence the radioactive decay constant, λ, can be taken as a measure of the specific activity (per particle); it follows that

$$S = \lambda N_A \text{ is a measure of the activity per mole} \qquad \ldots\ldots \quad \text{(ii)}$$

where N_A = Avogadro's constant = $6{\cdot}02368 \times 10^{23}$ molecules/mole

and
$$S = \frac{\lambda N_A}{M} \text{ is a measure of the activity per gramme} \qquad \ldots\ldots \quad \text{(iii)}$$

(M = molecular or atomic weight)

All three activities at (i) to (iii) are here expressed in terms of the number of disintegrations per second.

It is more usual to use the curie as the unit of measurement of activity. The curie, c, is that quantity of any radioactive nuclide in which the number of disintegrations per second is $3{\cdot}700 \times 10^{10}$; it follows from (iii) that

$$S = \frac{\lambda N_{\mathrm{L}} \times 10^{-10}}{M \times 3{\cdot}700} \quad (\mathrm{c/g}) \qquad \ldots. \quad \text{(iv)}$$

represents the activity per gramme in curies/gramme. Thus

$$S = \frac{6{\cdot}024 \times 10^{23} \times 10^{-10}\,\lambda}{3{\cdot}700\,M} = \frac{1{\cdot}628 \times 10^{13}\,\lambda}{M} = \frac{1{\cdot}128 \times 10^{13}}{MT} \quad (\mathrm{c/g}) \qquad \ldots. \quad \text{(v)}$$

If the measuring equipment gives the activity in terms of counts per second, its calibration factor, φ, must be determined. This factor is the ratio of the measured count (pulses/second) to the actual rate of disintegration (number of disintegrations per second). Thus

$$\varphi = \frac{\text{counting rate (pulses/second)}}{\text{rate of disintegration (number of disintegrations/second)}} \qquad \ldots. \quad \text{(vi)}$$

Solution 209. The first step is to determine the calibration factor φ. Since natural uranium is to be used for the purpose of calibration, it is necessary to know the specific activity of this material. The value, in curies, can be found as follows. The specific activities are, according to (v)

$$^{234}\mathrm{U}:\ S_1 = \frac{1{\cdot}628 \times 10^{13} \times 8{\cdot}8 \times 10^{-14}}{234} = 6122 \times 10^{-6}\,\mathrm{c/g} = 6122\,\mu\mathrm{c/g} \qquad \ldots. \quad \text{(vii)}$$

$$^{235}\mathrm{U}:\ S_2 = \frac{1{\cdot}628 \times 10^{13} \times 3{\cdot}1 \times 10^{-17}}{235} = 2{\cdot}148 \times 10^{-6}\,\mathrm{c/g} = 2{\cdot}148\,\mu\mathrm{c/g} \qquad \ldots. \quad \text{(viii)}$$

$$^{238}\mathrm{U}:\ S_3 = \frac{1{\cdot}628 \times 10^{13} \times 4{\cdot}89 \times 10^{-18}}{238} = 0{\cdot}3345\,\mu\mathrm{c/g} \qquad \ldots. \quad \text{(ix)}$$

Using eqn. (65), where

ξ_1 = weight fraction of ^{234}U
ξ_2 = weight fraction of ^{235}U
ξ_3 = weight fraction of ^{238}U

the activity of the isotope mixture will be given by

$$S = S_1\xi_1 + S_2\xi_2 + S_3\xi_3 = S_1\xi_1 + S_2\xi_2 + S_3(1 - \xi_1 - \xi_2) \qquad \ldots. \quad \text{(x)}$$

Substituting the values at (vii), (viii) and (ix) for S_1, S_2 and S_3 and using the data given at the beginning of the exercise for ξ_1, ξ_2 and ξ_3, the specific activity of natural uranium is found to be

$$S_0 = 6122 \times 0{\cdot}000058 + 2{\cdot}148 \times 0{\cdot}00715 + 0{\cdot}3345 \times 0{\cdot}9928$$
$$= 0{\cdot}7025\,\mu\mathrm{c/g} \qquad \ldots. \quad \text{(xi)}$$

It follows from (iv) that this corresponds to a rate of decay of $0{\cdot}7025 \times 10^{-6} \times 3{\cdot}700 \times 10^{10} \times 60$ counts/min g = $1{\cdot}560 \times 10^{6}$ counts/min g .... (xii)

The counting rate, as initially given, is 261,000 pulses/min g .... (xiii)

(vi), (xii) and (xiii) therefore give the calibration factor φ as

$$\varphi = 261{,}000/1{\cdot}560 \times 10^{6} = 0{\cdot}1673 \qquad \ldots. \quad \text{(xiv)}$$

The specific activity of the enriched uranium, initially given in counts/min g, can now be converted to curies per gramme; from (vi), one has $1{\cdot}635 \times 10^6/\varphi = 1{\cdot}635 \times 10^6/0{\cdot}1673$ disintegrations/min $\times$ g; analogously to eqn. (iv), this gives an activity of

$$S = \frac{1{\cdot}635 \times 10^6}{0{\cdot}1673 \times 3{\cdot}700 \times 10^{10} \times 60}\ \text{c/g} = 4{\cdot}40\ \mu\text{c/g} \qquad \ldots . \text{(xv)}$$

for the enriched uranium*.

From eqn. (x), one now has for the weight fraction ξ_1 of ^{234}U in the enriched sample of uranium:

$$\xi_1 = \frac{(S - S_3) - \xi_2 (S_2 - S_3)}{S_1 - S_3} \qquad \ldots . \text{(xvi)}$$

Using the value initially given for ξ_2, i.e. $\xi_2 = 0{\cdot}074$ (^{235}U content), the values for S_1, S_2 and S_3 in (vii), (viii) and (ix) and that for S in (xv), the above becomes

$$\xi_1 = \frac{(4{\cdot}40 - 0{\cdot}3345) - 0{\cdot}074\,(2{\cdot}148 - 0{\cdot}3345)}{6122 - 0{\cdot}3345} = 0{\cdot}642 \times 10^{-3}$$

$$= 0{\cdot}0642 \text{ per cent by weight of } ^{234}\text{U}$$

Note. 1 c of radium corresponds to approximately 1 gramme of radium; this is because the mol. wt. of radium is $M = 226$, $T = 1590$ years, $\lambda = 1{\cdot}38 \times 10^{-11}$ sec^{-1} hence, from eqn. (v);

$$S_{\text{Ra}} = \frac{1{\cdot}628 \times 10^{13} \times 1{\cdot}38 \times 10^{-11}}{226} = 0{\cdot}994 \text{ c/g of radium}$$

The original intention was to make 1 curie exactly equivalent to 1 g of radium. As long as the accuracy of measurement of the number of α-particles emitted by 1 g of radium per second was no better than ± 2 per cent, this was, in fact, true. Improvement in methods of measurement has, however, required a more precise definition. The definition of radioactive quantity (measured in curies) in terms of the number of disintegrations per unit time has the result that, after equilibrium has been established in a radioactive decay series — independent of half-life periods — all elements are present in equal radioactive quantity; this is because, at stationary equilibrium, exactly as many atoms of each element disintegrate as are produced, with the exception, of course, of the stable final member.

If two samples of different radioactive elements, having atomic weights M_1, M_2, masses G_1, G_2, decay constants λ_1, λ_2 and half-life periods T_1, T_2, show the same activity, one has the following relation between the number of atoms, N_1, N_2, in the two samples:
activity (1) = activity (2) or $S_1 G_1 = S_2 G_2$ or from eqn. (iv), $\lambda_1 N_A G_1/M_1 = \lambda_2 N_A G_2/M_2$ or, finally, where $N_1 = N_A \times G_1/M_1$, $N_2 = N_A \times G_2/M_2$

$$\lambda_1 N_1 = \lambda_2 N_2 \quad \text{and} \quad \frac{N_1}{T_1} = \frac{N_2}{T_2} \quad \text{or} \quad N_1 = N_2 \frac{T_1}{T_2} \qquad \ldots . \text{(xvii)}$$

since, according to eqn. (272):

$$\text{the half-life period } T = \frac{\ln 2}{\lambda} = \frac{0{\cdot}6931}{\lambda} \qquad \ldots . \text{(xviii)}$$

* One could, of course, also take the whole of the denominator in eqn. (xv), i.e. $\varphi \times 3{\cdot}700 \times 10^{10} \times 60$, as an apparatus factor for converting the count measured into curies. This would give the relation:

$$\frac{S\ (\text{counts/min sec})}{S_0\ (\text{counts/min sec})} = \frac{S\ (\mu\text{cg})}{S_0\ (\mu\text{cg})}; \text{ or, in the present case}$$

$$\frac{1{\cdot}635 \times 10^6}{261\,000} = \frac{S\ (\mu\text{c/g})}{0{\cdot}7025} \qquad S = 4{\cdot}40\ \mu\text{c/g}$$

It follows that the number of atoms in a quantity, say, of 1 c of any radioactive element may be obtained by multiplying the number of atoms of radium in 1 c of radium by the quotient of the half-life period for the element in question and that for radium. The relation at (xvii) is only another way of writing the expressions in eqn. (281); see also Exercise 184, *Note 2* and Exercises 178—183 on the subject of radioactivity.

Reading matter regarding Exercises 207—209 may be found in: VON HEVESY, G., *Radioactive Indicators*, Interscience Publishers, Inc., New York; VON HEVESY, G., *Künstliche radioaktive Isotope in Physiologie, Diagnostik und Therapie*, Springer, Berlin.

EXERCISE 210

An aircraft is powered by a high-temperature gas-nuclear reactor. ^{235}U is used as fission material. The thrust produced by the power plant is 30,000 kg wt. and the flight speed is 1000 km/h. (*a*) Calculate the rate of fission needed (number of disintegrations/sec) from the ^{235}U according to the required output from the reactor. The efficiency of the system is assumed to be 15 per cent. Calculation of the energy released during nuclear fission of ^{235}U is based on decay to the most abundantly occurring and stable end products $^{95}_{42}Mo$ and $^{139}_{57}La$ (+ neutrons + electrons) and on the total mass defect.

(*b*) By using the result obtained from (*a*), calculate the screening required to protect the crew against dangerous radiation. The screening must be effective against two types of radiation: (*i*) against gamma rays by using a layer of lead, the thickness of which should be calculated, and (*ii*) against fast neutrons by using a layer of water, the thickness of which should also be calculated.

Gamma quanta have an energy of 2 MeV; for this value, the attenuation coefficient in lead is $\mu = 0{\cdot}53\ \text{cm}^{-1}$; it may be assumed that 20 per cent of the gamma rays leave the reactor. The tolerance level for gamma rays of this type is 800 gamma quanta/(cm² sec). About 5 gamma quanta are released during each disintegration.

The absorption coefficient for fast neutrons in water is $m = 0{\cdot}215\ \text{cm}^{-1}$; it will be assumed that 10 per cent of the neutrons formed leave the reactor; an average of 2·5 neutrons are released for each disintegration. The tolerance level for fast neutrons is 22 neutrons/(cm² sec).

The distance between the reactor and the crew's cabin is $r = 30$ m.

Explanation. For the purpose of the present case, uranium fission takes place according to the equation

$$\left.\begin{aligned} &^{235}_{92}U + {}_0n^1 = {}^{236}_{92}U \\ &^{236}_{92}U = {}_zX + {}_{92-z}Y \rightarrow {}^{95}_{42}Mo + {}^{139}_{57}La + \text{electrons} + \text{neutrons} \end{aligned}\right\} \quad \cdots \quad \text{(i)}$$

The mass defect during reaction is usually calculated by using the physical atomic weight scale (i.e. the isotope ^{16}O, with a molar mass 16 g/mole$_{ph}$, is taken as the reference standard).

For the isotope:	^{235}U	$M_{ph} = 235{\cdot}12517$ g/mole$_{ph}$
	^{139}La	$M_{ph} = 138{\cdot}95020$ g/mole$_{ph}$
	^{95}Mo	$M_{ph} = 94{\cdot}93462$ g/mole$_{ph}$
for the neutron:	n^1	$M_{ph} = 1{\cdot}008986$ g/mole$_{ph}$

The rest mass of the electron is $m_e = 0{\cdot}91083 \times 10^{-27}$ g

The Avogadro constant is $N_{A\,(ph)} = k_A N_{A\,(ch)} = 1{\cdot}000279 \times 6{\cdot}02368 \times 10^{23}$

$= 6{\cdot}02536 \times 10^{23}$ molecules/mole$_{ph}$

$k_A = 1{\cdot}000279 = M_{ph}/M_{ch}$ is the conversion factor (Smythe factor) .... (ii)

between the physical and chemical atomic weight scales.

Conversion of the mass defect to energy is given by the Einstein mass–energy relation in eqn. (339).

The reader is reminded of terms familiar in mechanics:

$$\left.\begin{aligned} &\text{Power } N = \text{force } F \times \text{velocity } v \\ &1 \text{ kg wt.} = 9{\cdot}81 \times 10^5 \text{ dyn} = 9{\cdot}81 \text{ N (newtons)} \\ &1 \text{ mkg wt.} = 9{\cdot}81 \text{ mN} = 9{\cdot}81 \text{ J (Wsec)} = 9{\cdot}81 \times 10^7 \text{ erg (dyn cm)}. \end{aligned}\right\} \quad \ldots\ldots \text{(iii)}$$

As in the case of light waves, the attenuation of gamma rays and the absorption of neutrons obey an exponential law, i.e.

$$\Phi_f = \Phi_i \mathrm{e}^{-md} \quad \ldots\ldots \text{(iv)}$$

where Φ_f is the final intensity and Φ_i the initial value, d is the thickness of the medium and m (or μ) the natural extinction modulus (absorption coefficient, attenuation coefficient).

With the reactor as centre, emission of radiation spreads uniformly outwards into space. The surface density therefore decreases according to the inverse square law:

$$\Phi_i = I/4\pi r^2 \quad (I = \text{total radiation/sec}) \quad \ldots\ldots \text{(v)}$$

Solution 210. (*a*) The power of the aircraft is first calculated from (iii):

$$F = 30000 \text{ kg wt.} = 30000 \times 9{\cdot}81 \text{ N} \quad v = 1000 \text{ km/h}$$

$$= \frac{1000 \times 10^3}{3600} \text{ m/sec}$$

$$N_{\text{aircraft}} = F\,v = \frac{30000 \times 9{\cdot}81 \times 1000 \times 10^3}{3600} = 81{\cdot}75 \times 10^6 \text{ W} \quad \ldots\ldots \text{(vi)}$$

For a reactor efficiency of 15 per cent, the reactor must therefore be designed for an output of

$$N_{re} = \frac{81{\cdot}75 \times 10^6 \times 100}{15} = 545 \times 10^6 \text{ W} = 545 \text{ MeW} \quad \ldots\ldots \text{(vii)}$$

The mass defect during nuclear fission is now calculated.

The reaction equations at (i) show that, in the final balance, 236 − (95 + 139) = 2 units of mass, i.e. 2 neutrons, and 92 − (42 + 57) = −7 units of charge, i.e. 7 electrons, must remain on the right-hand side. The equation showing the balance must therefore be

$$^{235}_{92}\mathrm{U} + {}_0\mathrm{n}^1 = {}^{95}_{42}\mathrm{Mo} + {}^{139}_{57}\mathrm{La} + 2\,{}_0\mathrm{n}^1 + 7\,{}_{-1}\mathrm{e}^0 + \text{energy} \quad \ldots\ldots \text{(viii)}$$

From this, and using the data given in the explanation, one has for the mass balance:

^{235}U: $M_{ph} = 235{\cdot}12517$ g/mole$_{ph}$		^{95}Mo:	$M_{ph} = 94{\cdot}93462$ g/mole$_{ph}$
n^1: $M_{ph} = 1{\cdot}008986$ g/mole$_{ph}$		^{139}La:	$M_{ph} = 138{\cdot}95020$ g/mole$_{ph}$
$236{\cdot}134156$ g/mole$_{ph}$		$2\times$n^1:	$2\,M_{ph} = 2{\cdot}017972$ g/mole$_{ph}$
		$7\times$e^0:	$7\,M_{ph} = 0{\cdot}003842$ g/mole$_{ph}$
			$235{\cdot}906634$ g/mole$_{ph}$

where M_{ph} for an electron is given by

$$M_{ph} = m_e N_{A\,(ph)} = 0{\cdot}91083 \times 10^{-27} \times 6{\cdot}02536 \times 10^{23} = 0{\cdot}0005488 \text{ g/mole}_{ph}$$

i.e. $7\,M_{ph} = 0{\cdot}003842$ g/mole$_{ph}$.
Thus the mass defect for the conversion of 1 mole is

$$\Delta M = 236{\cdot}13416 - 235{\cdot}90663 = 0{\cdot}2275 \text{ g/mole}_{ph}$$

The mass defect per elementary disintegration is $\Delta m = \Delta M/N_{A\,(ph)}$:

$$\Delta m = 0{\cdot}2275/6{\cdot}02536 \times 10^{23} = 3{\cdot}776 \times 10^{-25} \text{ g per elementary disintegration} \quad \ldots . \text{(ix)}$$

Using the Einstein mass–energy relation [eqn. (339)] $E = \Delta m c^2$, where $c^2 = 8{\cdot}987524 \times 10^{20}$ erg/g, one obtains . . . . (x)

$$\left.\begin{aligned} E &= 3{\cdot}776 \times 10^{-25} \times 8{\cdot}987524 \times 10^{20} = 3{\cdot}394 \times 10^{-4} \text{ erg} \\ &= 3{\cdot}394 \times 10^{-11} \text{ watt-seconds per elementary disintegration} \end{aligned}\right\} \quad .. \text{(xi)}$$

According to (vii), the output of the reactor should be 545×10^6 watts; the rate of fission, i.e. the required number of elementary disintegrations per second, n, is therefore obtained from (vii) and (xi):

$$\left.\begin{aligned} n &= N_{re}/E = 545 \times 10^6 \text{ W}/3{\cdot}394 \times 10^{-11} \frac{\text{W sec}}{\text{elementary disintegration}} \\ &= 1{\cdot}6 \times 10^{19} \text{ elementary disintegrations per second} \end{aligned}\right\} \quad .. \text{(xii)}$$

Taking eqns. (ix)–(xii) together, one has

$$n = \frac{N_{re} N_{L\,(ph)}}{M_{ph} c^2} = \frac{545 \times 10^6 \times 6\ 02536 \times 10^{23}}{0{\cdot}2275 \times 8{\cdot}9875 \times 10^{20}} = 1{\cdot}606 \times 10^{19} \text{ disintegrations/sec} \quad \ldots . \text{(xiii)}$$

(*b*) (*i*) Screening of gamma rays. 5 gamma quanta (γ) are produced per disintegration and 20 per cent of the gamma rays leave the reactor; the total number of gamma quanta leaving the reactor is, therefore, $I_\gamma = 5 \times 0{\cdot}2 \times 1{\cdot}6 \times 10^{19}\ \gamma$/sec $= 1{\cdot}6 \times 10^{19}\ \gamma$/sec. It is known from (v) that the intensity of the gamma quanta at a distance r (cm) is $\Phi_{i(\gamma)} = I_\gamma/4\pi r^2$ and, from (iv), that this will be reduced by a layer of lead, of thickness d, to

$$\Phi_{f\,(\gamma)} = \Phi_{i\,(\gamma)}\, e^{-\mu d} = \frac{I_\gamma e^{-\mu d}}{4\pi r^2} \left[\frac{\gamma}{\text{cm}^2 \text{ sec}}\right] \quad \ldots . \text{(xiv)}$$

The residual intensity must not be greater than the tolerance level of 800 $\gamma/(\text{cm}^2\,\text{sec})$, so that, when $r = 30$ m $= 3000$ cm and $\mu = 0{\cdot}53\ \text{cm}^{-1}$:

$$800 = \frac{1{\cdot}6 \times 10^{19}\,\text{e}^{-0{\cdot}53\,d}}{4\,\pi \times 3000^2}$$

$$\text{e}^{-0{\cdot}53\,d} = \frac{800 \times 4 \times \pi \times 3000^2}{1{\cdot}6 \times 10^{19}} = 5{\cdot}65 \times 10^{-9}$$

Taking logs:

$$-0{\cdot}53\,d\,\log \text{e} = \log(5{\cdot}65 \times 10^{-9}) = -8{\cdot}248$$

$$d = \frac{8{\cdot}248}{0{\cdot}53 \times 0{\cdot}4343} = 35{\cdot}8 \approx 36 \text{ cm for the thickness of the layer of lead} \quad \ldots. \quad \text{(xv)}$$

in order to provide effective screening of the gamma rays.

(*b*) (*ii*) Screening of neutrons. The expression at (xiv) is also used for the absorption of neutrons (n), thus

$$\Phi_{f\,(\text{n})} = \frac{I_{\text{n}}\,\text{e}^{-md}}{4\,\pi\,r^2}\left[\frac{\text{n}}{\text{cm}^2\,\text{sec}}\right] \quad \ldots. \quad \text{(xvi)}$$

with a tolerance level of 22 n/cm² sec for neutrons and an absorption coefficient of $m = 0{\cdot}125\ \text{cm}^{-1}$ for fast neutrons. On the average, 2·5 neutrons are produced per disintegration and 10 per cent of these leave the reactor; it follows that the total number of neutrons, I_n, leaving the reactor per second, is

$$I_n = 2{\cdot}5 \times 0{\cdot}1 \times 1{\cdot}6 \times 10^{19} = 4{\cdot}0 \times 10^{18}\ \text{n/sec}$$

Hence, substituting numerical values in (xvi):

$$22 = \frac{4{\cdot}0 \times 10^{18} \times \text{e}^{-0{\cdot}125\,d}}{4\,\pi \times 3000^2} \quad \text{or} \quad \text{e}^{-0{\cdot}125\,d} = 6{\cdot}22 \times 10^{-10}$$

$$-0{\cdot}125\,d\,\log \text{e} = \log(6{\cdot}22 \times 10^{-10}) = -9{\cdot}206$$

$$d = \frac{9{\cdot}206}{0{\cdot}125 \times 0{\cdot}4343} = 169{\cdot}6 \approx 170 \text{ cm for the thickness of the water layer} \quad \ldots. \text{(xvii)}$$

for effective screening of the neutrons.

Literature—WINKLER W., Nuklearer Antrieb von Flugzeugen, *Neue Zürcher Ztg.* 1958 No. 371 (Technik)

SHOULTS, D. R., Test of a direct cycle nuclear turbojet system. *2nd International Conference on the Peaceful Uses of Atomic Energy*, Geneva 1958, A. Conf. 15/P/461e

COWAN, G. A., and ORTH, C. J., Diffusion of fission products at high temperatures from refractor 5 matrices, *2nd International Conference on the Peaceful Uses of Atomic Energy*, Geneva 1958, A. Conf. 15/P/613y

MURRAY, R. L., *Introduction to nuclear engineering*, Prentice Hall, New York, 1954

APPENDIX

CONSTANTS AND CONVERSION FACTORS

		Numerical value
c	speed of light	$2{\cdot}997\,92 \times 10^{8}$ m/sec
c_2	Planck's second constant ($= hc/k$)	$1{\cdot}438\,97$ cm deg.
e	elementary charge ($= F/N_A$)	$1{\cdot}601\,93 \times 10^{-19}$ coulomb
F	1 faraday (Faraday constant)	$96\,495{\cdot}1$ coulomb/equiv.
h	Planck's constant (quantum of action)	$6{\cdot}6252 \times 10^{-34}$ J $\times$ sec
k	Boltzmann constant ($= R/N_A$)	$1{\cdot}380\,28 \times 10^{-23}$ J/deg.
m_e	rest mass of an electron	$0{\cdot}910\,83 \times 10^{-27}$ g
m_p	rest mass of a proton	$1{\cdot}672\,39 \times 10^{-24}$ g $= 1836{\cdot}1\, m_e$
m_n	rest mass of a neutron	$1{\cdot}674\,57 \times 10^{-24}$ g $= 1838{\cdot}5\, m_e$
m_H	rest mass of hydrogen H^1	$1{\cdot}673\,40 \times 10^{-24}$ g $= 1837{\cdot}2\, m_e$
N_A	Avogadro constant	$6{\cdot}023\,68 \times 10^{23}$ molecules/mole
π	Ludolph number	$3{\cdot}141\,59$
R	gas constant $\left(= \frac{p_0 v_{0\,(\text{mol})}}{T_0}\right)$ (see also Energy Conversion Table, p. 340–341)	$8{\cdot}31\,439$ J/(deg. mole) $= 1{\cdot}98\,647$ cal/(deg. mole) $= 0{\cdot}082\,0544$ l. atm/(deg. mole)
$p_0 v_{0\,(\text{mol})}$ (for $p \to 0$, T_0)		$2271{\cdot}1$ J/mole
$T_0 = 0\,°C$		$273{\cdot}15$ °K (Kelvin)
v_0	molar volume of an ideal gas (at 1 atm, 0 °C)	$22\,414{\cdot}5$ Ncm³/mole
Y	Einstein constant (mass equivalent) $= c^2$ (see also Energy Conversion Table, p. 340–341)	$8{\cdot}987\,524 \times 10^{13}$ J/g
Z	constant in the wave number–energy relation (light equivalent) $= N_A hc$ (see also Energy Conversion Table, p. 340–341)	$11{\cdot}9641$ J cm/mole $= 2{\cdot}858\,46$ cal cm/mole $= 1{\cdot}239\,86 \times 10^{-4}$ e V cm/equiv.
1 atm	(1 physical atmosphere)	760 torr $= 1033{\cdot}23$ g wt./cm² $= 1013{\cdot}25 \times 10^{3}$ μb (dyn/cm²) $= 1013{\cdot}25$ mb
1 torr		1 mm Hg $= 1{\cdot}333\,22 \times 10^{3}$ dyn/cm² $= 1{\cdot}333\,22$ mb
1000 millibar		$750{\cdot}062$ torr $= 10^{6}$ dyn/cm² $= 1{\cdot}019\,72$ kg wt./cm²
1 eV	(1 electron volt; see also Energy Conversion Table, p. 340–341)	$1{\cdot}601\,92 \times 10^{-19}$ J
1 Å	[1 Ångstrøm (unit of measurement for the wavelength of light and atomic radii)]	1×10^{-8} cm
1 D	[1 Debye (unit of measurement for molecular dipole moments)]	1×10^{-18} electrostatic units of charge $\times$ cm (statcoulomb $\times$ cm)
$\ln x$		$2{\cdot}302\,59 \log x$
$\log x$		$0{\cdot}434\,294 \ln x$
$R \ln x$		$4{\cdot}5740 \log x$ cal/(deg. mol)
$\frac{RT}{F} \ln x$		$1.9840 \times 10^{-4}\, T \log x$ V

$$\frac{M_{\text{phys}}}{M_{\text{chem}}} = \frac{\text{phys. atomic weight } (O^{16} = 16{\cdot}000\,00)}{\text{chem. atomic weight } (\bar{O}_{\text{natural}} = 16{\cdot}000\,00)} = \text{Smythe factor } k_A = 1{\cdot}000\,279$$

i. e. $N_{A\,\text{phys}} = 6{\cdot}023\,68 \times 10^{23} \times 1{\cdot}000\,279 = 6{\cdot}025\,36 \times 10^{23}$ molecules/mole (phys.)

$1\, F_{\text{phys}} = 96{,}495{\cdot}1 \times 1{\cdot}000\,279 = 96\,522$ coulomb/equiv. (phys.)

ENERGY

	erg	J	cal_{15}	cm^3 atm	l. atm
1 erg	1	10^{-7}	$2{\cdot}389\,20 \times 10^{-8}$	$9{\cdot}869\,23 \times 10^{-7}$	$9{\cdot}868\,96 \times 10^{-10}$
1 J	10^7	1	0·238 920	9·869 23	$9{\cdot}868\,96 \times 10^{-3}$
1 g calorie cal_{15}	$4{\cdot}1855 \times 10^7$	4·1855	1	41·3077	$41{\cdot}3065 \times 10^{-3}$
1 cm^3-atmosphere (phys.) cm^3 atm	$0{\cdot}101\,325 \times 10^7$	0·101 325	$24{\cdot}2086 \times 10^{-3}$	1	$0{\cdot}999\,972 \times 10^{-3}$
1 l. atm	$101{\cdot}3278 \times 10^7$	101·3278	24·2092	1,000·028	1
1 mkg wt.	$9{\cdot}806\,65 \times 10^7$	9·806 65	2·343 01	96·7841	$9{\cdot}678\,14 \times 10^{-2}$
1 kWh	$3{\cdot}6000 \times 10^{13}$	$3{\cdot}6000 \times 10^6$	$8{\cdot}601\,12 \times 10^5$	$3{\cdot}552\,92 \times 10^7$	$3{\cdot}552\,83 \times 10^4$
1 eV	$1{\cdot}601\,93 \times 10^{-12}$	$1{\cdot}601\,93 \times 10^{-19}$	$3{\cdot}827\,33 \times 10^{-20}$	$1{\cdot}580\,98 \times 10^{-18}$	$1{\cdot}580\,94 \times 10^{-21}$
1 eV/equiv. (chem)	$96{,}495{\cdot}1 \times 10^7$	96,495·1	23,054·6	$9{\cdot}523\,33 \times 10^5$	952·306
1 eV/equiv. (phys)	$96{,}522 \times 10^7$	96,522	23,061·0	$9{\cdot}525\,99 \times 10^5$	952·572
Light equivalent/mole (chem). $Z = N_A h c$ wave number 1 ($\bar{\nu} = 1/\lambda\ cm^{-1}$) is equivalent	$11{\cdot}9641 \times 10^7$	11·9641	2·858 46	118·076	0·118 073
Mass equivalent $c^2 = Y$ gramme–mass 1 is equivalent	$8{\cdot}987\,524 \times 10^{20}$	$8{\cdot}987\,524 \times 10^{13}$	$2{\cdot}147\,30 \times 10^{13}$	$8{\cdot}870\,00 \times 10^{14}$	$8{\cdot}869\,75 \times 10^{11}$
gas constant $R \times$ (deg. mole)	$8{\cdot}314\,39 \times 10^7$	8·314 39	1·986 47	82·0567	0·082 0544

CONVERSION TABLE

mkg wt.	kWh	eV/equiv. (chem)	*Wave numbers* $(1/\lambda)$ (cm^{-1})	*Gramme-mass units*
$1{\cdot}019\,72 \times 10^{-8}$	$2{\cdot}777\,78 \times 10^{-14}$	$1{\cdot}036\,32 \times 10^{-12}$	$8{\cdot}358\,34 \times 10^{-9}$	$1{\cdot}112\,65 \times 10^{-21}$
0·101 972	$2{\cdot}777\,78 \times 10^{-7}$	$1{\cdot}036\,32 \times 10^{-5}$	$8{\cdot}358\,34 \times 10^{-2}$	$1{\cdot}112\,65 \times 10^{-14}$
0·426 802	$1{\cdot}162\,64 \times 10^{-6}$	$4{\cdot}337\,53 \times 10^{-5}$	0·349 888	$4{\cdot}657\,01 \times 10^{-14}$
$1{\cdot}033\,23 \times 10^{-2}$	$2{\cdot}814\,58 \times 10^{-8}$	$1{\cdot}050\,05 \times 10^{-6}$	$8{\cdot}469\,09 \times 10^{-3}$	$1{\cdot}127\,40 \times 10^{-15}$
10·3326	$2{\cdot}814\,66 \times 10^{-5}$	$1{\cdot}050\,08 \times 10^{-3}$	8·469 32	$1{\cdot}127\,43 \times 10^{-12}$
1	$2{\cdot}724\,07 \times 10^{-6}$	$1{\cdot}016\,28 \times 10^{-4}$	0·819 673	$1{\cdot}091\,14 \times 10^{-13}$
$3{\cdot}670\,99 \times 10^{5}$	1	37·3076	$3{\cdot}009\,00 \times 10^{5}$	$4{\cdot}005\,55 \times 10^{-8}$
$1{\cdot}633\,51 \times 10^{-20}$	$4{\cdot}449\,81 \times 10^{-26}$	$\dfrac{1}{N_{A\,(chem)}} = \dfrac{1}{6{\cdot}023\,68 \times 10^{23}}$	$\dfrac{8{,}065{\cdot}39}{N_{A\,(chem)}}$	$1{\cdot}782\,39 \times 10^{-33}$
9,839·76	$2{\cdot}680\,42 \times 10^{-2}$	1	8,065·39	$1{\cdot}073\,66 \times 10^{-9}$
9,842·51	$2{\cdot}681\,17 \times 10^{-2}$	$\dfrac{N_{A\,(phys)}}{N_{A\,(chem)}} = 1{\cdot}000\,279$	$\dfrac{8{,}065{\cdot}39\, N_{A\,(phys)}}{N_{A\,(chem)}}$	$1{\cdot}073\,96 \times 10^{-9}$
1·220 00	$3{\cdot}323\,36 \times 10^{-6}$	$1{\cdot}239\,87 \times 10^{-4}$	1	$1{\cdot}331\,19 \times 10^{-13}$
$9{\cdot}164\,72 \times 10^{12}$	$2{\cdot}496\,53 \times 10^{7}$	$9{\cdot}313\,97 \times 10^{8}$	$7{\cdot}512\,08 \times 10^{12}$	1
0·847 832	$2{\cdot}309\,55 \times 10^{-6}$	$8{\cdot}616\,39 \times 10^{-5}$	0·694 945	$9{\cdot}251\,03 \times 10^{-14}$

TABLE OF THE PERIODIC SYSTEM OF THE ELEMENTS

Group / Series	I	II	III	IV	V	VI	VII	VIII			I	II	III	IV	V	VI	VII	0
1	1 H 1·0080																	2 He 4·003
2	3 Li 6·940	4 Be 9·02											5 B 10·82	6 C 12·011	7 N 14·008	8 O 16·000	9 F 19·00	10 Ne 20·183
3	11 Na 22·991	12 Mg 24·32											13 Al 26·98	14 Si 28·09	15 P 30·975	16 S 32·06	17 Cl 35·457	18 A (Ar) 39·944
4	19 K 39·10	20 Ca 40·08	21 Sc 44·96	22 Ti 47·90	23 V 50·95	24 Cr 52·01	25 Mn 54·94	26 Fe 55·85	27 Co 58·94	28 Ni 58·69	29 Cu 63·57	30 Zn 65·38	31 Ga 69·72	32 Ge 72·60	33 As 74·91	34 Se 78·96	35 Br 79·916	36 Kr 83·80
5	37 Rb 85·48	38 Sr 87·63	39 Y 88·92	40 Zr 91·22	41 Nb 92·91	42 Mo 95·95	43 Tc (99)	44 Ru 101·1	45 Rh 102·91	46 Pd 106·7	47 Ag 107·88	48 Cd 112·41	49 In 114·76	50 Sn 118·70	51 Sb 121·76	52 Te 127·61	53 I (J) 126·91	54 X 131·3
6	55 Cs 132·91	56 Ba 137·36	57 La*) 138·92	72 Hf 178·6	73 Ta 180·95	74 W 183·92	75 Re 186·31	76 Os 190·2	77 Ir 192·2	78 Pt 195·23	79 Au 197·0	80 Hg 200·61	81 Tl 204·39	82 Pb 207·21	83 Bi 209	84 Po (210)	85 At (211)	86 Rn 222
7	87 Fr (223)	88 Ra 226·05	89 Ac 227·04	90 Th 232·05	91 Pa 231	92 U 238·07	93 Np (237)	94 Pu (242)	95 Am (243)	96 Cm (245)	97 Bk (249)	98 Cf (249)	99 Es (255)	100 Fm (254)	101 Md (256)	102 No (253)	103 Lw (257)	Acti- nides

*

Rare earths (Lanthanides)	58 Ce 140·13	59 Pr 140·92	60 Nd 144·27	61 Pm (145)	62 Sm 150·37	63 Eu 152·0	64 Gd 156·9	65 Tb 158·93	66 Dy 162·46	67 Ho 164·94	68 Er 167·2	69 Tm 168·94	70 Yb 173·04	71 Lu (Cp) 174·99

INDEX